QUALITATIVE ORGANIC MICROANALYSIS

COGNITION AND RECOGNITION
OF CARBON COMPOUNDS

BY

DR. FRANK L. SCHNEIDER

PROFESSOR OF CHEMISTRY, QUEENS COLLEGE OF THE CITY UNIVERSITY OF NEW YORK
FLUSHING 67, N. Y./USA

WITH 188 FIGURES

1964

NEW YORK
ACADEMIC PRESS INC.

VIENNA
SPRINGER-VERLAG

547
S 35-1

SPRINGER-VERLAG
VIENNA

Published in the U.S.A. and Canada by
ACADEMIC PRESS INC.
111 Fifth Avenue, New York 3, New York

Library of Congress Catalog Card Number 64-24670

Preface

The most important task of the analytical chemist, aside from the acquisition of experimental data, is the coordination and interpretation of such data in terms of the qualitative and quantitative composition of the test substance. As in the old tale of the blind men and the elephant, a single observation or test, not considered in conjunction with others, may lead to entirely erroneous conclusions. On the other hand, mere increase in the number of such tests, without regard to their need or to their relationship to each other, also may not suffice for drawing the correct inferences from the experimental evidence.

The deductive reasoning which is usually associated with the analytical chemist finds its greatest opportunity for application in the problems of cognition and recognition of carbon compounds. Since a rigid scheme of procedure tends to produce a corresponding rigidity of thought, the intent of the present book is to outline approaches which will minimize the chances of misinterpretation without restricting the analytical chemist in his choice of tests. The selection of subsequent tests or reactions should be governed by the results of the preceding ones rather than by an arbitrary list. The relationships of the various approaches (and the information derived from each) to the composition and constitution of the test substance are brought out in the discussion with the hope that they may serve as guide lines for such selection. These principles can, of course, be extended to other techniques such as infrared absorption, although the description and discussion of these lie outside the scope of the present volume.

The choice of milligram and centigram procedures (as well as some in the microgram range) in the experimental work is based upon their unique capabilities for the detection and demonstration of the details of a phenomenon and by this means providing additional information which will justify inferences beyond those ordinarily expected. For example, the wide divergence of the values of melting points as reported in the literature can often be understood or explained by observation of the overlapping or parallel phenonona usually hidden by the large-scale techniques which tend to give a summation of effects. These microtechniques have been taught by the author for many years in courses in qualitative analysis. He has received many reports from former students testifying to the great utility and value of these methods in their later industrial or academic research.

The tables of the values of the physical and chemical constants included in the book cover only the usual, commercially available compounds in the belief that these will be the ones most frequently involved in recognition. The properties of the less common substances may be found, of course, in standard reference works such as Beilstein.

The author wishes to express his appreciation of the stimulating criticisms of his former teacher and colleague, Dr. A. A. BENEDETTI-PICHLER and of Mrs. SCHNEIDER's patience and forbearance during the trying period of the writing of this book.

Sands Point,
Port Washington, New York, June, 1964

FRANK L. SCHNEIDER

Table of Contents

PART II

Preliminary Examination

PART III

Systematic Analysis

Tables of Physical Constants of Compounds and Derivatives
Classified by Orders, Genera, Divisions, and Sections

Contents

Introduction.

Every chemist concerned with the study of carbon compounds is confronted at intervals with the problem of identifying the substances with which he is working. These may be the reactants, the products, or the by-products. In some cases the problem is one of *recognition*, that is, the identification of substances previously isolated or prepared and described in the literature. At other times the problem is one of *cognition* or the determination of the constitution and structure of entirely new, hitherto unknown compounds. Since only rarely is sufficient information available to justify the assumption that the substance under investigation belongs to the first group, the approach must be broad enough to permit identification of compounds in either group. In either problem the chemist should be prepared to use any and all techniques available.

The essential steps in the procedures for the two types of investigations are shown in Table 1.

TABLE 1

Tests for Cognition and Recognition

Tests	Recognition	Cognition
Determination of physical constants	X	X
Elementary analysis		
Qualitative	X	X
Quantitative	—	X
Functional group analysis		
Qualitative (type)	X	X
Quantitative (number per molecule)	O	X
Preparation of derivatives	X	X
Determination of carbon structures; arrangement, place, and manner of addition of functional groups	O	X
Reconstruction by synthesis	—	X

X = always necessary
O = occasionally necessary

Recognition of Known Compounds. According to the theory of superposition, if the test substance* and a known compound agree qualitatively and quantitatively in all properties, the two are identical. In practice it is not necessary to test and measure *all* properties of the two materials. The number and sequence of the tests can be selected to provide positive and unequivocal identification but at the same time avoid redundant and unnecessary work.

The properties employed for comparison of the sample with known substances are usually the physical constants, either of the substance itself or of a suitable derivative. This assumes, of course, that these physical constants have not only been carefully determined for the known compound but have also been tabulated and made readily available in some system. The system which tabulates the properties of the largest number of compounds in a manner which permits easy and quick comparison with observed properties has the widest applicability and utility. In addition, since the values of the physical constants can be changed considerably by the presence of even small amounts of other substances, a further restriction on all systems of organic compound identification lies in the purity of the substance being identified. In the present volume a "pure" substance is considered one whose physical constants do not differ by more than the experimental error of determination from those accepted in the literature for that compound. If the tests for purity given in Chapter I show the test substance to be a mixture, it must first be separated into its components by one or more of the methods given in the same chapter.

Once the material used as sample for identification is considered pure, no further separations are required. However, a series of reactions must be carried out to place the compound into one of a number of groups and to thus narrow the field of search in the tables of properties. Thus the number of final identifying tests required to distinguish between the several remaining possibilities will also be reduced. Such reactions are the tests for the elements, the determination of type of functional group, the determination of solubility, etc.

The process of identification is, therefore, a series of tests which successively reduce the number of possible compounds with which the test substance may be identical. Some of these tests are chemical, others may be based on physical behavior.

It should be emphasized that in investigations involving organic compounds as much information as possible on the physical and chemical properties of a test substance should be obtained. The often slight dif-

---

* The term *test substance* is used in this book to designate the material under investigation. The term *sample* is reserved for the aliquot of the test substance employed in an operation or reaction.

ferences in properties between, e. g., two adjacent members of an homologous series or between two stereoisomers make a maximum of data imperative. Such investigations should be regarded as problems to be solved by any and all methods. The general procedures are outlined and some special tests are described but the selection and application must be determined by the behavior of the test substance as the analysis proceeds.

Cognition of New Compounds. Since the chemical and physical properties of new compounds are not described or tabulated in the literature and hence cannot be superimposed upon those of a known compound, it is necessary to first identify the constituent parts of the molecule, beginning with the elements, followed by the functional group or groups (type and number) and then to the basic carbon structure (ring, chain, etc.) to which these groups are attached. The next step is the determination of the manner in which these parts are joined together. This last is determined by breaking up the molecule into simpler, known compounds which can be identified by the *recognition* procedures. The reactions used in such breaking up are known as degradative procedures or reactions and serve also to help identify the basic carbon structure. They consist chiefly of oxidation, hydrolysis and alkali fusion.

In some cases final and complete proof of the constitution and structure of the compound must be supplied by re-synthesis.

A problem similar to the cognition of new compounds is met with in the case of compounds for which information concerning the properties is not available because of difficulty in locating the description of the compound in the literature. In such cases the cognition procedures must be followed.

The following are the steps in the cognition procedure in somewhat more detail.

1) Identification of elements. This is carried out exactly as in recognition.

2) Identification and determination of functional groups. This is also carried out as in recognition but the number as well as the type of each functional group in a molecule must be determined. An important factor is the interpretation of the results of the tests. In the case of multiple and different functional groups (such as amino acids, hydroxy acids, etc.) the characteristic properties of one group may be weakened or otherwise affected by the presence of the other or others. Even inert groups may prevent characteristic reactions through steric hindrance. The degradative procedures described below usually make it possible to resolve such difficulties. These procedures separate the functional groups as parts of the fragments resulting from the fracture of the original material.

3) The carbon structure is determined by (a) quantitative elementary analysis, (b) molecular weight determinations, (c) certain classification

tests such as bromine addition, permanganate oxidation, sulfuric acid solution.

4) Degradative procedures. These consist of oxidation (potassium permanganate, potassium dichromate), hydrolysis (acid and alkaline), and alkali fusion. The last is rather destructive and much material is lost, but it is most effective and useful for certain types of compounds such as oxygen heterocyclic compounds. The degradative reaction is followed by separation of the fragments and identification of these by the recognition procedures.

Systematic Analysis. To facilitate the comparison of the properties of a carbon compound with those listed in the original literature, a number of systematic procedures have been developed. These compile certain of the properties in a sequence which is intended to minimize the required number of tests and determinations. The procedure with the fewest steps, however, is not always the most desirable. A second, even more important, consideration is the number of compounds whose properties are listed in the tables of the procedure. Another very important concern is the provision such tables make for compounds which may exhibit *out-of-class* properties. For example, if the solubility of the sample in acid is used as a test, some compounds may not effectively show a sufficient basic character because of the presence of a second, acidic, functional group. An effective, efficient procedure should permit classification and identification of such compounds either by using a fixed sequence of tests and listing the compound under the first type for which a positive test is obtained or by listing it under all possible groups. Again, it should be emphasized that the steps in the actual procedure for the sample at hand must be selected by the analyst on the basis of the results obtained as the tests are performed.

The need for careful interpretation of results becomes obvious when the difficulties in the identification of carbon compounds but not encountered in inorganic analysis are considered. The reactions are, for the most part, non-ionic and often between reactants not even in the same phase. Thus the rates of reaction are low. Also equilibria are reached in most cases far from complete conversion and the rates of reaction are low. Yields of the product which is to serve as a means of identification or as a means of separation are often low. Since homologs or even two compounds with the same functional group but with the different carbon structure react similarly, separation by chemical means becomes most difficult. Hence the basic requirement is the isolation of a *pure* single substance prior to actual identification. The very first step, therefore, regardless of which procedure is employed, must be the purification of the sample or separation of the compound from other ingredients of the test substance.

Long experience with the various systems of analysis has led the author

TABLE 2
Classification According to Mulliken and Huntress

Order 1. *Compounds containing only C and H, or C, H, and O*

Suborder 1. Colorless Compounds

Genus 1. Aldehydes	A. Solids		B. Liquids	
2. Carbohydrates	A. Solids			
3. Acids	A. Solids	A_1 Soluble	B. Liquids	B_1 Soluble
		A_2 Insoluble		B_2 Insoluble
4. Phenols	A. Solids		B. Liquids	
5. Esters	A. Solids		B. Liquids	
6. Anhydrides, Lactones	A. Solids		B. Liquids	
7. Ketones	A. Solids		B. Liquids	
8. Alcohols	A. Solids	A_1 Soluble	B. Liquids	B_1 } acc. to
		A_2 Insoluble		B_2 } density
9. Hydrocarbons and Ethers	A. Solids	A_1 } acc. to	B. Liquids	B_1 } acc. to
		A_2 } sol., etc.		B_6 } density

Suborder 2. Colored Compounds

Generic Divisions	A. Solids	B. Liquids

Order 2. *Compounds containing nitrogen in addition to C, H, and O*

Suborder 1. Colorless Compounds

Genus 1. Acidic Species	A. Solids	B. Liquids
2. Basic Species	A. Solids	B. Liquids
3. Neutral Species	A. Solids	B. Liquids

Suborder 2. Colored Compounds

Generic Division	A. Solids

Compounds containing but one "additional" element

Order 3.	Chlorine	A. Solids	B. Liquids	B_1, $D > 1.15$
				B_2, $D < 1.15$
Order 4.	Bromine	A. Solids	B. Liquids	B_1, $D > 1.50$
				B_2, $D < 1.50$
Order 5.	Iodine	A. Solids	B. Liquids	
Order 7.	Sulfur	A. Solids	B. Liquids	

Compounds containing two "additional" elements

Order 50.	Nitrogen and chlorine	A. Solids	B. Liquids
Order 51.	Nitrogen and iodine	A. Solids	B. Liquids
Order 52.	Nitrogen and iodine	A. Solids	B. Liquids
Order 54.	Nitrogen and sulfur	A. Solids	B. Liquids
Order 70.	Sulfur and chlorine	A. Solids	B. Liquids

to adopt that of Professors S. P. MULLIKEN and E. R. HUNTRESS as the basis for the present volume. Some features of other procedures are included for use when the analyst may feel they can serve to advantage. It will be pointed out in later discussion of these features when and how they can be employed.

After determination of the most important physical constants of the test substance (melting point, boiling point, refractive index) as described in Chapter IV, it is classified on the basis of its elementary composition (Chapter III). These classes are known as *orders* and they are listed in Table 2 (*see* page 5).

The comparative rarity of the compounds of orders higher than Order II, the ease of characterization by elementary composition, and the use of Order I tests for functional groups usually make extended tests for these compounds unnecessary.

In the case of Order I and II compounds further classification is required after the qualitative elementary analysis in order to place the compound within a reasonably smaller group, the genus (Chapter VI). These grouping (generic) tests are carried out under carefully specified conditions. The genus is distinguished chiefly by the presence of a distinctive functional group but because of the difficulties mentioned before, other compounds which give a positive reaction in a given generic test are included in the tabulation of the members of that genus. Further division may also be made on the basis of color, state (solid or liquid at room temperature), solubility, density, etc.

At this point in the investigation the analyst should consult the tables in the back of this book to ascertain if a compound or compounds with the characteristics determined so far is listed. Reference to other works such as Beilstein or the journals may also be necessary or helpful. If such comparison of properties, observed and listed, indicates that the test substance may be a listed compound or one of several, final identification can be achieved by preparation of a derivative or by a quantitative determination such as that of neutralization equivalent, etc.

If the tables and literature reveal no compound with properties similar to those observed on the test substance, the procedure for *cognition* must be followed.

Part I.

Fundamental Techniques and Preparation of Sample.

Chapter I.

Fundamental Apparatus and Operations.

As pointed out previously, final identification of a substance is achieved by measurement of the physical constants either of the original material or of a derivative or degradation product. It is obvious that the certainty of the identification depends upon the reliability of the value of this constant. This in turn depends upon purity of the test substance. Aside from the application of analytical reasoning to the selection and interpretation of the reactions performed, the skill and care applied to the experimental work are the most important factors in obtaining the correct end product with satisfactory purity and thus successful analysis.

The difficulties inherent in reactions of carbon compounds impose a great demand upon the analyst's skill. Not only, as pointed out before, are these reactions usually far from complete but the final identification form is most often obtained only after an extended series of operations, each resulting in either some loss or contamination. Oils, volatile substances, and the like are lost either by evaporation or in the course of transferring the materials from one vessel to another. By-products, often with properties much like the desired product, are formed in each step.

Techniques must be employed which minimize such losses and contamination. This is especially necessary when quantities of the order of centigrams and milligrams are involved. Microtechniques, therefore, are generally distinguished from semi-micro or miniature techniques in that they make use of phenomena different from those used with larger quantities of material and are not merely based upon macro-sized apparatus reduced in scale. Some techniques are used in almost all analyses while others are used for only a few specific purposes. In this chapter the fundamental apparatus and operations only will be discussed.

Capillaries.

Preparation. Capillary tubes or *capillaries* are drawn from soft glass (in a few special cases, Pyrex) tubing about 6 to 8 mm in diameter. It is not advisable to use wider tubing or test tubes because the capillaries made therefrom will have walls too thin for further working. Heat the wide tube in a Bunsen flame so that a length of 1 to 3 cm (Fig. 1 *a*) becomes soft and workable. For a narrow capillary, heat only a short length; for a wide one, heat a greater length. Then remove the tube from the flame and pull the ends apart, gently at first and then with more force as the glass cools. Some practice will enable the analyst to determine the rate of draw-

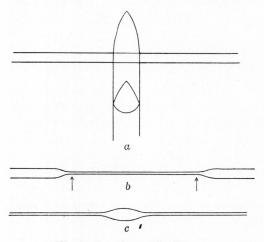

Fig. 1. Drawing a Capillary

ing required to obtain capillaries of uniform bore. The final capillary should have a bore of from a few tenths to about 2 mm. Cut the capillary from the wide tube at the points indicated by arrows (Fig. 1 *b*), at which the tubing becomes conical. The small ampule files or knives, obtainable from supply houses, have been found excellent for cutting capillaries. They cut easily and without crushing the capillary as ordinary files often do. Prepare a large number of capillaries of various diameters and keep in lengths of 15 to 20 cm in a stoppered test tube. The bulb-shaped portions (Fig. 1 *c*) remaining after the capillaries have been cut off can be used as centrifugal or contraction pipets for handling larger volumes of liquids.

Capillary pipets. Prepare these pipets by holding the middle of a length of capillary tubing, about 20 cm long, in the Bunsen or microburner flame until it just softens, Fig. 2. This point is usually reached at the moment the flame becomes yellow. Remove the tube immediately from the flame and quickly pull out to a much finer capillary. The bore of the latter should be from 0.05 to 0.1 mm. Break off the fine capillary about 1 cm from each wider one; the latter thus become pipets (Fig. 2a and b).

If the directions for a test call for a definite volume of a liquid, calibrate these pipets either by the use of another, larger calibrated pipet or by measurement of the bore using a microscope or lens. Partly fill (preferably with a colored liquid) a 1-ml Mohr-type measuring pipet (divided into tenths and hundredths of a milliliter). Read the volume to the nearest 0.005 ml. Touch the tip of the capillary pipet to the tip of the large pipet. The liquid will be drawn into the finer bore tube. When about 150 to 200 mm of liquid column have entered the capillary, take it away from the larger pipet. Read the volume in the latter again. The difference in the two readings is, of course, the volume of the liquid in the capillary, assuming that none has been lost during the transfer. Measure the length

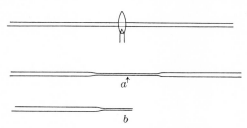

Fig. 2. Preparing a Capillary Pipet.

of the liquid column in the capillary. A simple calculation will give the volume per millimeter of length.

To calibrate by measurement of the cross-sectional area, cut off a small piece of the capillary and hold it in a vertical position under the microscope or lens (see Fig. 9) and measure the bore with a fine ruler or a calibrated ocular micrometer. Table 3 gives the volume per millimeter of length for capillaries of various bores.

TABLE 3
Capacity of Capillary Tubes

Bore mm	Capacity µl/mm length	Bore mm	Capacity µl/mm length
0.1	0.008	1.1	0.95
0.2	0.03	1.2	1.13
0.3	0.07	1.3	1.33
0.4	0.126	1.4	1.54
0.5	0.196	1.5	1.70
0.6	0.28	1.6	2.01
0.7	0.38	1.7	2.27
0.8	0.50	1.8	2.55
0.9	0.64	1.9	2.84
1.0	0.79	2.0	3.14

It is often possible to use uncalibrated pipets for measurement of relative quantities of reagents, etc. If it is assumed that the capillary has a uniform bore, the volume is directly proportional to the length of the liquid column. When a certain ratio of volumes of solutions is required but the actual volume of each is not important, the solutions can be measured in terms of length (mm) of liquid column in the capillary. Some procedures in the following pages, therefore, will specify the number of millimeters of reagent, etc. instead of microliters.

Transfer of Liquids. Liquids may be introduced into capillaries either by applying suction with the mouth or, better, by relying upon capillary attraction. If suction is used, the capillary should be long enough so that the analyst's face is sufficiently distant from the liquid being drawn up to enable him see the meniscus. It is helpful to stand a mirror

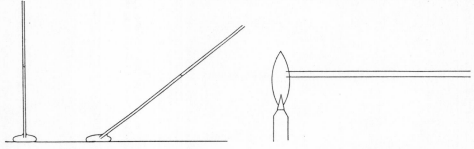

Fig. 3. Filling a Capillary.   Fig. 4. Sealing a Capillary.

on the table so that the reflection of the capillary and the level of the liquid in the vessel from which it is being drawn can be seen. When not too great a volume of liquid is to be taken up, merely dipping the capillary end into the liquid suffices to introduce the quantity required. The length of the liquid column drawn in can be regulated by inclining the capillary (Fig. 3). The more it is inclined, the more liquid will be drawn in. The liquid may also be drawn in by dipping the capillary farther into the liquid, closing the top with the finger when the desired length of column has entered, and then withdrawing; the disadvantage of this method is that the outside of the capillary is covered with the liquid for a considerable length. After a liquid has been drawn into a capillary, wipe off the outside of the end which has been in contact with the liquid with the edge of a piece of filter paper.

Capillaries are sealed by holding the very tip of the end to a flame, Fig. 4. The fusion of the glass should take place so that the walls of the tube collapse at the opening first and then on toward the center of the capillary. Since the presence of a solid (residue from evaporation, carbon, or ash from pyrolyzed liquid, etc.) will prevent perfect sealing, draw the liquid into the capillary some distance from the end being sealed. If the liquid in the capillary is a solution, draw in a very small amount of the solvent after the solution in order to wash the inside of the capillary. If washing with the solvent is not possible or permissible, pinch the softened end of the capillary with forceps when sealing.

Heating in capillaries. Heat the contents of capillaries by placing the tube in a hole in a metal heating block (*see* Fig. 17) or by heating in a liquid bath. The temperature can be controlled within narrow limits by the latter method. Place the capillary in a test tube which contains a liquid which boils at the temperature at which the heating is to be carried out. The capillary should be sealed at both ends if heated in this way. Bring the liquid to a gentle boil over the Bunsen or other heat source. When heating is completed, centrifuge the contents of the capillary to one end, Fig. 5. Scratch the empty end with a file and, holding it away from the face, break it off. Break off the other end in the same way if required. If the filled end is opened first, the contents will either fly out or spread out in a number of small drops throughout the capillary, thereby making recovery difficult.

Mixing in capillaries. If the contents of the capillary must be mixed, seal both ends and centrifuge the contents first to one end and then the other. Be certain that the capillary is shorter than the radius of the centrifuge, Fig. 6. If it is longer, it may break, or, at least, part of the contents will be centrifuged to one end and part to the other. A glass thread (*see* Fig. 14) can also be used for stirring. Do not leave such threads in the capillary while centrifuging as they will break and considerable broken glass will be added to the solid material in the capillary. When centrifuging capillaries, place them in centrifuge cones and then place the cones in the metal shells of the centrifuge, Fig. 6.

Drying in Capillaries. Draw out one end of a glass tube to a fine capillary. Bend the glass tube at a right angle and the capillary at a very obtuse angle, Fig. 7, so that it acts as a spring when placed inside the capillary containing the material to be dried. Allow air from a pump or other source to pass through a wash bottle containing concentrated sulfuric acid and then to the wide tube. Place a plug of cotton at the junction of the wide tube and capillary. Dip the sample capillary in a heating bath or block while passing the air through it. The temperature of the bath should be at or slightly above the boiling point of the solvent being removed.

Coloroscopic Capillaries. Faint colors can be detected in liquids by the use of the coloroscopic capillary. This consists of a capillary with a carefully sealed end, which is filled with the liquid and cut just below the meniscus of the latter.

Draw the liquid to be examined into the capillary. Seal one end carefully by rotating in the flame to form a rounded end. It is important

not to have it sealed so as to give a conical interior which would result
in the total reflection of the light used for illumination of the capillary,
Fig. 8a. Centrifuge the liquid to the sealed end. If a precipitate appears,

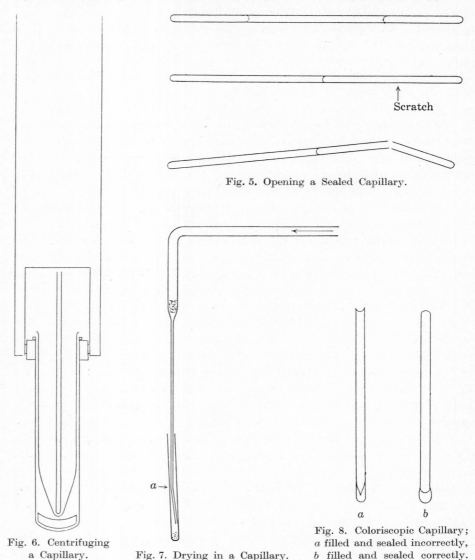

Fig. 5. Opening a Sealed Capillary.

Scratch

Fig. 6. Centrifuging
a Capillary.

a →

Fig. 7. Drying in a Capillary.

a   b

Fig. 8. Coloriscopic Capillary;
a filled and sealed incorrectly,
b filled and sealed correctly.

cut off the portion of the capillary with the precipitation. Seal the other
end as before and centrifuge the liquid to this end. Cut off the empty
portion of the tube just below the meniscus of the liquid. The tube should
be completely filled with liquid and contain no air bubbles. Now mount
it in a vertical position on a microscope slide by using a piece of modeling

clay or wax or a capillary clamp, Fig. 9. Place the slide on the microscope stage, the sealed end of the capillary having been dipped in a drop of water to form a better optical connection, and focus the microscope on the open end of the capillary. The field should show a bright circular band of light (the cross section of the capillary) and in the center of this a disk of the color expected if the test is positive. If the center of the bright ring is dark, add water (capillary pipet).

Microscope Slides.

The flat microscope slides used in inorganic microanalysis are not always suitable for organic work because organic solvents wet the glass much better than water, even when the slide is slightly "greasy" as when rubbed with the fingers. The drops of organic solvents therefore spread out in

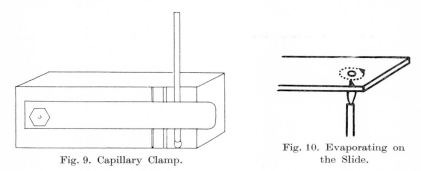

Fig. 9. Capillary Clamp.

Fig. 10. Evaporating on the Slide.

a thin film and make further work difficult. With aqueous solutions, of course, the ordinary slides are perfectly satisfactory. When organic liquids are used, it is best to employ slides with a concave or cylindrical depression, like those used in biological work. In many instances it will be found that cover slips can be used in place of microscope slides. This is especially true when a crystalline precipitation is being prepared for a melting point determination.

Heating on a Slide. It is not recommended that the usual wide (25 mm) slides be heated directly with a flame. They are apt to crack and break. If the sample must be heated in this manner, use a narrow slide (approx. 8 mm wide) and move the portion bearing the sample over the flame in a circular motion, Fig. 10. This will not only minimize thermal strains but also bring about evaporation at the edges of the drop and thus prevent spreading out of the liquid.

Direct heating is carried out best on a micro cover slip especially when determining melting points. To transfer a solid, prepare a slurry of the material with some liquid. Take this up in a wide capillary and transfer it to a cover slip. There remove the small amount of the liquid either

with a capillary pipet or by a triangle of filter paper, Fig. 11. Place the
cover slip on a melting point block. Examine it with a lens and remove
any adhering filter paper fibers or other impurities by means of a needle

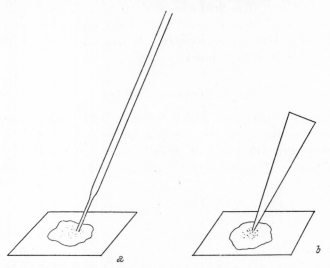

Fig. 11.   Transfer of a Solid; *a* transfer of slurry; *b* removal of liquid with filter paper.

or glass thread (*see* page 29). First heat gently and slowly to the boiling
point of the solvent, if possible, and then, when the material is dry, cover
it with a second cover slip and continue the heating until the substance
melts.

Microcones.

The centrifuge tubes used in microanalysis, called cones or microcones,
are usually of 1- or 2-ml capacity. Most laboratory supply houses now
offer centrifuges with heads especially made for these sizes of tubes but
adapters can be purchased for the same purpose to fit any hand or electrical
centrifuge.

Microcones are used with larger quantities of material than used in
capillaries or on microscope slides, i. e., several milligrams. Liquids are
introduced by means of a capillary pipet or a centrifugal pipet, Fig. 12.

Mixing in Microcone. Reagents and sample are mixed by means
of a glass thread. Make this by holding a capillary in the flame of a microburner until the portion in the flame fuses to a solid, Fig. 13*a* and *b*. Then
take it from the flame and draw it out quickly, as in making a capillary
pipet, Fig. 13*c*. Cut the thread of glass so that a piece about 5 cm long
is left attached to the capillary. The latter serves as a handle. Hold the
cut end of the thread briefly in the flame until it softens and forms a bead.
Hold the thread horizontally during the heating so that the bead will

hang to one side of the thread, Fig. 13d. When the thread with the bead
is twirled between the forefinger and the thumb and at the same time
drawn in and out of the solution in the centrifuge cone, a very thorough

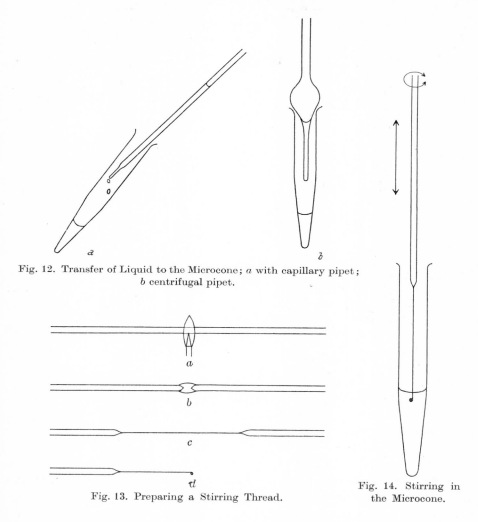

Fig. 12. Transfer of Liquid to the Microcone; a with capillary pipet;
b centrifugal pipet.

Fig. 13. Preparing a Stirring Thread.

Fig. 14. Stirring in
the Microcone.

agitation will result, Fig. 14. Remove the thread before centrifuging,
however, as it may break in that operation.

Stirring can also be accomplished in a centrifuge cone by means of the
flea stirrer or the electromagnetic stirrer described under Microbeakers
below.

Cleaning Microcone. Microcones should be cleaned as soon after use
as possible to prevent the drying of solutions with consequent adhesion
of residues difficult to redissolve or remove. After use fill the microcone

with the proper solvent, allow it to stand for a while in order to get as much of the residue as possible into solution; then draw off the liquid. This can be done best by the use of an apparatus shown in Fig. 15. Then add more solvent and rinse the cone several times with fresh solvent. Should any solid adhere to the cone, loosen it by means of a stiff narrow feather or a *pipe cleaner*, that is, a cotton cord wound on a wire. If necessary, use a strong alkali solution to dissolve or loosen all the residue. Dry cones

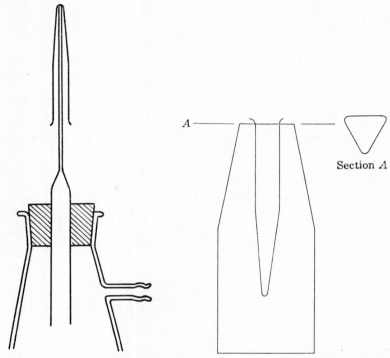

Section *A*

Fig. 15. Cleaning of Microcones, $^2/_3$ nat. size.

Fig. 16. Heating on the Steam Bath, nat. size.

by centrifuging and sucking off the drop of liquid collected at the bottom in this way; then put the cone away in a box.

Heating in Microcones. Microcones can be placed upon the water bath by means of a conical glass tube with a triangular opening at the narrow end, Fig. 16. This may be supported by a metal tube of slightly wider internal diameter fastened to a water bath ring. Place this tube on the water bath and drop in the cone. It will be held by its rim on the triangular opening. For heating at other temperatures a brass, copper, or aluminum block, drilled to hold the microcone snugly, is recommended. This block can also be drilled with a hole about 2.5 mm in diameter for capillaries and another about 7 mm in diameter for a thermometer. The

hole for the cones should be just wide enough to permit the conical portion
to enter but not the cylindrical part.   Clamp the block on a ring stand
with the bottom projecting through a piece of asbestos paper, Fig. 17.
The same arrangement may also be used for heating reflux tubes.

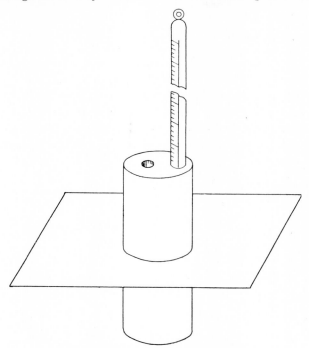

Fig. 17. Heating Block, $^2/_3$ nat. size.

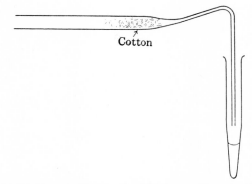

Cotton

Fig. 18. Evaporating in the Microcone, $^2/_3$ nat. size.

Drying in Microcones.   Evaporation or removal of solvent can be
carried out in microcones by the use of a stream of air. The set-up is shown
in Fig. 18.   The air or other gas may be supplied from a source of compressed air or gas or it may be obtained from an aspirator if the evapo-

ration does not require too much time. The cone may be placed in a water
bath or heating block. An electrically heated wire coil inside the air inlet
tube has been suggested by KURTZ (1).

Phase Separation in Microcones. At this point only the simple,

Fig. 19. Use of Capillary Pipet.

unmodified cone will be considered. Modifications which provide certain
advantages for specific uses will be described in a later chapter.

The separation of phases based upon differences in density of the phases
is accelerated greatly by the use of a centrifuge. When centrifuging results

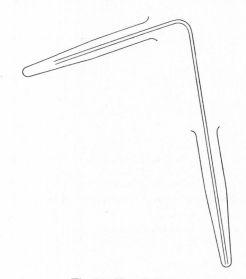

Fig. 20. Use of Siphon.

in clean-cut separation of the two phases, remove the upper phase by
using either a capillary pipet or a capillary siphon. If a capillary pipet
is used, incline the cone toward the horizontal as far as possible and lay
the capillary in it. The tip should not touch the liquid. When in the proper
position, the tip of the pipet should touch the uppermost wall of the cone
and the pipet itself should rest on the lower edge of the mouth of the cone,
Fig. 19. Then push it continuously farther into the cone with one finger,
keeping the tip under the surface of the liquid, until it almost touches
the interface of the second phase. Then remove the pipet, keeping it in
a horizontal position. Centrifuge the cone once more and remove, by
means of the emptied capillary pipet, any upper layer which may collect.

The capillary siphon is a capillary bent into the form of an inverted **V**. One arm of the **V** should be longer than the other. Place the long arm into an empty microcone. Hold this cone with the palm and little finger of the right hand and the siphon between the forefinger and thumb of the same hand. Hold horizontally by the thumb and forefinger of the left hand the cone containing the liquid to be siphoned off. Gradually insert the shorter arm of the siphon into this cone and draw off the upper layer as described above with the capillary pipet, Fig. 20. A larger volume of liquid can be removed by the siphon at one time since most of the liquid is drained into a second cone.

Spot Plates.

Color tests particularly can be carried out in the depressions of a spot plate. Spot plates made of white porcelain, black glazed porcelain, and clear glass are now obtainable. The latter, if Pyrex, has a slight greenish yellow tint which should be taken into consideration when making color tests.

In general, spot plates of any kind should be used only when a very decided color change is to take place. Faint colorations, even when viewed on a white porcelain plate or on the glass plate against a white background, do not show up very well and can easily be mistaken for a shadow.

Reflux Tubes.

Because of the large surfaces of a reflux system consisting of a flask, stopper, and condenser, such a set-up does not lend itself to work with small quantities. The small amount of liquid would spread itself over these surface, and be lost. Furthermore, cork and rubber stoppers absorb certain liquids and vapors and thus cause the latter to be lost.

A simple micro reflux apparatus is made from a glass tube 4 to 5 mm in diameter and 100 mm long, blown out at one end into a bulb 6 to 7 mm in diameter, Fig. 21 *a*. A constriction near the open end facilitates sealing, Fig. 21 *b*. If no precipitate is formed in the reaction, place some asbestos at the bottom of the bulb to absorb the liquid. Introduce the liquid test substance and the reagent by means of a long capillary pipet directly into the bulb. Seal the open end of the tube and place the bulb and lower portion of the tube in a heating bath or heating block. The upper end of the tube should project above the top of the block so that any condensate which may form in this portion can readily be seen. If too large a condensate forms, remove the tube from the bath or block, centrifuge the condensate back into the bulb, and resume the heating. When the heating is completed, cool the tube and first cut off the tip of the capillary end to release the pressure. Then cut the wider portion of the tube at *a*,

2*

Fig. 21c. By inverting this portion of the tube into the lower bulb portion, any liquid or condensate in it can be washed back into the bulb.

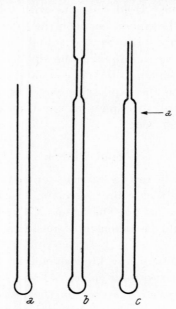

Fig. 21. Reflux Tubes; nat. size.

Microbeakers.

In some cases the larger capacity of the microbeakers will be found desirable or necessary. These microbeakers may have flat, round, or conical bottoms, Fig. 22. The latter two forms are preferable since they permit

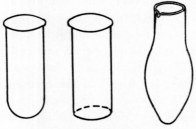

Fig. 22. Microbeakers.

concentration of the sample in a small area. Treatment of substance is the same as with the cones except that centrifugation is not used with the microbeakers.

Mixing in Microbeakers. Stirring is effected by passing a stream of gas bubbles through the liquid by means of a *flea* stirrer or an electromagnetic stirrer.

Stirring by means of an air or gas stream has the advantage of avoiding introduction of another device with additional surface and it can provide the inert atmosphere required in certain reactions such as titration of acids or bases. Pass the air or gas through a purifying system (sulfuric acid, soda-lime, etc.) and then through a 6- to 7-mm tube which is drawn down to a capillary 60 to 80 mm long. A plug of asbestos or cotton at the junction of the capillary and the wide tube will serve to catch any entrained droplets or particles. Bend the capillary at an angle of about 115° to the wide tube as shown in Fig. 23 and insert its end into the liquid

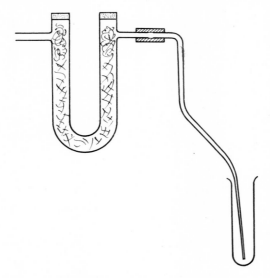

Fig. 23. Stirring with a Gas Stream.

to be stirred. Adjust the stream of gas to provide sufficient stirring without spattering or splashing.

Stirring with a *flea* stirrer is required when the material must be completely enclosed. Make a flea by enclosing a small amount of soft iron powder in a short length of capillary tubing. The size of the flea is governed by the volume of liquid being stirred and the size and shape of the container. Mount an electromagnet (the type used in door bells or buzzers is sufficiently large and powerful) so that its poles are at the level of the surface of the liquid being stirred. The circuit of the electromagnet should include a *flasher* of the type used either for automobile directional signals or for intermittent operation of advertising signs and the like. The former type is used when the magnet is powered directly by a battery or from a transformer and the latter is placed in the power line ahead of the transformer. These flashers will alternately close and open the circuit to the magnet, thus causing the flea to rise and then to drop back.

Electromagnetic stirrers are usually fine glass rods fastened to the vibrator of an electric buzzer or bell. The frequency or amplitude of the vibration should be adjusted so keep the movement of the glass rod within a few hundredths of a millimeter.

Heating in Microbeakers. Microbeakers can usually be heated directly over the flame if required. The device shown in Fig. 24 is used

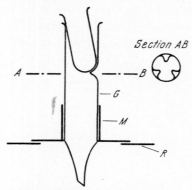

Fig. 24. Heating Mikrobeakers.
M metal ring
R water bath ring
G glass jacket

with a water bath. Metal blocks are less desirable as they do not permit observation of the contents of the beaker.

Filtration in Microbeakers. This will be discussed later under "Preparation of the Sample." *See* page 52.

Drying in Microbeakers. Drying can be achieved by heating on a water bath, possibly with assistance of a stream of air, Fig. 18 as described under Microcones. If a filterstick is employed to separate a precipitate, the apparatus described on page 55 under "Preparation of the Sample" should be used.

Determination of Weight.

If the analyst has access to a microchemical balance of the KUHLMANN type, samples for the various quantitative determinations can be weighed out easily enough. One of the following two substitutes will serve for most purposes of organic qualitative analysis.

Ordinary Analytical Balance. It has been shown that analytical balances found in most laboratories can be used in place of microchemical balances if not too great a precision is required. Since the quantitative determinations required for distinction between some compounds, such as homologs, as, e. g., neutralization equivalents and saponification numbers, do not require a very high precision, such analytical balances can readily be used with excellent results. The method of weighing follows.

With the pans empty or with almost equal weights on both pans, bring the rider exactly into position so that front and back legs are in line with the mark on the rider scale. Use only the divisions indicating whole milligrams. Use the pan arrest alone, keeping the beam arrest in the released position. Release the balance and allow the beam to swing. Disregard the first two complete swings. Take readings by regarding the center of the scale as zero and reading the inflections to the left as minus and those to the right as plus. Read each division as 10 units. Take three

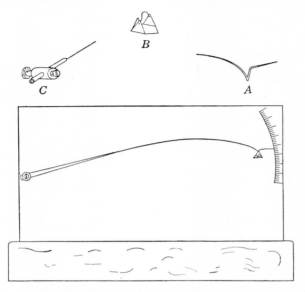

Fig. 25. Glass Fiber Balance, $1/3$ nat. size.

consecutive readings. For example, the readings may be — 15, + 26, and — 13. Calculate the deflection by averaging the results on one side and adding the results algebraically. Thus, in the example, the deflection would be $1/2$ [— 15 + (— 13)] + 26 = + 12. Then shift the rider 1 mg and determine the deflection again. Dividing 1 mg by the algebraic difference between the two deflections gives the value in milligrams for each unit of the pointer scale. This, of course, is the reciprocal of the sensitivity of the balance. Weigh the sample in the usual way but calculate the fractions of the milligram from the value of the division and the deflection instead of determining them by adding weights to the balance pan or by moving the rider. In this way it is possible to weigh to the nearest hundredth of a milligram. This suffices for this type of work if the samples weigh 6 to 10 mg.

Salvioni or Glass Fiber Balance. A simple modified form of the Salvioni balance is shown in Fig. 25. A glass or clear plastic plate about

15 cm $\times$ 25 cm is mounted vertically along its long edge in a slot in a wooden base board. A clamp (Fig. 25 C) is fastened at the center of one side through a hole in the plate at this edge or on the edge itself. Through this clamp is passed a glass or quartz rod, 2 cm long, which has been drawn out into a fine fiber at one end. The free end of this fiber is bent into a hook as shown in Fig. 25 A. The tip may be blackened with India ink to render it more easily visible against the background. A white paper or plastic scale is fastened to the right side of the plate in such a position that the tip of the fiber will pass over the scale. A tiny pan can be constructed of a square piece of aluminum or platinum foil, approximately 5 mm $\times$ 5 mm, by bending up three corners and passing a wire handle through holes in two of these, Fig. 25 B. This is hung on the hook. The clamp is turned so that the tip of the fiber indicates zero when the empty pan is in place. The scale is calibrated by placing small pieces of wire of known weight on the pan. The weight of these pieces of wire can readily be determined by weighing a piece of fine wire, 50–75 mm long, on an analytical balance and then cutting off lengths corresponding to half a milligram. The length is measured carefully, if necessary under a microscope with a calibrated ocular micrometer.

A number of torsion spring balances are available on the market with a considerable range of loads and sensitivities.

When the directions call for a sample of approximate weight, it is not necessary to weigh out this amount. After the analyst has had some experience working with samples of a few milligrams, he will be able to estimate the amount required accurately enough for qualitative purposes. In the case of liquids, if the specific gravity is known, a capillary pipet of known bore can be used and the proper volume taken. If the specific gravity is unknown, the average value of 0.85 for organic liquids can usually be assumed.

The Microscope.

Although a milligram or centigram sample of any carbon compound listed in the tables can be identified without the use of the microscope, this instrument can be as invaluable in the identification of carbon compounds as in inorganic analysis. In fact, as can be seen from the following pages, considerable time and work can be saved if a microscope is used. Its use is not restricted to identification of crystalline form but includes the observation and measurement of other properties such as refractive index and extinction directions. As investigation of the optical properties of various carbon compounds and their tabulation continues, these properties will become of greater importance in the identification of the compounds and will permit further reduction in the time required for identification.

The microscope which will best serve the organic analyst should be fitted with the following equipment: a calibrated rotating stage, objectives 4 × and 10 × and an ocular 8 × (with cross hairs if possible), plane and concave mirrors, substage condenser, polarizer, and analyzer.

The reader is referred to the literature for detailed directions on the use of the microscope and on the measurement of the optical properties.

Reagents.

Aside from the usual laboratory reagents such as acids and alkalies, identification of carbon compounds requires a considerable number of special reagents. While the quantities of these reagents used in the tests are quite small, usually only a few milligrams or microliters, many of them react with the air or moisture in the air, while others decompose or change spontaneously. Larger quantities of these reagents should therefore be kept on hand so that fresh, unchanged material can be taken from under the surface layers or from the supernatant liquid. Bottles which are fitted not only with stoppers but also with ground-on caps are best suited for the protection of sensitive reagents. The reagents should be kept either in dark closets or in boxes to minimize the effect of light.

The directions for making up reagents are given under the notes for the various tests; care should be taken to follow them closely since the result of a test may depend upon such care.

Chapter II.

Preparation of the Sample.

Tests for Purity.

Unlike inorganic substances, carbon compounds cannot be identified by means of a sequence of "separation" reactions. Individual members of an homologous series, for example, could not be separated from each other for the purpose of identification by purely chemical reactions. Nevertheless, final identification of a substance is made, as pointed out before, by measurement of the physical constants of what is assumed to be a single, pure compound. It is obvious, therefore, that the first task of the analyst is to determine whether his test substance is (a) a pure substance, (b) a mixture with one major component and some minor impurities, or (c) a mixture of substances in other proportions. In the case of (b), subjecting the test substance to recrystallization, distillation, etc., usually suffices to free it of impurities. In the case of (c), however, all of the components

are regarded as *major* and are to be separated, purified, and identified
and both chemical and physical methods of separation can and should
be employed.

To determine into which group the test substance falls requires a number
of tests. The result of these tests will also usually permit distinction between
test substances of types (*b*) and (*c*). Inasmuch as it is assumed in micro
work that the amount of available substance is small, the determination
of the purity should be carried out as far as possible by methods which
permit recovery of the sample or which aid in the identification of the
substance at the same time. Such methods include determination of
physical constants, microscopic examination, determination of solubility,
and examination by the schlieren method.

1) In the determination of the boiling point or the melting point, the
behavior of the substance during the heating often gives an indication
of its purity. In the boiling point determination (page 115) if the droplet
rises slowly from the bottom of the capillary to the level of the surface
of the bath liquid over a temperature range of more than 1 or 2 degrees an
impurity is present. It need not be present in high concentration, however,
to cause this effect. It is the difference in the vapor pressure of the components which determines the size of the temperature interval.

2) In the determination of the melting point under a lens or the microscope
the individual particles or crystals can be observed. If some of these melt
and others do not, the presence of a mixture is indicated. However, if the
individual crystals themselves are impure, they will all melt within the same
temperature range. Therefore, after the melting point or melting range
has been determined, the melt should be allowed to congeal again and
observed carefully during this process. Supercooling may take place
and steps should be taken to prevent this. Appearance of simultaneous
liquid and solid phases which persist over a temperature range of ten
degrees or more should be regarded as evidence of impurities.

3) In the determination of the refractive index of solids by the immersion
method (page 124), one component of a crystalline mixture may "disappear" when immersed in a standard liquid while the crystals of another
component remain more or less sharply defined (35, 70).

4) Solid test substances should be examined under the microscope.
Crush and spread out a small amount in a thin layer between two microscope slides. Observe the material remaining on one slide. Look for differences in the crystal form, color, and refractivity of the individual particles.
Owing to the possibility of polymorphism, differences in crystal structure
need not necessarily mean that the test substance is a mixture of two or
more components. However, the difference should be noted and further
tests for homogeneity of the test substance should be applied. Differences in color are more indicative of impurities.

5) The polarizing microscope offers a further possibility for establishing the purity of the test substance. The differences in appearance of singly and doubly refracting substances during examination between crossed nicols under the microscope, determination of melting point, or determination of refractive index, can sharply distinguish between two or more species of particles.

6) The purity of the test substance may also be established by means of the *schlieren* test. In the case of liquids carry out a fractionation, e. g., in an Emich tube (page 33) and allow the distillate to flow into the residue in the schlieren cell (page 131). The appearance of schlieren indicates the presence of impurities. If the test substance is a solid, recrystallize some of it and use saturated solutions of the original substance and the recrystallized material as static and fluid samples. This method is very sensitive; it will detect traces of impurities which would not interfere with the identification of the principal component.

7) Solubility tests may be helpful in determining the purity of solid test substances, particularly if these happen to be mechanical mixtures. Furthermore, while the results of tests (2), (3), (4), and (5) may indicate a mixture, the components may be separate chemical entities or they may be modifications of one compound, e. g., polymorphs. If the latter, they exhibit the same solubility in any given solvent. A quick and simple method of determining solubility is described on page 149. To ascertain if any of the test substance has dissolved in cases where complete solution does not occur, take up the clear liquid in a capillary pipet and transfer to another, clean, spot on the slide and pass solvent-free air over it. It is also advisable to subject the undissolved material to another treatment of solvent-laden air. If some of the sample dissolves and some remains undissolved, even upon additional exposure to solvent, the test substance can be regarded as a mixture. The behavior of certain substances as described on page 75 must be kept in mind in interpreting the results of this test.

8) Differences in specific gravity as shown when a powdered sample is dropped into liquids of varying density have been used for demonstrating the existence of mixtures as well as for separating the components.

9) A test which may provide considerable information on the character of the sample and which should be carried out before further steps are taken is the ignition test. Place a particle (about 0.01 mg) on a platinum microspatula (made by flattening about 5 mm of the end of a 0.5 mm platinum wire fixed in a glass rod or needle holder) and hold it in the colorless flame of a microburner. It is desirable to use one of the adjustable types of microburners because they give a much smaller and finer flame. Do not hold the sample directly in the flame; heat the wire about 1 cm from the flattened end and then move it so that the sample is gradually brought into the flame, Fig. 26. This will prevent loss of the sample by spattering.

During the heating observe the following: (*a*) any melting or sublimation, (*b*) nature of the flame when the substance begins to burn, (*c*) nature of the combustion (flash, quiet, explosive), (*d*) nature of the residue after ignition.

a) An approximate idea of the melting point can be obtained by the amount of heating required in this test. Other phenomena such as loss of water of hydration, sublimation, etc., can also be observed and will be of assistance in later work on the sample.

b) The substance may burn with a non-luminous, luminous, or smoky flame. This will be an indication of the carbon-hydrogen ratio in the compound. If the ratio of hydrogen to carbon is high, the substance will

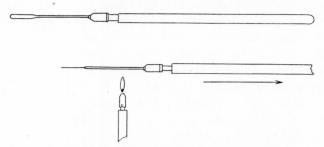

Fig. 26. Heating on the Microspatula; nat. size.

burn with a non-luminous flame and is probably a paraffin or a simple derivative of a paraffin with a carbon to hydrogen ratio of $1:2+$. A luminous flame indicates a higher content of carbon, a ratio of carbon to hydrogen of $1:2$ as in olefines, cycloparaffins, and simple derivatives. An even higher ratio of carbon (carbon to hydrogen $1+:1$) produces a smoky flame and is indicative of aromatic compounds. Colored flames (other than yellow) are produced by compounds which contain metals, usually of the alkali or alkaline earth groups. If a residue remains, it should be heated further at higher temperature. If it was black and disappears on further heating, it was carbon. If the residue seemed to be undergoing swelling during formation, the sample was probably a carbohydrate or an acid like citric or tartaric. If the black residue partly disappears on further heating but a part remains despite continued heating, it may be the oxide or oxides of the heavy metals. If the residue is white it may be the carbonate of an alkali or alkaline earth metal or it may be silica as from silicones. It may also be an inorganic salt remaining from drying or salting out. The residue should be subjected to the usual inorganic qualitative analysis unless the quantity indicates that it was a merely minor impurity.

c) Rapid, almost instantaneous, combustion of the sample indicates high hydrogen content. If the combustion is so rapid that sputtering or explosion result, a high oxygen content as in nitro compounds is indicated. During the combustion, particularly if this is rapid or explosive, the odor, if any, of the combustion products should be noted. Sharp acrid odors of oxides of nitrogen or sulfur or the *burnt hair* odor of nitrogeneous compounds are easily detected.

d) The types of residues after combustion have been mentioned. Usually addition of a drop of water and a test with litmus silk will demonstrate the presence of an alkali or alkaline earth carbonate and a flame test will confirm the identification. Otherwise a systematic analysis must be carried out.

The approximate ratio of the components of a mixture can be established in the case of solids in tests (2), (3), (4), (5), and (8) by comparison of the numbers of particles showing similar behavior. In test (7) the relative quantities of dissolved and undissolved give this information. Subjecting liquid test substances to fractional distillation and then applying the above tests again will serve to indicate the degree of admixture with such materials.

Separation of Minor Components and Impurities.

Distinction is made between the removal of components which are present in only small concentrations and separation of components present in more or less equal proportions. As pointed out before, recrystallization or distillation usually suffices for the former. The latter is designated as separation of mixtures and is discussed in a separate section. Obviously, some of the more efficient methods employed to remove impurities are also applicable to separation of mixtures. Hence, the former methods will be discussed first.

Mechanical Separation.

If the test substance is a solid mixture, it may be possible, if the individual particles are sufficiently large, to pick out enough of the kind desired to provide a sample for analysis. Or, if there are only a few of one kind of particles, these may be regarded as the impurities and may be picked out and the residue used as sample. This selection may save considerable time by avoiding or minimizing other, more time-consuming procedures.

A binocular microscope is preferred for this operation but the usual monocular type with low magnification (and therefore a large working distance) and with proper illumination and contrasting background is also suitable. Spread the test substance out on a microscope slide in a thin layer. Examine the slide under the microscope, separating the particles as much as possible by means of a glass or platinum needle, Fig. 27. When the various kinds of particles have been studied sufficiently to be recognized again, bring one of them to the center of the field. Moisten the point of the needle by rubbing a drop of glycerol on the back of the hand, wiping off all excess, and then drawing the point of the needle over this spot. Bring the point of the needle under the objective of the microscope and, while looking into the ocular, move the point of the needle around until it appears in the field. It will naturally appear indistinct because the microscope is focused on the slide. Bring the point of the needle directly over the particle to be removed, lower it until it touches the particle, carefully raise it again, and then take it out from under the microscope and touch it to a droplet of water at the end of the slide or on another slide.

Repeat this procedure until sufficient material has been removed to form a sample or until the sample under examination has been purified as completely as possible by this method.

Care must be taken not to use too much glycerol. Mechanical removal of impurities usually does not result in a clean and complete separation.

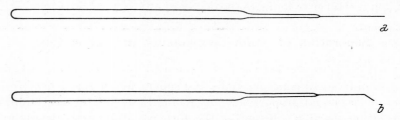

Fig. 27. Needles for Work under the Microscope; *a* platinum, *b* glass. $^2/_3$ nat. size.

Often the particles of the mixture are so small or so close that the needle will remove not only the one particle desired but also others. If the drop of water which acted as receiver is then evaporated, a second mechanical separation in the same manner can be carried out.

If the point of the needle is bent as shown in Fig. 27 b, the needle can be brought under the objective in a horizontal position and then turned on its axis to bring the point into contact with the single particle desired.

As mentioned, if a background of proper contrasting color is employed, the recognition of the particles is facilitated. When the two or more substances have the same color or are both colorless, the polarizing microscope may be of help if one or another of the components is birefringent and the other not.

Particularly when working with natural products or forms such as cells or tissues or when isolating occlusions, the various micromanipulators may be used, *see* Volume 3 of this series. A number of these are available in somewhat simplified forms which are more adapted to microchemical work than the usual biological instruments. These permit working with very small amounts of material and also, because of the greater surety of the movements as contrasted with hand-manipulation, permit more perfect separation.

Distillation

One of the basic physical methods of separating liquids from solids or liquids from other liquids is distillation. Simple distillation involves merely the vaporization of the liquid without decomposition or vaporization of the solid. At first glance this may seem to be a simple matter of evaporating one component and leaving the other, non-volatile, component. Actually, in view of the comparative volatility of so many substances and the possibility of co-distillation, simple evaporation rarely takes place. Practically all of the devices and equipment described in the literature, therefore, are fractionating distillation apparatus.

A large number of these have been described. They range from such simple devices as Chamot's (27) crucible covered with a microscope slide to very complicated pieces of apparatus for the separation of multiple components. Inasmuch as most of them are designed for a specific problem of separation, it is advisable to select the proper apparatus to meet the requirements of the specific problem and sample. Table 4 summarizes the uses and scope of the various devices and will aid in the selection of the most appropriate and effective apparatus. The manipulative details for the more versatile or useful devices are given below. The methods of using the others can be seen from the diagrams and the descriptions.

TABLE 4

Types of Distilling Apparatus

Apparatus	Volume		Boiling Point		Components		Difference in Boiling Point		Proportions of Components	
	Small	Large	High	Low	Two	More than Two	Small	Large	A	B*)
WIDMER (146)	x	x		x		x	x		x	
DUFTON (38)		x		x		x	x		x	
BERING (15)		x				x	x		x	
GARNER (57)		x	x	x	x			x		x
LAPPIN (96)		x	x	x	x			x		x
GROSS and WRIGHT (67)		x		x	x			x		x
ERDÖS and LÁSZLÓ (48) (reflux)		x		x	x		x	x		x
EMICH (tube) (43)	x			x		x	x		x	
EMICH (flask) (44)	x			x		x	x		x	
MORTON and MAHONEY (105)	x			x		x	x		x	

*) A = Approximately equal
B = Differing widely

TABLE 4

Types of Distilling Apparatus—(Continued)

Apparatus	Volume		Boiling Point		Components		Difference in Boiling Point		Proportions of Components	
	Small	Large	High	Low	Two	More than Two	Small	Large	A	B*)
CRAIG (31)	x			x		x	x		x	
GAWALOWSKI (60)	x			x		x	x		x	
YOUNG (151)	x			x		x	x		x	
BERNHAUER (16)		x	x			x		x	x	
GOULD, HOLZMAN, and NIEMAN (reflux) (65)	x			x		x	x		x	
BENEDETTI-PICHLER and SCHNEIDER (10)		x		x	x		x			x
EMICH-SOLTYS (129)	x		x		x		x		x	
EMICH-ALBER (1)	x		x		x		x		x	
WRIGHT (149)	x		x			x	x		x	
PREGL (114)		x	x		x		x			x
PEAKES (109)		x	x			x	x		x	
FRAENKEL, BIELSCHOWSKY, and THANNHAUSER (53)		x	x			x	x		x	
KLENK (89)		x	x			x	x		x	
SCHRADER and RITZER (127)		x	x			x	x		x	
TIEDCKE (136)		x		x		x	x		x	
ELLIS and WEYGAND (42)	x		x			x	x		x	
BABCOCK (4)	x		x			x		x		x
BENEDETTI-PICHLER and RACHELE (11)	x			x	x			x	x	
BAILEY (6)	x		x		x			x	x	x
GOULD, HOLZMAN, and NIEMAN (molecular) (65)	x		x			x		x	x	
PASCHKE, KORNS, and WHEELER (108)		x	x		x			x	x	
RUSHMAN and SIMPSON (123)		x	x			x		x	x	
BREGER (23)		x	x			x			x	
ROPER (120)		x	x			x			x	
POZZI-ESCOT (112)	x		x		x			x	x	
ERDÖS and LÁSZLÓ (49) (steam)	x		x		x			x	x	

Fractional Distillation.

If the volume of the original sample is large, i. e., several milliliters, an apparatus such as described by WIDMER (148) (Fig. 28), DUFTON (38) (Fig. 29) *see* also BERING (15), GARNER (58) (Fig. 30), LAPPIN (97) (Fig. 31),

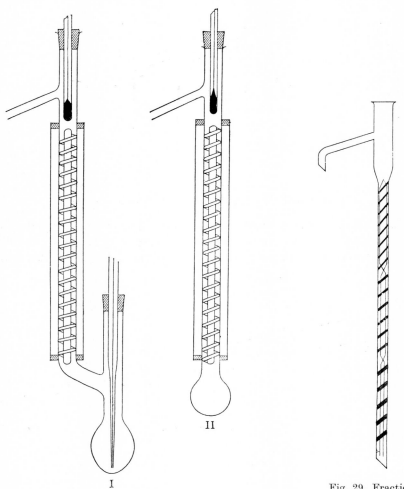

I

II

Fig. 28. Fractionation Apparatus of WIDMER, $^1/_3$ nat. size.

Fig. 29. Fractionation Column of DUFTON.

or GROSS and WRIGHT (67) (Fig. 32) can be used. ERDÖS and LÁSZLÓ (48) describe an apparatus for distilling off a product after a reaction in which refluxing was required, Fig. 33.

Emich Fractionation Tubes. For the fractionation of quantities smaller than 1 ml, EMICH's fractionation tubes (43) are best suited. The operation is simple and quick.

Organic Analysis

The apparatus consists of a piece of Pyrex tubing about 60 mm long
with a bore of about 4 mm, Fig. 34. The tube is constricted at the middle

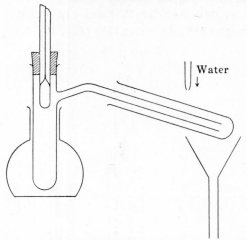

Fig. 30. Distillation Apparatus of GARNER, $^2/_3$ nat. size.

and sealed at one end. A short piece of glass rod is sealed to this end to
serve as a handle. In use, insert the handle into another glass tube about
15 cm long to facilitate manipulation. Pack some acid-washed and ignited

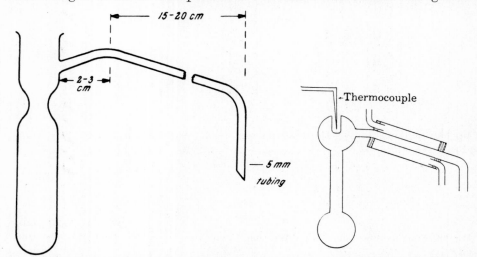

Fig. 31. Fractionation Apparatus of LAPPIN,   Fig. 32. Fractionation Apparatus
$^1/_3$ nat. size.   of GROSS and WRIGHT.

asbestos tightly inside of the sealed end. Sufficient asbestos to absorb
all the liquid to be distilled must be used. Dry the tube thoroughly by
heating it in a Bunsen flame until no more moisture appears. After allowing the tube to cool, introduce the test substance (1 to 3 drops) from a

capillary pipet directly onto the asbestos. Centrifuge into the asbestos
any liquid which may adhere to the walls of the tube. Remove the last
traces of liquid from the upper part of the tube by drawing the upper
end through the Bunsen flame. This is particularly necessary with high-
boiling and viscous liquids. After this part of the tube has cooled, heat
the end of the tube containing the asbestos by holding it about 4 cm above
a small (2 cm) Bunsen flame. Hold the tube at an angle of about 45°
and rotate continuously during the heating, Fig. 35. A ring of condensate

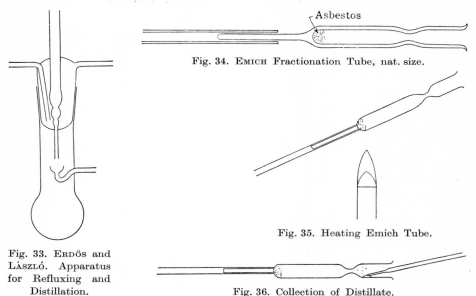

Asbestos

Fig. 34. EMICH Fractionation Tube, nat. size.

Fig. 35. Heating Emich Tube.

Fig. 33. ERDÖS and
LÁSZLÓ. Apparatus
for Refluxing and
Distillation.

Fig. 36. Collection of Distillate.

will appear above the asbestos. Continue the heating carefully so that
this ring will rise slowly and *steadily*. When it has reached the constriction,
stop the heating; when the ring passes the constriction into the open end
of the tube, hold the tube in a horizontal position. The condensate collects
in a drop or droplets and can be taken up by a capillary pipet, Fig. 36.
After cooling, centrifuge the remainder of the liquid in the tube back
into the asbestos and repeat the process. The boiling point of the various
fractions can be determined by the procedure given on page 115; the fractions
with the same boiling point (or within the desired range) can be combined
to form the sample for the analysis.

MORTON and MAHONEY (106) have modified the EMICH fractionation
tube and are able to obtain as many as 70 fractions from initial samples
of only 23 mg. They use capillary tubes 1.5 to 2 mm in bore and 130 mm
long, packed with glass wool, Fig. 37. An insulating jacket of either glass
or asbestos tubing is placed over the middle portion of the tube. The
distillations are carried out as follows.

3*

Pipet a single drop of the test substance into the fractionation tube
and centrifuge until the drop is forced below the constriction to the bottom.
Attach the wet filter paper condenser and the insulating jacket and place
the tube in the metal block used for the heating. This block is drilled to
hold the tubes to a depth just below the constrictions near the top. The
block is covered with an asbestos jacket. Apply heat gradually. The paper

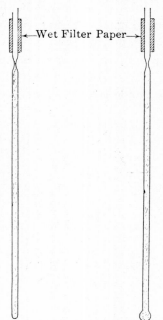

←—Wet Filter Paper—→

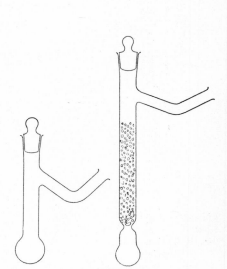

Fig. 37. Fractionation Apparatus of MORTON and MAHONEY,
$^2/_3$ nat. size.

Fig. 38. EMICH Fractionation
Flasks, $^1/_2$ nat. size.

condenser should be wet, and a stream of air directed against it will keep
it cool. When the first tiny droplet of condensate appears above the constriction, stop heating and remove the asbestos jacket of the tube. Take
out the capillary and centrifuge the droplet back into the tube. During
the centrifuging the block should cool off 4 to 5 degrees. Replace the capillary
in the block and heat again. Repeat this heating, removal of capillary,
centrifuging, and cooling three or four times, taking care each time to
note the lowest temperature at which enough liquid for a boiling point
determination will condense above the constriction in one to one and a
half minutes. Then collect a fraction by touching the tip of a boiling
point capillary (*see* page 115) to the droplet. After the determination of the
boiling point and the centrifuging of the fractionation capillary, replace
the latter in the block. The block should not have cooled more than 2
degrees. Repeat for the next fraction.

When only a few fractions are expected, that is, when the number of components is small, the small fractionation flasks of EMICH (44) (Fig. 38), CRAIG (31) (Fig. 39), GAWALOWSKI (60) (Fig. 40), YOUNG (153) (Fig. 41), BERNHAUER (16) (Fig. 42), and GOULD, HOLZMAN, and NIEMAN (65) (Fig. 43) are recommended.

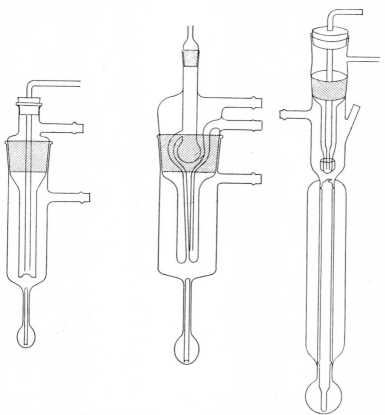

Fig. 39. Fractionation Apparatus of CRAIG, ½ nat. size.

Emich Fractionation Flask. As can be seen from Fig. 38, it is possible to fit the EMICH flasks with a column which can be filled with packing material or to extend the column into a small one of the RASCHIG type as in the Young modification, to use a vacuum jacketed column as in the GOULD, HOLZMAN, and NIEMAN apparatus, or to introduce a thermometer as done by ALBER (1). In the first three modifications the object is to improve the efficiency of the column.

Introduce the liquid to be distilled into the bulb of the flask from a capillary pipet, taking care not to allow any of the liquid to get on the upper walls of the flask. Heat the bulb over a microburner. When the condensate ring appears in the knee-shaped portion of the apparatus, stop the heating. Remove the distillate by means of a capillary pipet. The residue can also be removed in the same way. It is advisable to use some means of insuring quiet boiling, such as boiling capillaries (*see* below).

Benedetti-Pichler and Schneider Rectification Flask (14). This apparatus (Fig. 44) is used to isolate small quantities of one component

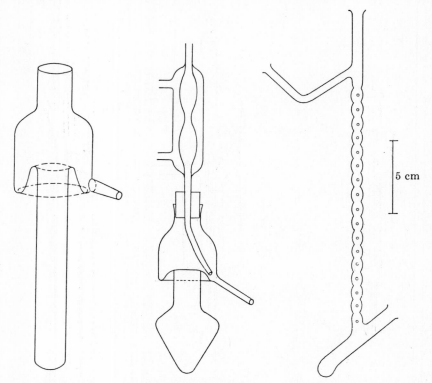

Fig. 40. Fractionation Apparatus of GAWALOWSKI,
½ nat. size.

Fig. 41. Fractionation
Apparatus of YOUNG.

5 cm

from a liquid mixture. The method is applicable only when the boiling point of the component to be isolated is lower than that of the rest of the mixture.

First thoroughly clean the rectification flask with hot chromic-sulfuric acid, then rinse with tap water and finally with distilled water. Clamp the flask in the position shown in the figure and dry the tube above the small bulb *a* by stroking with a Bunsen flame. After the tube has cooled to room temperature, introduce about 1 gram of 20-mesh granular zinc into the bulb through the funnel connected to the side tube. Then add the liquid sample. Close the side tube by replacing the funnel with a short length of glass rod. Hang a strip of wet filter paper around the knee of the tube, *b*. Heat the bulb by a large flame of a microburner until the

liquid begins to boil quietly. Then reduce the heating so that the ring
of condensate rises slowly and steadily. When it enters the knee of the

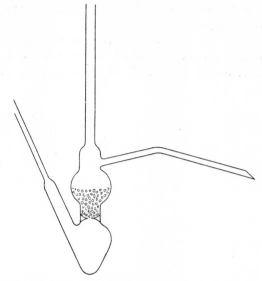

Fig. 42. Fractionation Flask of BERNHAUER, ½ nat. size.

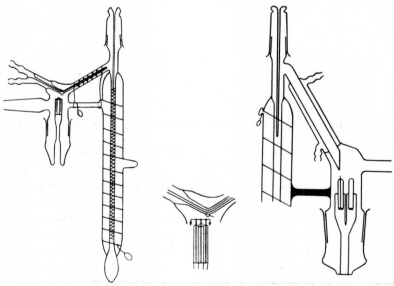

Fig. 43. Fractionation Apparatus of GOULD, HOLZMAN and NIEMAN.

tube, reduce the heating further so that no more distillate enters the knee.
When the substance has a boiling point over 65° C the burner can be
removed entirely, but with substances such as ethyl ether removal of the
burner would result in condensation of the vapor in the tube. In turn,

the air would be drawn back into the tube and this might bring about
the re-evaporation of the low-boiling condensate and its return to the main
portion of the liquid still in the bulb. Remove the distillate in the knee
with a capillary pipet.

The volume of the bulb of this flask is determined by the concentration
of the desired component. If the concentration is low, a large volume
of the original solution must obviously be taken in order to ensure a distillate

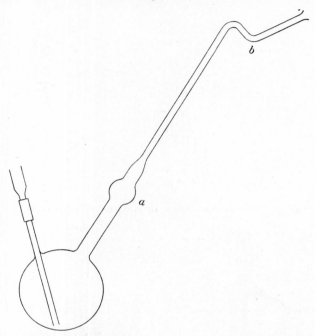

Fig. 44. Rectification Flask of BENEDETTI-PICHLER and SCHNEIDER, ¼ nat. size.

of sufficient size for further analysis. Flasks with volumes of 5, 50, and
100 ml are able to accommodate most samples. In the case of highly
volatile distillates such as ethyl ether, it is helpful to immerse the knee
at *b* in a cooling bath such as a solid carbon dioxide-acetone mixture.

General Precautions. Practically all types of the micro distilling apparatus
depend for their functioning upon the principle that a narrow glass tube
acts as a fractionating column of high efficiency. Certain precautions
must be observed, however, in order to obtain the best results.

1) The apparatus must be perfectly clean. Since the ring of condensate
consists of a liquid of which the composition must change at a constant
rate, there must be no sudden changes such as might occur if the hot
liquid dissolved some material adhering to the walls of the tube. Furthermore, the ring must ascend unbroken, and there must not be present
any contamination which would cause the ring to break.

2) The rate of boiling must not be too high. The fractionation depends upon the repeated condensation and evaporation of the distilled substance on the walls of the tube. If the rate of evolution of vapor from the liquid

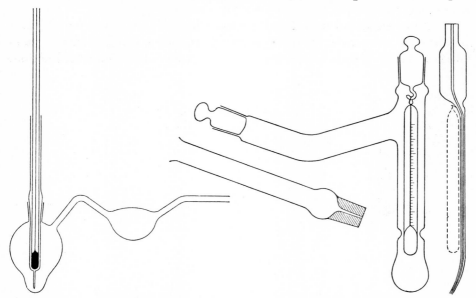

Fig. 45. Vacuum Distillation Apparatus of SOLTYS, $^1/_3$ nat. size.   Fig. 46. Vacuum Distillation Apparatus of ALBER, nat. size.

is too high, the vapor will pass directly through the tube without much condensation on the walls.

3) The boiling must be even and quiet. The vapor should be given off at a constant rate so that condensation and re-evaporation of the distillate

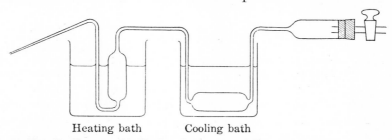

Heating bath   Cooling bath

Fig. 47. Vacuum Distillation Apparatus of PREGL.

take place at a constant rate and the ring advances evenly and slowly. If, for example, a large bubble of vapor bursts forth from the boiling liquid, the vapors will be forced past the ring of condensate and establishment of equilibrium conditions will be prevented. Well-controlled heating and the use of boiling capillaries, zinc dust, sodium bicarbonate, or asbestos are essential.

4) The apparatus should be shielded from sudden changes in temperature. It should not be placed where cold drafts of air might strike it.

For a detailed study of the operating conditions of micro distilling apparatus the reader is referred to the work of Rose (123).

Vacuum Distillation. Liquids with a high boiling point or low temperature of decomposition are separated into their components by distillation under reduced pressure or by so-called molecular distillation.

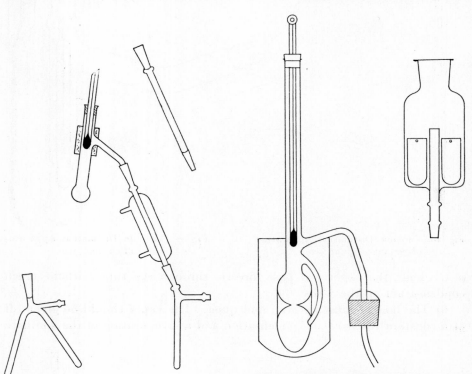

Fig. 48. Vacuum Distillation Apparatus of Peakes, $^1/_3$ nat. size.

Fig. 49. Vacuum Distillation Apparatus of Fraenkel, Bielschowsky, and Thannhauser, $^2/_3$ nat. size.

Some of the types of microapparatus used in ordinary fractional distillation can also be adapted for distillation under reduced pressure. The Emich fractionation flasks, for example, have been modified by Soltys (131) and also by Alber (1), as shown in Figs. 45 and 46, by the addition of a capillary inlet and a connection for the vacuum pump. The manipulation is otherwise the same as with the original Emich apparatus. Wright (151) has eliminated the ground joint of the Soltys apparatus and replaced it with a side inlet capillary which is sealed off after introduction of the sample. The Pregl (115) apparatus (Fig. 47) can readily be made by the analyst himself out of a test tube.

For larger volumes of liquids, the apparatus of PEAKES (110) (Fig. 48), FRAENKEL, BIELSCHOWSKY and THANNHAUSER (53) (Fig. 49), KLENK (90) (Fig. 50), SCHRADER and RITZER (129) (Fig. 51), TIEDCKE (138), ELLIS

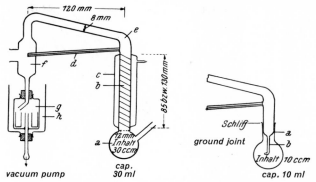

Fig. 50. Vacuum Distillation Apparatus of KLENK.

and WEYGAND (42) (Fig. 52), or BABCOCK (4) (Fig. 53) can be used. All but the last also permit the collection of several fractions without discon-

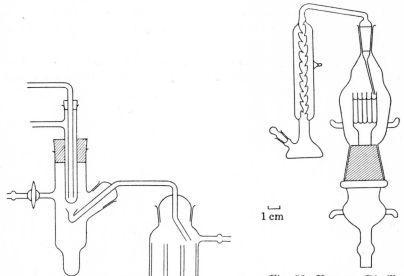

Fig. 51. Vacuum Distillation Apparatus of SCHRADER and RITZER.

Fig. 52. Vacuum Distilla-tion Apparatus of ELLIS and WEYGAND.

tinuing or interrupting the distillation. BERNHAUER (17) describes several types of micro or semi-micro receivers (Figs. 54 and 55).

Distillation Below the Boiling Point. High boiling substances can sometimes be distilled without decomposition at low temperatures by a process similar to sublimation. This is molecular distillation. It is based on the principle that at reduced pressures the free mean path of the molecules is large enough to permit them to move out of the field of attraction of the mass of the liquid and to reach a condensing surface. For achieving this, a fairly high vacuum of the order of 10^{-3} to 10^{-4} mm

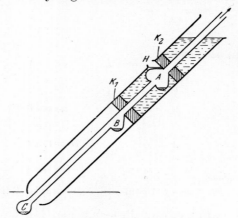

Fig. 53. Vacuum Distillation Apparatus of BABCOCK.

mercury; a condensing surface which can be brought sufficiently close to the heated sample; and a means of spreading out the sample in a thin, broad film are required.

BENEDETTI-PICHLER-RACHELE Apparatus.   The apparatus described by BENEDETTI-PICHLER and RACHELE (12) (Fig. 56) permits the distillation

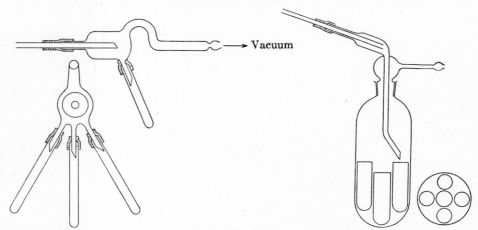

→ Vacuum

Fig. 54. Receiver for Vacuum Distillation   Fig. 55. Receiver for Vacuum Distillation
      of BERNHAUER, ½ nat. size.   of BERNHAUER, ½ nat. size.

of very small quantities (10 to 50 µl) below the boiling point without the use of vacuum. The sample is introduced into a tube with a 6-mm bore and 20 to 30 mm long, sealed at one end. This tube is placed in a vertical position in an electrically heated metal block and heated to a temperature

about 10 degrees below the boiling point of the liquid.   The condensing
surface is the sealed end of a capillary tube, 60 mm long and 1.5 mm wide

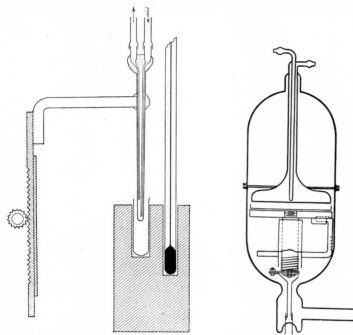

Fig. 56. Distillation Apparatus of
BENEDETTI-PICHLER and RACHELE,
$^2/_3$ nat. size.

Fig. 57. Molecular Distillation
Apparatus of BAILEY.

at the lower end, through which cold water is circulating.   The capillary
is lowered by means of a rack and pinion to within a millimeter or two

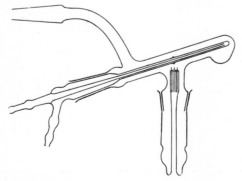

Fig. 58. Molecular Distillation Apparatus of GOULD, HOLZMAN, and NIEMAN.

of the liquid being distilled.   The condenser is raised from time to time
during the distillation and the condensate removed by means of a capillary
pipet.

The apparatus of BAILEY (7) (Fig. 57) consists of two halves joined by ground surfaces. The upper half holds the condenser while the lower holds the tray with the sample. This rests on an electrically heated hot

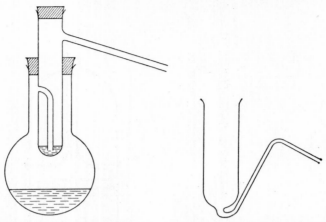

Fig. 59. Steam Distillation Apparatus according to POZZI-ESCOT.

Fig. 60. Receiver according
to SOLTYS, nat. size.

plate. This plate can be raised or lowered to adjust the distance between evaporating and condensing surface.

Other molecular distillation apparatus are those of GOULD, HOLZMAN and NIEMAN (65) (Fig. 58), PASCHKE, KORNS and WHEELER (10), RUSH-

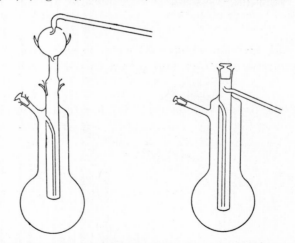

Fig. 61. Steam Distillation Apparatus of ERDÖS and LÁSZLÓ, 1/3 nat. size.

MAN and SIMPSON (125), BREGER (23), and ROPER (122). The first uses a water cooled tube as condensing surface which is inclined to permit the condensate to flow to a flange from which the condensate is drained off into one of several receivers through capillaries.

Steam Distillation. Steam or codistillation of small quantities can be carried out by the use of the apparatus of POZZI-ESCOT (113), Fig. 59. The material to be distilled is placed in the inner vessel, water in the outer. SOLTYS (131) recommends the use of a special receiver (Fig. 60) for the separation of the distillate and the water to avoid losses inherent in the use of separatory funnels.

ERDÖS and LÁSZLÓ (49) have modified POZZI-ESCOT's apparatus as shown in Fig. 61 to facilitate the introduction of the sample. The apparatus on the left is designed for difficultly volatile substances.

The saturation of the aqueous phase with a salt such as sodium chloride or potassium carbonate will reduce the time required for steam distillation and increase the volatility of compounds which are otherwise difficult to distil.

Recrystallization.

Although recrystallization from a solvent is usually employed in the purification, when carried out on the micro scale it may also be used for the separation of liquid mixtures because of the ease of freezing small quantities of material. The speed of working makes it possible to cool a solution to crystallization temperatures far below 0°C with solid carbon dioxide and to filter off the crystals before they melt again. On the other hand, recrystallization can be also carried out by converting all components to the liquid state by raising the temperature above the melting point and then allowing cooling to the point at which one component crystallizes out. This is performed best in a zone melting apparatus as described below.

The technique to be used in microrecrystallizations depends upon the quantity of material available and upon the point reached in the scheme of analysis. For very small quantities or in making a final test under the microscope, the microscope slide is used. In the preparation of derivatives, the capillary tube or the micro cone is preferred. The latter is best suited for the purification of larger quantities of material. Still larger amounts can be handled in microbeakers and with the various filters described below.

Recrystallization on the Microscope Slide. It often becomes necessary to carry out a recrystallization on a microscope slide or cover glass, as, for example, when, during the determination of the melting point under the microscope, the sample gives evidence of being impure. In such a case, place a drop of the solvent on the solid on the slide by means of a capillary pipet. Prepare another long capillary pipet and keep it at hand. Heat the solvent on the slide by moving the latter in a circular motion over a micro flame. This prevents cracking of the slide. When as much solid as possible has dissolved (excess undissolved solid should remain), draw up the liquid into the clean capillary pipet and transfer it to another part of the same slide or to another slide. Cool it there by either merely letting it stand or, if rapid cooling is desired, by placing it on a metal block which has previously been cooled to a low temperature by ice or carbon dioxide snow. After crystallization has taken place, remove the liquid first with a capillary pipet having a fine

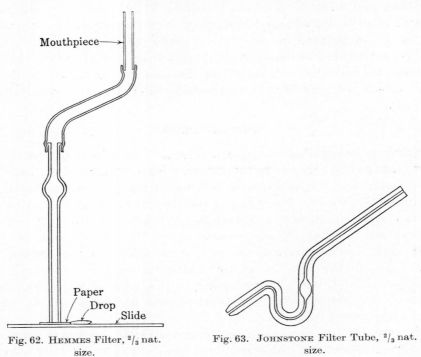

Mouthpiece→

Paper
Drop
Slide

Fig. 62. HEMMES Filter, ²/₃ nat.
size.

Fig. 63. JOHNSTONE Filter Tube, ²/₃ nat.
size.

tip and then touch the point of a triangular piece of filter paper to the crystal mass, *see* Fig. 11, page 14. The individual crystals can be separated by the paper and the liquid thus removed more completely. Final drying may be accomplished by waving the slide over a microflame. The liquid may also be removed from the precipitate by other methods.

The HEMMES (73) filter consists of a tube (Fig. 62) with one end ground flat. A piece of filter paper is placed beside the test drop and the filter is held vertical with the ground end pressed tightly against the filter paper. Suction is then applied to the other end of the tube and the liquid thus drawn into the tube. JOHNSTONE (81) (Fig. 63) has modified the HEMMES filter to permit working from an angle with greater ease. MALJAROFF (102) (Fig. 64) described another device which is somewhat like the HEMMES filter but consists of two parts. The upper is like the HEMMES tube, the lower has a fine tip. The adjoining ends of the two are ground flat and are

held together by a spring. The filter paper is placed between these two
ground ends and the two parts are put together as shown. The precipitate

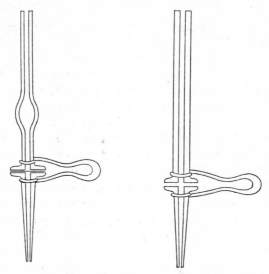

Fig. 64. MALJAROFF Filter Tube, $^2/_3$ nat. size.

is drawn up and held in the lower part and the filtrate in the upper. JURANY
(80) uses a tube with a permanent fritted glass filter.

If the desired substance does not readily crystallize from the cooled
solution, evaporation of part of the solvent may be necessary. Direct a

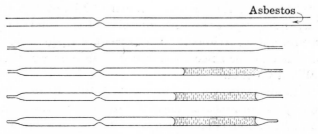

Fig. 65. Recrystallization in the Capillary.

stream of warm air from a capillary (*see* page 17) on one edge of the drop.
Evaporation at this point will cause the appearance of a few crystals.
These will seed the remainder of the drop.

Recrystallization in Capillary Tubes. Fit an asbestos plug into
a capillary, 7 to 8 cm long and 1 to 3 mm in diameter, at a constriction
about 2.5 cm from one end, Fig. 65. Then draw the ends into points.
Dissolve the material to be recrystallized, if a solid, in the minimum volume
of hot solvent either on a slide or in a depression of a spot plate. Of course,

when liquid samples are used, no previous solution is necessary. Draw 30 to 50 μl of the solution or liquid into the larger portion of the tube. Take care not to wet the asbestos plug with the solution. Then seal the dry end and allow it to cool. The cooling of the sealed end causes the liquid to be drawn in and away from the open point. Seal this end. Cool the enclosed liquid to the crystallizing temperature by immersing in a cooling mixture (ice and salt or carbon dioxide snow and acetone, etc.). The cooling should be slow in order to obtain as large crystals as possible. The speed of the cooling process can be reduced by dipping the tube momentarily into the cooling mixture, removing, dipping it in again, and repeating, holding the tube in the mixture for a longer period each time until the first crystals appear. Then leave the tube in the mixture until crystallization is complete. After crystallization place the tube in a microcone (Fig. 66) and centrifuge the mother liquor through the asbestos plug. The crystals will remain in a packed layer at the constriction. Cut the capillary at *A* and *B* and push the crystals out by means of a glass rod. The mother liquor may be recovered from the other portion of the capillary tube and reworked if desired.

If necessary, the separation of the crystals and mother liquor by centrifugation can be carried out at lower temperatures by using the arrangement shown in Fig. 67.

The same basic procedure is used for recrystallization of a mixture of solids. Melt the mixture in a microcone or a microbeaker and heat about 10° to 20° higher. Draw the liquid up into the capillary with constriction as described above. When the first crystals or turbidity appears, place the capillary in a microcone as shown in Fig. 67 but with warm or hot water (depending upon the melting point of the solid) in place of the freezing mixture, and centrifuge. This procedure requires several reworkings of the mother liquor since the impurities usually remain dissolved in the uncrystallized portion.

Another technique which uses the capillary tube is also due to EMICH. This technique permits repeated recrystallizations in the same tube with intermediate melting point determinations. Use a capillary with a 1.5-mm bore and about 100 mm long. Draw the hot saturated solution of the substance to be recrystallized into one end of the capillary, then seal the other end in the flame. Centrifuge the solution to the sealed end and seal also the open end. The crystallization should take place on cooling. If this does not occur, the solution is supercooled, in which case cool it further by dipping the capillary into carbon dioxide snow or by wrapping it in cotton and allowing ether to drip upon it. The original solution may also not have been sufficiently supersaturated. In this event, concentrate the solution somewhat by opening the tube and inserting a fine capillary 0.3 to 0.5 mm in diameter, which is bent at an obtuse angle at *a* so that it acts as a spring and holds the crystallizing tube, Fig. 7, p. 12. In the wide, upper part the capillary tube widens to 5 to 6 mm in diameter. Place a plug of cotton at the point where the tube widens out. Blow air which has passed through a wash bottle containing concentrated sulfuric acid through the capillary. Place the crystallizing tube in a heating bath and heat to about 100° C or slightly above the boiling point of the solvent.

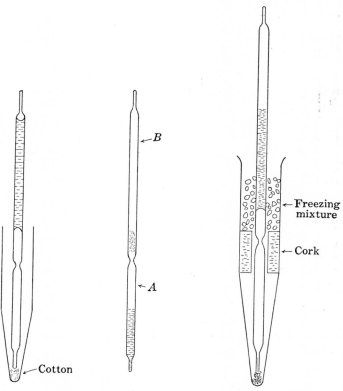

Fig. 66. Separation of Liquid and Solid with the Centrifuge.

Fig. 67. Separation by Freezing and Fractional Melting.

When the volume of the solution in the crystallizing tube has been reduced as desired, remove the air tube and seal and cool the crystallizing tube as described above. After crystallization, cut off the empty end of the capillary and pack down the crystals with a glass rod and centrifuge. Remove the mother liquor by means of a fine capillary. Repeat the packing, centrifuging, and decanting until the crystals are as dry as possible. Final drying is accomplished in the same way as the evaporation of the solvent. The determination of the melting point of the crystals can then be carried out in the same tube, if desired. *See* also HÄUSLER (11).

4*

Recrystallization of Larger Quantities. The primary objective in the design of apparatus for recrystallization of small quantities is to ensure maximum recovery of the desired material, that is, minimum loss of solution and crystallized material. Therefore, filters such as paper which can absorb and hold both liquid and solid should be avoided or at least have

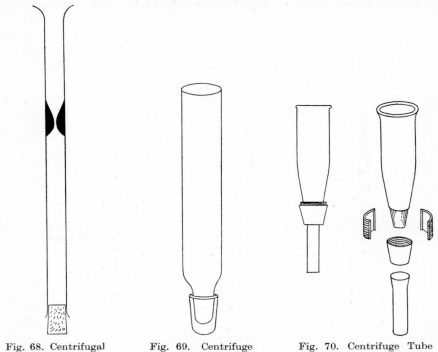

Fig. 68. Centrifugal Filter of PREGL, nat. size.

Fig. 69. Centrifuge Tube of FRIEDRICH, $^2/_3$ nat. size.

Fig. 70. Centrifuge Tube of ELEK, $^2/_3$ nat. size.

the area of contact kept very small. Again, since organic liquids, the usual solvents employed, tend to spread out over a wide area on glass, the apparatus should keep the liquid confined to prevent the formation of a thin layer of solid which is difficult to collect and recover.

The apparatus which has been devised for recrystallization can be placed in one of two classes: (1) combination precipitation vessels and filters, (2) separate precipitation vessel and filter.

Under the first heading are the filter beaker, EIGENBERGER filter, centrifugal filter, and the separable centrifuge tubes.

The centrifugal filter of PREGL (116) (Fig. 68) is a larger version of the crystallization capillary described above. An asbestos plug at the constriction acts as filter. FRIEDRICH (54) describes centrifuge tubes with removable bottoms, Fig. 69, which are ground onto the upper part of the tube. ELEK (41) uses the same idea but the bottom of the cone is screwed in place instead of being ground on, Fig. 70. The crystals are collected in the bottom and can readily be separated from the mother liquor. KLATT (88) and LIEB and SCHOENIGER (101) hang a tube with turned edges and a fused-in glass filter plate in the centrifuge tube. The material to be filtered is placed in this inner tube. The precipitate remains on the filter plate while the liquid passes through into the centrifuge tube. This is a modification of the SKAU tubes used in macro work. *See* also HOUSTON

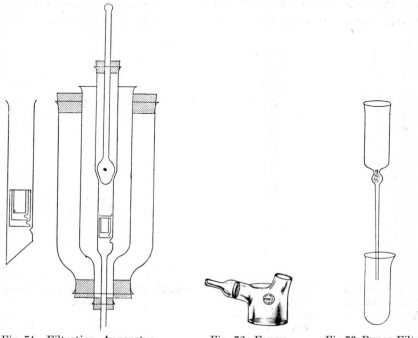

Fig. 71. Filtration Apparatus   Fig. 72. EMICH   Fig.73. PREGL Filter,
of EIGENRERGEB, $^2/_3$ nat. size.   Filterbeaker. $^2/_3$ nat. size.

and SAYLOR (78), CRAIG (32), LANGER (96) and KATO (82). The EIGEN-BERGER filter (10) can be used for quantities from several milligrams to centigrams. It consists of a series of short glass tubes, closed at one end and fitting into each other as shown in Fig. 71, which act as support for the filter paper. The use of the funnel arrangement (similar to that of KIRK and CRAIG (86) makes it possible to carry out the filtration at lower-than-ordinary temperatures, the space between the funnel and the outer double-walled vessel being filled with a cooling mixture such as solid carbon-dioxide and ether. The filtration can further be carried out under pressure after the plug in the funnel has been removed.

The filter beaker (Fig. 72) is quite flexible in its use, permitting solution, heating, cooling, and filtration in the same vessel. The only disadvantage lies in difficulty in removing the precipitate.

When working with separate filters and crystallization vessels, larger quantities can be employed but there is a greater possibility of loss during the transfer of the crystal-mother liquor slurry to the filter. The crystallization vessels may be either centrifuge tubes or microbeakers.

PREGL (117) uses a microbeaker and a funnel made by drawing out a test tube (Fig. 73) in conjunction with a SCHWINGER suction filter Fig. 74. Filter the hot solution (which must not be completely saturated), through cotton in the funnel and cool the filtrate while stirring. After crystallization, filter with suction through the SCHWINGER filter. The filter in the latter

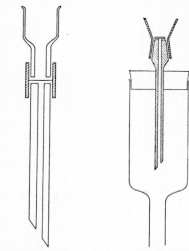

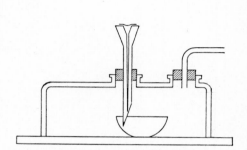

Fig. 74. Suction Filter of SCHWINGER, ²/₃ nat. size.

Fig. 75. YAGODA Modification of SCHWINGER Filter, nat. size.

Fig. 76. Use of EMICH-DONAU Filter Capillary.

is a circular piece of hardened filter paper held between the two sections of tubing. Remove the crystal mass from the filter by separating the upper portion and pushing the crystals out with a glass rod which has a diameter just slightly less than the bore of the filter tube. BEROZA (19) suggests using Tygon or other transparent plastic tubing to join the two parts of the filter to permit observation of the process of filtration. It has been suggested that the upper part can also be connected to a pressure system to improve rate and thoroughness of filtration. YAGODA (152) substitutes a ground joint for the rubber tubing (Fig. 75). The method of operation can be seen from the figure.

DONAU dishes can also be used for recrystallizations. These dishes, made of platinum foil, were designed for use with a NERNST balance in quantitative work. However, the ease and simplicity of manipulation recommend them for organic preparative work. They are easily made of platinum foil about 0.004 mm thick; the platinum foil is stamped out

with a glass rod of the proper diameter (8 to 10 mm) as stamping die and
a rubber with a hole slightly larger than the glass rod as the base. A circular
piece of foil is laid over the hole in the stopper and the glass rod is pushed
on the foil into the hole so that the foil is formed into a cup. The bottom
of one dish is perforated with numerous fine holes made with the point
of a needle to form the filtering dish. A handle of platinum wire can readily
be welded on one edge of the cups if desired. Filtration is carried out on a
DONAU (37) filter capillary, Fig. 76. This consists of a glass tube of capillary

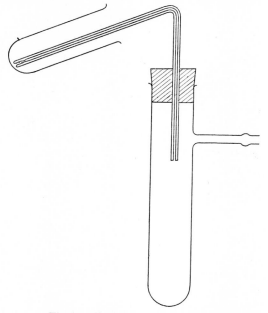

Fig. 77. Use of Immersion Filter, $^2/_3$ nat. size.

bore, widened at the top to 12 to 15 mm with the orifice also slightly flared
and the top ground flat. On this is placed a circular piece of filter paper
with a paraffined edge. The filter is placed in a suction flask or suction
bell jar. The DONAU dish is laid on the filter paper, the material to be
filtered is introduced into the dish and suction is applied. The precipitate
can easily be removed from the platinum dish after washing. The adhering
paper or asbestos fibers which may prove a nuisance with the other filters
are avoided. An inverted porcelain or fritted glass filterstick (see below)
may be substituted for the filter capillary.

  With easily soluble substances it is better to use an immersion filter
as described by EMICH (45). This is a modification of the filterstick. Place
an asbestos plug in a bell-shaped enlargement at the end of a glass tube.
Bend the tube at an angle of about 45°. Insert the other end of the tube
in a suction flask or side-arm test tube (Fig. 77). Carry out the solution

and crystallization of the substance in a microbeaker as in the PREGL method described above. Use the end of the filter tube containing the asbestos to push the crystals together in the microbeaker while applying suction to draw out the mother liquor. For final drying insert a piece of hardened filter paper in the crystal mass, stopper the microbeaker with a cork and allow it to stand.

The porcelain filtersticks as well as those with sintered glass filter disks can be used for recrystallization purposes since the crystal mass can easily be removed from the filter surface unadulterated with fibers of

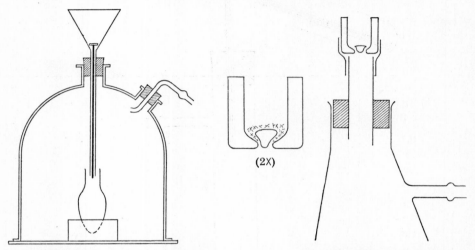

Fig. 78. Filtration with WILLSTAETTER Button.

Fig. 79. Filter Crucible of BAILEY.

(2X)

asbestos or paper. CRAIG (32) describes a filterstick with an easily removable paper disk filter.

The microcone of EMICH can also be used for recrystallization. The mother liquor is removed by centrifuging and decanting through a capillary siphon as described on page 18.

The WILLSTAETTER button, consisting of a glass rod flattened at one end and inserted into the stem of an ordinary funnel, is recommended by SOLTYS. He suggests that the surface of the flattened end be roughened to make the suction effective over the entire surface of the filter paper and not merely at the edges. This can be achieved by pressing the hot softened end of the glass rod against the surface of a file. The paper used should be about 2 mm larger in diameter than the button. It is fixed to the button by first moistening with water and applying suction, then washing the water out with alcohol, and finally washing with the solvent used in the recrystallization. The use of a bell jar on a ground glass plate, as shown in Fig. 78, makes it possible to collect the filtrate in any type of vessel.

BAILEY's filter crucible (6) can readily be made by the analyst himself. Its construction and operation can be seen from Fig. 79.

SOLTYS (131) recommends the use of a microbeaker with a conical bottom, Fig. 22, page 20. This permits the use of a comparatively large original volume of liquid but concentrates the residue in the point as in a microcone instead of allowing it to form a thin layer over a large surface.

General Notes on Recrystallization. The efficiency of the separation of impurities from the major component by recrystallization is dependent to the highest degree upon the choice of the solvent.

The most desirable solvent is one in which the major component, usually the material under investigation, is much less soluble than the other constituents, usually the impurities or by-products. A consideration of the possible other constituents can often lead to the proper choice of solvent. For example, in the preparation of a derivative, the original sample substance, the reagent, the derivative, the reagent product, and any by-products from the reaction of the reagent and the solvent, etc., should be predictable. The solubilities of these in various solvents can be obtained from the literature. In other cases, certain solvents will be recommended in the procedures for the preparation of derivatives, etc. as they have been found most effective. If such information is not available, it is determined fairly easily by the use of the solubility apparatus described on page 149. The use of mixed solvents should also be considered.

After the proper and most effective solvent has been ascertained, the sample is dissolved in it using either a capillary, a microcone, or a microbeaker. Introduce the solid into the capillary tube in the same way as in filling a melting point tube. Add the solvent either by suction or by the use of a capillary pipet with a fine tip. Then seal the capillary at both ends and heat by placing inside an ordinary test tube and passing this through the flame of a Bunsen burner. Possible distillation of the solvent is overcome by occasional centrifuging back to the solid.

When using a microcone or microbeaker, use little of the solvent at the beginning and add more after the mixture has been heated, usually on a water bath. Stir the solvent and solid thoroughly during the heating. Filter the mixture quickly through cotton or other filter to remove insoluble material before allowing it to cool and crystallize.

If too much solvent has been used with the result that the solution is unsaturated even when cold, some of the solvent must be removed by evaporation. Some methods of evaporation have been described above. SOLTYS recommends the use of *micro boiling stones*, made by fusing a tiny piece of unglazed porcelain into the end of a glass thread. He states that the use of such a boiling stone or boiling capillaries is essential for evaporation without loss when microbeakers are used. Such boiling stones may also be used in distillations. Another method of producing the same result but with larger volumes is shown in Fig. 80. The operation is self-evident. If the solvent is fairly volatile, the solution may be subjected to a stream of pre-heated air. Radiant heat from as, for example, from a lamp ("infra-red" heating bulb) will also bring about gentle but rapid evaporation.

The removal of the last traces of solvent after the separation of the crystals from the mother liquor can also be accomplished by evaporation in vacuum. A more complete discussion of this will be found below under Drying and Removal of Solvent.

Often a substance will not crystallize despite the fact that the solution is supersaturated. This may be due to the presence of certain inorganic salts. *See* page 85. Cooling to very low temperatures will not always

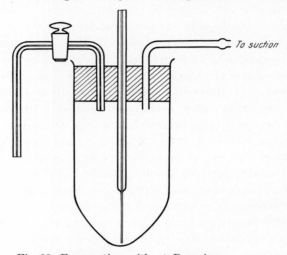

Fig. 80. Evaporation without Bumping.

produce crystals. For an excellent discussion of the subject of inducing crystallization, the reader is referred to MORTON (105). According to AMELINK (3), the stimuli for crystallization can be divided into the "mechanical" and the "chemical". The former include warming, scratching, and local drying by warming. Addition of another solvent, addition of a solid substance, and seeding are the "chemical" stimuli. DENIGÈS (36) suggests rubbing a microscope slide with a crystal of the substance and then placing a drop of the super-saturated solution upon the same spot. Another device is to dip a glass thread into the supersaturated solution, withdraw it and, after evaporating the minute quantity of the solution adhering to it, then dip the thread back into the solution. The solid at the end of the thread seeds the remainder of the solution. Stirring rods which have been previously used in the crystallization of the substance, since they may still carry sufficient traces of the substance, can sometimes be used to induce crystallization. If the solvent is water or some other substance which is readily absorbed, e. g., by a desiccant, the arrangement shown in Fig. 81 may be used to cause crystallization on the microscope slide. *See* also SCHOORL (128). TSCHERMAK-SEYSENEGG (141) suggests *seeding through the tube wall* by freezing the solvent by local cooling.

Fig. 81. Evaporation in Well Slide.

The addition of diluents such as water or solvent other than that originally used may also cause the crystallization to begin. Whether or not this would be effective can be determined quickly by the apparatus and procedure on p. 149.

Zone Melting.

A technique which was developed chiefly for its value in the preparation of very pure inorganic materials has been found to be extremely effective in the purification of carbon compounds. In fact, these have properties

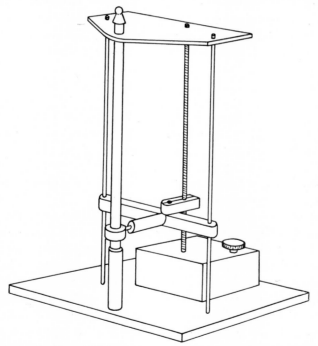

Fig. 82. Apparatus for Zone Melting. Courtesy of Microchemical Service, Douglaston, N.Y.

such as low heat conductivity, which make the method even more efficient. SCHWAB and WICHERS (130) purified benzoic acid and acetanilide from a melt by slow fractional melting and subsequent freezing. After three

repetitions of the melting and solidification, benzoic acid of 99.91% purity
was converted to 99.997% purity. It was found that two repetitions were
comparable to eleven recrystallizations of benzoic acid from benzene or
25 from water. GOODMAN (62) has summarized the principles and the
practical conditions of zone melting, as the technique is now known, particularly when applied to carbon compounds with low vapor pressures and
which decompose on distillation. A semimicro apparatus for zone melting
is described by HANDLEY and HERINGTON (69). It consists of a glass tube,
2.5 to 6 mm in bore, which contains the powdered substance to be purified.
This tube is supported in a vertical position and is raised slowly, at a rate
of 2 cm per hour, through a narrow region of high temperatures. This region
is produced by focusing the radiant energy from an incandescent lamp on
a spot on the tube. Another device by SCHNEIDER uses a hot wire and a
narrow microscope slide or capillary. The movement of the tube or the
wire is governed by a slow speed motor such as used in electric clocks.
While the time required for one transit or *pass* of the heated zone seems
long, it is certainly less than that required for the recrystallization needed
for reaching the same end purity. Once the zone melter has been set up
and in action, no further attention is required. Most commercial models
have limit switches which shut off the motor at the end of the pass or
reverse the direction of movement of the heater. *See* Fig. 82.

Extraction.

Extraction of a solid mixture is somewhat similar to recrystallization
in that it is based upon solubility differences between the components of
the mixture. However, in the case of the former, the major or the
desired component should preferably be the more soluble one. Again, the
choice of the solvent is of primary importance. The same general con-
siderations apply as with recrystallization.

Extraction of Solids. The simplest micromethod consists of adding
a droplet of the solvent (which may be hot) to a milligram or less of the
solid sample on a slide. After stirring with a glass thread and allowing it
to stand for a time, draw up the liquid in a fine capillary pipet. Repeat
the process with further droplets of solvent until no more dissolves. Collect
the extract on another part of the slide or on a second slide and there
concentrate it for further investigation.

If the solvent is very volatile, a capillary can be employed in place of
the microscope slide. Put the solid in a capillary tube with a bore of about
2 mm, sealed at one end, using the method of filling a melting point tube.
Add solvent by means of a capillary pipet. Seal the open end and centrifuge
the solvent to the end containing the solid. Then heat the capillary by placing
in a test tube which, in turn, is held in the flame, or in a centrifuge tube

which is placed on the water bath. From time to time centrifuge the capillary or shake it like a clinical thermometer to return the distilled solvent to the solid. Remove the capillary from the heat, allow it to cool, centrifuge, and cut open the empty end. Remove the extract with a capillary with a fine, drawn-out point. If desired, add another aliquot of fresh solvent and repeat the process. Sometimes it will be helpful if,

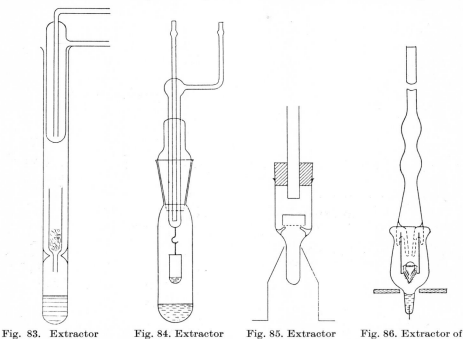

Fig. 83. Extractor of GARNER, ½ nat. size.

Fig. 84. Extractor of FULTON, ²/₃ nat. size.

Fig. 85. Extractor of HETTERICH, nat. size.

Fig. 86. Extractor of GETTENS, ²/₃ nat. size.

during the heating, the contents of the sealed capillary are centrifuged several times back and forth from one end to the other.

A variety of types of apparatus has been devised for the continuous extraction of samples up to 1 gram in weight. Most of these depend upon the distillation of the solvent and the slow filtration of the solution of extract back to the boiling vessel. GARNER's (59) apparatus consists of a *cold finger* condenser inserted into a test tube. The test tube is indented at three places near the bottom (Fig. 83) to hold a small funnel. The sample to be extracted is wrapped in filter paper and inserted in the funnel. Similar apparatus is described by LACOURT and GURFINKEL (95) and by PRATT (114).

FULTON (56) describes an extraction apparatus (Fig. 84) in which the sample is placed in a glass tube 15 mm long with a bore of 4 mm, which has a small opening on the bottom over which a thin layer of cotton is placed. The weight of the boiling vessel is but 8.5 grams. Thus the solvent can be evaporated from the extract and the latter weighed directly. The condenser is ground into the boiling flask.

HETTERICH's device (75) for the extraction of vehicle from dried paint is a simple one. The sample is placed on a disk of filter paper which in turn is

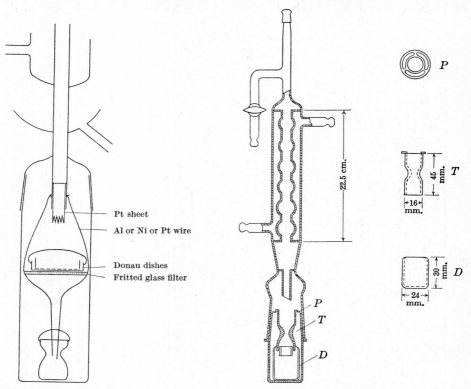

Pt sheet

Al or Ni or Pt wire

Donau dishes
Fritted glass filter

22.5 cm.

P

45 mm.   T

←16→
mm.

30 mm.   D

←24→
mm.

P

T

D

Fig. 87. Extractor of GORBACH,
$^2/_3$ nat. size.

Fig. 88. Extractor of TITUS and MELOCHE.

placed in a glass cup which has a perforated bottom, Fig. 85. The cup is held in the boiling vessel by indentations in the latter. The solvent is held in the narrow portion of the boiling vessel. An air condenser usually suffices.

Refinements of the HETTERICH extractor are required for special purposes. For example, GETTENS (61) has changed the shape of the cup so that the solid particles remaining after the extraction are kept in a fixed position, an advantage when the location of the components is important, as in the examination of paintings, etc. The cup is a perforated platinum cone which holds a filter paper cone. A piece of platinum wire is fused into the bottom of the boiling vessel to prevent superheating or violent ebullition, Fig. 86.

When the extract is to be weighed, the devices of GORBACH (64) (Fig. 87) or TITUS and MELOCHE (139) (Fig. 88) can be used. In both, the sample is placed in a small container which is held by a larger vessel. GORBACH (64) uses a DONAU dish (*see* page 54) for holding the sample; TITUS and MELOCHE use a thimble made from a glass tube, one end of which is closed by a piece of filter paper held in place by a glass ring very much as cloth in embroi-

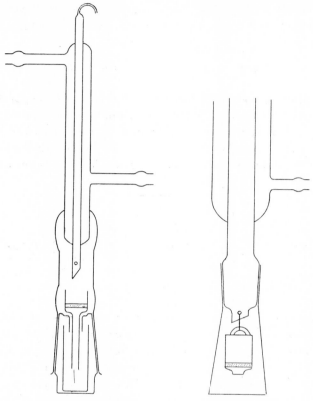

Fig. 89. Extractor of
BROWNING, $^2/_3$ nat. size.

Fig. 90. Extractor of
BLOUNT, $\frac{1}{2}$ nat. size.

dery rings. The BROWNING (25) extractor is a simplified form of the TITUS and MELOCHE extractor (Fig. 89).

BLOUNT (22) describes an apparatus for the simultaneous extraction and recrystallization of small amounts of material. The sample, which may be the impure crystals, is held in a small fritted glass filter crucible, Fig. 90. The latter is hung from the end of a condenser which is ground into the small boiling flask. After the extraction, the condenser is removed and the solution is evaporated to the crystallizing point.

When larger quantities of material are available, small, modified Soxhlet extractors can be used. WASITZKY (145) describes two types, one for solvents of ordinary boiling points, the other for high-boiling solvents. COLEGRAVE (30) uses an ordinary test tube, 25 mm by 150 mm, in which the Soxhlet thimble is held by three indentations. The condenser is the *cold finger* type. The ordinary filter paper extraction thimbles are used in both the WASITZKY and the COLEGRAVE apparatus.

Extraction of Liquid Samples. The extraction of liquid samples can be carried out in capillary tubes, using the same technique as for solids. Particular care must be taken to secure thorough mixing by

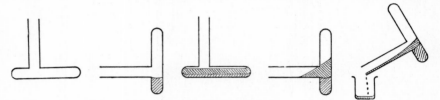

Fig. 91. Contraction Pipt, $^1/_3$ nat. length.

repeated centrifuging back and forth to get a clean cut separation of the two liquid layers at the final centrifuging, and to remove the uppermost layer carefully. This latter can be done best by the use of the contraction pipet, Fig. 91. These pipets are made from the bulb-shaped pieces of tubing left after two capillaries have been drawn from a 6-mm tube. Draw

Fig. 92. Extraction Tube of KÖNIG and CROWELL.

out the capillary at one end to a still finer one and seal the other end. The latter is used as a handle. Heat the bulb in the flame and insert the fine capillary into the liquid to be drawn off. The cooling and contraction of the air in the bulb draw in the liquid. Since the extraction capillary and the pipet can be held horizontally in the hands in this way, no suction with the mouth being necessary, the interface between the two liquids is easily observed and one liquid can be drawn off almost completely without taking any of the second liquid with it. Cut off the sealed end of the contraction pipet and blow the contents out into a centrifuge cone or onto a slide. Run a preliminary experiment to determine the relative densities of the solvent and the sample to make certain which forms the upper layer.

Centrifuge tubes or microcones can also be used for liquid-liquid extraction. Thorough and continuous stirring is, of course, imperative. Decantation of the upper layer follows centrifuging, using either a capillary pipet or a capillary siphon.

KÖNIG and CROWELL (93) use T-tubes. The construction and use of these tubes is evident from Fig. 92. GORBACH (63) designed pipets of the form shown in Fig. 93. When the pipet is held almost horizontally, it can be shaken without loss of material. If held as shown in the upper sketch

in Fig. 93, the less dense liquid can be drawn off. When held as shown
in the lower part of Fig. 93 or vertically, the more dense liquid flows out
upon careful release of finger pressure on the wide end. Forms of separatory funnels for use with micro quantities have been devised by, e. g.,
BROWNING (26), FABIAN (50), ALBER (2), and KIRK (85). With the first
(Fig. 94) the rubber tubing is pinched to force the liquid of greater density

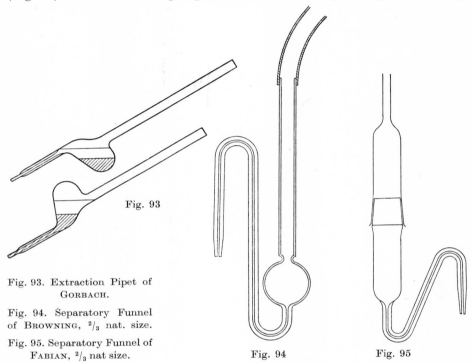

Fig. 93

Fig. 93. Extraction Pipet of
    GORBACH.

Fig. 94. Separatory Funnel
of BROWNING, $^2/_3$ nat. size.

Fig. 95. Separatory Funnel of
    FABIAN, $^2/_3$ nat size.

Fig. 94

Fig. 95

out of the capillary. The ground joint of FABIAN's funnel (Fig. 95) permits
easy introduction of the liquids. ALBER modified the SPAETH sedimenta-
tion funnel by using a three-way stopcock and graduating the funnel. The
KIRK funnels use capillary stopcocks or tubes in place of the lower stopcock of the usual separatory funnel. The conventional stopper is replaced
by a three-way stopcock which, when connected to a vacuum, permits a
stream of air to be drawn through the liquids when the funnel is held
vertically with the lower capillary stopcock open.

    Continuous extraction of liquids can be carried out by the use of
LAQUER's apparatus (98), the construction and operation of which can
be seen from Fig. 96. This apparatus can be used, of course, only when
the liquid to be extracted has a higher specific gravity than the solvent.
The apparatus of BARRENSCHEEN (8) is similar. STETTEN and GRAIL (133)
have made the extractor more compact by placing the extracting vessel

inside the vessel containing the boiling solvent, Fig. 97. This keeps the
solvent hot and aids in the extraction. BERNHAUER (18) describes a somewhat larger apparatus which can be used also with liquids of lower specific

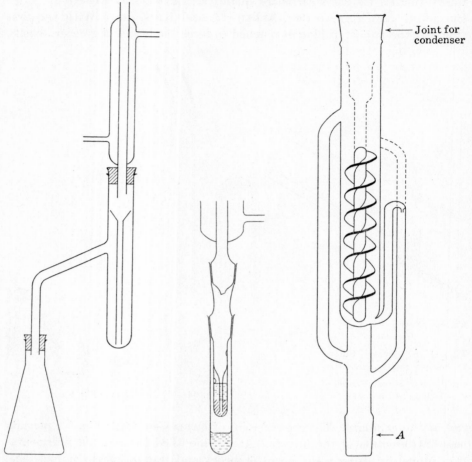

Joint for
condenser

A

Fig. 96. Continuous Extractor   Fig. 97. Extractor of   Fig. 98. Extractor of
of LAQUER, ¹/₃ nat. size.   STETTEN and GRAIL.   BERNHAUER.

gravity, Fig. 98. When the solvent is lighter, a long-stemmed funnel is
placed inside the spiral. This catches the condensed solvent and leads it
to the bottom of the layer of liquid to be extracted. The solution of
extract drains off through the side tube to the boiling flask which is
attached at A. When the solvent is heavier, the funnel is omitted and
the return is through a siphon as shown in the figure.

CLAUSEN (29) devised an apparatus for the extraction of small amounts
of lactic acid from large volumes of urine. KIRK and DANIELSON (87)
have described apparatus for the extraction of samples of 0.5 ml.

While the above methods and apparatus are quite effective when the solubilities of the components are quite different, when the solubilities are of the same order, separation by extraction procedure requires multiple extraction somewhat analogous to the action of fractionating columns in distillation. This procedure has been named countercurrent distribution and has proven a very efficient tool for the isolation and separation of closely related substances. Since the apparatus is more complex than the type described heretofore, the reader is referred to the original papers of CRAIG (33), CRAIG and POST (34), RAUEN and STAMM (120), GRUBHOFER (68), RAYMOND (121), TSEHESCHE and KÖNIG (140), and WEYGAND (147) for details and procedures.

Sublimation.

Since not all carbon compounds sublime, it is possible to carry out separations which might otherwise present difficulties. Furthermore, when the substance can be sublimed, it is a simple matter to obtain well-formed crystals suitable for microscopic examination and identification, as, for example, with aldomethones, synthetic medicinals, and amino acids.

The apparatus for sublimation can be divided into two groups: those which have no means of measuring the temperature and those which have. Often the former suffice but sometimes pains must be taken to carry out the sublimation at or below a certain temperature to avoid simultaneous sublimation or distillation of another substance or thermal decomposition of the material. HOFFMAN and JOHNSON (76) state that the temperature of sublimation is not a fixed point but can be placed within definite limits if a standard apparatus is used. Not only the vapor pressure but also the distance between the surface of evaporation and the surface of condensation is important. The vapor pressure in some cases never goes beyond a certain point as, for example, a few millimeters for indigo. When the distance is small there is some doubt as to whether the transfer of material is actually sublimation or "some other kind of mechanical phenomenon".

Sublimation from Slide to Slide. For quick work the sublimation can be carried out between two watch glasses clipped together or from one microscope slide to another, the slides being held in the hands. Since microscope slides are apt to crack when heated, the one carrying the sample can be replaced by a microspatula of nickel, platinum foil, a mica plate, or a microcrucible. When two slides are used, the heated slide should be a narrow one, i. e., one made by cutting a slide of usual size lengthwise into thirds. Bring the sample into close contact with the slide by wetting the material on the slide with water and then drying it thoroughly. The layer of material should not be too thick. Hold the narrow slide in one hand and a wide slide in the other hand. Allow the wide slide to rest at an angle on the edge of the narrow one (Fig. 99) away from the sample. Heat the latter over a microflame, slowly at first until the degree of heating required for sublimation is determined. Remove the slide from the flame at frequent intervals, every five seconds or so, and move the wide slide over the heated sample. If sublimation is taking place, the sublimate can be seen condensing on the wide slide. In some instances it is necessary or advisable to place a drop of water on the upper surface of the wide slide to aid condensation. When the condensation of material has ceased, return the wide slide to its first position and again heat the sample over the burner. Repeat the process until no further sublimation takes place. This is determined by

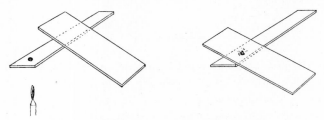

Fig. 99. Sublimation from Slide to Slide, $1/3$ nat. size.

using a clean portion of the wide slide for the condensation. If no sublimate appears on the clean surface, the removal of volatile material is complete. Collect the sublimate within a fairly small area. If microscopic examination is to follow, the condensate should not form too thick a layer.

When some degree of temperature control is desired or required, one of the following types of apparatus may be employed. In these the receiver is separated from the subliming surface by a glass ring, glass threads, asbestos paper, or the like. KEMPF (83) recommends that the sublimation take place at as low a temperature as possible and that the receiver be as close as possible to the sample, that is, from 0.1 to 0.01 mm. He secures these conditions by using an apparatus consisting of an electrically heated plate with automatic temperature control and very thin platinum or brass foil or mica plates for separating the sample and receiver. The material is heated for hours and possibly under vacuum. He is thus able to sublime a great many substances including nearly all classes of organic compounds. For our purposes, however, it will suffice to place the substance on a slide on a metal heating block (drilled to hold a thermometer) or on a crucible filled with mercury, laying two or three glass threads with a diameter of less than 0.1 mm on the spread-out sample and placing a cover glass on the threads. Heat the block or crucible with a burner.

For larger quantities, KUERSCHNER (94) uses two Petri dishes. One is placed open side downward on an asbestos-wire gauze to form a sort of air bath. The sample is spread out on the upper side of the dish and a glass ring is used to separate it from the receiver, the second Petri dish. The latter is set on the ring, open side up, and can be filled with water.

Other sublimators are those of TUNMAN (142), ROSENTHALER (124), MAYRHOFER (104), and JENNERICH (79).

Sublimation in Tubes. When the microscopic examination of the sublimate is not the immediate object, one of the tube type of sublimators can be used. For very small quantities, capillaries sealed at one end are employed by BENEDETTI-PICHLER (10). After placing the substance in

Fig. 100. Slide for Collecting the Sublimate, $^2/_3$ nat. size.

the tube and bringing it to the sealed end by tapping, draw out the capillary about 30 mm from the sealed end into a finer capillary. Then place the sealed end to the depth of the sample in an aluminum heating block which is fitted with a thermometer or the same length on a hot stage and raise the temperature until sublimation is complete. If necessary, of course, the temperature can be kept at one point. Heating of the aluminum block under such circumstances is best carried out by means of a microburner.

For larger quantities PREGL (118) devised the sublimation tube to be used in conjunction with his regenerating block. This tube is 20 cm long and 7 mm in outer diameter, sealed at one end and open at the other

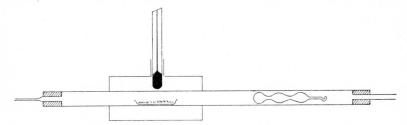

Fig. 101. Sublimation Tube of SOLTYS, $^1/_4$ nat. size.

if the sublimation is to be carried out at normal pressure. If it is desired to employ a vacuum, the tube is constricted to a fine capillary near one end and the other end is connected to a vacuum pump. After sublimation is complete, the tube is cut open and the sublimate is pushed out by means of a sharp-edged glass rod.

PREGL's tube was modified by SCHÖLLER (126) who placed a narrow microscope slide with the ends bent as shown in Fig. 100 and with a small handle fused on one end over the substance to be sublimed in the tube, to act as receiver.   The sublimate can then be examined immediately under the microscope.

SOLTYS (131) advises using the KEMPF method first to determine whether the substance is actually sublimable. For purification purposes he recommends the tube sublimator. Place the sample (in glass or porcelain boat) in the tube, Fig. 101. If the substance is a viscous liquid, transfer it to the boat by absorbing it in asbestos and placing the latter in the boat.

Wipe out the original container once or twice with asbestos which has been moistened with the proper solvent. After placing the boat in the tube, apply suction carefully without heating. When no foaming can be observed with full vacuum, begin heating carefully. From about 50°C up the heating can be rapid. A sublimate (solid or liquid) is obtained at a greater or smaller distance from the metal block depending upon the volatility of the substance. Cut the tube and remove the larger portion of the sublimate, if solid, by means of a spatula. If the sublimate is in the form of a thin film, remove it by fixing the tube into the neck of a small flask containing a small amount of solvent (Fig. 102), and dissolve the sublimate by refluxing.

If the subliming substance is very volatile, it may be sucked through and out of the tube entirely. This may not be

Fig. 102. Removal of Sublimate.

prevented entirely by cooling but a plug made of a glass tube with constrictions as shown in Fig. 101 will keep the sublimate in the tube.

Solid crystalline substances, according to the same author, are best purified by a tube sublimator with a fritted glass filter. The construction of the apparatus and the method of operation can be seen in Fig. 103.

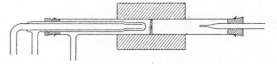

Fig. 103. Filtered Sublimation according to SOLTYS,
$^1/_3$ nat. size.

Vacuum Sublimation. Other vacuum sublimators have been described by EDER (39) (Fig. 104), WERNER and KLEIN (146), WAGENAAR (144), MARBERG (103), and HORTVET (77). WERNER and KLEIN (146) improved the apparatus of EDER by adding a ground-in condenser, Fig. 105; the sublimate is collected upon a cover slip just as in the sublimator of EDER. MARBERG's apparatus is designed for semi-micro sublimation at low temperatures and high vacuum. The HORTVET apparatus was used by HOFF-

MAN and JOHNSON (*see* above) in the investigation of the sublimation temperatures of thirty seven substances. These authors give the sublimation temperatures for these substances at atmospheric pressure and at a vacuum of 0.5 to 1 mm. Photomicrographs of some of the substances are included. The sublimation block of CLARKE and HERMANCE (28) is

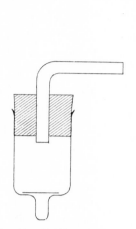

Fig. 104. Sublimation
Apparatus of EDER,
$^2/_3$ nat. size.

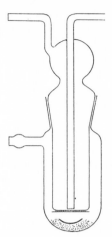

Fig. 105. Sublimation
Apparatus of WERNER
and KLEIN, $^1/_2$ nat. size.

thermostatically controlled and electrically heated and is fitted with a water-cooled condenser.

KOFLER and DERNBACH (92) have devised a sublimation chamber to be used in conjunction with the KOFLER-HILBCK microscope hot stage (*see* page 113). The formation of the sublimate (under vacuum if desired) can be observed under the microscope and the temperature noted. The hot stage of FISCHER (51) was designed for carrying out microsublimations.

An interesting use of sublimation, somewhat akin to gas chromatography, is KOFLER's adsorption sublimation. This will be discussed later, p. 83.

Drying and Removal of Solvent.

Before the physical constants can be determined or before the sample for a quantitative analysis or estimation can be weighed, all traces of water or other solvent which may have been used in the purification of the substance must be removed. Furthermore, before some substances can be purified by recrystallization from certain solvents, all water must be removed. For example, moist solids can be recrystallized from solvents such as acetone and alcohol in which the water is soluble, but not from benzene or carbon tetrachloride.

For simple drying the ordinary desiccator may be used, the sample being placed on a small watch glass or in a microboat which in turn is placed on a large watch glass or plate in the desiccator. EMICH (46) suggests using a Canada balsam bottle as a microdesiccator. A micro gas chamber

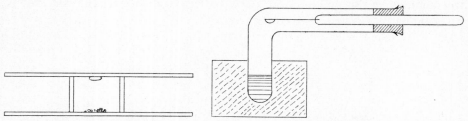

Fig. 106. Drying Chamber.   Fig. 107. Microdesiccator of GARNER, $^2/_3$ nat. size.

made by placing a glass ring on a microscope slide and another slide on top of the ring (Fig. 106) also serves as a drying chamber. The desiccant is either a drop of concentrated sulfuric acid hanging from the upper slide or a small piece of calcium chloride placed beside the sample on the lower

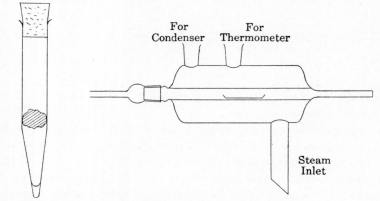

Fig. 108. Drying in the Microcone, nat. size.   Fig. 109. Drying Apparatus of VETTER.

slide. GARNER (58) makes a microdesiccator out of a test tube as shown in Fig. 107. In some cases material prepared in a microcone can be dried without transfer by putting a piece of calcium chloride above the substance as shown in Fig. 108 and stoppering the cone with a cork. This is particularly useful when working with liquids.

The usual method of removing excess solvent by pressing the crystal mass out on a porous plate, employed with macroquantities, obviously cannot be used with microsamples. The solvent must be removed by evaporation. Inasmuch as the removal of the last traces may require the attainment of a higher vapor pressure than that at room temperature and atmospheric pressure, the use of vacuum and high temperature is called for. These conditions are also required for the removal of water from substances which form hydrates or are very hygroscopic. Occasionally the passage of dry air or inert gas over the substance being dried can be substituted for vacuum evaporation.

The drying of a substance in a capillary tube has been described on page 12 in the discussion of recrystallization in the capillary. This procedure is especially applicable to the preparation of derivatives. If larger quantities are available or another type of container has been used in the preparation of the substance, the usual drying ovens can often be employed. In such cases the substance is handled as described above when using the ordinary desiccators. EMICH (48) also recommends a small STAEHLER block. PREGL (119) places the substance in a platinum boat and heats the latter on a metal block which is bored for a thermometer. The block is placed on a support and is heated by a microburner. SOLTYS (132) uses the drying

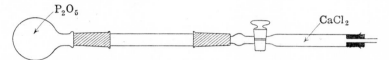

Fig. 110. MUENSTER's Modification of PREGL's Vacuum Desiccator.

block of PREGL (118) for vacuum drying. A small watch glass carrying the sample is placed on the previously heated drying block and the latter is placed on a wire tripod in the ordinary vacuum desiccator. This is then evacuated. The high heat capacity of the block and the low loss due to the vacuum keep the block hot for a long time. Substances just recrystallized can be dried in this way very quickly so that melting points and other physical properties can be determined very soon after preparation of the material.

FUHRMANN (55) has described a device for drying small amounts of solids, which makes it possible to use microboats, microbeakers, or tubes as containers for the substance. The apparatus of NOLLER (108) can also be used for beakers, flasks, or centrifuge cones. HECHT's (72) is fitted with an inverted funnel for drawing off the vapors to hasten evaporation.

Drying under vacuum can also be carried out by means of the Abderhalden drying pistol, the substance being placed in a microboat. A very simple apparatus has been devised by SWINDELLS (135). The material to be dried is placed in a glass tube sealed at one end, a Nichrome wire heating coil is inserted into the tube, and the tube is evacuated and sealed. Current is passed through the coil and thus the substance can be heated in the absence of air. PREGL's tube desiccator can, of course, be used with vacuum. The device of VETTER (143) for the determination of water (Fig. 109) can also be used as a vacuum drier by replacing the inlet tube with a very fine capillary and connecting the other end to a vacuum pump. MÜNSTER's (107) modification of PREGL's tube desiccator is shown in Fig. 110. The center portion which holds the microboat containing the substance to be dried is placed in the regenerating block of PREGL or other heating

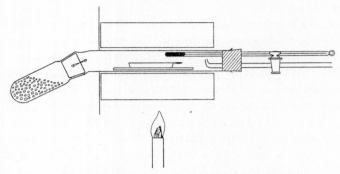

Fig. 111. Vacuum Desiccator of BLANK.

apparatus. The bulb on the left is filled with the proper drying agent. A vacuum desiccator something like a "micro drying pistol" has been designed by BLANK (20). The desiccant is contained in the vessel at the

TABLE 5
Drying Agents

Solvent to be removed	Absorbents
Water	$CaCl_2$, KOH, NaOH, H_2SO_4, P_2O_5, silica gel, anhydrous salts
Alcohol, ether	H_2SO_4, paraffin (paraffin-impregnated filter paper), silica gel, activated carbon
$CHCl_3$, C_6H_6, CS_2, ligroin	Paraffin (above), olive oil, silica gel, activated carbon
HCl, acetic acid, other volatile acids	KOH, NaOH, $Ca(OH)_2$
NH_3, pyridine, other volatile bases	H_2SO_4. P_2O_5

left (Fig. 111), which is fitted to the rest of the apparatus by a standard taper ground joint to permit quick replacement.

Solvents other than water can usually be removed in the same way as water using, however, absorbents which take up the solvent in question. Table 5 lists a number of the absorbents or adsorbents which can be used for the common solvents.

The activated carbon should be of the gas-adsorbent type such as used in solvent recovery systems.

In removing solvents other than water, it has been found that simply passing a stream of air or other gas over the substance being dried, after it has been heated, will remove the solvent quickly. This can be done by using BENEDETTI-PICHLER's (11) drying tube and block, Fig. 112.

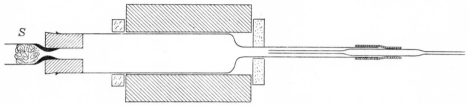

Fig. 112. Drying Tube of BENEDETTI-PICHLER, $^1/_3$ nat. size.

It is possible to dry substances under vacuum or in an inert gas by closing the tube with a stopper S through which is fitted a glass inlet tube with a very fine capillary bore or by connecting the inlet with a source of inert gas.

Liquids and solutions can be dried by the addition of a solid absorbent which is not soluble in the liquid being dried. After allowing the liquid to stand in contact with the dehydrating (or absorbing) agent for some

TABLE 6
Drying Agents For Liquids

Calcium chloride	Cannot be used with alcohols, amines, or phenols
Potassium hydroxide	For amines and cyclic bases
Potassium carbonate, anhydrous sodium sulfate, or anhydrous magnesium sulfate	For sensitive compounds which can be decomposed by stronger agents

time (several hours if necessary) filter off the latter. Care must be taken not to add too much drying agent. Drying is usually not complete. Some of the dehydrating agents which can be used are given in Table 6. The last three substances are recommended for drying unknowns.

It is also possible at times to dry a solid by dissolving it in a nonaqueous solvent such as ether and then drying the solution as described above.

An important factor in the selection of a dehydrating agent or absorbent is the possibility of the formation of a stable compound such as a solvate between the desiccant and a component other than the one which it is

desired to remove.   For example, calcium chloride, so commonly used
as a desiccant in inorganic work, is greatly limited in its applicability in
organic procedures because of its ability to form stable addition compounds
with a wide variety of substances including acetone, acetamide, glycerol,
mannose, amines, and esters.   The lists of these compounds given by
PFEIFFER (112) and GREENBAUM (66) will be helpful.

Separation of Mixtures.

The foregoing discussion was concerned principally with the removal
of impurities from the major component.   While many of the methods
described can also be used, as has been pointed out, when the various
components are present in more or less equal proportions, there are cases
in which the properties of the components are so close in nature that the
separation will become difficult and unsharp.   Criteria in the tests for
purity cannot always distinguish between a test substance containing
a low concentration of impurity (hence only a slight difference between
physical constants of pure and impure substances) and mixtures of two
chemical entities with very similar properties and consequent similar slight
difference in physical constants of pure substance and mixture.

Separation is achieved on the basis of difference in physical properties,
chemical properties, or both.   The physical methods are preferred, of
course, since they involve no change in the chemical nature of the test
substance.   These will, therefore, be discussed first.

The first differentiation to be made between the types of mixtures,
the first step in physical separation, is the determination as to whether
the sample is homogeneous or heterogeneous.   The former class includes
solid-solid solutions (mixed crystals), liquid-solid solutions, liquid-liquid
solutions, and gas-liquid solutions.   The second class includes suspensions
of solids in liquids, emulsions and mixtures of solid particles.

Heterogeneous Mixtures.

Since two or more phases already indicate a marked difference in at
least some properties, mixtures of this type present the least difficulty
in separation.

Suspensions.   The solid phase may be either coarsely granular, in
which case simple filtration suffices, or it may be colloidal in nature.   The
latter requires resort to the various means of coagulation.   These include
ultra high speed centrifugation, so-called *ultra* filters, and dialysis.   The
first two methods require special apparatus available through commercial
supply houses.   Reference will be made only to the membrane filter of
THIESSEN (137).   For dialysis, on the other hand, little in the way of apparatus is required and this can be made by the analyst himself in most cases.

Essentially dialysis involves the use of membranes which are permeable to both solvent and ionic solutes but impermeable to colloidal particles. Various types of membranes may be used, such as parchment paper, collodion, and cellophane. Since dialysis is a process involving diffusion, it will take place more rapidly at higher temperatures. Furthermore, in certain cases it may be possible to make use of the charge on the ionic solute by placing positive and negative electrodes on either side of the membrane with resultant increase in the rate of transport of the ions. Microdialysis apparatus has been described by WOOD (150); BAER (5); TAYLOR, PARPART, and BALLENTINE (136) and a micro electrodialyser by KEYS (84).

In some cases colloidal suspensions can be coagulated by evaporating the liquid phase and then adding fresh, pure solvent. The possibility of mechanical occlusion of soluble material makes this method less preferable.

Emulsions. Emulsions can also be separated sometimes by ultra-centrifuges. At other times addition of a salt or other electrolyte to a high concentration will produce separation into two layers, especially if the electrolyte is very soluble in one phase.

Solid Mixtures. If the particles are sufficiently large, mechanical separation as described on page 29 can be used. If this is not feasible, differences in solubility or density can be employed. The former property involves extraction and one of the procedures described on page 60 ff. should be tried. If a sufficiently great difference in density exists between the components, a series of liquids of different densities is used. These liquids would, of course, not be solvents for any of the components. A list of liquids which can be used and the method of employing them are described in the publication of SULLIVAN (134).

If the densities or particle sizes are not sufficiently different to permit efficient separation by the methods listed above, heterogeneous mixtures should be regarded and treated as homogeneous ones.

Homogeneous Mixtures.

Under this classification are found solid solutions (mixed crystals), solid-liquid solutions, liquid-liquid solutions, and gas-liquid solutions.

Solid Solutions. Since separation requires breaking of the crystal lattice, the sample must be partly or completely vaporized, fused, or dissolved. Vaporization involves sublimation and the sample should be tested and treated as described above under this heading. If care is taken to control the temperature, it should be possible to carry out a fractional sublimation in case more then one component is volatile. Raise the temperature slowly and observe the sublimate as it forms, using a lens to note if there is any change in color, form, or state. If, after sublimation starts, the temperature is kept at that point until no further sublimate forms and some material is still left on the heated surface, change the receiver before raising the temperature further.

Zone melting is effective in separating components of solid mixtures. For this purpose the passes are made in one direction only and the temperature of the heater should be kept just above the melting point of the highest melting component. PFANN (111) has demonstrated the efficiency of the method by separating Halowax, a wax mixture used in electrical

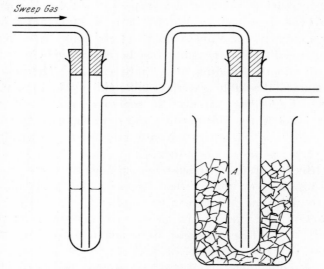

Sweep Gas

Fig. 113. Separation of a Gas from a Liquid.

condensers, into components differing considerably in their dielectric constants and in their melting points.

Although zone melting is much more effective, some mixtures must be separated by recrystallization from or extraction with liquid solvents because of their instability at higher temperatures.

Solid-Liquid Solution. If no codistillation takes place, separation of a solid solute from a liquid solvent is achieved most easily by simple evaporation of the solvent. Use a simple distilling apparatus with condenser to recover the liquid fraction as well as the solid one. If codistillation does take place, it will be necessary to fractionate the distillate.

Liquid-Liquid Solutions. Aside from fractional distillation, liquid-liquid solutions can be treated only by extraction or by fractional crystallization. The latter again depends upon a considerable difference in melting points and upon these melting points being in an attainable range. For example, if cooling of the solution with ice or carbon dioxide snow results in solidification of at least one component, the method can be used. But if none solidify it is not advisable to try lower temperatures. Extraction is of advantage only if one or more components are water soluble and the rest not. The organic solvents usually do not differentiate sufficiently between various carbon compounds to make them valuable as separating agents. Fractional or steam distillation provides the best physical method of separation.

Liquid-Gas Solutions. The term "gas" is meant to include compounds boiling at or below room temperature. Examples of this type of mixture would be the low boiling petroleum fractions, Formalin, etc. Fractional distillation and preferential adsorption offer the only feasible

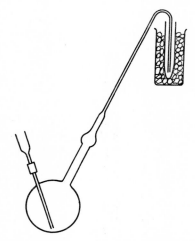

Fig. 114. Fractionation Flask of BENEDETTI-PICHLER-SCHNEIDER.

methods of physical separation. Evaporation of the more volatile components takes place at such a low temperature that unless the solvent has a very low vapor pressure at that temperature, heating should be avoided. It is best to use a sweep gas for the removal of the gaseous component and a freezing mixture or adsorbent as condensing agent. An apparatus which may be used is shown in Fig. 113. The trap A is immersed in solid carbon dioxide or liquid air. It may be replaced by an absorption tube of the PREGL or similar type filled with activated carbon of the gas-purifying type. Recovery of the adsorbed gas is accomplished by heating the absorption tube in a PREGL regenerating block or similar apparatus.

If the solvent has a high boiling point (100° or over) the BENEDETTI-PICHLER-SCHNEIDER fractionation flask as modified for quantitative work (13), Fig. 114, will be found satisfactory. Again, a cooling bath of liquid air or a solid carbon dioxide and acetone mixture must be used.

Preferential Adsorption. It is sometimes possible to accentuate the differences in solubility of substances in a given solvent by combining extraction with adsorption. The techniques which employ this principle include chromatographic, selective, and sublimation adsorption.

Chromatographic Adsorption. (21, 24, 99) Chromatographic separation of the components of a mixture depends upon (*a*) differences in the affinity of the components for an adsorbent or (*b*) differences in the solubility of the components in two different solvents. Undoubtedly there are other mechanisms involved such as ion-exchange, but a detailed discussion is beyond the scope of this book.

The media on which the separation occurs may be columns of an adsorbent such as activated carbon, silica gel, alumina for the first cited

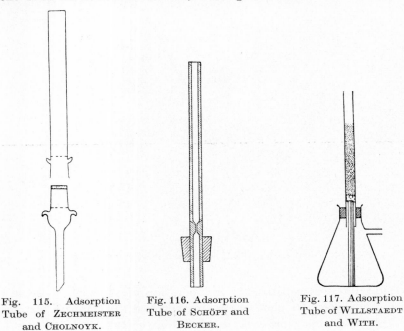

Fig. 115. Adsorption Tube of ZECHMEISTER and CHOLNOYK.

Fig. 116. Adsorption Tube of SCHÖPF and BECKER.

Fig. 117. Adsorption Tube of WILLSTAEDT and WITH.

systems and strips or sheets of paper for the second. After separation the components of the mixture may be recovered from the columns by successive elution and from the paper by cutting the strip or sheet into pieces so that each contains only one component. Unless the substances are colored, fluoresce, or emit radiation it is necessary to determine their location on the paper by the use of a developer, that is, a reagent which will give a colored product with the compound sought. This obviously can be a disadvantage when a pure substance alone is desired.

Table 7 summarizes some of the paper chromatographic procedures which have been described for the separation of various types of compounds, either as such or as derivatives. The following discussion will concern itself only with column chromatography.

The two steps in column chromatography are (1) separation (or retention) of the components on the medium and (2) their removal from the column.

Type of Compound	Derivative	Common Solvent System	Color Indicator
Alcohols	Xanthogenates	n-Butanol : 2% aq. KOH	Sodium nitroprusside and hydroxylamine HCl
	3,5-Dinitrobenzoates	Heptane : methanol	1-Naphthylamine
	3,6-Dinitrophthalates	iso-Pentanol : NH$_4$OH : H$_2$O	NaOH and ethyl acetoacetate
Phenols	Methylolphenols	n-Butanol: NH$_4$OH	p-Nitrobenzenediazonium fluoborate (Derivative is colored)
	Phenylazobenzenesulfonates	sec.-Butanol : aq. Na$_2$CO$_3$	
Aliphatic acids			
Volatile (C$_1$–C$_9$)	Hydroxamates	n-Pentanol : formic acid : H$_2$O	Ferric chloride
H$_2$O-sol., non-vol.		Ethanol : NH$_4$OH : H$_2$O	Thymol blue
α-Keto acids	2,4-Dinitrophenyl-hydrazones	tert.-Pentanol : ethanol : H$_2$O	NaOH
Higher fatty acids	Hydroxamates	Ethyl acetate : tetrahydro-furan : H$_2$O	Ferric chloride
Aromatic acids		n-Butanol : (NH$_4$)$_2$CO$_3$: H$_2$O	Methyl red
Aldehydes and Ketones	2,4-Dinitrophenylhydrazones	Ethyl ether : petrolic ether } Ethanol : petrolic ether }	NaOH
Carbohydrates		Phenol : H$_2$O } n-Butanol : acetic acid : H$_2$O }	{ 3,4-Dinitrobenzoic acid { Aniline and phthalic acid, 1-naphthol
Amines		n-Butanol : acetic acid : H$_2$O	Triketohydrindene (ninhydrin)
Amino acids		Phenol : H$_2$O	Triketohydrindene (ninhydrin)
		2,6-Lutidine : 2,4,6-collidine : H$_2$O }	
	Dinitrophenyl aminoacids	n-Butanol : acetic acid : H$_2$O }	
		n-Butanol : H$_2$O	(Derivative is colored)

Details of the procedures listed in this table are given, among others, by BLACK, DURRUM and ZWEIG (20), BRIMLEY and BARRETT (24), and LEDERER and LEDERER (98).

The various types of micro chromatographic columns are shown in Figs. 115, 116, 117, 118, 119, 120.

Although the efficiency of separation is dependent in some degree upon the adsorbent, use either silica gel or aluminum oxide if the nature

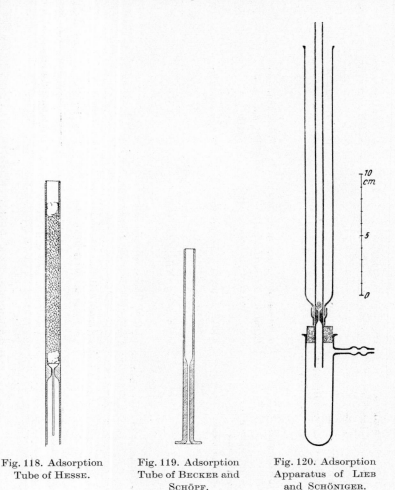

Fig. 118. Adsorption   Fig. 119. Adsorption   Fig. 120. Adsorption
Tube of HESSE.   Tube of BECKER and   Apparatus of LIEB
                           SCHÖPF.   and SCHÖNIGER.

of the test substance is unknown. Suspend the adsorbent in an inert solvent such as petrolic ether or benzene. A vacuum may be used to assist in the filling of the column. Add enough adsorbent so that the tube is about three quarters full. A little pure sand added to the top may prevent disturbance of the adsorbent layer. Wash with 2 to 3 ml of the solvent. In the case of tubes which cannot be closed at the bottom, add the solution of the sample when the suspending liquid has dropped to about 3 mm above the top of the settled adsorbent.

Add about 1 ml of a 1% solution of the test substance to the top of the adsorbent tube. When this has drained to the top of the adsorbent column, add the eluting solvent, 1 ml at a time, and collect the eluate, also 1 ml at a time, in microbeakers. Evaporate each portion of eluate to determine if any of the sample is being extracted. Continue to add the eluant until either no further residue is obtained upon evaporation of the extract or, if no residue at all has been obtained, until 10 ml of the solvent have been used. In the latter case repeat with another solvent.

The elution is based upon the displacement of the adsorbed substance by the eluant. In the investigation of unknown mixtures the usual solvents are, in order of use, petrolic ether, petrolic ether-benzene mixtures in ratios of from 4:1 to 1:4, benzene, benzene-ether mixtures, ether, and ether-methanol mixtures. The discussion of adsorbents and eluting solvents by FISCHER and IWANOFF (52) may serve as a guide in the selection of the most efficient ones if something concerning the character of the sample is known.

Selective Adsorption. This term is applied to separations which use the new synthetic zeolites. These are crystalline sodium or calcium aluminosilicates which have been heated to remove the water of hydration. The resulting crystals are highly porous but the pores are of molecular dimensions and are uniform. Small molecules may enter but not large ones and thus separations based on differences in molecular size are possible. For example, they can be employed to separate n-butane from isobutane. Also, by combining the action of several types or combinations of these zeolites with conventional adsorbents such as activated carbon or silica gel, it is possible to carry out separations of such mixtures as n-propanol and n-butanol, aromatics and aliphatics, etc.

The separations may be carried out by either shaking the liquid in a stoppered flask with the adsorbent and then filtering or by drawing the liquid or gaseous sample through a column of the adsorbent. The adsorbed material is recovered either by desorption by heating or by displacement with water. After regeneration in this manner the adsorbent can be used again.

Sublimation Adsorption. The separation of substances by adsorption has also been utilized by KOFLER (91) in his *sublimation adsorption*. It is applicable, although not restricted, to substances which have an appreciable vapor pressure at temperatures below their melting points. It has been pointed out in a preceding section that a great many substances can be sublimed, many more than usually believed. In sublimation adsorption a carrier gas (air or other inert gas) is saturated with the vapor of the sample at reduced pressures and at temperatures usually below the melting point of the sample and then drawn through a column of adsorbent heated to the same temperature. By varying pressure, temperature, and rate of flow through the column, separation of the components can be achieved. If the solid substances are not sufficiently volatile at temperatures below their melting points, they can be heated to liquefaction to provide the necessary vapor pressure. Most of the components of mixtures suited to this method of separation are usually very readily adsorbed by the ordinary adsorbents and hence little separation would be effected. It is necessary, therefore, to work with less effective adsorbents such as silica gel, Floridin XS, etc. However, since the capacity of the adsorbent decreases with increasing temperature, the more active adsorbents must be used when the sublimation temperature is high. An adsorbent which permits release of the adsorbate at temperatures 20° to 30° above the melting point of the latter is most satisfactory.

After volatilization of the sample and adsorption, the column is eluted by drawing air or inert gas through it with gradual, slow rise in temperature. The rate of gas flow is very important. In general, a rate of 0.1 liter per minute at pressures of 20 to 25 mm (obtainable with aspirator pump) is recommended. The gas stream issuing from the top of the adsorbent layer impinges on a cooled copper rod which acts as condenser. The sublimate which collects there can be removed for further testing. In the case of more complex mixtures the condenser should be changed frequently as the temperature is raised. It is possible to obtain as many as ten fractions in this way.

Condensation in capillary spaces as distinct from real adsorption can also take place in the pores of the adsorbent. However, working under reduced pressure as described will prevent this. Sublimation adsorption has been used successfully to convert impure "technical" grade compounds into extremely pure ones by a single sublimation through the adsorption column. Mixtures such as one of o-, m-, and p-nitroaniline can readily be separated.

Ion-Exchange Separations. Ion exchanging materials may be inorganic or organic. The former are limited in their applicability since they are stable only over a narrow pH range, soluble in acid solution, and peptized by alkaline fluid. Only the organic type will be considered. Most organic ion exchanges are copolymers of styrene and divinyl-benzene. Their action may be physical or chemical. By choice of the pore size of the exchanger (determined by degree of cross-linkage) it is possible to separate large from small molecules as with the selective adsorbents. So-called *ion-exclusion* separates ionic from non-ionic substances by making use of the difference in the ability of the two to displace the liquid phase inside the exchanger particles. The most useful action of the exchangers is, however, their function as chemical reagents in which the reagent and one of the products are insoluble in water. Thus, excess reagent does not contaminate the sample and yet the desired component is removed simply and completely. As the name indicates, the reactions involve the component or components which are ionic. Therefore it is possible not only to remove ionic material from non-ionic but also to separate weakly ionized materials from strongly ionized substances. For example, acids and salts can be removed from glycerine, alcohol, or amino acids; and mixtures such as mono-, di-, and triethanolamines or mono-, di-, or trichloracetic acids can be separated. Ionic materials in low concentration can be taken up on an exchanger and eluted in more concentrated form.

When the ion-exchangers act purely as chemical reagents, the following reactions can be regarded as taking place. R signifies the water-insoluble copolymer network of a resinous ion-exchanger, A, A_1, and A_2 are anions and M, M_1, and M_2 are cations.

Cation exchanger:
$$RM_1 + M_2A \rightleftharpoons RM_2 + M_1A$$
$$RH + MOH = RM + H_2O$$
$$RH + MA \rightleftharpoons RM + HA$$

Anion exchanger:
$$RA_1 + MA_2 \rightleftharpoons RA_2 + MA_1$$
$$ROH + HA = RA + H_2O$$
$$ROH + MA \rightleftharpoons RA + MOH$$

As shown, four of these reactions are reversible and tend to reach a state of equilibrium. When the reaction is to proceed to the right (*loading*) dilute solutions are used. In running the reaction to the left (recovery or regeneration) concentrated solutions of the regenerant are used. By dilute is meant the order of 0.1 normal, by concentrated, 1 normal to 10 normal. This use of dilute solutions is often a limiting factor in the application of the exchangers.

Procedure. The ion-exchange resins should be the analytical grade or should be conditioned prior to use. Such conditioning involves, e. g. for a cation exchanger, washing the resin with hydrochloric acid to remove iron, with distilled water to remove colloidal material, and finally with sodium hydroxide. It is then washed free of alkali with water. Similar treatment must be given other resins to obtain them in the proper condition.

The tube for holding the resin may be a simple glass tube either constricted near the bottom end to support a glass wool plug or fitted with a fritted glass or other filter at this point. These serve to hold the resin in place. The upper end is either fitted with a separatory-type funnel or connected to a leveling bulb device for introducing the sample solution. Microcolumns have tube diameters of between 2.5 mm and 7 mm with 6 mm as the optimum size. The ratio of diameter to height of resin column should be 1 to 10. Figure 121 shows the apparatus of KLEMENT (89). Since some resins swell appreciably when reacting or being regenerated, allowance must be made for this when determining the length of the tube.

The resin is added to the column in the form of a water suspension. Add the resin to about two volumes of water in a flask and allow to stand

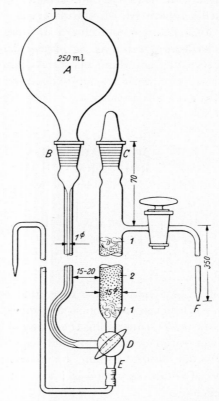

Fig. 121. Ion exchange column. *1* Cotton plug; *2* Exchange resin.

for one or two hours. Then stir to remove all air bubbles and pour portions of the slurry into the column. Allow each portion to settle, applying air under pressure at the top if necessary to expel the water more rapidly. Add more resin suspension when the water is within one centimeter of the resin layer in the tube.

The sample solution is usually added to the top of the column through funnel or leveling bulb at a rate of 3 to 5 ml per minute for a 6-mm column. Solutions which might dissolve or oxidize the resin of the exchanger must not be used. Allow the sample solution to flow through the column as completely as possible. Since the sample meets fresh exchanger on its passage downward, the reaction should be complete unless the exchanger is overloaded. Wash the column by adding water in the same manner as the sample to remove any sample solution remaining. Collect the *effluent* (do not confuse with the eluant!) and treat it further by other methods to recover the components which it might hold. Treat the column to recover the adsorbed components. The solution used for this purpose must contain the appropriate ion at the proper concentration. For example, if acetic acid (or acetate ion) has been adsorbed, elute the column with 1 m ammonium carbonate. Use a mineral acid to recover the cation from a cation exchanger. Add the eluting solution again in the same way as the sample. Treat the *eluant* further for recovery of the adsorbed component in its original form.

Batch operation is also employed with ion-exchangers but it is not as satisfactory as the column method. The extent to which exchange takes place is limited by the selectivity (preference for certain ion species) of the resin at equilibrium and, therefore, unless the selectivity is extremely favorable, only a relatively small portion of the total capacity of the resin is utilized. The technique does possess the advantage of rapidity. Merely mix the resin and the sample solution in a flask, stir and allow to stand. Then filter, wash, and recover the adsorbed material by treatment with an appropriate solution in another flask.

By proper conditioning of the resin it is possible to carry out other separations. For example, by using the bisulfite form of an anion exchanger, aldehydes and ketones have been separated from alcohols. In other cases, certain anion exchangers appear to have the effect of removing whole molecules of acids. An excellent series of papers on separations of classes of organic compounds by ion-exchangers has been published by GABRIELSON and SAMUELSON (57).

Chemical Separations. Since the primary concern of the analyst in dealing with mixtures is to obtain the components in the same form as they occurred in the original test substance, chemical means of separation are a last resort. The mere addition of a reagent increases the complexity of the original problem. The selection of a reagent should therefore have the following as desirable objectives.

1) The reagent should produce a difference in the solubility, volatility, or adsorbability of the components of the mixture.

2) It should be possible to detect the stoichiometric end point. Since all of the components of a mixture usually require identification, unreacted component or excess reagent would contaminate the remainder of the mixture.

3) The product of the reaction should be such that a regeneration of the original substance is possible. For example, reacting an acid component with a base permits the recovery of the acid by treating the product (salt) with a stronger acid.

4) There should be no change in the character of the remainder of the mixture. Addition of an acid reagent, for example, for the removal of a basic component, should not cause a rearrangement of another component to produce another species.

These requirements sharply restrict the possible reagents for general use on an unknown test substance. A few specific reagents which might be used for special cases will be mentioned under the discussion of the individual genera. It should also be pointed out that a further separation by physical means is usually required after the chemical treatment.

The following outlines the procedure for chemical separations.

I) Titration: A) With acid.
               B) With base.

II) Neutralization: A) With acid.
                     B) With base.

III) Treatment of Reaction Result:

   A) Homogeneous: 1. Extraction.
                     2. Distillation.
                        a. Fractional.
                        b. Vacuum.
                        c. Steam.
                     3. Evaporation.

   B) Heterogeneous: 1. Filtration.
                       2. Decantation.
                       3. Extraction.

IV) Recovery of Original Component:
    A) Evaporation of solvent, if non-aqueous.
    B) Re-solution.
    C) Release of free acidic or basic compound.

The largest classes of compounds with similar reactivity are the acidic and basic groups. Reaction with a mineral acid or a metallic base results in salt-type compounds with markedly different volatility and solubility. In the case of the acidic compounds, most of the salts with the alkali metals are water-soluble; the salts with heavy metals such as silver are insoluble in water as well as in organic solvents. Most of the salt-type products of the basic compounds are also water-soluble. The determination of the stoichiometric end point is readily possible for acids and bases. The first step is, therefore, the determination of the exact quantity of acid or base required to just neutralize the basic or acidic component of the mixture.

I) Titration. This is carried out on a separate sample unless the indicator or the alcohol used do not interfere with later tests.

A) Test for Acid. Dissolve 5 mg of the test substance in 2 ml of water and add 1 drop of phenolphthalein indicator solution. Using the apparatus and precautions described on page 182, titrate with 0.02 n sodium hydroxide. If the end point is reached with less than 0.5 ml of base, repeat the titration but use 2 ml of neutral alcohol in place of the water. Titrate to a pink color which persists for one minute. If more than 0.5 ml of the base are used in the first or second titration, the substance is regarded as acid. If less than 0.5 ml used, the acidic material is only a minor impurity or the base was consumed by a reaction other than neutralization.

B) Test for Base. Dissolve 5 mg of the test substance in 2 ml of neutral alcohol and add 4 to 5 drops of thymol blue indicator solution. Titrate with 0.02 n hydrochloric acid to a distinct pink which persists for one minute. If less than 1 ml of the acid is required, the compound is not sufficiently basic for separation by this means.

II) Preparation of Salt. If the sample shows a sufficient basicity or acidity, calculate the volume of 1 n base or acid which must be added for neutralization of a definite weight of the test substance. Add this to the sample in either water or alcohol solution, as indicated by the titration results.

III A) If the neutralized solution is homogeneous, that is, no precipitate or no second liquid phase forms, add an equal volume of water and examine again. If the solution is still homogeneous, extract a small portion with ether and allow the ether to evaporate from the extract at room temperature. Evaporate another portion of the solution on a water bath. The evaporation will indicate if the entire sample is readily volatile, if a difficultly volatile liquid residue remains, or if a solid residue remains. If the residue is a viscous liquid, try a steam distillation and a vacuum distillation of another portion of the solution.

III B) If the result of the reaction is a mixture of solid and liquid, filter off the solid. If a mixture of two or more immiscible liquids results, decant the upper layer after centrifuging. Try the miscibility of alcohol and ether with the two fractions. If one or both of the solvents is immiscible with the liquid, use it to extract a small portion and determine if any component has been dissolved.

IV) Regeneration of Original Component. After the extraction, distillation, filtration, or other removal of the non-reacted portion of the original material, recover the salt by first evaporating any remaining non-aqueous solvent. Dissolve the residue in water and treat with either sulfuric acid or sodium hydroxide to displace the weaker acid or base. Separate this from the sodium sulfate or sodium chloride in the usual ways.

Other Reactions. While most other reagents can be used only in special, limited, cases, it is sometimes possible to predict a possible second component if the nature of one is known. For example, if a second component is found together with an aldehyde, it is reasonable to expect this to be the oxidation product of the aldehyde, namely, an acid. It is therefore possible to select a more specific reagent such as sodium bisulfite for aldehydes or halogens for unsaturated hydrocarbons and phenols. An interesting type of compound which offers considerable opportunity for what might otherwise be a difficult separation is the inclusion compound or adduct. The use of urea in separating the chemically inert hydrocarbons is an example.

Part II

Preliminary Examination.

Chapter III.

Elementary Analysis.

Carbon.

Although it is assumed that only compounds of carbon are being analyzed and hence a test for carbon is more or less superfluous, there may be instances when such a test is advisable or desirable. The ignition test (page 27) will, in the majority of cases, give evidence of the presence of carbon but there will be exceptions. Volatile substances simply evaporate or sublime and some non-volatile substances do not char. For example, metallic salts of organic acids will not necessarily show the presence of carbon when subjected to the ignition test. They may appear to decompose but purely inorganic substances may also decompose when heated. Furthermore, some inorganic compounds such as the nitrates of some of the heavy metals will decompose when heated and leave a residue of a black oxide which might be mistaken for carbon. In doubtful cases, therefore, a test for carbon should be carried out.

EMICH (9) describes a very delicate test for carbon but a test of such sensitivity is unnecessary for most work. He also gives another procedure which is less sensitive but much more quickly carried out.

Place the substance in a Pyrex capillary with a bore of 0.5 to 1 mm and seal at one end. Introduce liquids by means of a capillary pipet and solids by means of a glass thread. After introduction of the sample, seal the other end. Heat the section of the tube above the sample first, then the sample itself, so that the vapors must pass the glowing spot. The carbon usually appears as a shining mirror. When the tube is cut open and the mirror is heated, it should prove to be combustible. The procedure of PEPKOWITZ (24) is an adaptation of the first test by EMICH mentioned above.

BEHRENS (2) heats the substances with sodium or potassium nitrate and tests the resulting melt for carbonate by precipitation as the strontium salt. ROSENTHALER (26) suggests a wet combustion (not micro) for the detection of carbon. SOZZI and NIEDERL (27) mix the test substance with ammonium sulfate and carry out a sodium fusion to detect carbon as either cyanide or as methyl amine.

Carbon can also be detected by the silver permanganate fusion of KÖRBL (20) described below. At the conclusion of the reaction the combustion tube will contain a large quantity of carbon dioxide. Immediately place a small rubber bulb over the top of the tube. Hold the combustion tube into a test tube which contains 0.2 to 1 ml of barium hydroxide solution so that the tip is close to the surface of the solution. Then press the rubber bulb to force about 5 ml of gas through the tip. The precipitate of barium carbonate on the surface of the solution is a positive test for carbon.

Water.

No test is necessary for the detection of hydrogen since, once the organic nature of the compound has been established by the carbon or ignition test, the further classification of the compound by elementary analysis does not depend upon the presence or absence of hydrogen. If, however, the presence of hydrogen must be determined, the fusion with silver permanganate described below may be of assistance. The droplets of water formed in the reaction in the upper part of the combustion tube are removed by means of a capillary pipet and identified as water either by means of the reagents for water (anhydrous copper sulfate or calcium carbide) or by determination of the boiling or freezing point.

The presence of water, however, may affect the value of the physical constants or may cause side reactions in later identification tests. Hence a test for the presence of water should be made.

Place a small lump of calcium carbide (about the size of a poppy seed) in a microcone. Add 100 μl of anhydrous ether and a few drops (from a capillary pipet) or a few micrograms of the test substance. Cork the cone tightly and allow it to stand for 10 minutes. Centrifuge and decant the ether layer into some freshly prepared cuprous chloride solution in another microcone; stir and centrifuge. A reddish precipitate indicates the presence of water in the sample.

Notes.

1) Prepare the reagent by adding 20 ml of water to 1 g of mixture consisting of 32 g anhydrous copper sulfate, 13 g sodium chloride, and 10 g sodium bisulfite. Bring to a boil and, after the precipitate of cuprous chloride has settled, decant the supernatant liquid and wash the precipitate once by decantation. Add 3 ml ammonia (sp. g 0.90) and dilute the solution to 35 ml with distilled water.

2) Commercial calcium carbide may contain occluded acetylene which can be removed by boiling the carbide with about twice as much anhydrous solvent and then evaporating off all the solvent.

Another, less sensitive, test for water consists of sealing the sample (or a solution of the sample in absolute alcohol or ether) in a capillary tube with a few milligrams of anhydrous cupric sulfate. The capillary is allowed to stand for at least two hours with occasional centrifuging back and forth to mix the liquid with the solid. A blue tinge of color in the cupric sulfate layer indicates the presence of water. A blank must be carried out simultaneously on the solvent.

Oxygen.

The test for oxygenated compounds developed by DAVIDSON (5) depends upon the fact that ferric thiocyanate (ferric hexathiocyanatoferriate) is soluble in compounds containing oxygen, nitrogen, or sulfur but not in compounds of carbon and hydrogen alone. Therefore it can be used to distinguish between, e. g., hydrocarbons and oxygenated compounds of Order 1. The test is carried out on a microscale as follows.

Dissolve 1 g ferric chloride and 1 g potassium thiocyanate separately in 10 ml methanol and mix the solutions. Filter off the precipitated potassium chloride. Break up some pieces of a new porous plate in a mortar to a granular powder. Transfer the ground material to a test tube and add the reagent solution. Stopper and shake thoroughly. Pour off the liquid and transfer the porous plate particles to a watch glass. Separate the particles and drain off the liquid still remaining. Allow the particles to dry in the air. Preserve the dry material in a stoppered vial.

Add a particle of the reagent to a drop of the liquid being tested in the depression of a spot plate. With solids use a saturated solution of the sample of test substance in a hydrocarbon or halogenated hydrocarbon. The solvent must be tested first and must react negatively. Stir with a glass thread. The appearance of a deep wine-colored solution is a positive test.

Positive tests are always reliable but certain aromatic ethers and a few other substances fail to give the test. GOERDELER and DOMGÖRGEN (15) found the ferric thiocyanate solubility test superior to the iodine solubility test.

Other Elements.

The detection of other elements requires decomposition of the sample to convert these elements into radicals which can be detected by the usual inorganic tests. Such decomposition is usually pyrolysis in the presence of absorbing media which provide the oppositely charged radical. Some of these media absorb all of the sought-for elements, others are limited to the detection of one or two. The latter will be described under the element.

Decomposition of the Substance.

Sodium Fusion. This is one of the oldest methods but it possesses certain disadvantages. Although carrying out the sodium fusion on a microscale greatly facilitates the destruction of the excess sodium and practically eliminates the danger of an explosion, the manipulation is more difficult. The conditions of the fusion may also lead to the loss of nitrogen (16), especially in compounds containing a high percentage of nitrogen and a low content of carbon. In the case of highly volatile compounds, the sample may be lost before it is decomposed (11). With care and the exercise of certain precautions the sodium fusion test will give good results.

Place 5 to 10 µg of the test substance in a capillary tube with a bore of 2 mm. From a sodium capillary (page 226), having an outside diameter slightly less than 2 mm cut a 3-mm length, and drop it over the sample. Heat the tube starting from about 5 mm above the sodium and moving down. After cooling crush the tube in a drop of water contained in a depression of a spot plate. Transfer the solution to a centrifuge cone, centrifuge, and decant. Test the solution for the various elements.

It has been recommended that in the case of aliphatic compounds a nitrogen-free carbonaceous material such as starch be added prior to the sodium fusion.

WIDMARK (29) modifies the fusion by heating 1- to 5-mg samples with sodium at 500° in sealed ampules to assure complete reaction.

MENVILLE and PARKER (22) use a sodium dispersion in benzene to determine the halogen content in larger samples (several hundred milligrams) of organic compounds.

Sodium Dispersion. PATRICK and SCHNEIDER (23) have used sodium dispersions for the decomposition of the test substance. In dispersions the surface of the sodium is protected from reaction with the atmosphere by the non-reactive dispersing medium. The very large surface area of the finely-divided sodium greatly increases the rate of reaction. The high reducing power of the sodium in this form converts nitrogen, even when in the highly oxidized form of the nitro compounds, into ammonia, and the difficulties met within the detection of the cyanide are eliminated.

Place the sample of test substance (1 µg to 1 mg, depending upon the content of the element to be detected) into a capillary tube sealed at one end or into a microcone. Add 5 to 10 times as much sodium dispersion. In the original work the dispersing medium was toluene but other media are available and it appears that a medium with a higher boiling point than toluene would be more desirable to avoid evaporation of the medium during transfer. The medium should, of course, contain no other elements than carbon, hydrogen, and possibly oxygen. Place a piece of sensitized red litmus paper (*see below* under nitrogen) over the mouth of the centrifuge tube or in the open end of the capillary. Warm the tube gently over a micro-flame. All nitrogen compounds tested by the authors, from acetamide to nitrobenzene, gave positive tests for nitrogen without further treatment. Test for sulfur by first destroying the excess sodium with ethyl alcohol, warming if necessary to achieve complete reaction. Transfer the liquid to a clean microcone and acidify with dilute nitric acid. Immediately after acidification, place a piece of moistened lead acetate paper over the mouth of the tube. Darkening of the test paper indicates, of course, the presence of sulfur.

Magnesium–Potassium Carbonate Fusion (1, 12). Bend a Pyrex capillary tube of about 1-mm bore as shown in Fig. 122. Introduce the magnesium powder-potassium carbonate mixture (1 part of magnesium

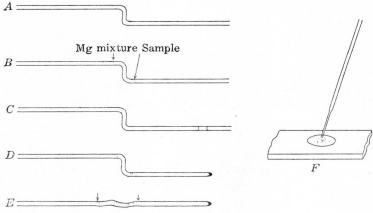

Fig. 122. Magnesium Fusion.

powder ground in an agate mortar with 2 parts of anhydrous potassium carbonate) at one end and pack in with a glass thread so that the entire cross section of the tube is filled. The layer of carbonate mixture should be about 5 mm long. Introduce the sample at the other end. Dip the sample end into a vial of anhydrous ether so that a droplet of ether, about 2 mm long, rises in the tube. In the case of liquids, introduce the ether before the sample. Seal the tube at the sample end by heating in a micro flame and pinching the softened end shut with forceps. During the filling and sealing operations, handle the tube only at the ends. The ether evaporates during the heating, the vapor displacing the air in the tube. Heat the portion of the tube containing the carbonate-magnesium mixture to glowing, then hold the tube in a Bunsen flame so that both the magnesium mixture and the sample are heated at the same time. In this way the sample is distilled over the glowing mixture. After cooling, cut the tube at the points shown in the figure and place the piece containing the fused mass in a previously moistened depression of a spot plate. Crush the tube, preferably with a porcelain spoon or the small end of a porcelain pestle. The moisture film on the plate will prevent the pieces from flying off the plate. Place a drop of hot water on the residue and, after allowing it to stand for a few minutes, draw it off into a fine capillary pipet. The tip of the pipet should be too fine to permit the solid to be drawn up with the liquid. Should any solid particles be drawn up with the liquid, seal the pipet at the wider end and centrifuge the contents to this end. Cut the capillary just above the surface of the liquid and draw off the clear centrifugate in another capillary pipet. This clear liquid is used for the tests for the elements.

It is most important that the potassium carbonate be absolutely dry. Since the nitrogen is absorbed by the magnesium, any moisture in the potassium carbonate would immediately decompose the magnesium nitride with the consequent loss of nitrogen.

Calcium Oxide-Zinc Fusion. JOHNS (19) has reported that this fusion as described by EMICH (8) is very reliable and is so sensitive for nitrogen that it is best not to use it at its extreme limit of sensitivity unless very small quantities or concentrations of nitrogen are important. The procedure has been modified by BENNETT, GOULD, SWIFT, and NIEMAN (3) as follows.

Prepare a combustion tube from a freshly cleaned Pyrex tube 12 cm long and 3 mm in outer diameter. Three centimeters from one end constrict a 2- to 3-mm portion to an inside diameter of 0.6 to 0.7 mm. Place a plug of acid-washed and freshly ignited asbestos into the long arm of the tube and press it firmly into the near side of the constriction with a clean glass rod. Mix equal parts of calcium oxide (prepared by igniting calcium oxalate) and 80-mesh zinc powder (free from sulfur and arsenic) and introduce the mixture into the long arm of the tube in small portions and with tapping to build up a column of 20 mm. Take up the sample in a thin-walled capillary of 0.5-mm bore and 10 to 15 mm long. Place this tube on the calcium oxide-zinc layer and seal the end of the combustion tube by heating and pinching the softened glass shut with forceps. Insert about 1 cm of the open end of the combustion tube into a sleeve made of a 40-mm length of 5-mm Pyrex tubing. For the detection of ammonia place a piece of red litmus paper (*see below* under Nitrogen) into the other end of the sleeve. Cut a hole about 10 mm × 30 mm in a wire gauze and place the gauze on a ringstand or tripod. Lay the combustion tube assembly on the gauze so that the portion containing the calcium oxide-zinc is over the hole. First heat the asbestos plug to a dull-red glow with a small sharp flame, then move the burner to the reagent zone to heat this to glowing and finally heat the sample. This heating should not require more than two minutes.

The elements are sought both in water extract of the combustion mixture and in the residue itself. Seal the short arm of the tube and open (*Caution*) the long arm near the end. Heat the sealed end of the short arm and then allow it to cool. During the cooling add several drops of water so that they will be drawn into the combustion mixture. After 10 to 15 seconds centrifuge the liquid through the asbestos to the closed end of the tube. Cut the tube about 5 mm above the meniscus of the liquid and use the liquid in the tests for the halogens.

After removal of the liquid as described above, warm the solid remaining in the tube to remove any water. Then cut the tube open near the middle of the combustion mixture and transfer all the solid by gentle tapping into the depression of a culture-type microscope slide. Use this for the tests for sulfur, arsenic, and phosphorus.

JOHNS (19) has found that the calcium oxide is not necessary when testing only for the halogens and sulfur but not for nitrogen.

Silver Permanganate Fusion. An interesting procedure which, it is claimed, permits the simple and rapid identification of C, H, N, Cl, Br, I, P, As, and Hg is that of KÖRBL (20). The oxidizing agent is the thermal decomposition product obtained when silver permanganate is heated in portions of about 2 g each in a test tube at 150°. This product is a black, graphite-like material.

Prepare the silver permanganate by treating a boiling solution of 19.4 g potassium permanganate in 400 ml water with 20.4 g solid silver nitrate. After the latter has dissolved allow the solution to cool and the silver permanganate will crystallize out. Collect it on a glass suction filter, wash with 150 ml cold water, and then transfer to 400 ml of boiling water. Filter the latter solution through a glass filter and wash the crystals obtained upon the cooling of the filtrate with distilled water. Dry at 60 to 70°. The yield is about 18 g. This is then pyrolytically decomposed as described above.

When an organic compound is heated with the reagent, combustion starts as a rule at low temperatures and with glowing of the reaction mixture. Carbon is oxidized to CO_2 and hydrogen to H_2O. Part of the nitrogen is converted to silver nitrate. Sulfur is found in the reaction mixture as Ag_2SO_4 and $MnSO_4$. The halogens form the corresponding silver salts, phosphorus and arsenic are retained as phosphate and arsenate, while mercury is obtained in the free state.

Draw out a glass tube of 4-mm bore to a fine tip at one end. Constrict the tube to a diameter of 0.3 mm at a point 6 cm from the tip and cut off the tube 9 cm from the constriction, Fig. 123.

Introduce a plug of freshly ignited asbestos into this tube and press it together above the constriction. Mix 0.1 to 1 mg of the test substance with about 50 mg of the oxidizing reagent, introduce the mixture into the combustion tube and press it against the asbestos plug. Finally introduce a second asbestos plug thereby wiping the upper part of the tube clean and keeping the reaction mixture in place.

Decompose the test substance by cautiously heating the mixture for a few seconds by means of a micro-flame.

Another more or less universal reagent for the decomposition of organic compounds is sodium peroxide. This is used, however, only in a special "bomb". For details of the method, which is also used for quantitative determinations, *see* ELEK and coworkers (6, 7). WILSON (30) carries out

Fig. 123. Qualitative Combustion according to KÖRBL.

the test for nitrogen, sulfur, and halogen on a microscale by fusing the sample with sodium carbonate and sucrose (or zinc and sodium carbonate) in a capillary.

Nitrogen.

Direct Method. The EMICH method for the detection of nitrogen mentioned above requires running a blank each time the test is carried out and the sample should be kept small since traces of incidental impurities may give a positive test which may be mistaken for a nitrogen content in the test substance.

Fit a capillary of the shape shown in Fig. 124 with an asbestos plug. Take up the asbestos with a platinum-tipped forceps, ignite it in the flame for a moment, trim it to the proper size, and then push it into the tube from the wide end. Heat the tube around the asbestos until the glass softens and holds the asbestos. With a microspatula place some calcium oxide at the point x, then about 1 μg of the test substance, and finally some more calcium oxide. If the test substance is liquid, it can be introduced through a capillary pipet. Mix the lime and the sample by stirring with

a platinum wire or by tapping the tube. Seal the wide end of the tube.
Dip the point of a piece of hardened filter paper, cut in the form of an
isosceles triangle, 4 to 5 mm long and as wide as the bore of the tube, into
red litmus solution so that the indicator rises about 1 mm from the point.
Push this paper, point foremost, into the tube to within 1.5 to 2 cm of the
asbestos plug. Heat the lime-sample mixture with the micro flame beginning
at the portion nearest the asbestos plug. Then move the tube into a small
Bunsen flame and strongly heat the entire section of the tube containing
the lime-sample mixture until it collapses. This forces the ammonia to
move over the test paper. The litmus solution may be prepared by adding

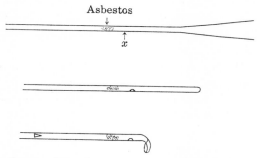

Fig. 124. Emich's Test for Nitrogen, nat. size.

sulfuric acid to a concentrated alcoholic solution of litmus until the pH
is 1.5 to 1.0. Brown and Hoffpauir (4) use 8-quinolinol-zinc complex for
detecting ammonia in place of the litmus. The ammonia-8-quinolinol-zinc
fluoresces greenish yellow under ultraviolet light. For substances containing nitrogen in combination with oxygen, add copper powder to the
lime mixture.

In the Sodium Fusion. Treat the solution from the sodium fusion
in a centrifuge cone with some ferrous sulfate solution. Heat the cone and
then centrifuge. Draw off the clear liquid in a capillary pipet, blow out
on a slide, and acidify with hydrochloric acid. It may be necessary to
wait for a time before the flakes of Prussian blue appear. Observe against
a white background, If the solution appears green, draw up the liquid
into a capillary pipet and touch the tip of the pipet to a piece of filter
paper. This will serve to concentrate any blue particles of precipitate in
a small area and make them more readily visible.

In the Magnesium-Potassium Carbonate Fusion. Treat a drop of
the solution from the magnesium-potassium carbonate fusion with a drop
of 4% ferrous sulfate solution. After stirring and allowing it to stand for
a minute, draw off the clear liquid into a capillary pipet, blow it out on
a white spot plate, and add a drop of concentrated hydrochloric acid.
The Prussian blue color appears if nitrogen is present. When both nitrogen

7*

and sulfur are present, the test for nitrogen by the ferrocyanide reaction becomes doubtful. If, however, the filtrate from the fusion mixture is first tested for the presence of sulfur (*see below*) and then, if this test is positive, for nitrogen by means of the ferric thiocyanate test, a red coloration will appear if nitrogen is present. Carry out the thiocyanate test by adding a drop of ferric chloride solution to the filtrate from the fusion mixture.

In the Calcium Oxide-Zinc Fusion. As mentioned in the description of the decomposition technique, nitrogen is detected by the change of the color of the litmus paper in the sleeve. Ordinary litmus paper may not be sufficiently sensitive for this test. Suspend strips of ordinary blue or neutral litmus paper in distilled water and add just enough sulfuric acid to change the color of the paper to pink. Then wash the papers with distilled water until a piece of the treated paper when pressed against a piece of neutral litmus paper will not turn the latter red. Press the prepared papers between sheets of soft filter paper and then store in a moist condition in a sealed container. The presence of nitrogen in the sample is indicated by a change in color from pink to blue at the end of the litmus strip nearer the open end of the combustion tube. Any color obtained should be compared with that obtained in a blank test. Although exposed strips of litmus very quickly lose their blue color when allowed to stand in contact with air, comparisons may be made as long as 15 minutes after a combustion if the paper strips are placed between two microscope slides immediately after exposure.

In the Silver Permanganate Fusion. Introduce 0.1 to 0.2 ml distilled water into the wide end of the combustion tube so that the water completely fills the cross section of the tube. Attach a rubber bulb or injection syringe and slowly force the liquid through the combustion tube and into the tip. For detection of the nitrogen (as NO_2, HNO_2, or HNO_3) put a small part of the solution on the surface of a 1% solution of diphenylamine in concentrated sulfuric acid.

Halogens.

In the Sodium Fusion. The extract from the sodium fusion can be used for the detection of the halogens. However, if sulfur or nitrogen is also present, a preliminary treatment is necessary to remove the cyanide and sulfide ions before the silver nitrate can be added. To accomplish this, add 3 m sulfuric acid in slight excess to the extract from the fusion in a centrifuge cone and boil to expel the HCN and H_2S. Then add the silver nitrate.

In the Magnesium-Potassium Carbonate Fusion. Acidify the clear liquid from the magnesium-potassium carbonate fusion with nitric acid by inverting the slide on which a test drop rests over the mouth of a bottle of the concentrated acid. Add silver nitrate either in the form of a tiny crystal or as a drop of the solution. Take care not to touch the portion of the combustion tube containing the fusion mixture with the fingers since sufficient chloride is left on the glass from such contact to give a positive test for this element. Handle this portion of the tube with the forceps in any case. Should a positive test for the halogens be obtained, it is advisable to make further tests to determine the specific halogen and type of halogen compound under consideration. For the latter see page 279.

In the Calcium Oxide-Zinc Fusion. For testing the presence of halogens in the aqueous extract from the calcium oxide-zinc fusion, draw a 4- to 5-mm column of the liquid into a capillary tube of 1- to 1.5-mm bore. Add 3 to 4 mm of a 0.5 m silver nitrate solution which is 3 m in nitric acid. The formation of a white or light yellow precipitate within 30 seconds indicates the presence of cyanide, chloride, bromide, or iodide.

If nitrogen has been found to be present, transfer the remainder of the aqueous extract to a micro beaker by means of a capillary pipet and add one drop of a solution which is 1 molar in sodium acetate and 0.1 molar in acetic acid. Cover the beaker with a circle of filter paper impregnated with one drop of a reagent freshly prepared by mixing equal volumes of 0.015 molar aqueous cupric acetate and half-saturated aqueous benzidine acetate. The appearance of a blue spot on the paper within a few seconds indicates the presence of cyanide. If cyanide is present, remove the filter paper and heat the mixture in the beaker gently on a hot plate or water bath until the test for cyanide with fresh cupric acetate-benzidine test paper is negative. Then carry out the tests for the halogens as below.

After removal of the cyanide, test the remaining solution for halogen again with silver nitrate as above. If a positive test is obtained, the tests for distinguishing between chlorine, bromine and iodine are carried out.

Draw 5 to 6 mm of the aqueous extract into a capillary and add 3 to 4 mm of freshly prepared 0.0035 molar aqueous chloramine T, then 3 to 4 mm of a fluorescein reagent (50% aqueous ethanol solution 0.00075 molar in fluorescein and 0.12 molar in acetic acid), and finally another 3 to 4 mm of chloramine T solution. When viewed against a white background, the appearance of a pink color is indicative of bromide or iodide. No color should be obtained in blank tests on properly prepared reagents.

If the chloramine T test was positive, draw another 3 to 4 mm of the aqueous extract into a capillary and add an equal volume of freshly prepared nitrite reagent (mixture of equal volumes of 0.5% starch solution, 1 molar sodium nitrite and 6 molar acetic acid). The appearance of a blue or black color indicates the presence of iodide. No color should be obtained in blank tests.

Obviously, if a positive test was obtained with the silver nitrate and negative tests for bromide or iodide, the halogen must have been chlorine.

In the Silver Permanganate Fusion. *Chlorine and Bromine.* To the combustion tube add 0.1 to 0.2 ml 6 *m* NH₃ and transfer the ammonia extract of the reaction mixture to a microcone, again using a rubber bulb to effect removal of the liquid. Acidify with nitric acid and collect the precipitate, consisting of AgCl and AgBr, for further examination as above.

Iodine. Wash the combustion tube with 6 *m* NH₃ until acidification of the washings no longer produces a turbidity of AgCl or AgBr. Then extract the residue in the combustion tube with 0.1 to 0.2 ml 30% silver nitrate solution in which AgI is readily soluble. Dilute the extract in a microcone with water and silver iodide-nitrate will precipitate. Upon further dilution this will become AgI.

Other Tests for Halogens.

Other means of distinguishing between chloride, bromide, and iodide include the following.

Bromine can be detected in the extract from the sodium fusion or the magnesium-potassium carbonate fusion by placing a drop of the extract on a slide and adding a drop of concentrated ammonia. Beside this drop place a drop of 0.1 molar or 0.01 molar silver nitrate solution. Join the two by another drop of concentrated ammonia. Allow the ammonia to evaporate. If bromine is present, thin blue-gray hexagonal or triangular plates of silver bromide will precipitate out.

The bromoplatinate can also be used for differentiating between chlorine and bromine. Acidify a drop of the neutral fusion extract with sulfuric acid and to this add a drop of 1% potassium sulfate and a drop of 1:1000 solution of platinum sulfate. Allow the drop to evaporate to the point at which crystals appear. The potassium bromoplatinate precipitates in orange-red to deep brown crystals or plates. The precipitate appears all over the drop, not merely at the edges, as is the case with the chloroplatinate.

The formation of the characteristic crystalline precipitate of 2,4,6-tribromphenylenediamine when bromine is brought into contact with a solution of *m*-phenylenediamine sulfate can also be used to distinguish bromides from the other halides (21). Place a drop of the solution to be tested on a microscope slide and strongly acidify by adding a drop of 3 molar sulfuric acid. Convert the slide into a gas chamber (page 72) by placing a glass ring around the drop and covering the ring with another slide, on the underside of which is a drop of *m*-phenylenediamine sulfate (about ¹/₂₀ saturated aqueous solution to which a *trace* of sulfuric acid has been added). Lift the top slide, add some powdered potassium dichromate to the test drop, and replace the cover. The crystals are fusiform needles, single or in clusters, highly refractive, and strongly birefringent. Gentle warming is of advantage when small amounts of bromine are involved but do not heat to the point of forming steam. Chlorine and iodine give no such precipitate. Iodine may condense in oily drops if present in large amounts but these drops disappear when exposed to air.

If it is necessary to confirm chlorine, the conversion to chromyl chloride can be used. A similar gas chamber is employed. Treat the test solution on a microscope slide with some powdered potassium dichromate and then evaporate to dryness. Place the glass ring around the residue and add a small drop of concentrated sulfuric acid. Cover the ring with a second slide bearing a drop of water on its underside. Allow the whole apparatus to stand for five to ten minutes. This permits the chromyl chloride, a heavy vapor, to diffuse to the upper drop of water where it is hydrolyzed to H_2CrO_4 and HCl. Care must be taken to avoid any spattering of the lower drop or any other contact with the upper drop. Remove the upper slide, invert and evaporate to dryness. Dissolve any residue in a small drop of water and add a tiny crystal of silver nitrate. The characteristic precipitate of silver dichromate is a positive test for chlorine.

Procedure of Wilson and Wilson. (32) This procedure permits detection of chlorine, bromine and iodine separately or in mixtures. It uses 2 molar nitric acid, 0.02 molar silver nitrate, 18 molar ammonia (d = 0.88), 3 molar ammonia, and 0.18 molar ammonia. Place a drop (0.2 ml) of the test solution on a slide and acidify with the nitric acid. Add a large drop (0.1 ml) of the silver nitrate solution and evaporate just to dryness. Heating beyond this point may result in loss of silver chloride. Wash twice with water, using a capillary pipet to remove the wash liquid. Evaporate to dryness, cool, and extract the residue with a large drop of 0.18 molar ammonia, stirring well.

Remove the clear liquid in a capillary pipet and transfer to a slide. To carry out the transfer, blow out a small drop on the slide, allow it to dry, blow out a second drop on the residue from the first, and so on, until the entire filtrate has been evaporated within a small area. Dissolve the residue in a minimum of 3 molar ammonia, cover with a small watch glass, and set it aside, labeling it Drop A. Wash the residue from this extraction twice with a large drop of 3 molar ammonia, then stir and filter. Extract the residue with 18 molar ammonia, drawing the extract into a capillary pipet. Centrifuge and blow the clear liquid out on a slide. Cover the drop with a watch glass and set it aside after labeling it Drop B. Wash the residue from this extraction twice thoroughly with 18 molar ammonia. Dissolve the residue in a drop of pyridine. This is Drop C. Table 8 gives the results to be expected in the possible cases.

TABLE 8

Interpretation of the Test According to Wilson and Wilson.

Halide	Drop A	Drop B	Drop C
Cl	Octahedra, squares, and cubes *	Nil or trace of dust	Nil
Br	Dust (may show triangles and pentagons) †	Many long triangles and hexagons, field clear	Nil
I	Nil	Nil or dust	Characteristic pyridinium crystals ≠
Cl plus Br	Small squares and cubes and nodules §	Many triangles and hexagons, field fairly clear	Nil
Br plus I	Dust (may show triangles and hexagons)	Triangles and hexagons	Characteristic pyridinium crystals
Cl plus I	Octahedra, squares, and cubes	Nil or dust	Characteristic pyridinium crystals
Cl, Br, and I	Small squares, cubes and nodules	Many triangles, hexagons, field fairly clear of dust	Characteristic pyridinium crystals

　　* Large octahedra, cubes, or squares; highly refractive.
　　† Many hexagons and triangles; large. Colors vary: blue-gray, pink, green, yellow, and mauve.
　　≠ Transparent, oblong crystals with frequent V-shaped re-entrants at ends. In pairs, crossed, or in clumps piled on top of each other spirally around vertical axis.
　　§ Numerous transparent small squares and crystals of square outlines are characteristic of chloride.

The Beilstein Test for Halogens. Although very sensitive, this has been reported (28) to be not entirely reliable, because some nitrogenous compounds also give a positive test. In addition, GILMAN and KIRBY (14) have shown that many carboxylic acids also give a positive test. Place some copper oxide on the loop of a platinum wire and heat it briefly until the oxide adheres to the wire. Place the test substance on the copper oxide and insert the loop in the non-luminous flame of a Bunsen burner, first in the inner and then in the outer zone near the edge. The carbon will burn first and the flame will be luminous but then the characteristic green or blue color will appear. The amount of halogen can be approximately measured by the duration of the flame coloration. It is advisable to use this as a preliminary test before carrying out a fusion test.

Hayman's Modification of the Beilstein Test. (17) The author claims that it has never given positive results with any compound not containing a halogen except materials containing copper.

Heat a section of Monel metal tubing, about 1 cm in diameter, to cherry red heat over a Bunsen burner fitted with a wing top. Take up the material to be tested in a platinum loop if it is a liquid or on a platinum microspatula if a solid. Hold it 1 cm below the Monel tube. As the substance decomposes in the flame, the products are swept up and around the hot metal. If halogen is present, a flare, any shade between green and blue, will appear. Comparison of the length of time the flame is colored with that given by control samples of known composition can be used for estimation of the percentage of halogen present.

GARNER (13) describes a test for halogens which he claims is very sensitive. He refluxes the carefully filtered sample with pyridine for 15 minutes, cools it, and then adds water. After filtration and acidification with nitric acid, silver nitrate is added. See also HUNSDIECKER (18).

Test for Fluorine (3). The solubility of silver fluoride prevents the detection of fluorine at this point in the analysis of fusion extracts. The test for this element is therefore carried out on a separate sample of the original test substance.

Place approximately 1 mg of the liquid or finely powdered sample in the depression of a culture-type microscope slide and convert to a gas chamber by means of a glass ring. Add ten drops of the oxidation mixture (mix 33 ml 85% phosphoric acid and 67 ml of 30% fuming sulfuric acid in a 250-ml glass stoppered flask and add 6 g chromium trioxide and 1 g potassium periodate). Cover the ring immediately with a small watch glass with a drop of water on its underside. Allow to stand for five minutes and then, after placing a few drops of water in the concave upper side of the watch glass, heat the slide (preferably on a metal block to avoid cracking) until the mixture in the chamber begins to fume and then for 30 seconds more. Remove the drop on the underside of the watch glass with a capillary pipet and transfer it to a centrifuge cone or small test tube. Add one drop of 6 molar formic acid and one drop of 2% hydrazine hydrate solution. Heat the mixture to between 50° and 60°. After 20 seconds add 1 ml of water, one drop of 3 molar sodium hydroxide, and two drops of 0.12% alcoholic sodium alizarinsulfonate and mix thoroughly. Prepare a similar solution of all the reagents used in a similar tube for comparison of the colors. To each tube add one drop of 0.0005 molar thorium nitrate, mix by gentle shaking, and compare the colors. If fluorine was present in the sample, the drop from the gas chamber will be yellow and the comparison solution pink. One drop (0.05 ml) of the thorium solution is equivalent to about 2 μg of fluorine and by dropwise addition of the thorium nitrate solution a rough titration and estimation can be carried out. The authors state that from 15% to 50% of the fluorine content of the sample can be collected in this way in the gas chamber.

Sulfur.

The aqueous extracts from both the sodium fusion and the magnesium-potassium carbonate fusion can be tested for sulfur by acidifying a drop with acetic acid and adding a drop of lead acetate solution. A black precipitate indicates sulfur.

To test for sulfur in the calcium oxide-zinc fusion, use the culture slide, with the solid residue remaining after the water extraction of the fusion mixture, as the lower portion of a gas chamber. Add four drops of 9 molar perchloric acid to this residue and immediately complete the chamber with a glass ring and another slide bearing a drop of 1 molar lead acetate on its underside. A black or brown precipitate in the lead acetate drop two to three minutes later is a positive test for sulfur.

EMICH (10) mixes one volume of the test substance (slightly moistened) with four to ten volumes of carbonate-chlorate mixture (six parts of sodium carbonate with one part of potassium chlorate) on a piece of platinum foil or a narrow microscope slide. The mixture is heated over an alcohol flame (fuel gas may contain mercaptans or other sulfur-bearing warning agents) until no further action is visible, dissolved in water, and tested with barium chloride after being acidified with hydrochloric acid.

Test volatile or difficultly oxidizable substances for sulfur by heating with nitric acid in a sealed quartz or Pyrex capillary tube. The capillary should have a heavier wall than usual, i. e., it should have a wall thickness of almost 1 mm. Seal the tube after introduction of the sample and acid and heat to 300°C. After cooling, open (*Caution*) and blow the liquid out on a microscope slide. Evaporate the liquid to dryness, take up with concentrated hydrochloric acid, and again evaporate to dryness. Add a drop of dilute hydrochloric acid, warm the slide until complete solution takes place, and then add a kernel of calcium chloride. The characteristic crystals of calcium sulfate appear if sulfur is present.

In the case of the silver permanganate fusion test for sulfur by transferring the aqueous extract remaining from the nitrogen test (*see above*) from the combustion tube to a microcone and treat with 0.05 ml of 5% barium nitrate solution. The precipitate of $BaSO_4$ appearing if sulfur was present in the test substance can be centrifuged off and tested further if desired.

Phosphorus.

Phosphorus is tested for either by reaction with ammonium molybdate or a spot test.

In Capillary or Cone. Use either the acid extract remaining after the test for sulfur in the calcium oxide-zinc fusion, or from the separation of the silver halides in the silver permanganate fusion, or after wet oxidation of the original test substance (*see* above under Sulfur). Add ammonium molybdate to the acid solution in a microcone or capillary and heat on the water bath. If a yellow precipitate is obtained, the test is positive for phosphorus. It can be confirmed further by dissolving the precipitate in ammonia after washing and then reprecipitating with magnesia mixture. Wash the precipitate carefully and examine single crystals under the microscope.

Spot Test. Prepare the reagent paper for the spot test for phosphorus by placing a few drops of a 0.03 molar solution of ammonium molybdate in 3 molar nitric acid on a piece of No. 1 Whatman filter paper or the equivalent and drying the paper at 80° to 90°. Transfer 5 to 8 mm of the acid extract from the fusion with a capillary pipet to a spot on this paper. Follow with the addition of 5 mm of a 0.0027 molar solution of benzidine in 1.8 molar acetic acid and an equal volume of saturated aqueous sodium acetate. The presence of the phosphorus is indicated by the formation of a blue spot. This should always be compared with one obtained in a blank test.

A microtest for phosphorus, arsenic, and antimony is described by WILSON (31).

Arsenic.

Arsenic can be tested for simultaneously with sulfur but the test is not positive since phosphorus may give phosphine under the same conditions and this will react like arsine. It is better, therefore, to use a test such as the MARSH test.

Silicon.

The test for silicon is carried out on the residue after ignition of the sample.

Place the sample in a platinum crucible and ignite until the residue is white. Cool, add a drop of concentrated sulfuric acid and an amount of sodium or calcium fluoride equal to the residue left from the ignition. Cover the crucible immediately with the platinum lid which bears a small drop of water on the underside. On the upper side of the lid, place a large drop of water for cooling. Warm the crucible and contents. After a minute transfer the small drop of water to a varnished or plastic microscope slide by touching the lid to a drop of water on the slide. Add a crystal of sodium chloride. If, upon evaporation, crystals of sodium fluosilicate appear, the test is positive. The crystals should be pale red, six-sided prisms or plates,

rosettes, and stars which must be sought under the microscope with small
iris opening because the index of refraction of the solid is close to that
of the mother liquor.

Metals.

Organo-metallic compounds of most types will leave a residue upon
ignition of the compound in air or oxygen. This residue will consist of the
oxide or the carbonate of the more active metals or the free metal in the
case of gold, etc. The carbonates (possibly sulfates) will be formed if the
metal is an alkali or alkaline earth; the heavy metal carbonates decompose
to the oxide at the temperatures of the ignition. Such ignition residues
should be analyzed according to the usual procedures for inorganic
substances.

The volatility of mercury excludes simple ignition as a means of decom-
posing the original carbon compound in which it may occur. Wet combustion in open vessels has also been found by PREGL and VERDINO (25)
to be unsatisfactory. They recommend decomposition with nitric acid in
sealed tubes as used for sulfur. The resulting solution is tested for mercury by displacement of the metal by copper or by precipitation of the
cobalt mercuric thiocyanate.

Quantitative Elementary Analysis.

Cognition procedures require quantitative determination of the elements
as well as qualitative. The micro procedures for such determinations are
described in detail in texts on quantitative organic microanalysis to which
the reader is referred. The results of such determinations are converted
into the ratios of the elements in the compound to obtain the empirical
formula. The determination of molecular weight, as described on pages
136 to 143, then permits a molecular formula to be set up. The constitution
of the compound can, however, be finally determined only after identification of the functional groups and their location in the molecule.

Chapter IV

Determination of Physical Constants.

The physical constants of both the original compound and at least
one of its derivatives must be determined for the final recognition of a
substance. As pointed out before, in addition to serving to identify a
substance the physical constants may indicate its purity.

The physical constants usually employed include boiling point, melting
point, density, refractive index, optical rotation, and molecular weight.

Of these, only the first three are usually required for recognition but the others may be required in some cases, particularly if the possible compounds with which the sample may be identical possess constants which are quite similar. In cognition procedures, aside from molecular weight, the physical constants of the original substance serve chiefly as a check on purity. Naturally, once derivatives or degradatives have been prepared, these are identified by determination of their physical constants. Aside from the properties listed, others which are particularly useful with some types of compounds will be described.

An important point to be kept in mind in selecting a method for the determination of a particular constant and evaluating the result of that determination is the reliability of this constant given in the literature. If, for example, the melting point of a compound is determined by a different method or with a different accuracy, comparison of the two values is of doubtful validity. To give comparable data and therefore be determinate in identification, the methods must be comparable. In other words, differences in values obtained must be ascribable only to differences in the chemical composition, not to experimental observations. Judgment must be exercised, therefore, in accepting any value as a standard.

When working with a material of unknown composition and with sources for values of constants which do not specify how these were obtained, it is necessary that allowance be made for such differences by assuming that the value obtained for the physical constant lies within a certain *range* rather than being a single, determinate value. Thus, when the first measurement of boiling point or melting point is made on a test substance and reference is made to the tables or the literature to learn what substances must be considered, all compounds in the class or genus which boil or melt 5 or 10 degrees above and below the observed value must be considered. Similarly, the derivative selected for final identification of the test substance should be one which shows a marked difference in boiling or melting point between individual members of the group. Repeated purifications of test substance or derivative will usually show a decreasing change in boiling or melting point as the true value is approached.

The values of the physical constants can be determined within limits of accuracy which are rather broad. However, since, for example, molecular weights differ by more than a single unit (hydrogen) in the great majority of cases, a high precision is not required. In an homologous series the individual members differ in molecular weight by at least 12 units and hence the permissible error is large. On the other hand, other physical properties may differ by very small quantities, as with densities. The value of the determination of the physical constants depends, therefore, upon the use to which it is put, i. e., for distinction within a class as in the identification of hydrocarbons (see page 233) or for distinguishing between several types.

Of greater interest is the possibility of using physical constants as a means of establishing the structure of compounds. Unfortunately, while there seems to be considerable basis for such a relationship, too little is known as yet to permit a general application. The direction in which this effort is being made is exemplified by the work of EISENLOHR (49), SMITH (144), and FAJANS and KNORR (52) in relating refractivity and structure of a compound and in that of GILMORE, MENAUL, and SCHNEIDER (65) in establishing a relation between structure and refractive index, density, and boiling point. The latter authors present charts to show how these properties can be used to shorten and simplify the analyses required in connection with research. For the relationship of infrared spectra, Raman spectra, etc. the reader is referred to texts on these subjects.

Centers of rotatory power may be due to either asymmetry of chemical groups or may be induced by other influences such as a magnetic field (the FARADAY effect). Prediction of the optical activity of any given structure can be made only by the application of involved theory and is not yet generally useful. The use of optical rotatory power to identify the groups present in a new substance rests, therefore, on the comparison of observed rotation with that of models having the postulated asymmetric groups.

CASTLE (27) and BILES (15) have presented some evidence to show a relationship between melting point and refractive index, and the latter paper discusses the orientation of atoms and molecules with respect to this problem.

Melting Point.

CAUTION: Before heating more than a few micrograms of the sample substance, perform a preliminary test as described on p. 27 to determine the behavior of the substance on heating.

The melting point may be defined as the temperature at which the solid substance is at equilibrium with the pure corresponding liquid. Any method for determining the melting point must attain this condition. For purposes of simplification of technique, methods which approximate this condition have been used. The capillary method is one of these. While it can be used for many purposes, it must be kept in mind that it is open to several sources of error which may lead to erroneous results. Among those are superheating, temperature lag between reading device and heating bath, false equilibrium, etc.

Capillary Tube Method. The ordinary method consists of observing the disappearance of opacity of the contents of a capillary tube fixed to a thermometer and placed in a heating bath. The capillary should be 0.75 to 1 mm in diameter, thin-walled, and 3 cm in length. It should be drawn from a 5-mm tube. One end is sealed and the other should have its edge ground perfectly flat.

Grind the sample in an agate mortar and pack it tightly in the tube by means of a wire. The layer of test substance in the tube should not exceed 2 mm. Attach the capillary to the thermometer with a rubber band or by merely wetting the thermometer and the outside of the capillary with the bath liquid and touching the two together. The capillary should be either to the right or to the left of the thermometer scale so that the latter is not obscured. Light from a window or a lamp should come from behind the bath. The heating bath fluid should be a low-melting wax or, better, a silicone fluid. The thermometer should be calibrated to permit correction for partial immersion, etc.

SCHMALFUSS and BARTHMEYER (131) describe the procedure to be followed in the determination of the melting point of a volatile substance by the capillary method. Draw out a tube to capillaries (Fig. 125). Drop the

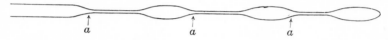

Fig. 125. Preparation of Melting Point Tubes for Volatile Substances.

test substance into the sealed end, or sublime the sample under reduced pressure (4 mm) into the capillaries and seal off the latter at the points marked "a". Then use these tubes to determine the melting point as described above.

Instead of a thin-walled capillary BLANK (16) uses two cover glasses. The sample is placed between them and they are then placed beside the thermometer in a tube in a THIELE tube.

Somewhat more complex apparatus has been devised by SPERONI (146) and McMULLEN (102). For the details refer to the original publications. The author of this volume (132) pointed out the error due to the time required for the eye to be moved from observation of the sample to the scale of the thermometer. His suggestion of a reading device which moved with the mercury of the thermometer has been embodied in the melting point apparatus of HOOVER.

Melting Point Blocks. In place of the heating bath with its attendant disadvantages such as non-uniform temperature, etc., metal blocks of various types have been proposed. The simplest apparatus of this type consists of an aluminum or copper block drilled vertically about halfway through with a hole for the thermometer and a smaller hole for the melting point capillary. Another hole is drilled horizontally so that it passes through the bottom of the hole for the capillary. This permits observation of the sample. A light is placed behind the block and the latter is heated by a microburner. At first very little or no light will pass through the horizontal hole but when the substance melts, the light can be observed. Cover glasses or pieces of mica fastened over the ends of the horizontal hole eliminate air currents which may affect temperature equilibrium.

This simple apparatus has been modified and refined by a number of authors. FRIEDEL (55) projects the image of the melting point tube on a screen and observes the changes in this way. WALSH (157) uses a 50-power microscope and thus can observe a single crystal. MASON (99), IZMAÏLOV and TKACHENKO (77), and DUNBAR (45) use an electrically heated block. MORTON and MAHONEY (104) describe an electrically heated copper block with an optical system for observation of the sample and an air jet for rapid cooling of the block. RASSOW (119) uses a cylindrical block and a thermocouple of platinum-platinum rhodium in place of a thermometer. For substances with a high melting point, RAY and DAYAL (122) use a platinum wire bent into the form of a V. The substance is placed upon a mica platform and the apex of the V is touched to a crystal of the substance. The wire is connected to a source of current and the fusion of the crystal is observed through a telescope. The current is measured by means of a milliameter and this reading is related to the temperature by calibration with known substances.

A neat little apparatus is described by BURT-GERRANS (24). It consists of a silver disk 25 mm thick and 60 mm in diameter. A shallow circular depression is machined in the center of the upper side. In this is placed a cover glass bearing the crystals of the test substance which is covered with another, larger, cover slip, the latter resting on the upper surface of the disk. The disk is heated electrically by a coil of wire on the outer perpendicular surface. The temperature is determined by means of a thermocouple inserted into a narrow hole in the side of the disk. The hole is cut at an angle so that it slopes downward, ending directly under the depression. The coil and disk are insulated. If reflected light is used, the crystals can be observed with a lens.

The apparatus of JOHNS (81) is somewhat similar but a vertical hole drilled under the center of the depression in the block permits observation by transmitted light. He uses aluminum in place of silver for the block and a thermometer in place of the thermocouple. The thermometer is calibrated by using the melting points of very pure compounds. This eliminates the need for corrections. Both the BURT-GERRANS and the JOHNS blocks are very useful because they make it possible to use a single crystal.

The apparatus of MA and SCHENCK (97) can also be used for the determination of melting points using a magnifier or a small telescope.

Melting Point on the Microscope Hot Stage. The determination of the melting point under the microscope gives perhaps the most accurate results. The moment at which the solid passes over into the liquid phase can be determined very readily by the disappearance of the sharp edges of the crystals and, in the case of anisotropic substances, by the disappearance of birefringence. The more delicate control of the temperature will often permit holding the temperature at which the solid and liquid phases are in equilibrium. Changes such as dehydration, sublimation, and decomposition can be observed in the course of the determination.

A great number of hot stages has been described. They are all electrically heated and differ only in the method and the region of heating, in the method of determining the temperature, and in the specific purpose for which they have been designed. Thus some are intended for melting point determinations, some working with micromanipulators at higher temperatures, some for sublimations, and so on. AMDUR and HJORT (3), DEININGER (40), VORLAENDER and HABERLAND (156), WEYGAND and GRUENTZIG (158), KLEIN (86), GRANICK (67), MULLER (105), JANÁK (78), NIETHAMMER (112), FUCHS (51), KOFLER and HILBCK (88), and ZSCHEILE and WHITE (166) have all designed hot stages. ZSCHEILE and WHITE's stage provides for working in an inert atmosphere. KOFLER and HILBCK's stage (later further improved) is one of the best, because it is adaptable not only for melting point determinations but also for fusions, sublimations, and other work at higher temperatures.

Some of these hot stages are comparatively simple and can be constructed by the analyst himself or by a mechanic; others are more complex and are produced only by skilled instrument manufacturers.

General Precautions in Melting Point Determinations. When the melting point blocks of BURT-GERRANS or JOHNS or any of the various hot stages are used, several points must be kept in mind. Because single crystals are being observed and the temperature of melting is taken when the edges of the crystals begin to "dissolve," a more exact melting point is obtained than when the usual capillary method is employed. In the latter all the crystals must be completely molten before the melt appears clear. Owing to the time required for complete fusion, the temperature of the bath usually rises somewhat above the true melting point during this time. Since the melting points given in the literature are based for the most part on observations with the capillary method, the melting points as determined on single crystals are usually 1 to 2 degrees lower. This fact has been pointed out by a number of investigators, notably CLEVENGER (35) and LINSER (96). LINSER discusses the errors and precautions to be considered in using KLEIN's hot stage but his observations are applicable to nearly all these devices. He points out that the thickness of the cover glass and the rate of heating are as important as in the capillary method. Naturally, the degree to which these factors affect a determination depends upon the construction of the particular hot stage or block used. It is advisable for the analyst using such a device to determine the melting points of a number of known substances of high purity and thus learn the characteristics of his own apparatus.

DANGL (31) uses a microscope hot stage for the study of paraffins and stearin in polarized light. He is able to determine the melting points of these substances very easily since the "structure" of the solid becomes visible between crossed nicols. GARNER (60) points out that some substances undergo chemical changes during the heating in a melting point determination and hence two consecutive determinations on the same sample may give considerably different results and neither may be the correct value because only partial conversion from one form to the other may have taken place.

The reader is referred to *Die Methoden der organischen Chemie*, Volume I, by HOUBEN-WEYL, for a discussion of melting point determination and crystal structure.

In addition to greater accuracy, the microscope hot stage presents a number of advantages over the capillary method. It is possible to obtain more information than the mere melting point. KOFLER, KOFLER and, MAYRHOFER (89, 90) have pointed out that changes can be observed in many substances during the heating before the melting point is reached. Some substances sublime from the slide to the cover slip. The sublimation temperature as well as the appearance of the sublimate may be characteristic of the substance. Hydrated substances sometimes occur as mixtures of various steps of hydration which show a different behavior on heating. In the case of substances which exist in different modifications, it is often possible, on heating under the microscope, not only to observe the transition from one modification to another but also to determine the transition points of the various forms in succession. Furthermore, since the higher vapor pressure of the unstable form makes it more readily sublimable, it is often possible to observe volatilization of this form before its melting point is reached. At the same time crystals of the stable form will grow. In other cases, in the temperature range between the melting points of the stable and the unstable forms, the drops of molten form crystallize again. The foregoing shows once more that the melting points obtained by the use of a hot stage will not necessarily agree with those obtained by the capillary method. The same authors found that, for substances which decompose on heating, the melting points found by the use of the hot stage are often higher than those found by the capillary method. They recommend that in all cases the literature should state that the melting point was determined between cover glass and slide and they propose the abbreviation "micro m. pt.". At this point it should be mentioned that differences between the value of the melting point as given in the literature and that obtained by the use of a block or hot stage can be resolved by taking a "mixed melting point". If a sample of the known compound is mixed with a sample of the test substance, the mixture should have a sharp melting point and this should agree with that obtained for the known or the unknown alone if the two are identical. Obviously, in the case of the cognition of a new substance, in view of the absence of a comparison substance, mixed melting points cannot be used.

When using a hot stage in carrying out a melting point determination, carry out a preliminary determination. If no decomposition occurs, allow the sample to congeal again, and then raise the temperature very gradually as the melting point is approached and finally hold it constant when both solid and liquid coexist. In this way any lag in the thermometer or thermocouple is eliminated as completely as possible. If a change other than simple melting occurs, use a fresh sample of the test substance for the second determination.

If polarized light is used, anisotropic phases are easily perceived and equilibria between anisotropic and isotropic (liquid) phases may be recognized without difficulty.

Boiling Point.

Emich Method (5). This method depends upon the high surface tension of a liquid in a very fine tube and upon the sharp increase in vapor pressure near the boiling point.

The method uses from 0.1 to 2 μl of sample. Use a capillary about 10 cm long and from 0.4- to 1-mm bore, according to the viscosity of the sample. Draw out one end for a length of about 1 cm to a diameter of 0.05 mm. Touch this fine point to the liquid test substance and allow the liquid to rise in the tube until at least 1 mm of the wider portion of the capillary is filled. Then hold the capillary slightly inclined from the horizontal with the fine end uppermost and seal the latter by touching to the edge of a Bunsen flame. A tiny bubble of air must be trapped between the sealed end and the liquid (Fig. 126). If no bubble appears when the tube cools, cut the tube open and repeat the sealing to include a bubble. The bubble must not be large; in fact, it must not

Fig. 126. Capillary for the Determination of the Boiling Point.

be longer than the fine portion of the tube. Attach the capillary to a thermometer (page 111) and insert in a heating bath so that about 4 cm of its length is immersed. Heat as in the melting point determination with vigorous stirring of the bath liquid. As the boiling point is approached, the drop begins to move and to rise in the tube. The moment it reaches the level of the meniscus of the bath liquid, read the temperature. This is the boiling point.

Careful studies (12) have shown that in pure substances the temperature range in which the droplet rises from the bottom to the surface of the bath liquid is not more than 1 or 2 degrees. This interval is greatly increased when the test substance is impure (mixture) or when the sample decomposes below the boiling point. It is obvious that in a mixture the droplet begins to rise at the temperature at which it boils; during the rise a fractionation takes place and if only a small amount of the lower-boiling component (the impurity) is present, the droplet reaches the surface of the bath liquid at the boiling point of the major component.

Observation of Boiling Point and Boiling Range under the Microscope (160). This procedure of WIBERLEY, SIEGFRIEDT and BENEDETTI-PICHLER uses about 0.01 µl of test substance and employs the KOFLER hot stage.

Heat a capillary tube, 1 to 2 mm in diameter and 50 to 100 mm long, near one end in a micro flame. By first fusing the glass to a solid and

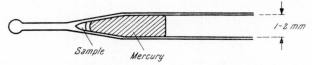

Sample   Mercury   *1-2 mm*

Fig. 127. Determination of the Boiling Point on the Microscope Hot Stage.

then drawing it out and off, form a blunt, cone-shaped, seal as shown in Fig. 127. The taper should not be too long. Introduce about 10 µg of the liquid test substance on the inside wall of the capillary by means of a glass thread or capillary pipet and centrifuge it to the point of the cone. Follow this with a droplet of mercury introduced by means of a capillary pipet narrow enough to fit easily into the capillary and long enough to reach to the bottom. Connecting this pipet to a hypodermic syringe will permit good control of the mercury ejected and permit the latter to be placed so close to the sample that the intervening air space is not more than a few times the sample volume.

Bend the capillary into a U-shape to have it fit within the rim of the KOFLER hot stage with the sample over the center opening of the stage. Do not heat the sample end of the tube during this operation and make certain that the tube is not sealed. Place the capillary on the stage so that the entire sample is in the field. Use a magnification of about 50 times. Place an aluminum plate, 2 mm thick, 15 mm wide, and 50 mm long, and provided with a 3-mm slot, around the sample end of the capillary to provide a uniform temperature. Place the glass baffle of the stage crosswise over the capillary and the top plate of the stage in place. Focus on the meniscus of the sample and observe this during the test. Begin the heating of the stage. The liquid will gradually be converted into vapor and its volume will decrease. Pure substance will vaporize within a short temperature range and the point of complete vaporization is the boiling point. By permitting the sample to cool and heating again the determination may be repeated as often as desired. A quick return of the mercury upon condensation of the sample is indicative of a pure substance and is possibly the best signal for reading the boiling point.

For determining the boiling *range*, a larger sample is used and the volume of liquid vaporized is measured at intervals and plotted against the temperature reading at those points.

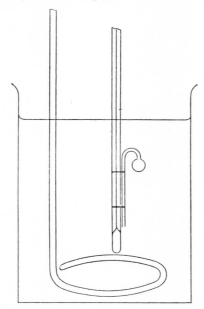

Fig. 128. Boiling Point Determination according to SMITH and MENZIES.

Siwoloboff Method (138). This method uses small quantities of material but by no means as little as EMICH's method.

Place a few drops of the test substance in a small tube and insert a capillary sealed at one end, open end downward, into the liquid. Attach the tube to a thermometer and heat in a bath until a continuous stream of bubbles emerges from the inner tube. Stop heating and allow the bath to cool, stirring continuously. Note the temperature at the moment bubbles stop issuing from the capillary.

Smith and Menzies Method. A modification of the SIWOLOBOFF method is that of SMITH and MENZIES (141). The liquid (0.03 to 0.1 g) or the pulverized solid is placed in the bulb (Fig. 128). The capillary is 3 to 4 cm long and not less than 1 mm in diameter. The substance is heated until bubbles issue in a steady stream. The boiling point is determined when, on cooling the bath, the bubbles just cease coming from the tube.

Other micromethods for the determination of the boiling point are those of JONES (80), SCHLEIERMACHER (130), and ARREQUINE (5). Details are given in the original papers.

Boiling Point at Non–Atmospheric Pressure. For the determination of boiling points at pressures other than 760 mm, HANSEN (71)

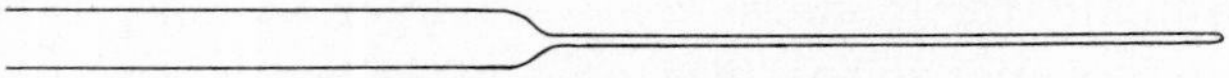

Fig. 129. Boiling Capillary of GARCIA, $^2/_3$ nat. size.

placed EMICH's boiling point capillary with the thermometer in a flask connected to a vacuum pump. GARCIA (59), however, found that leaving the air bubble below the droplet of liquid in the capillary gave incorrect

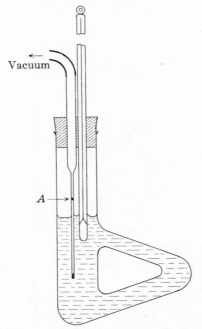

Fig. 130. Determination of the Boiling Point at Reduced Pressure according to GARCIA.

results when the pressure above the droplet was reduced. His procedure, which gave him correct results, is as follows. Prepare a tube of the dimensions shown in Fig. 129. Introduce 2 to 5 µl of the sample into the wider part of the tube by means of a capillary pipet and centrifuge it to the bottom of the narrow portion. Connect the tube to a vacuum pump and lower the pressure to the desired point as indicated on a manometer. Insert the tube into a Thiele melting point tube as shown in Fig. 130 and submerge it 25 to 30 mm below the surface of the bath liquid. Place the thermometer bulb as near to the capillary as possible and just below the surface of the bath liquid. Heat slowly; when the temperature is close to the boiling point some of the liquid will recondense in the cooler portion of the tube above the liquid level of the bath. Continue heating cautiously until a droplet which completely fills the cross section of the tube starts to form (*A*, Fig. 130). (If the bath is heated too rapidly or too far above the boiling point of the sample, more than one droplet will probably form and an incorrect result will be obtained. In this event the liquid must be centrifuged back into the capillary and the heating repeated.) Allow the

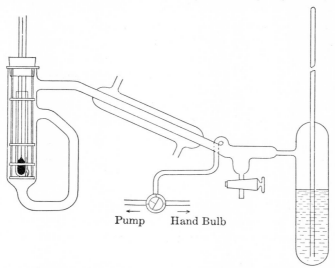

Fig. 131. Boiling Point Apparatus of HAYS, HART, and GUSTAVSON.

bath to cool slowly. The droplet will descend with the cooling of the bath; the temperature at which it reaches the level of the liquid in the bath is the boiling point.

The apparatus of ROSENBLUM (126) or that of HAYS, HART, and GUSTAVSON (73) can also be used. The latter permits determinations at higher as well as lower pressures as might be required when working at higher altitudes. Its operation can be seen from Fig. 131. In the ROSENBLUM apparatus the thermometer with the boiling point tube attached is placed through a cork in a side arm test tube which contains some of the bath liquid. The test tube is then placed in the heating bath and the side arm is connected through a condenser to a manometer and a vacuum pump.

Density.

Solids. In general, the density is more important as a means of identification for liquids than for solids. In fact, the specific gravity of a small amount of solids is almost never determined for this purpose. Should it become necessary, however, to do so for a special purpose, the suspension method of RETGERS (123) or DE JONG (41), in which the particles of the solid are mixed with liquid non-solvents of various known densities can be employed. If the particles sink in the liquid, they are obviously denser than the latter; if they float, they are less dense. The liquids are changed until one is found in which the solid particles remain suspended at any level. The solid then has the same density as the liquid. SULLIVAN (151) made a study of the most useful and economical liquids for separations of mixtures by utilizing the difference in specific gravity. His list of suggested liquids may be helpful in the determination of the density as described above. Other liquids are given by THIEL and STOLL (153) and CLERICI (34). Methods based on STOKES's law are described by BEHRENS (9) and HABER and JAENICKE (70). In these methods the rate of fall of a particle of the solid through a liquid of known viscosity is measured and the specific gravity is calculated. BEHRENS uses a set of standard solids and estimates the density of the unknown by comparing its rate of fall with that of the standards. Results good to the first decimal are obtainable. The HABER and JAENICKE method gives much more precise results. If larger quantities of the solid are available, a pycnometer of one type or another can be used. The WINCHELL pycnometer (163) uses 0.03 to 0.04 ml of material with specific gravities ranging from 4 to 7.5. KSANDA and MERWIN (92) use even less. DE CRINIS (39) determines the specific gravity of small pieces of animal organs by impaling them on silver wire and determining the apparent loss of weight upon immersion in water by the use of a torsion balance. He uses samples of 200 mg and more. CALEY (25), BLANK (17), and BLANK and WILLARD (18) determine the density of solids by measuring the displacement of a liquid in calibrated tubes. BLANK uses a minimum of 20 mg but CALEY works with much larger quantities. BLANK and WILLARD's cell, described on page 122, can, of course, be used for the determination of the density of solids as well as of liquids. First ascertain whether the solid in question is more dense than the liquid being used. Place some liquid in the cell and focus on the upper surface. Introduce a weighed amount of the solid test substance into the cell, making sure that none floats on the surface of the liquid. Again focus on the surface of the liquid and measure the displacement and the volume of the solid as described on page 122. The density of the solid can then be calculated. In some cases the dimensions of a crystal can be measured carefully under the microscope and its volume calculated. The weight can be determined on a microbalance (23).

Liquids. *Pycnometer Method.* The density of liquids may be determined by the use of a pycnometer. This may be merely a small one of the usual form with a capacity of 0.1 ml. The liquid test substance is introduced by means of a capillary pipet which must reach to the bottom of the pycnometer. FISCHER (54) describes a "filling" pycnometer for determining the density of a solution which is then transferred directly into a polarimeter tube. The pycnometer of CLEMO and McQUILLEN (33) uses only about 2 mg of sample and gives the density to the third decimal place. The dimensions of the pycnometer are given in Fig. 132. Fill the pycnometer,

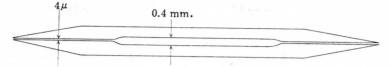

Fig. 132. Pycnometer of CLEMO and McQUILLEN.

which has been tared against a glass tube, by placing it in the liquid test substance which is slightly cooler than room temperature. Wipe off the excess or allow it to evaporate. The fine capillaries will sufficiently prevent loss from within the pycnometer. Then place it on the microbalance.

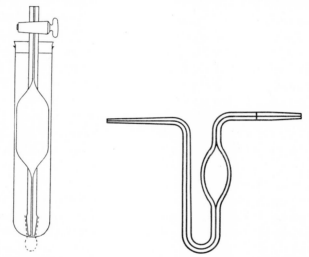

Fig. 133. Pycnometer
of YUSTER and
REYERSON.

Fig. 134. Pycnometer of ANDERSON.

In five minutes the pycnometer reaches temperature equilibrium and can be weighed.

YUSTER and REYERSON (165) described another type of pycnometer. They claim a precision of $\pm$ 0.1 mg in weighing the pycnometer while using as little as 0.1 ml of liquid. Draw up the liquid from the test tube into the bulb (Fig. 133) and to the mark in the upper tube. Then close the stopcock, remove the pycnometer from the test tube, and place the cap over the lower end.

Variations of the weighing pipet of PREGL (118) have been devised by ALBER (1). A self-filling micro pycnometer is described by ANDERSON (4) and is shown in Fig. 134.

Falling Drop Method. A number of investigators have determined the density of liquids by placing a drop of the liquid being tested in another liquid of known density and observing whether it rises or falls or remains stationary. DETRE (42) introduces a drop of the test substance into liquids of various densities. The liquid in which the drop does not rise or fall has the same density as the sample. LINDERSTRØM-LANG (95) improved this method by using a *specific gravity gradient* made by mixing kerosene and bromobenzene in varying ratios in a vertical glass tube so that the density of the mixture is lowest at the top and highest at the bottom. The gradient is measured by introducing 0.1-μl drops of liquids of known density from a micropipet. The positions of these drops are observed on an ocular micrometer. The drop of liquid of unknown density is introduced in the same way and, after a period of 10 minutes, its position is compared with those of the other drops and its density is thus determined. The falling drop method consists in allowing a drop of the test substance to fall through a column of liquid of slightly lower density. The time required for it to pass between two marks is noted and the density is calculated by comparing this time with that required for drops of liquids of known density. This method is described by FENGER-ERIKSON, KROGH and USSING (53) and HOCHBERG and LA MER (14). The latter authors use from 0.001 to 0.01 ml of the test substance. It is essential in the use of these methods that the size of the drops be exactly the same. For details as to the method of producing such drops the reader is referred to the original papers. The density can be determined to the fifth decimal.

Blank and Willard Method. BLANK and WILLARD (18) describe a very simple method for the determination of the density of liquids when a microchemical balance is available. A small cell is made by cementing a short length of glass tubing on a microscope slide. The slide is cut off close to the tube so that the weight is reduced to a minimum. The inside diameter of the tube is measured very exactly. It is assumed that the diameter is uniform along the short length used. The authors suggest a diameter of approximately 1 cm but this can obviously be reduced to cut down the amount of liquid sample. Introduce the liquid into the cell and weigh it. Then place the cell under the microscope. First focus on the upper surface of the slide. To facilitate this, the slide can be lightly scratched outside the cell. Raise the tube of the microscope by means of the vernier or fine adjustment until the surface of the liquid is sharply focused. This can be made more readily visible by dusting it with lampblack. The distance through which the microscope tube was raised is the height of the liquid column and this, with the inside diameter of the cell, is used to calculate the volume of the liquid sample. If the microscope is not equipped with a fine adjustment marked in millimeters, the vernier knob can easily be calibrated to read distances by using objects of various thicknesses which have been measured by a micrometer caliper. The same authors describe a method based on the balanced column of liquids.

Schlieren Method. In general it is not necessary in qualitative organic analysis to determine the density to a high degree of precision. In the scheme of analysis of MULLIKEN-HUNTRESS (106) the specific gravity is used chiefly in the identification of the hydrocarbons. In this classification it is not necessary to know the value of the density but merely whether it lies in one range or another. For such work the schlieren method of EMICH (51) (*see* also page 131) can be used with great economy of time and equipment. All that is required is a number of standard liquids in which the sample is soluble and the densities of which are known and which lie on the boundaries of the ranges mentioned above. The sample is allowed to run into one of these standards after another and the direction of flow is observed. If the schlieren rise, the sample is lighter than the standard, if the schlieren descend, the sample is heavier. If the schlieren spread out or diffuse without ascending or descending, the sample has the same specific gravity as the standard. STRUSZYNSKI (150) suggests that the capillary pipet from which the sample is allowed to flow into the standard be shaped as shown in Fig. 135. He also suggests that the schlieren be made more readily visible by adding a small amount of dye (not enough to affect the specific gravity) to the test substance. For further details *see* page 131. CAP (26) uses a method somewhat like the schlieren technique. He sets a capillary containing the sample on the surface of a standard liquid. If the sample is lighter than the standard, nothing happens. If it is heavier than the standard, a transposing action takes place in that the standard liquid

Fig. 135. Schlieren Pipet according to STRUSZYNSKI.

rises in a column in the interior of the capillary and the sample descends along the inside walls of the capillary.

Other methods for the determination of the density are those of GICKLHORN and NISTLER (62) and of LEWIS and McDONALD (94) and GILFILLAN (63). The GICKLHORN and NISTLER method is based upon the fact that two miscible liquids of equal density, when placed in contact with each other, have an interface of very low stability. They use sugar solutions of known density for comparison with the unknown. The LEWIS and McDONALD method uses a float which is placed in the liquid to be tested. The temperature of the liquid or the pressure upon it is changed until the float neither rises nor falls. The same determination is carried out with pure water. The method is not applicable over more than a rather

narrow range of densities. A micro buoyancy balance is described by
EIGENBERGER (48) who states that it can easily be built by the analyst.
It uses 0.2 to 0.5 ml and permits determination of the density to the fourth
decimal place. GILL and SIMMS (64) describe a hydrometer for use in determining the specific gravity of oils.

Refractive Index.

Solids.

The refractive index of solids is not as important in organic qualitative
analysis as in inorganic. Nevertheless, it is a value which can be determined
very easily by the immersion method and the determination is non-destruc-
tive of the sample. This method depends upon the fact that colorless
transparent objects are visible because of the difference in refractive index
of the object and its surrounding medium. If a solid object is immersed
in a liquid and the outlines of the object vanish or almost vanish, the
liquid and the solid have the same refractive index. Naturally, the solid
must not be soluble in, or react with, the liquid. If a series of liquids of
different refractive indices is used, an unknown solid can be placed in each
liquid in turn until one is found in which the solid becomes invisible or
nearly so. As a guide for the selection of the immersion liquid, one of two
methods of determining whether the liquid or the solid has the higher
refractive index should be used. These two methods are (1) the use of the
BECKE line and (2) the use of oblique illumination.

Use of Becke Line. Place a few thin crystals of the solid test substance
on a slide, cover with a cover glass, and transfer to the stage of the microscope. Focus on a single crystal with clear-cut outlines. Bring a drop
of one of the standard liquids (*see below*) to the edge of the cover glass
by means of a glass rod or capillary pipet so that it is drawn between the
slide and the cover glass. Then observe the crystal, using axial illumination
with the iris diaphragm almost closed. Focus the microscope on the outline of the crystal so that it becomes a single dark line. Slowly raise the
body tube of the microscope (still looking into it) for a short distance.
A fine bright line will appear beside and parallel to the dark outline of the
crystal. This bright line is called the BECKE line. If the BECKE line is
on the crystal side of the outline, the solid has the higher index of refraction;
if on the liquid side, the liquid has the higher index. Next, lower the body
tube first to the point of sharp focus and then beyond; the BECKE line
will move into the medium of lower refractive index. It is advisable to
apply the BECKE line test by both raising and lowering the tube of the
microscope. From the result of the above observation, decide whether
to use next a liquid of higher or lower refractive index. In this way it is

possible to determine that the index of refraction of the test substance lies between two values. If greater precision is required, make up mixtures of the two standard liquids (if they are miscible) to values of the refractive index lying between these two values until the right value is obtained. It must be remembered, of course, that very precise determinations of the refractive index require the use of monochromatic light but such precision is usually not necessary in organic work.

For organic compounds which are soluble in the liquids ordinarily used as standards, aqueous solutions of potassium mercuric iodide are employed. For lists of media suitable for organic compounds see SCHNEIDER and ZIMMERMAN (133) and BEHRENS and KÜSTER (11).

Use of Oblique Illumination. This is based upon the fact that if an object is illuminated by unilateral oblique transmitted light it will be unsymetrically shaded, the shaded side of the object depending upon whether the object or the surrounding medium is more highly refractive. If the crystal has the higher refractive index, it will appear shaded on the side opposite that from which the oblique light comes. Remove the condenser from the microscope and open the iris diaphragm wide. Adjust the mirror (plane side so that the best possible illumination is obtained) and then, while looking continually at the crystal (which has been previously focused), swing the mirror to the left until the boundary of a shadow appears in the field and continues across until it almost reaches the opposite edge. If the crystal has a higher refractive index than the liquid, a very bright streak or center of light will have appeared in the crystal. This center of light will move as the mirror moves; that is, if the mirror is moved to the left, the center of light will move to the left, or, if the mirror is moved to the right, the light will also move to the right. If conditions are reversed, that is, if the crystal has the lower index of refraction, the center of light will move in the direction opposite that of the mirror.

The newer microscopes with built-in illuminators do not lend themselves readily to the use of this procedure. To obtain the oblique illumination it is necessary to manipulate the condenser and the side of the shading will depend upon the characteristics of the microscope. If such microscopes are used, therefore, it is advisable to determine the behavior of a known substance.

Anisotropic Crystals. For anisotropic crystals the observed refractive index depends upon the direction of travel and upon the plane of vibration of the light. Consequently, there are minimum and maximum refractive indices. If an anisotropic crystal is examined by the immersion method, no liquid will be found in which the crystal is invisible unless plane polarized light is used and the crystal is in an extinction position.

For tetragonal, hexagonal, and trigonal crystals there are two principal refractive indices, the highest and the lowest. When performing the BECKE test with ordinary light, the BECKE line will be seen to move outward into the liquid upon raising the tube of the microscope if the refraction of the liquid exceeds the maximum refraction of the crystal. The BECKE line will move into the crystal if the refraction of the liquid is below the minimum refraction of the crystal. For liquids of intermediate refractive index the BECKE line will be partially within and partially without the crystal provided that the light does not travel parallel to the axis of isotropism.

In order to observe one refractive index at a time it is necessary to use polarized light and to adjust the plane of polarization to admit only one of the directions of vibration within the crystal. The crystal must also be viewed vertically to its principal axis and it must be definitely known that it is hexagonal or tetragonal. Rotate the crystal between crossed nicols and determine the position of extinction. This is the position at which the brightness of the crystal becomes a minimum. The vibration directions in the crystal are then indicated by the cross-hairs of the eyepiece. After removing one of the nicols (usually the analyzer) determine the refractive index by the immersion method. Then rotate the crystal 90° and repeat the determination for the second vibration direction. Observation of a few crystals in random position will show one index to be constant and the other to vary. The constant value is the refractive index for the *ordinary* ray and may represent either the minimum or the maximum value.

Orthorhombic, monoclinic, and triclinic crystals each have three refractive indices: a minimum (α), a maximum (γ), and an intermediate value (β) which is the refractive index for light traveling along the axes of isotropism.

For a general presentation of the principles involved in the immersion method of determining the refractive index, the reader is referred to SLAWSON and PECK (139) especially for details for birefringent materials. SAYLOR (128) discusses the relative accuracy of the BECKE Line and the oblique illumination methods together with the so-called double diaphragm method. KOFLER (81) describes the procedure to be followed with melts. Since these are isotropic they have but one refraction index. In such cases splinters of glasses of a variety of refractive indices are immersed in the molten sample and then examined as described above.

VON ENGELHARDT (155) has devised an instrument for estimating the refractive index of particles of ultramicroscopic size.

Liquids.

Refractometers. The index of refraction is also a very important constant in the identification of liquids, particularly those which are chemically inert, such as hydrocarbons. The ABBE or dipping refracto-

meters can be employed for determining this constant. For a discussion
of these instruments see, e. g., FULWEILER (58). A number of inexpensive

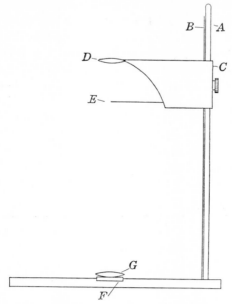

Fig. 136. Refractometer of SMART and HOCKING.

substitutes have been devised, among them those of JELLEY (19), STANCIU
(148), SMART and HOCKING (140), EDWARDS and OTTO (47), and NICHOLS (108).

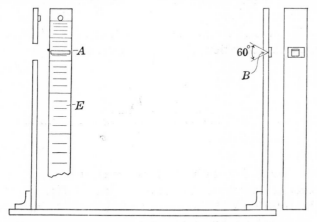

Fig. 137. Refractometer of EDWARDS and OTTO, ¼ nat. size.

The last three pieces of equipment can be constructed by the analyst
himself or by almost any laboratory technician. The device of NICHOLS
as modified by ALBER and BRYANT (2) uses but 6 to 7 μl. SMART and HOCK-
ING's refractometer is shown in Fig. 136. The rod A is made of wood and

bears a scale B marked off in millimeters. A carriage C bearing the lens D can be moved up and down this rod. Below the lens and also fastened to the carriage is a wire with a fine white-enameled point E. This point should be directly below the center of the lens D. A mirror F is set into the base and a lens G is placed over the mirror. The carriage is moved up or down until the point of the wire and its image in the mirror coincide (position F). The position of the carriage is noted on the scale. A drop of water is then placed between the lens G and the mirror and the carriage is again adjusted

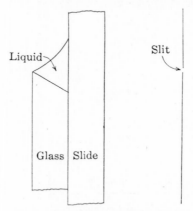

Fig. 138. Vertical Section through Cell, enlarged.

until the point of the wire and the image coincide (position F_1). This is repeated with the use of a drop of the liquid under investigation in place of the drop of water (position F_2). The position of the carriage is noted after each adjustment. From these data the index of refraction can be calculated with the equation given in the original paper:

$$\frac{n_{\mathrm{H_2O}} - 1}{n - 1} = \frac{\dfrac{1}{F_1} - \dfrac{1}{F}}{\dfrac{1}{F_2} - \dfrac{1}{F}}$$

A device similar to JELLEY's which can readily be made by the analyst himself, is that of EDWARDS and OTTO shown in Fig. 137. The authors state that the total cost of the instrument is four dollars. The slit A is illuminated from behind by monochromatic light and is viewed through a small aperture B. This aperture is covered by a prism made from a cover slip whose edge has been ground off to an angle of 45° and which is cemented to a microscope slide as shown in Fig. 138. The liquid is placed between the beveled edge of the cover slip and the microscope slide. When the prism is placed over the aperture, the effect is that of a camera lucida in which the virtual image of the slit is seen on the scale E in a position which indicates the value of the refractive index of the liquid. Details on the grinding of the cover slips and construction of the other parts of the apparatus as well as the calibration of the scale are given in the original article.

Immersion Method. The microscope can also be used for the determination of the refractive index of liquids or melts. The immersion method described above for solids can also be used for liquids if a number of solid standards (insoluble in the liquid being tested) are used. Lists of such solids are to be found in the literature (30). Special glasses of different refractive indices can also be made up for use as standards (87). KIP-LINGER (84) describes a method for determining the refractive index of liquids which employs an ordinary microscope fitted with a special lens with an opening to contain the liquid sample. MÖHRING (103) describes a microscope chamber for measuring the refractive index of liquids. This chamber consist of two slides cemented together with a circular hole drilled into the upper one. A scale is placed on the bottom of the cell thus obtained. A glass prism made of two wedges cemented together at the hypotenuse faces, one wedge with a refractive index of 1.47 and the other 1.91, is placed over the scale so that the marks are half covered. Owing to the arrangement of the wedges the refractive index of the prism changes from 1.47 at one end to 1.91 at the other. A liquid with a refractive index lying between these two values is placed in the cell and the half of the scale not covered by the prism is brought into focus under the microscope. Only the one line on the scale lying under the point of the prism which has the same index of refraction as the liquid will be sharply in focus at this setting of the microscope. The scale is empirically calibrated by the use of liquids of known refractivity.

Duc de Chaulnes Method. Another microscopic method is that originally developed by the DUC DE CHAULNES (44). It is based upon the fact that, when an object is viewed through a medium the surface of which is normal to the line of vision, the image will appear to be in a plane above that of the object, the amount of the displacement being dependent upon the thickness and refractive index of the medium. The technique of CHAMOT and WRIGHT (32) employs a cell made by cementing a perforated brass disk with plane parallel surfaces onto a microscope slide. The cement, of course, must not be soluble in the liquids to be tested.

KIRK and GIBSON (85) make the cell by boring a hole 1 mm in diameter and 5 mm deep in a glass plate 6 mm thick. Fill the cell "rounding full" and lay the cover glass upon it and press it down into contact with the cell. Avoid surplus liquid. Set the fine adjustment at the lower limit of its range so that the same portion of its movement will be used for the measurements of each liquid. Then, looking through the portion of the

cover glass projecting over the cell (*see* Fig. 139), focus the microscope
with the coarse adjustment on a mark (scratch or ink mark) on the upper
surface of the slide. Next, move the slide so that the cell with the liquid
is under the objective. Use the fine adjustment to focus on the upper
surface of the slide again, counting the number of divisions the fine adjustment knob is moved. The measurement should be repeated at least three
times and the results averaged.

Using the same cell and the same microscope, measure the displacement of the mark with at least three liquids, of which the refractive indices
have been determined with a refractometer. Choose these liquids to give
values which represent the minimum, maximum, and middle of the range

Fig. 139. Cell of Kirk and Gibson, 5 times nat. size.

in which future determinations are to be made. More liquids may be used
to give more points on the curve. Prepare a good-sized graph of displace-
ments plotted against refractive indices. The curve is nearly a straight
line and it passes through the point: displacement 0, $n = 1.00$. To determine the refractive index of an unknown, the displacement is measured
and the refractive index is read from the graph.

Schlieren Method. In the Mulliken-Huntress classification of
compounds according to their refractive indices, it is not necessary to
actually determine the value of this constant. As with the density, it is
only necessary to determine whether it lies within one range or another.
In other words, one need only know whether the refractive index is above
or below certain values. This determination can be carried out most rapidly
by employing the schlieren method of Emich (129). This method is based
upon the fact, when one liquid is allowed to flow into a second, miscible,
liquid which has a different refractive index, the zones of mixing, the
so-called schlieren, are visible with proper illumination if the indices of
refraction of the two liquids differ by as little as one unit in the fourth
decimal place. If the two liquids have the same refractive index no simple *
schlieren appear.

It a suitable illumination is employed it is also possible to determine
which of the two liquids has the higher refractivity. Thus, if a series of

---

* Schlieren can be obtained with liquids of identical refraction but of a different
type. *See* E. Schally, *Monatsh. 58,* 399 (1931).

liquids of known refractive indices is used and the unknown tested against
them, it is easy to determine in which range the refractive index of the
unknown substance lies.

The test is carried out as follows. The cell may be either a special one
which has a large cross-sectional area but only a small capacity (0.1 ml)
(*see* Fig. 140) or, more simply, a short length of glass tubing with a bore
of 4 mm and a length of about 40 mm, sealed at one end, Fig. 141. Fill
about three fourths of the cell of the first type or about one-fourth of the
cell of the second type with the liquid of known refractive index. This is

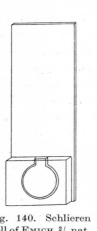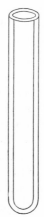

Fig. 140. Schlieren
Cell of EMICH, $^2/_3$ nat.
size.

Fig. 141. Tube
for Schlieren
Observation
$^3/_4$ nat. size.

the "static" sample. Draw the liquid test substance into a capillary pipet.
This is the "fluid" sample. The size of the bore of the capillary pipet
tip depends upon the viscosity of the liquid used. For viscous liquids the
bore should be about 0.2 mm; for liquids of low viscosity it should be
half as large. The amount taken should be great enough so that the liquid
will just flow out slowly when the pipet is held vertically. It is sometimes
advisable to prevent the flow of the liquid sample until the pipet has been
properly inserted in the cell. To accomplish this, attach a short length
of fine-bore rubber tubing to the upper end of the capillary. Draw in the
liquid column so that the bottom is a short distance above the tip of the
pipet. This draws in an air bubble which keeps the liquid in the pipet.
Hold the rubber tubing closed and insert the pipet into the static sample.
Then squeeze the tubing to push out the air bubble and the flow of liquid
will start. In most cases this device is not necessary.

The proper illumination is essential for maximum sensitivity of observation. View the cell against a background which is half light and
half dark. This can be furnished by the vertical edge of a window frame,

the frame being dark and the light from the sky or the reflection of a light-colored building being bright. Another background can be made by covering half a piece of dull black paper with a sheet of white paper and holding it so that the line of separation is vertical. This can be illuminated by a lamp placed in front of the observer but facing away from him toward the paper. Hold the cell some distance in front of the background so that the boundary between light and dark zones appears immediately beside the opening of the pipet in the cell. When the fine tip of the pipet is lowered into the static sample, the fluid sample begins to flow out and mix with the liquid in the cell. If the two liquids differ in refractive index, the stream of the fluid sample forms a schlieren which is bright on one side and dark on the other. In the case of the cell with parallel sides, if the shadow of the schlieren is opposite the dark region of the background, the refractive index of the fluid sample is higher than that of the static sample. If the shadow is on the same side, the static sample has the higher refractivity. In the case of the tubular cell, the reverse is true; that is, if the dark regions of both schlieren and background are on the same side, the fluid sample has the higher refractive index, and vice versa.

Thus by the use of two or three standard liquids the range in which the refractive index of the substance under examination lies is quickly determined. If a more precise determination is desired, the number of standard liquids and the number of tests must be correspondingly increased. MAYRHOFER (101) has used this method for the determination of the refractive indices of essential oils.

Crystallographic Properties.

Reference to certain tests and methods of identification discussed later in this book indicates the growing interest of analysts in the polarizing microscope as a means of identifying compounds without resort to destructive reactions. The properties which can be determined in this way and which have been tabulated for various types of compounds include: (A) crystal habit, (B) crystal system, (C) interfacial angle, (D) refringence, and (E) extinction. The last two are discussed under Crystal Optical Properties, p. 133.

A) Crystal Habit. Solids rarely crystallize in perfect geometric forms. They may be grouped, incomplete, developed in one direction more than in another, etc., depending upon the external conditions at the time of formation. However, these forms, which are designated the habit, may be quite characteristic and may also indicate the crystallographic system to which the material belongs. The various designations and categories of habits will be seen from the tables under the various types of compounds for which these properties have been determined.

B) Crystal System. The crystallographic system to which the substance belongs may be recognized by its behavior when examined with polarized light as described below. Only rarely can this property be determined by mere examination.

C) Interfacial Angle. It has long been known that, although a particular substance can produce crystals of all sizes and habit, the angles between the faces of such crystals are always the same for the same substance. When grown under the usual conditions, e. g., on a microscope slide, crystals will develop chiefly at their angles, producing few faces and simple habit. If the rate of growth is too high, the growth at the edges and corners will be so much greater than on the plane faces that long, dendritic, platy, or acicular crystals will be formed. Nevertheless, the interfacial angles will be maintained. Furthermore, certain interfacial angles are extremely characteristic for crystals not in the cubic system.

When crystals of sufficient size are available, these angles can be measured by a goniometer. The CODD-MOORE two-circle goniometer (36) measures the angles between the faces of very small crystals by catching reflections from the various faces in a telescope which is moved around the crystal on a graduated scale.

D) Profile Angles. If the faces between which the angle is to be measured are perpendicular to the plane of the microscope stage, the angle will be a true interfacial angle. Usually, however, the crystal lies on one face on the slide and the other faces are oblique to the plane of the stage. The angle between the edges (or faces) as observed is therefore not the true interfacial angle but a projection of it onto the plane of the stage. SHEAD (135) has suggested that these *outline* or *profile* angles be used for identification as well as the actual interfacial angles. Such profile angles can be measured with a microscope fitted with a rotating stage. DONNAY and O'BRIEN (43) describe methods for converting the observed values of the profile angles into actual interfacial angles, thus making it possible to use the tables of interfacial angles such as those of BARKER (8).

This author has devised a system of rules for classifying the values of the interfacial angles to facilitate identification of a substance on the basis of this property. The compilation of these values is known as the BARKER Index of Crystals (116) and includes some 10,000 substances. See also PORTER (115), KOMÁREK (91), SIERRA (136), VAN ZIJP (154), TERPSTRA (152), DAVIES and HARTSHORNE (38), BOLD'IREV (20), and WHERRY (159).

Crystal Optical Properties.

By the crystal optical properties is meant the behavior under the microscope in polarized light. By application of the following tests in sequence the test substance can be placed in certain groups or the tests will characterize the compound to permit identification if used with tables such as those of WINCHELL (162) or those listed in this book under the headings of the various types such as the amino acids.

Birefringence. The Nicol prisms are set in the crossed position and the condenser lenses are removed, so that so-called parallel light is used, and the object slide shielded to exclude reflected light. The crystals of the test substance are placed on a slide and spread out so that they are oriented at random. One of two things may be observed with these crystals.

a) The crystals remain dark in all positions. The crystals are isotropic and belong to the cubic system. Amorphous substances show the same behavior. It is assumed that the material is not influenced in its ability to refract light by pressure or internal stress or strain. Very fine threads and objects such as starch kernels usually show a phenomenon similar to double refraction. With platelets rotation of the stage may not suffice to bring out birefringence and it will be necessary to inspect these also in up-ended position.

b) The crystals of many substances will change from bright to dark or the reverse when the stage is rotated, that is, they are doubly refracting. They therefore belong to any other system than cubic. Further observation places these crystals in one of two classes depending upon the position (direction of axes of isotropism) in which these crystals behave like singly refracting bodies, i. e., do not brighten the field upon rotation of the stage.

α) There is only one direction in which the crystal does not brighten when rotated between crossed nicols: the crystal is optically uniaxial. It belongs to the hexagonal or tetragonal system. The direction of the optic axis coincides in this case with the principal crystallographic axis.

β) There are two directions in the crystal in which the crystal does not brighten the field when rotated between crossed nicols; viewing along these axes never gives a complete extinction, the crystal always remains at least gray: the crystal is optically biaxial. It belongs to the rhombic, monoclinic or triclinic systems.

Extinction. If a birefringent crystal is observed between crossed nicols while the stage is rotated slowly through 360°, the crystal will generally appear dark in four positions which are 90° apart. These positions, in which the crystal behaves like a singly refracting one, are called *extinction positions*. In defining extinction positions, the principal edges of the crystal are usually considered, that is, those by which the crystal is chiefly defined (e. g., in a needle-shaped crystal, the longitudinal edges). These positions can be marked by turning the eyepiece so that they will coincide with the crosshairs. Two cases are possible:

a) Parallel extinction.   If, in the extinction position, the pricipal edges are parallel, or perpendicular, to the planes cf vibration of the nicols (which are at the same time the directions of vibration of the two components of light in the specimen), the extinction is said to be *parallel*. This occurs quite often with needle-shaped crystals (Fig. 142 *A*).

b) Oblique extinction.   If, in the position of extinction, the principal edge forms an angle with the planes of vibration of the nicols varying between 0° to 90° but at neither limit, the extinction is said to be *oblique*

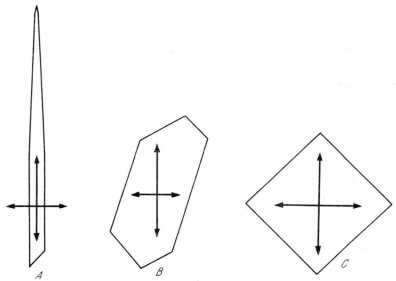

Fig. 142. Extinction Positions and Directions of Vibration. *A* parallel extinction; *B* oblique; *C* symmetrical.

(Fig. 142 *B*).   The crystal has oblique extinction.   By *extinction inclination* is meant the angle which the principal edges form with the planes of vibration of the nicols and the vibration directions in the crystal.

c) Symmetrical extinction.   If, in the extinction position, the planes of vibration of the nicols bisect the angle between two adjacent crystal edges, the crystal is said to possess *symmetrical* extinction (Fig. 142 *C*). This is a special case of parallel extinction.

Other Optical Properties.   These can be observed and measured by the use of a polarizing microscope.   For details the reader is referred to CHAMOT and MASON (31), WINCHELL (161), and HARTSHORNE and STUART (72). See also lists of optical properties of compounds given by ASHTON, HOUSTON, and SAYLOR (6), GROTH (68), KEENAN and HANN (83), MAYRHOFER (100), BEHRENS and KLEY (10), HAAS (69), BOLLAND (21), WOOD and AYLIFFE (164), HULTQUIST, POE, and WITT (76), CASTLE *et al.* (28, 29), and DUNBAR and KNUTESON (46).

Molecular Weight Determination.

Some authors, as, for example, KAMM (82) do not regard the determination of the molecular weight as an important or worthwhile step in the identification of an organic compound. It is felt that the time required to set up the necessary apparatus and carry out the determination can be used to much better advantage by performing several other tests. Such statements do not apply, as KAMM also points out, to most of the microprocedures. Furthermore, the determination of the molecular weight is essential in the cognition of hitherto undescribed compounds. The procedures which are given on the following pages have been selected from the many in the literature on the basis of simplicity, ease of making the apparatus, and speed of manipulation.

Rast-Soltys Method. (120, 145) This method is based upon the large depression of the melting point of camphor. The camphor must be as pure as possible; it must be resublimed before use if necessary.

Grind the camphor to a powder in an agate mortar after moistening with a little ether. After grinding, spread it out on a watch glass or sheet of paper for few hours to allow the ether to evaporate completely. Determine the melting point and the molecular melting point depression; use a pure substance of known molecular weight for the latter determination. The melting point capillaries should be thin-walled and about 4 cm long with a bore of 2 to 3 mm. They should be tapered somewhat to facilitate the introduction of the material. Seal the smaller end, taking care not to form a point or heavy drop of glass. Weigh the capillary on a microbalance. Then introduce the sample by means of a filling tube made from a smaller capillary, about 5 cm long, which fits into the first (Fig. 143). A thin glass rod, 6 cm long, which can easily be inserted into the filling tube is also used. Place the test substance on a glass plate or watch glass. Press the filling tube into the substance, remove, and carefully wipe off the outside so that no particles of the substance remain adhering to the surface. Then insert it into the melting point tube (which can be supported in a cork) until it almost reaches the bottom. Use the glass rod to push the sample out of the filling tube. Withdraw the latter and examine the melting point tube to see if any of the material is adhering to its walls. Should there be any, bring it to the bottom by tapping or scratching with a tile as in filling an ordinary melting point tube. Then weigh the tube again. Add camphor (about ten times the weight of the sample) in the same way as the sample, taking care not to touch the latter. Weigh the tube again. Now seal it by heating with the flame of a microburner about 15 mm from the sealed end until the tube collapses and then draw out to a fine thread (Fig. 144) 4 to 5 cm long. Attach the sealed tube to a thermometer in the usual melting point bath. The thermometer need not be a particularly accurate one, although HOUBEN recommends the use of a "normal" thermometer to avoid the necessity of stem corrections. If possible, use one with a range of 120 to 180° in fifths of a degree. First heat the mixture to melting in order to dissolve the sample in the camphor. After cooling again, heat carefully, raising the temperature at a rate of not more than 2 degrees per minute with a microburner. Long before the melting point is reached, the mixture will begin to look like thawing ice. It finally will become a turbid liquid in which, by the aid of a lens, one can see a delicate crystal skeleton which permeates the entire melt in the beginning but dissolves

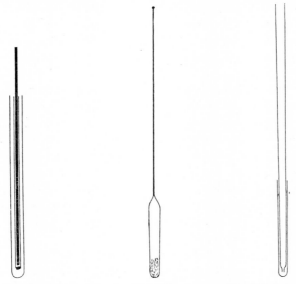

Fig. 143. Introduction of   Fig. 144.   Fig. 145. Introduction
Sample by Filling Tube.   Sealing of Tube.   of Liquid Samples.

from the top downwards during slow temperature rise. The temperature at which the last crystals disappear is used in the calculation. Repeat the melting point determination to check the first result.

A simpler procedure with larger quantities of material may be used. Carefully clean a small test tube with cleaning solution. Dry and then set it into a cork and weigh on the balance. Weigh in several milligrams of the test substance followed by ten to twenty times as much camphor. Fuse and mix the contents of the tube by dipping the test tube into a hot sulfuric acid or paraffin bath. After cooling, remove the mixture and place in an agate mortar or on a watch glass. Transfer some to a thin-walled melting point tube in the usual way by pressing the latter into the kernels of the mixture and then pushing the material down into the tube with a glass rod. Seal the tube as described above and determine the melting point.

HOUBEN (75) and SOLTYS (145) have applied this method to the determination of the molecular weight of liquids. The latter introduces the liquid into the weighed melting point tube by means of a capillary pipet (Fig. 145). A centrifuge may also be used to advantage for this. The outside of the pipet is carefully wiped after it has been filled to prevent liquid from adhering to the walls of the melting point tube and thus not mixing with the camphor.

Barger Method. If drops of two solutions, one osmotically stronger than the other, are placed in a capillary, the concentrations of the two tend to become equal as the solvent passes from the more dilute to the more concentrated droplet. The stronger solution grows at the expense of the weaker. With a sufficiently volatile solvent this change can be observed in a few minutes under the microscope. If the test solution is compared with solutions of known molality, the molecular weight of the test substance can be determined.

Various non-volatile substances such as azobenzene or benzil may be used as standard substances of known molecular weight. Using a buret, dilute a solution of known concentration to 0.2, 0.4, 0.6, 0.8 molal, etc. Should these limits be too wide, intermediate concentrations such as 0.45, 0.5, 0.55 may be prepared by proper dilution of the standard solution. The limit of error of the molecular weight determination is set by the error in the preparation of the solutions. The solvent employed is usually pyridine because most carbon compounds are soluble in it. It need not be particularly pure; in fact, even mixtures can be employed as solvents in this method.

Make the test solutions in small ampules or tubes with a bore of 3 to 4 mm and about 15 mm long by weighing out in them several milligrams of the test substance and 50 to 100 mg of the solvent. Then seal the tube. When ready to carry out the determination, cut the tube open, remove the required amount in a capillary, and seal the tube again. If larger amounts of the substance are available, larger vessels and an ordinary analytical balance can be used in the preparation of the test solutions. The standard solutions are preserved in long-necked ampules. These should have a capacity of 2 ml and a neck 16 cm long and wide enough to permit the introduction of a capillary. They can be filled by evacuating and sealing of the neck at a previously constricted point and then pushing it into a vessel containing the solution so that the tip breaks off.

The actual determination is carried out in capillaries with a bore of 1 to 2 mm and 10 to 15 cm long. Hold the capillary between the thumb and middle finger with the index finger closing the upper end. Dip the lower end into the standard solution. By releasing the pressure of the index finger, allow a column of liquid, 5 to 10 mm long, to enter. Then close the upper end again, remove the capillary from the solution, and tilt it so that upon releasing the pressure of the finger again, the column of liquid slides down

the capillary until it is about 2 to 3 mm from the filling end. Then press
the finger tightly upon the tube, wipe off the filling end of the tube, and
touch it to a drop of the test solution. Allow only a very small biconcave
drop to enter. Permit this drop to slide down the tube as the drop of standard solution did, but do not bring them into contact with each other. In
the same way introduce a drop of the same size of the standard solution,
followed by another of the test solution. After 2 to 4 drops of each solution
again allow a column of 10 to 15 mm of standard solution to enter. Since
capillary action is usually not sufficient for this, dip the capillary deeper
into the solution and regulate the amount of entering liquid by the pressure
of the finger. When all the drops have been introduced, allow them to slide
down the tube until the last column is about 1 cm from the filling end.
Then seal this end.

Draw out (147) the other end of the tube to hairbreadth for a distance
of 2 cm. Do not break off the funnel-shaped portion attached to the hair.
Break off the sealed end of the capillary and tilt the tube so that the liquid

Fig. 146. Barger Molecular Weight Determination.

flows back through the hair to the point at which the tube widens out again.
Draw out the other end of the tube to hairbreadth for 2 cm, breaking off
the empty wide portion of the capillary attached to this hair. Tilt the tube
so that the liquid runs into this hair and fills it. Seal in the microflame.
Some liquid should remain in the funnel at the other end so that the hair
at this end is still filled. Break off the funnel and pass the hair through a
microflame to expel a small portion of the solution before sealing it.

Fasten the capillary to a microscope slide by means of wax or modeling
clay. In Fig. 146 the black drops are the standard solution, the others being
the test solution. Measure only the small drops by placing the slide with the
tubes in a flat glass dish (which can be made by fastening four glass rods
with wax to the edges of a glass plate about 40 by 20 cm) and filling the
latter with water until the tubes are just covered. The drops chosen for
measurement should be long enough to permit accurate measurement and
yet not exceed the length of the micrometer scale of the microscope ocular.
Focus the microscope on the axis of the capillary so that the drops are
sharply defined. Measure the length of the drops at intervals to note
whether the test solution or the standard solution gives off solvent. Prepare
another capillary by using a standard solution of higher or lower concentration as indicated by the first experiment. When a standard solution is
found that neither gains nor loses solvent, the molality of the test solution
is the same as that of the standard solution. Of course, it is not necessary
to secure exact equilibrium between test and standard solution. If, for

example, a 0.4 molal solution gives off solvent to the test solution while a 0.5 molal solution takes up solvent, the molality of the test solution must lie between 0.4 and 0.5. For many purposes this suffices, but if desired, the tests may be continued with the use of standard solutions of concentrations between 0.4 and 0.5 molal, in steps small enough to satisfy the required precision.

A number of improvements have been made in this basic procedure. FRIEDRICH (56) recommends the use of a capillary about 10 cm long, drawn out to hair-fine capillaries at both ends. This is clamped between the halves of a one-hole rubber stopper on a suction tube. The comparison solution (no more than 2 cm) is drawn up to half the length of the capillary by sucking

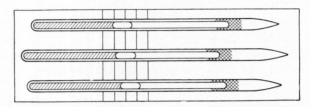

Fig. 147. Modification of Barger Method by NIEDERL and Coworkers.

with the mouth, followed by the air bubble and finally the test solution. The fine ends are then sealed. FRIEDRICH discusses the precision and technique of the Barger method in great detail in the paper cited above.

An ingenious modification which greatly reduces the time for a determination is that of NIEDERL and co-workers (109, 110). Instead of introducing the test and comparison solutions in the same capillary tube, with consequent contamination, they are placed into separate tubes which are sealed at one end. These are placed with the open ends facing each other in a third, larger, tube which can be evacuated. In this way the rate of evaporation is increased permitting changes in the respective volumes to be observed in a much shorter time. The construction and arrangement of the capillaries and outer tubes can be seen from Fig. 147.

Other modifications of the Barger procedure are described by RAST (121), SCHWARZ (134), SIGNER (137) and BERL and HEFTER (14).

To reduce the time required for a determination by measuring the differences in vapor pressures of the standard and the test solutions instead of observing changes in the volumes, NASH (107) used a modification of the SMITH and MENZIES (141) submerged bulblet method for vapor pressure determination. He uses a sample of 2 to 3 mg and the determination requires about two hours.

Other methods of determining the vapor pressures of small volumes of solutions and thus obtaining the molecular weight are the micro-isoteniscope of STEINBACH and DEVOR (149) and the procedure of GOULD, HOLZMAN, and NIEMAN (66) which is a modification of the EMICH boiling point determination. *See* also PERMAN (114) and the third BLANK and WILLARD method below.

Blank and Willard Methods.   Most of the other methods for the determination of molecular weights on a microscale require apparatus

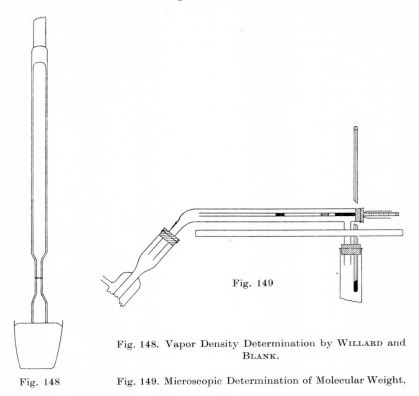

Fig. 149

Fig. 148. Vapor Density Determination by WILLARD and BLANK.

Fig. 148

Fig. 149. Microscopic Determination of Molecular Weight.

which is more or less complicated. Among these are the PREGL-BECKMANN (117), RIECHE (124), NIEDERL and SASCHEK (111), RIESENFELD and SCHWAB (125), LAKSHMINARAYAN and NYAK (93), SMITH and MILNER (143), BRATTON and LOCHTE (22), PEAK and ROBINSON (113), and BENSON (13). However, BLANK and WILLARD (19) have described three methods which require comparatively simple apparatus and which can be carried out quickly.

The first method of these last named authors is based upon the measurement of the pressure required to bring the volume of the vapor of a known weight of the unknown liquid to a given value. Weigh the sample in a small bulb and insert into a tube as shown in Fig. 148 which is originally filled with mercury. A mark is placed at the constricted portion of the tube. The volume of the tube up to the mark is previously determined.

After introduction of the sample, invert the tube into a small dish also partially filled with mercury. Place the dish and tube in a heating bath. Raise the temperature of the bath until the substance is completely vaporized and the mercury pushed out to the mark. Then read the temperature after the mercury levels have been adjusted. When the weight of the sample, the volume of the vapor, the pressure (barometric + head of mercury), and the temperature of the vapor (i. e., of the bath) are known, the molecular weight can be calculated. A somewhat similar method is that of SÁNCHEZ

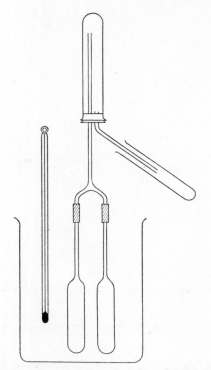

Fig. 150. Vapor Pressure Method of WILLARD and BLANK.

(127) who uses a shortened mercury thermometer. A weighed amount of the substance in a small tube is placed in the thermometer and heated by steam. The calibrated tube shows the volume. As the author himself states, "approximate exact" results are obtained.

The second BLANK and WILLARD method uses much smaller quantities and requires the use of a microscope or magnifier. Fig. 149 shows the apparatus and set-up. Place a weighed drop of the substance between two drops of mercury in a capillary with a bore of between 1.5 and 3 mm. Heat the capillary in a vapor bath to volatilize the sample. One of the mercury drops is fixed and the other is free to move. When the internal diameter of

the tube and the distance between the mercury drops are known, the volume
of the vapor can be determined. The temperature of the vapor bath, the
atmospheric pressure and the weight of the sample complete the data
necessary for the calculation of the molecular weight.

The third method of BLANK and WILLARD depends, like the BARGER
method, upon the differences in vapor pressure due to difference in molecular
concentration. In the following equation M_1 and M_2 are the molecular
weights of the standard and unknown substances, W_1 and W_2 are the weights
of the solutes in the two solutions, and V_1 and V_2 are the volumes of solvent.

$$M_1/M_2 = W_1 V_2/W_2 V_1$$

If equal weights of the standard and the unknown substances are taken
($W_1 = W_2$) the molecular weights are inversely proportional to the volumes
of the solvents when the vapor pressures of the two solutions have become
equal. The apparatus used is shown in Fig. 150. The standard substance
should have a molecular weight of about 100. Make up solutions of the
standard and the test substance to a concentration of 0.01 g/ml. After
weighing the solutions, place them in the heating bath. Heat the bath until
the solutions have boiled down to a state of equilibrium. This requires from
20 to 30 minutes. Then cool and weigh the bulbs. Since the weight of the
solvent is proportional to the volume, the weights may be substituted in
the volumes in the calculation after deducting the weights of the solutes.

Specific Rotation.

The specific rotation of solutions with a volume of about 0.2 ml can
be determined with the usual polarimeter if the polarimeter tubes of EMIL
FISCHER are employed. These tubes are 5 or 10 cm long and have a bore
of 1.5 mm and a volume of 0.1 to 0.2 ml. They can be placed directly
into the polarimeter. The tubes are made of colorless glass and are en-
cased in hard rubber to prevent interference from incident light. The
density of the solutions is determined by a pycnometer of the usual form
but with a volume of 0.1 ml. It is filled by means of a capillary pipet
and weighed to the nearest 0.05 mg. The density may also be determined,
of course, by any of the methods listed on pages 120 to 124.

In place of the polarimeter tubes described, capillaries made of black
glass with a bore of 0.4 to 0.5 mm and a length of 5 or 10 cm can be used
with a corresponding decrease in the volume of solution required. With
such tubes the ordinary polarimeter with three fields cannot be used
but a WILD "polaristrobometer" can be. The capillary tube is fastened
into a wider tube by means of two rubber stoppers. A sodium vapor lamp
serves as light source if the shorter tube is used. For the 10-cm tube an

arc light is required. The ends of the capillaries are closed by means of small cover glasses about 3 mm in diameter. They adhere readily to the ends of the capillaries.

Another rapid-filling capillary polarimeter tube has been described by SMITH and EHRHARDT (142).

At the suggestion of the author of the present volume, MARION (98) adapted the ordinary polarizing microscope equipped with a graduated rotating stage for use as a polarimeter by the addition of a simple analyzer constructed from a few square centimeters of Polaroid film. A sample of only 150 µl is required. The analyzing unit (Fig. 151) consists of a metal frame which can be attached firmly to the graduated stage by means of

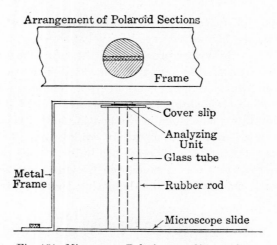

Fig. 151. Microscope Polarimeter, $^2/_3$ nat. size.

a knurled machine screw ordinarily used in a fastening a mechanical stage to the microscope. The frame must be high enough so that it barely clears the top of the cell. The two small pieces of Polaroid are located beneath a hole drilled in the metal frame concentric with the optical axis of the microscope. The sections of Polaroid are cut so that their planes of polarization include an angle of approximately 5° when the segments are mounted in place with a slight overlap.

The cell is essentially a hard rubber rod drilled to hold a length of 2-mm outer diameter glass tubing fastened to a microscope slide for easy manipulations. The height, 5.15 cm (effective length 5 cm) is selected so that the rack and pinion gears of the microscope adjustment are engaged and allow focusing (the thickness of the cover glass on top must also be taken into consideration).

The frame is bent from a strip of aluminum (2.5 cm wide) so that the distance between the microscope stage and the top of the frame is 5.25 cm.

This provides for sufficient clearance for the cell. A 5-mm hole is bored in the frame and the Polaroid is fastened underneath.

In use the microscope is focused on the slightly overlapping intersection of the two pieces of Polaroid film. This junction should approximately bisect the field and, when the stage is rotated, the mid-point of the intersection should remain in the center of the field. Coupled with the manner of mounting the Polaroid film, this procedure gives a field roughly halved, in which the intensity of light will be uniform only at the zero point.

A magnification of 100 times is sufficient. A higher magnification serves no useful purpose and does not increase the precision of measurement. Best results are obtained when a compromise plane of focusing is selected midway between the Polaroid and the top level of the liquid in the cell.

Make up the solution in a 1-ml volumetric flask by weighing out 100 to 250 mg of the test substance on an analytical balance and dissolving in sufficient solvent. Naturally, if a microbalance is available, much less sample is required. Draw a portion of the solution up in a capillary tube, place the tip of the latter carefully in contact with the bottom of the cell, and expel the liquid slowly. As the cell fills, withdraw the capillary, always keeping the tip below the surface of the liquid. The surface tension of the liquid will cause a hill of liquid to form above the top of the cell. Slip the cover glass on top, cutting off the excess liquid with the glass. Remove the excess liquid with a piece of filter paper. This draws the cover glass tightly against the top of the cell and ensures the complete filling of the cell. It is important that no air bubbles be enclosed in the cell. Check the absence of air bubbles by holding the cell directly at a light; a translucent disk of light free from any dark spots indicates complete filling.

To obtain the zero point, fill the cell with distilled water and manipulate it until it is in the field of view. Use a sodium vapor lamp as a source of monochromatic light. Rotate the stage until both halves of the field are equally extinct. Regulate the intensity by the substage iris diaphragm until the zero point illumination is sufficient to provide a sharp zero point. It was found that the zero point obtained in this way is the same as that when no cell at all was used. Determine the angular difference between this zero point and the similar position obtained with the sample in the cell.

The specific rotation can be calculated by means of the formula:

$$\text{Specific rotation} = l\,a/d \text{ for pure liquid}$$
$$= 100\,a/l\,c \text{ for solutions}$$

where a = observed rotation, l = length of tube in decimeters, d = density of liquid, and c = grams of substance in 100 ml of solution.

Chapter V.

Solubility.

The determination of the solubility of a substance in various solvents is an important step in the identification of carbon compounds. It may be used in the classification of a substance, in the determination of the existence of, or distinction between polymorphs, in the selection of the proper solvent for the recrystallization of a compound, and for identification by the crystallization of a definite form.

KAMM (7) and SHRINER and FUSON (10) place a substance in a definite group according to its solubility behavior. MULLIKEN and HUNTRESS (8) use the solubility for subdiving the genera, particularly the hydrocarbons. It must be kept in mind that a purely qualitative test is not sufficient. Furthermore, there is no sharp dividing line between "soluble" and "insoluble" and an arbitrary ratio of solute to solvent must be taken as criterion. This ratio will vary according to the solvent and the physical state of the solute. The usual value taken for the solubility ratio is 1 part of solute to 25 parts of solvent. If this ratio is exceeded (e. g. 1:30) the compound is designated as insoluble; if it is below this value (e. g. 1:20) the substance is considered as soluble. Borderline cases are placed in both classes and tested for in each. The ratio of solute to solvent may be determined either by adding increments of the solvent to a fixed quantity of the solute or vice versa, whichever is more convenient.

CHAO-LUN TSENG (2) has suggested a more logical definition of solubility. Instead of an arbitrary limit separating "soluble" and "insoluble" he proposes a solubility scale as follows: Scale 1: less than 5 parts solvent; Scale 2: 5 to 10 parts solvent; Scale 3: 10 to 50 parts solvent; Scale 4: 50 to 100 parts solvent; Scale 5: insoluble in 500 parts solvent.

Solvents.

When used for purposes of classification the solubility of a test substance should give an indication, at least, of the nature of its composition. Thus, solution of a water-insoluble material by hydrochloric acid would indicate that the material possesses a basic-reacting functional group. This reasoning can be used only within narrow limits.

The classification solvents are divided into reactive and inert types. The reactive solvents give the most information as to the chemical character of the substance under examination but even this information may be too broad or too indefinite to be of great help to the analyst. While it may be possible to predict the solubility of a known compound in certain reactive solvents, the reverse process is open to too many variables. The solubility of a compound in a chemically reactive solvent depends not only upon the presence of a certain functional group but also upon the position of that group in the molecule, the presence of other functional groups, the size and shape of the carbon frame, and the possibility of parallel or secondary reactions. The classification of a substance of unknown composition on the basis of solubility therefore becomes a more or less empirical matter based upon arbitrarily set standards. Again, even when the conditions are set, some substances will be borderline cases and must be sought in two or more solubility classes.

In the case of inert solvents there is even less upon which to base conclusions regarding the chemical composition of the sample. The lack of correlation of polarity with solvent power has been pointed out in the literature for over forty years. The rules of thumb such as "like dissolves like" have too many exceptions to be used as bases for the classification of compounds. An example is the high solubility of cellulose acetate in a mixture of ethanol and methylene chloride when neither solvent dissolves this material by itself.

On the other hand, if determination of solubility is required for separation of the components of a mixture or for selection of the best solvent for recrystallization, some knowledge of the nature of the sample is available and can be used. The separation procedures using reactive solvents have been discussed under Chemical Separations in Chapter II. The selection of a solvent for recrystallization can often be based on the solubility parameters of the solute and the solvent. For a discussion of the theoretical basis for these parameters see HILDEBRAND and SCOTT (5). The basic rule in the application is that for maximum solution the solubility parameter of the solvent should be equal or as close as possible to that of the solute. If the solubility parameter of no single solvent is close enough to that of the solute, a mixture can be employed, as with ether and ethanol for nitrocellulose. In such cases, the mean of the solubility parameters of the two solvents should be as close as possible to that of the solute for maximum solubility. The approximate value of the solubility parameter of a compound, if not known, can be calculated closely enough for this purpose by the formula of SMALL (11):

$$\delta = d\Sigma G/M$$

where δ is the solubility parameter, d is the density, ΣG is the sum of all the molar attraction constants in the molecule and M is the molecular weight. Table 9 (1) gives values for the molar attraction constants of the more common groups. The table should not be used for alcohols, amines, carboxylic acids, or other substances with strongly hydrogen bonded groups unless such functional groups constitute only a small part of the molecule so that the proportional error is not so great.

The values of solubility parameters of solvents (1) are given in Table 10.

10*

Determination of Solubility.

GARDNER and LINDE (3) determined the solubility in deep-well slides, using about 5 mg of solid or about 0.01 ml of the liquid test substance and 0.15 ml of solvent. The solid was weighed out on a modified SALVIONI balance. For the quantities usually employed in microanalysis, three procedures are available, namely, the capillary, the schlieren, and the

TABLE 9

Molar Attraction Constants G of the More Common Groups

Group		G	Group	G
—CH$_3$		214	COO esters	310
—CH$_2$—	single-bonded	133	CN	410
—CH<		28		
>C<		− 93	Cl (mean)	260
CH$_2$=		190	Cl single	270
—CH=	double-bonded	111	Cl twinned as in >CCl$_2$	260
>C=		19	Cl triple as in —CCl$_3$	250
			Br single	340
CH≡C—		285	I single	425
—C≡C—		222		
			CF$_2$ n–fluoro–	150
Phenyl		735	CF$_3$ carbons only	274
Phenylene *(o, m, p)*		658		
Naphthyl		1146	S sulfides	225
Ring, 5 membered		105–115	SH thiols	315
Ring, 6 membered		95–105	ONO$_2$ nitrates	∼440
Conjugation		20–30	NO$_2$ (aliphatic nitro	
			compounds)	∼440
H (variable)		80–100	PO$_4$ (organic phosphates)	∼500
O ethers		70		
CO ketones		275	Si (in silicones)	− 38

solvent vapor method. The former is used when the actual solvent-solute ratios are desired, the latter two are best when the solubility in a definite solvent (simple or mixed) is questioned.

Schlieren Method. The appearance of schlieren on the addition of a solute to a solvent will depend upon the degree to which the amount of solute will change the refractive index of the solvent. If refractivity is regarded as an additive property, the change in refractive index will depend upon two factors: (1) the difference in the refractive indices of the solvent and the solute, and (2) the concentration of the solute. Theoretically, therefore, the appearance of schlieren cannot be a measure of the concentration of the solute only. It has been shown experimentally, however (9), that, within certain limits, schlieren can be used as a direct meas-

TABLE 10
Solubility Parameters of Solvents

Aliphatic hydrocarbons			Isopropyl isobutyrate	7.9
Isobutylene	6.7		Methyl amyl acetate	8.0
Low odor mineral spirits	6.9		Butyl butyrate	8.1
Pentane	7.0		Sec. butyl acetate	8.2
Hexane	7.3		Sec. amyl acetate	8.3
Heptane	7.4		Isobutyl acetate	8.3
Octane	7.6		Isopropyl acetate	8.4
			Amyl acetate	8.5
Aromatic hydrocarbons			Butyl acetate	8.5
Xylene	8.8		Cellosolve acetate	8.7
Ethylbenzene	8.8		Propyl acetate	8.8
Toluene	8.9		Butyl cellosolve	8.9
Benzene	9.2		Ethyl acetate	9.1
Tetralin	9.5		Propyl formate	9.2
			Dibutyl phthalate	9.4
Other hydrocarbons			Methyl acetate	9.6
Methylcyclohexane	7.8		Ethyl lactate	10.0
Turpentine	8.1		Butyronitrile	10.5
Cyclohexane	8.2		Acetonitrile	11.9
Dipentene	8.5		Propylene carbonate	13.3
			Ethylene carbonate	14.7
Chlorinated hydrocarbons				
2,2-Dichloropropane	8.2		**Ethers**	
Carbon tetrachloride	8.6		Diethyl	7.4
1,2-Dichloropropane	9.0		Dimethyl	8.8
Chloroform	9.3		Dichloroethyl	9.8
Trichloroethylene	9.3		Dioxane	9.9
Tetrachlorethylene	9.4		Cellosolve	9.9
Chlorobenzene	9.5			
Methylene chloride	9.7		**Alcohols**	
Ethylene dichloride	9.8		Butyl carbitol	8.9
o-Dichlorobenzene	10.0		Butyl cellosolve	8.9
			Diethylene glycol	9.1
Ketones			2-Ethylhexanol	9.5
Diisobutyl	7.8		Carbitol	9.6
Diisopropyl	8.0		Cellosolve	9.9
Methyl isobutyl	8.4		Methyl isobutyl carbinol	10.0
Methyl amyl	8.5		n-Octanol	10.3
Methyl propyl	8.7		2-Ethylbutanol	10.5
Diethyl	8.8		n-Hexanol	10.7
Isophorone	9.1		Sec. butanol	10.8
Diacetone alcohol	9.2		n-Pentanol	10.9
Methyl cyclohexanone	9.3		n-Butanol	11.4
Methyl ethyl	9.3		Cyclohexanol	11.4
Cyclohexanone	9.9		Isopropanol	11.5
Acetone	10.0		n-Propanol	11.9
Cyclopentanone	10.4		Ethanol	12.7
Cyclobutadione	11.0		Ethylene glycol	14.2
			Methanol	14.5
Esters			Glycerol	16.5
Isobutyl n-butyrate	7.8			

ure of the solubility. In using schlieren for this purpose the sensitivity of the observation must be reduced. This is accomplished by using a cell made of glass tubing (*see* page 131) in place of the cell with plane parallel sides and by changing the method of illumination.

Technique for Liquids. The substance to be tested is used as the fluid sample. Fill the schlieren tube with the solvent to serve as the static sample. Draw the fluid test substance into a capillary pipet, the diameter of whose tip may vary from 0.5 to 1 mm. The more viscous the substance, the wider the tip should be. Hold the schlieren tube so that the illumination is obliquely downwards, as obtained, for example, by holding the tube below the horizontal edge of a lamp shade or below the horizontal cross bar of a window. The illumination should not be too intense. When only very small amounts of substance are available, introduce the fluid sample into the static sample by first absorbing it in a very small piece of (ignited) porous tile which has been fixed in a platinum wire and then dipping the tile into the static sample. With an inert solvent such as water or ether, a piece of ashless filter paper may also be used. If schlieren appear, the substance is classified as soluble.

Technique for Solids. First prepare a saturated solution of the solid substance by placing a drop of the solvent in a depression of a spot plate and adding the solid until some remains undissolved. With solvents which are pure substances, a saturated solution may also be prepared by making up a solution on the spot plate and allowing the solvent to evaporate until a crust appears. Then take up the clear solution in a capillary pipet and let it flow into the static sample (solvent). With solvents which are already solutions, such as 5% hydrochloric acid and 5% potassium hydroxide, place a control consisting of several large drops of the solvent in an adjacent depression of the spot plate and allow to stand until the fluid sample has been taken up in the pipet. Then use the control as a static sample. In this way differences in the refractive indices of the static and fluid samples which might result from partial evaporation and consequent concentration of the solvent solution are avoided. Follow the same technique as for liquids from this point on.

Solvent Vapor Method. (6) If the solvent is added slowly by exposing the test substance to a stream of air which has been saturated with the solvent vapor, it is possible to observe (usually with a lens) the details of the solution process. For example, if only part of the sample dissolves, it can readily be observed if this is due to low solubility of a pure compound or to the presence of a mixture of a soluble and an insoluble substance. Particles which are soluble lose their sharp outline and appear to melt. When air containing no solvent is then passed over the droplets of solution, the solvent evaporates and crystals of the solute appear. These may exhibit characteristic shapes.

An absorption tube as used for semimicro combustion is used as a chamber. Scatter a few crystals or particles of the sample upon the surface of a narrow (6 mm) microscope slide and place this in the chamber (Fig. 152). A hand lens giving a magnification of 5 to 10 diameters, clamped above the chamber, suffices for observation of the individual particles. Fill the gas-wash bottle about half full of the solvent to be used. Open the first three-way stopcock to permit air to enter the gas-wash bottle. Then slowly open the second stopcock to permit the air to leave the apparatus.

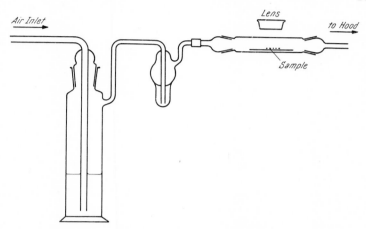

Fig. 152. Solubility Test by Solvent Vapor Method, ½ nat. size.

In the case of combustible solvents it is advisable from a safety standpoint to lead the air through a tube to a hood or window. The air should pass through the chamber at the rate of 400 to 500 ml per minute. Too high a rate does not permit saturation of the air with the solvent as it passes through the wash bottle. If the rate is too low, the solvent is brought to the sample too slowly. If the sample is soluble in the solvent, the particles will lose their sharp outlines and appear to melt. The time required for this phenomenon to take place is indicative of the relative solubility of the substance. Very soluble materials will show this behavior in less than 30 seconds, fairly soluble ones in 1 to 3 minutes and insoluble substances show no change in as much as 15 minutes of exposure to the solvent-laden air.

If air containing no solvent is passed over the droplets of solution on the slide by turning the three-way stopcocks, the solvent will be re-evaporated and the crystals of the solute reappear. As mentioned, these may exhibit characteristic shapes, which will be detailed later under the discussion of the types of compounds.

Another possibility for quantitative measurement exists with this method. If the gas-wash bottle is placed in a bath of hot water or the temperature of the air is raised before passing it through the solvent, the effect of increasing the concentration of the solvent vapor in the air stream and the higher temperature of the solvent can be observed.

Capillary Method. If the minimum or any other solute-solvent ratio is required, the solvent is added to a known quantity of the solute in small portions until complete solution has been attained. With the quantities of test substances used as samples in this work, capillary tubes must be employed.

Liquids. Dip a capillary tube, about 70 mm long and with a bore of 0.5 mm into the sample until a droplet about 2 mm long (0.1 µl) is drawn

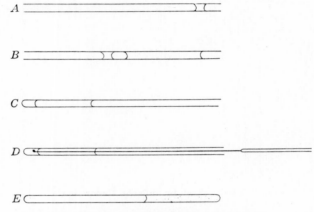

Fig. 153. Determination of Solubility in the Capillary.

up, Fig. 153 A. Then tilt the capillary so that the droplet slides a few millimeters down the tube. Dip the end into the solvent until a droplet about 10 mm long is drawn in, Fig. 153 B. Seal the end of the capillary and centrifuge the solvent and the solute to the closed end. Now mix the solute and solvent in one of two ways. In the first method insert a glass thread with the end fused to a droplet, Fig. 153 D, into the capillary and stir the two liquids by drawing the thread in and out of the tube and at the same twirling it between the fingers, thereby giving it a rotatory as well as translatory motion. In the second method of mixing, seal the open end of the capillary and centrifuge the liquids back and forth from one end of the capillary to the other. In this way the liquid of greater density is always thrown to the end of the capillary and on being centrifuged to the other end must pass through the lighter liquid. Complete and thorough mixing is thus obtained.

After mixing, determine the degree of solubility by examining the resulting droplet. This is done best with a microscope; use a narrow diaphragm opening and the condenser. If the droplet is perfectly clear and homogeneous, the liquids are completely miscible. If the droplet appears turbid, Fig. 153E, or if two separate phases appear, the sample has not dissolved completely. In such a case, cut the capillary at the empty end, add another 10 or 20 mm of solvent by means of a capillary pipet, and mix again. The quantity of solvent taken at one time can, of course, be increased or decreased as desired. If the droplet appears turbid or if two phases persist after the addition of 50 mm of solvent, the sample is designated as insoluble in that solvent.

Solids. Introduce the test substance into a capillary as in the filling of a melting point tube. The weight of the sample can be determined by weighing on a glass or quartz fiber balance (SALVIONI), torsion spring balance, or the like. Take about 0.1 mg. Add the solvent as with liquids but use the maximum amount of solvent permissible under the definition of what constitutes "soluble" without determining the exact solvent-solute ratio of a saturated solution. That is, if the ratio 1 part of solute to 25 parts of solvent is used, take 25 times as much solvent by weight as solute. If a residue remains after mixing, the substance is designated as insoluble; if none remains undissolved, the substance is soluble. Although the volume of the solid cannot be determined by the length of the solid layer in the capillary, a diminution of the volume on adding additional solvent can often be accurately determined.

Should the solid remain at one end of the capillary after centrifuging instead of passing from one end to the other with the liquid, the sample must be stirred with the glass thread as described for liquids.

Application of Solubility Data.

Knowledge of the solubility of a compound will also serve to decide if two materials having different melting points but apparently alike in all other properties are isomers or polymorphs. If the latter, they will show the same solubility while the former will differ in this property also.

The solubility of organic compounds in sulfuric acid can be used for separation and classification. *See* discussion under Hydrocarbons and also GILLESPIE (4).

Several schemes of analysis have been proposed which use differences in solubility as a basis for separating carbon compounds into smaller groups and thus reduce the number of chemical or other tests which must be carried out for final identification. Two of these are KAMM's (7) and that of SHRINER and FUSON (10). As can be seen from the following tables, the separation is not sharp because of the factors mentioned above. The tables are included in the present volume as an aid to the analyst in furnishing another tool for arriving at an unequivocal conclusion as to the identity of the compound under investigation.

TABLE 11
Solubility Classification According to Kamm

Soluble in Water: Groups I and II

Soluble in Ether (I)	Insoluble in Ether (II)
1. Alcohols (low mol. wt.) 2. Aldehydes (low mol. wt.) 3. Ketones (low mol. wt.) 4. Other neutral oxygenated compounds 5. Acids (mostly low mol. wt.) 6. A few anhydrides 7. A few esters, phenols, etc. 8. Amines (mostly low mol. wt.) 9. Neutral nitrogen compounds 10. Miscellaneous	1. Polybasic acids, hydroxy acids, etc. 2. Polyhydroxy alcohols, sugars, and certain derivatives 3. Some amides, amino acids, amines, etc. 4. Many sulfonic acids and other sulfur compounds 5. Many salts 6. Miscellaneous

Insoluble in Water: Groups III, IV, V, VI, and VII

Soluble in Dilute HCl (III)	Soluble in Dilute KOH (IV)	Indifferent Compounds of C, H, and C, H, O		Indifferent Compounds* Containing N or S* (VII)
		Soluble in Cold Conc. H_2SO_4 (V)	Insoluble in Cold Conc. H_2SO_4 (VI)	
1. Primary amines	1. Acids	1. Alcohols	1. Saturated aliphatic hydrocarbons	1. Nitro compounds (tertiary)
2. Secondary amines	2. Phenols	2. Aldehydes	2. Aromatic hydrocarbons	2. Amides and negatively substituted amines
3. Tertiary amines	3. Some amides, imides, etc.	3. Ketones and quinones	3. Halogen derivatives of VI_1	3. Nitriles
4. Hydrazines	4. A few nitro compounds and oximes	4. Ethers and acetals	4. Halogen derivatives of VI_2	4. Nitriles, nitrates, azo & hydrazo compounds, etc.
5. Miscellaneous	5. Some thiophenols, sulfonic and sulfinic acids	5. Esters and lactones		5. Sulfones, sulfonyl derivatives of secondary amines
	6. A few enols	6. Anhydrides		6. Mercaptans, sulfides, sulfates, etc.
	7. Miscellaneous	7. Unsaturated hydrocarbons		7. Miscellaneous

* Halogen compounds are not listed **separately** but are met in each of the seven groups in accordance with their solubility behavior. Similarly certain nitrogen and sulfur compounds will fall in Groups I, II, III, and IV.

TABLE 12

Solubility Classification According to Shriner and Fuson

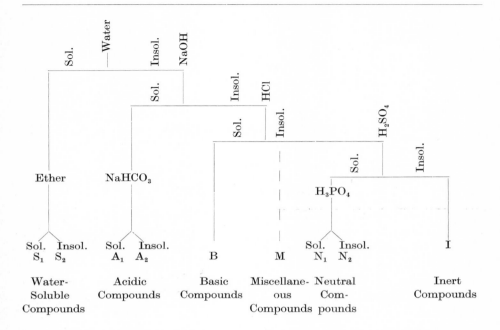

Class S_1: Almost all compounds of low molecular weight except (a) low-molecular-weight hydrocarbons and their halogen derivatives and (b) low-molecular-weight compounds which are strongly polar.

Class S_2: Water-soluble salts of all kinds, many polyhydroxy compounds, polybasic acids, hydroxy acids, amino acids, some amides, amines, and sulfur derivatives.

Class A_1: Acids and a few negatively substituted phenols such as picric acid.

Class A_2: Weakly acidic compounds such as oximes, imides, amino acids, sulfonamides or primary amines, primary and secondary nitro compounds, enols, phenols, and certain mercaptans.

Class B: Amines except diaryl- and triarylamines.

Class M: Nitro compounds, amides, negatively substituted amines, nitriles, azo compounds, hydrazo compounds, sulfones, sulfonyl derivatives of secondary amines, mercaptans, thioethers, and others.

Class N_1: Alcohols, aldehydes, methyl ketones, alicyclic ketones, and esters with fewer than 9 carbon atoms.

Class N_2: All aldehydes, alcohols, ketones, and esters with more than 9 carbon atoms, quinones, ethers, and unsaturated hydrocarbons. Anhydrides, lactones, and acetals may be found here as well as in Classes S_1 and N_1.

Class I: Saturated aliphatic hydrocarbons, aromatic hydrocarbons, and halogen derivatives of these constitute the inert class.

Part III.

Systematic Analysis.

Chapter VI.

Compounds of Order I.

After the elementary analysis and the determination of the physical constants have narrowed down the number of possible substances which the unknown may be, the latter is classified as a definite genus of compound by the use of *generic* tests. These are usually carried out in a definite sequence so that each test will identify but one or, at most, two *genera* of compounds.

Schemes based upon the solubility behavior of organic compounds require fewer classification tests. In all other respects, however, the schemes are the same as those which are based on the elementary composition of the substance. In the present book, the sequence of tests will follow that of the MULLIKEN-HUNTRESS scheme as outlined in Table 2, p. 5.

In this scheme the compounds are divided first into *orders*, that is, according to their elementary composition. The next classification is according to genera, which are groups of compounds showing the same behavior to certain tests. Each genus may be further separated into divisions and sections on the basis of physical properties such as color and physical state, rather than upon chemical behavior. The division is followed by so-called *classification* tests, such as the neutralization equivalent, which may help to identify the individual substance or merely give additional information which will aid in narrowing down the field of search as in the detection of unsaturation in acids. Finally, the tests for specific compounds are carried out. These may consist of mere verification of the melting and boiling point if the determination of the order and genus of the compound indicates only one substance with such chemical properties and with such a melting point or boiling point or they may include the preparation of one or more derivatives or the preparation of a crystalline form of the substance which may be identified under the microscope by one or more of its characteristics.

Most of the qualitative techniques described in the following pages were developed by the author and his coworkers and are based on methods suggested in the mimeographed edition of *"A Systematic Course of Instruction in the Identification of Organic Compounds"* by MULLIKEN and HUNTRESS. The microtechniques were for the most part published in separate papers (49, 50, 55 etc.). Where the microprocedures were developed by others or were based on methods other than those of MULLIKEN and HUNTRESS, a note to that effect is made at the proper point.

It is the consensus that color reactions are not sufficiently distinctive or reliable to be used as confirmatory tests. They are very useful in indicating what the test substance might be but cannot be used for the final decision on the identity of the compound. Reference is made to original work in the case of some of these color reactions but the determination of the value to be placed upon the results of such tests is left entirely up to the reader.

The discussion of the tests and procedures for each genus will consist of (1) the generic test or tests (2) the divisional tests if any, (3) the classification reactions (4) the preparation of derivatives, (5) degradative procedures, (6) chemical separation procedures, and (7) quantitative functional group determination. As pointed out in the introduction the selection of the procedures to be used is left to the judgment of the analyst as he ascertains facts about the test substance in the course of the analysis.

Aldehydes.

Generic Test.

Place two drops (from a capillary pipet) of the fuchsin-aldehyde reagent in a shallow depression of a white porcelain spot plate. Add a tiny drop (0.02 to 0.05 μl) of the test substance to the reagent drop, stirring if necessary. A distinct pink, red, or purple color develops within two minutes if the test substance is an aldehyde. In the case of solids place a tiny crystal of the test substance in the spot plate depression. Add just enough aldehyde-free alcohol to dissolve it and then the reagent as above. With water-insoluble liquids, proceed as with solids, using 0.02 to 0.05 μl of the test substance.

Notes.

1) Prepare the reagent by dissolving 0.2 g of certified basic fuchsin in 10 ml of a freshly prepared, cold, saturated, aqueous solution of sulfur dioxide. Allow the solution to stand (several hours) until all pink color has disappeared. Dilute with water to 200 ml and keep in a tightly stoppered amber bottle. Do not expose it unnecessarily to light and air.

2) Substances of fruity or aromatic odor which fail to react positively in this test should be boiled with a drop of a solution of one drop of 12 molar hydrochloric acid in 5 ml of water. Take a drop of the solution as test substance in the test.

3) WIELAND and SCHEUING (164) have suggested the following as probable reactions.

$$
\text{(structure)} \quad \begin{array}{c} \text{NH}_2 \\ \text{N}\!\!<\!\!\begin{array}{l}\text{H}\\\text{H}\\\text{Cl}\end{array} \\ \text{NH}_2 \end{array} \xrightarrow{+\text{H}_2\text{SO}_3} \quad \text{HO}\cdot\text{O}_2\text{S}-\text{C}\!\!<\!\!\begin{array}{c}\text{NH}_2\\\text{HN}_2\\\text{NH}_2\end{array} \xrightarrow{+\text{SO}_2}
$$

$$
\text{HO}\cdot\text{O}_2\text{S}-\text{C}\!\!<\!\!\begin{array}{c}\text{NHSO}_2\text{H}\\\text{NH}_2\\\text{NHSO}_2\text{H}\end{array} \longrightarrow \text{HO}\cdot\text{O}_2\text{S}-\text{C}\!\!<\!\!\begin{array}{c}\text{NHSO}_2-\overset{\text{H}}{\underset{\text{OH}}{\text{C}}}-\text{R}\\\text{NH}_2\\\text{NHSO}_2-\overset{\text{H}}{\underset{\text{OH}}{\text{C}}}-\text{R}\end{array}
$$

$$
\text{C}\!\!=\!\!<\!\!\begin{array}{c}\text{NHSO}_2-\overset{\text{H}}{\underset{\text{OH}}{\text{C}}}-\text{R}\\\text{NH}\\\text{NHSO}_2-\overset{\text{H}}{\underset{\text{OH}}{\text{C}}}-\text{R}\end{array}
$$

Since the final compound is not the regenerated original parafuchsin, instead of being light pink it has a distinct bluish tinge. The original pink color can be restored by compounds which remove sulfurous acid such as free alkalies, organic bases, or some hydrolyzable salts, or even by heating.

Classification Tests for Aldehydes.

Tollen's Test. Draw 10 to 15 mm of TOLLEN's silver nitrate reagent into one end of a capillary of 0.5-mm bore and add 2 mm of the liquid or 10 to 20 micrograms of the solid test substance. Seal the other end and centrifuge the contents of the capillary to this end. Then seal the open end also. Centrifuge the liquids back and forth a few times, if necessary, to ensure thorough mixing and then allow them to stand for 5 minutes without heating. A black or brownish black precipitate of metallic silver or a mirror on the glass indicates that the compound has reducing properties. Because of the instability of the contents, cut the capillary open after the test and throw it into a waste crock.

Notes.

1) Prepare the reagent just before use by mixing equal volumes of 10% aqueous sodium hydroxide and 10% silver nitrate in 6 molar ammonia.

2) The ammoniacal silver nitrate solution can be reduced by compounds other than aldehydes. Although a large excess of ammonia reduces the sensitivity of the reaction, it will also reduce the number of compounds other than aldehydes which may react positively (101).

Sodium Bisulfite Addition.   Place a small drop of the liquid aldehyde or of the concentrated ether solution of a solid test substance on a slide beside a droplet of the bisulfite reagent. Join the droplets and mix by means of a glass thread. If no precipitate appears on mixing, test for the evolution of heat by touching the finger to the under side of the slide directly beneath the merged drops. If much heat is evolved, lay the slide on a cold surface such as a cold metal block. When cold, examine for a precipitate.

Notes.

1) The reagent is prepared by adding 2 to 3 ml of alcohol to 10 ml of a fresh, cold, saturated solution of pure sodium bisulfite. Any precipitated solid is filtered off.

2) Failure to obtain a precipitate does not necessarily mean that the sample is not an aldehyde since many of the addition products are too soluble to appear as precipitates and the rate of formation is slow in some instances. The marked evolution of heat may therefore serve as an indication of a reaction.

3) The reaction that most probably takes place in the addition of sodium bisulfite is

$$R-C\overset{\displaystyle O}{\underset{\displaystyle H}{\big<}} \quad + NaHSO_3 \quad \longrightarrow \quad R-C\overset{\displaystyle H}{\underset{\displaystyle S-O_3Na}{\big<}}OH$$

The data on the formaldehyde bisulfite compound support the above structure for the addition product. The addition products of aldehydes (and methyl ketones other than those containing a phenyl group or other aromatic substituent and compounds containing the =CO group as part of a carbon ring) are easily formed and insoluble in ether, infusible, and non-volatile. The reaction is reversed by the addition of sodium carbonate or hydrochloric acid.

Differentiation of Aliphatic and Aromatic Aldehydes. (11)

Nitration. Treat the sample of aldehyde in a centrifuge cone or a capillary with an equal volume of 16 molar nitric acid, if necessary with warming. Only vanillin is attacked by 6 molar acid at ordinary temperatures. Nitration will give decisive results for benzaldehyde, cinnamaldehyde, piperonal, and vanillin but other aromatic aldehydes give an inconclusive yellow or brown oil as do the higher aliphatic aldehydes.

Formation of Triphenylmethane Derivatives. Precipitate the aldehydes by shaking with aniline and a little acetic acid. Add aniline and aniline hydrochloride to the precipitate, evaporate on a slide and heat (to about 170°) until a coloration appears at the edge of the drop. After cooling stir the melt with a drop of hydrogen peroxide and heat again until the coloration has spread through the entire sample. A reagent blank is colored black-brown on heating. Warm with dilute acetic acid to bring the colored material into solution. Soak a fiber of silk or wool in the solution of the triphenylmethane compound and convert into the dye by heating with hydrochloric acid. Aromatic aldehydes give violet dyes; aliphatic aldehydes give red compounds of the rosaniline group with much greater difficulty. With dimethylaniline, aromatic aldehydes give green colors of the malachite green series, aliphatic aldehydes give methylated rosanilines. Dimethylaniline does not seem to be as well suited for these tests since, unlike aniline, it does not give precipitates in solutions of the aldehydes and it gives an oxidation product of a lively green color which does not adhere to silk or wool as a dye. If it is desired to work with dimethylaniline, the green color which appears on warming without the action of oxidizing agents should be regarded as a positive test; otherwise a dyeing test is necessary.

Derivatives of Aldehydes.

Methones. To the dimethyldihydroresorcinol (methone) reagent in a centrifuge tube add an excess of the dilute (1% to 5%) aqueous solution of the aldehyde. Some aldehydes precipitate immediately and others remain in solution or precipitate only very slowly because of the relatively large solubility of the products in alkali. Acidify the mixture carefully (to avoid dehydrating the methones) with 3 molar hydrochloric acid and allow it to stand for several hours. Filter off the precipitate, wash several times with water, and dry in the desiccator over calcium chloride.

Notes.

1) The reagent is prepared by gently heating 1 g to 2 g of dimethyldihydroresorcinol in 100 to 200 ml of distilled water, with some 3 molar sodium carbonate added, until complete solution takes place. After cooling, filter to remove impurities as well as any excess reagent.

2) With some aldehydes with longer carbon chains, the aqueous reagent gives gummy or resinous products and small yields. In such cases a 50% or a saturated alcoholic solution of the reagent is employed with the aldehyde added in alcoholic or aqueous solution. Either solvent will give well-crystallized products after the slow evaporation of the alcohol. Heating will cause resinification.

3) For the crystallographic and optical properties of the methones and their anhydrides see KLEIN and LINSER (79).

4) This reagent was first prepared and used by VORLAENDER (158) and later by NEUBERG (105, 106) and KLEIN (81, 82) and their students.

Sublimation of Methones. Spread the aldimethone as flat as possible on a slide. Place a few glass threads, 0.5 mm thick, on this and then place a cover glass over all. Heat the slide on a melting point block or other metal block. Raise the temperature of the block until crystals of a sublimate begin to appear. Note the temperature at this point and then continue the heating. The more slowly the sublimation is carried out, the better the crystals of the sublimate will be. Some aldimethones will condense as drops which crystallize only after standing or on cooling.

Notes.
1) The aldimethones are easily sublimable. Sublimation should be carried out before each melting point determination to purify the product and, if necessary, to separate different aldehydes.

2) When substances sublime in drops, crystals are formed when the drops cool and congeal; these crystals melt appreciably higher than the sublimation temperature indicates.

3) The different sublimation temperatures permit separation of individual aldimethones. Actually only those whose sublimation points lie sufficiently far apart can be separated. Aside from the fact that is it difficult to keep the temperature constant, even between relatively wide limits (5° to 10°), mixed crystals of the two substances may form because they both sublime simultaneously. Such mixed crystals show new properties and other melting points which depend upon composition and cannot be used for identification. Thus, from a mixture of formaldimethone and acetal-dimethone, crystals melting at 151° were obtained.

Methone Anhydrides (79). Boil the aldimethone with a few milliliters of 40% sulfuric acid for about 2 hours in a micro extraction apparatus until all of the sample is in solution. Then precipitate the excess acid with solid, finely ground barium hydroxide. The excess acid would increase the solubility of the aldimethone anhydride. Stir the resulting mass thoroughly with petrolic ether and decant the clear extract. If the mass is too compact, add a little more water. Evaporate the ether in a vacuum (*see* page 71). The anhydrides remain as a residue. In this way the anhydrides are obtained without appreciable loss.

Notes. The reaction is:

2) The anhydrides are insoluble in water, give no ferric chloride reaction, but have definite melting points and characteristic crystal forms.

Phenylhydrazones, Semicarbazones, etc. Use Pyrex beakers 10 mm high and 10 mm in diameter. The upper edge should be ground flat. It is advisable to have some larger beakers also in case the sample should be large as in the case of natural products. Place the sample of test substance in the beaker. If the substance is a solid, add a few drops of water to prevent the drying up of the reagent drop; but if the test solution contains more than 20% alcohol, dilute it with water to bring this down to 10% because a higher alcohol content would cause the reagent drop to spread over the cover glass. Immediately after introduction of the sample, cover the beakers with half a slide (25 × 40 mm) which carries the reagent drop on its under side. To prepare the slide, grease it slightly by rubbing it between the fingers and then place a drop of the reagent on it with a thin glass rod. The reagent drop should be no larger than 2 mm in diameter. When the reaction is so great that the reagent drop becomes a crystal mass almost immediately, repeat the test with a more dilute sample so that the crystals of the product will be better formed. Take care to place the reagent drop as near to the center of the mouth of the beaker as possible and at least 3 mm above the solution being tested. Warm the beaker gently on a water bath or a small electric hot plate. As soon as a crystalline precipitate can be recognized with the naked eye in the suspended drop, or when numerous small drops of water from on the slide, remove the latter and cover the drop with a cover glass (approximately 18 mm × 18 mm) and place to one side to cool. In some cases, particularly with weak reactions, the crystals form only on cooling. Usually 10 minutes suffice for this although a longer period may be necessary.

Remove the excess reagent by washing with distilled water as follows. Place a strip of filter paper, 2 cm wide and 20 cm long, at one edge of the cover glass and add drops of distilled water at the opposite edge. Continue the dropwise addition of water until the filter paper strip is moistened to a length of 15 to 18 cm. Then, with a fresh piece of filter paper, remove the rest of the liquid under the cover glass by touching filter paper to the space between the cover glass and slide. Remove the cover glass. Part of the crystals will be on the slide and part on the cover glass. They will still be moist. Place the cover glass, crystal side up, on a second slide and warm both slides gently on a hot plate or remove the remainder of the wash liquid by blowing gently with a stream of air. Examine under the microscope to determine whether all of the liquid has been removed. In the case of oily test substances, it is advisable to wash with petrolic ether to remove the remainder of the oily substance, the precipitate being insoluble in the ether. Wash as with water for one half minute. The usual drying in a desiccator or in vacuum is entirely unnecessary.

Before the melting point determination, cover the crystals on the first slide with a cover glass and invert the cover glass over the second slide so that the crystals are protected.

Determine the extinction under a polarizing microscope and then proceed to the determination of the melting point. Since two preparations with crystals are available, it is possible to determine the melting point twice in each case. Determine the approximate melting point with one sample. In the second sample, carry out the melting point determination in the usual way, that is, heat rapidly to within 10° to 15° of the melting point and then slowly.

Notes.

1) Both aldehydes and ketones react with phenylhydrazine as follows:

$$>C=O + H_2N \cdot NHC_6H_5 \quad \rightarrow \quad >C=N \cdot NHC_6H_5 + H_2O$$

2) The BEHRENS (9) method for the preparation of the phenylhydrazones of aldehydes, consisting in placing a drop of the aldehyde solution on a slide and then adding a small drop of the reagent solution, has been shown by GRIEBEL (61) to be uncertain since small amounts of aldehydes in solutions which contain other carbon compounds cannot be detected. The method described above, that of GRIEBEL and WEISS (62) as modified by FISCHER (47) and FISCHER and MOOR (48), has proved very satisfactory for mixtures as well as for pure aldehydes and ketones.

3) The reagents are as follows:

p-Nitrophenylhydrazine (m.pt. 161°), saturated solution in 15% (2.5 molar) acetic acid.

p-Nitrobenzhydrazide (m.pt. 210°), saturated solution in 30% acetic acid.

o-Nitrobenzhydrazide (m.pt. 123°), saturated solution in 30% (5 m), acetic acid.

Semicarbazide (m.pt. 163°), 10% solution in water with 10% sodium acetate or more concentrated solutions. (A reagent consisting of 2 g semicarbazide and 2 g sodium acetate in 6 g of water also gives satisfactory results.)

Semioxamazide, saturated solution in water or in 30% (5 m) acetic acid.

Other phenylhydrazides and benzhydrazides are used in the concentrations given above.

In all cases the reagents should be stored in small glass-stoppered tubes and kept not longer than three or four days. Do not use corks. Solutions older than four days will give products with unsharp melting points.

4) The test substance may be pure or an aqueous solution; wines, oily liquids, etc. may be used directly.

5) The crystalline forms are not sufficiently characteristic or constant to be usable.

6) A number of substances will sublime just before, or 15° to 20° below, the melting point onto the cover glass. Thus new crystals and drops of condensate form, which should not be confused with drops of the melt. In observing the melting point, only the isolated crystals and not those lying in clusters should be observed. The latter may melt at lower temperatures because of possible occlusion of some reagent. In the case of the semioxamazones, which melt between 200° and 300°, place the preparation on a hot stage heated to 200° and heat rapidly, the rate at the melting point being 4° to 6° per minute. Several o- and m-derivatives melt on decomposition. In such cases the melting points depend upon the rate of temperature rise. Raise he temperature as rapidly as possible to about 10° below the expected melting point, then raise it 4° to 6° per minute; at the moment of the melting point it should not be rising more than 2° per minute. In this way reproducible results can be obtained.

7) The sensitivity of the test is several tenths of a microgram. The semicarbazides are less sensitive reagents than the nitrophenyl or nitrobenzhydrazines but they give sharp melting points. When only small amounts of product are obtained, carry out the washing under a lens or microscope to prevent loss of material.

8) Readily volatile substances are treated at room temperature in a microbeaker with a capacity of 0.5 to 1 ml. In some cases, with ethereal oils for instance, it is not necessary to remove the sample from the bottle; merely place the cover glass with the reagent drop downward over the mouth of the bottle containing the test substance. If heating is necessary with such oils, some of the oil appears on the cover glass in addition to the crystalline products. Remove it with petrolic ether.

9) Polymorphism may become evident. By the microprocedure only the lowest melting form is obtained, whereas the macroprocedure usually produces the higher melting form.

10) For the crystallographic and optical properties of these derivatives see BEHRENS-KLEY (12), EMICH (43), and the original papers of GRIEBEL and WEISS, FISCHER, and FISCHER and MOOR.

2,4-Dinitrophenylhydrazones.

To approximately 40 µl of the reagent in a microcone add an equal volume of 95% alcohol and 3 to 4 mg of the aldehyde. Heat in a boiling water bath for one minute. Add a drop of 12 molar hydrochloric acid from a capillary pipet, and then resume heating for two minutes. Add water until a turbidity appears and then allow the solution to cool. Recrystallize the product from alcohol.

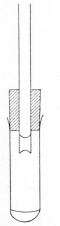

Fig. 154. Preparation of Derivatives for Volatile Aldehydes, nat. size.

Notes.

1) The reagent is prepared by refluxing 1 g of solid 2,4-dinitrophenyl hydrazine with 100 ml alcohol. The change in the color of the solution to yellow or orange when the acid is added indicates that the latter aids in the elimination of water from the intermediate addition product of the reagent and the carbonyl compound (3).

2) A second procedure similar to that of FISCHER and MOOR (*see* above) can be used for volatile aldehydes. Place the aldehyde in a microbeaker and the reagent in the end of a tube inserted in a stopper in the microbeaker, Fig. 154. The tube should have a bore of about 3 mm. This method of holding the reagent prevents it from spreading out in a thin film, as it would if a watch glass were used. The reaction proceeds more slowly in this method than in the one given above.

4) Here again polymorphic forms may be obtained and cis-trans isomerism has been observed (20, 122). These properties may account for variations in reported melting points.

5) For a description of the crystallographic and optical properties of the 2,4-dinitrophenylhydrazones see BRYANT (22) and MATTHIESSEN and HAGEDORN (99).

Methyl Nicotinium *p*-Toluenesulfonate Hydrazones.

Modification of method of ALLEN and GATES (4). Dissolve 3 to 4 mg of the reagent and an excess of the carbonyl compound in 15 µl absolute alcohol in a reflux tube. Seal the tube and heat in the water bath for 15 minutes. Cool, cut open the tube with the usual precautions, and transfer the contents to a centrifuge tube. Centrifuge and decant. Transfer the crystals to a microscope cover glass for determination of the melting point. Remove the remaining liquid with a fine-tipped capillary pipet or by means of a piece of filter paper. Determine the melting point. Recrystallize from absolute alcohol or from alcohol-ether (1:1 mixture) to constant melting point.

Note.

The reagent is prepared by mixing 15 g ethyl nicotinate, 18.6 g methyl-*p*-toluenesulfonate and 50 ml absolute alcohol and refluxing for four hours. After cooling, add 6 g of 85% hydrazine hydrate in 10 ml absolute alcohol. Reflux again for 15 minutes. On cooling and initiating crystallization, the product will separate slowly and is filtered off. It is sufficiently pure for preparation of derivatives.

For identification of aldehydes by formation of characteristic crystalline forms other than those given by BEHRENS-KLEY, the reader is referred to ROSENTHALER (128) for a description of the crystalline precipitates obtained by the reaction with barbituric acid and to FOSSE, DE GRAEVE, and THOMAS (51) and KOFLER and HILBCK (83) for the tests for formaldehyde.

Degradative Procedures.

Aldehydes themselves can be reduced to the corresponding alcohol, but a better procedure is the conversion to the acid by oxidation.

Carry out the oxidation by adding drops of a 5% aqueous solution of potassium permanganate to a suspension of 1 part aldehyde in 20 parts of a 5% sodium hydroxide solution. Stir thoroughly until no more manganese dioxide is formed and a pale pink color of permanganate persists. Destroy the excess permanganate with a drop of alcohol. Then warm the solution on the water bath to 60° or 70° to coagulate the manganese dioxide and then centrifuge. Evaporate the decantate to about one-fourth of its volume and acidify with dilute hydrochloric acid to precipitate the organic acid. This may be identified as described under Acids.

Chemical Separation of Aldehydes.

By Oximes and Semicarbazones. The reaction of aldehydes with hydroxylamine is from 92 to 100% complete. The carbonyl compound is regenerated by hydrolysis of the oxime, etc., with hydrochloric acid. To 5 to 6 mg of the test substance in a reflux tube add 90 µl of 12 molar hydrochloric acid. Seal the tube and heat in a boiling water bath for 30 minutes (in some cases 15 minutes will suffice). Cool the tube, open the tip with the usual precautions, and add 2 volumes of water. Centrifuge and decant the clear liquid. Steam distil this liquid and extract the distillate with ether three or four times. Dry with anhydrous sodium sulfate and distil off the ether. The residue will consist of the aldehydes. In the case of very volatile aldehydes such as the low-molecular weight members of the aliphatic series, further reactions must be carried out on the ether extract without removal of the solvent.

By Bisulfite Addition Products. The reaction of aldehydes with sodium bisulfite can be reversed (46, 89, 150) and the carbonyl compound recovered. Because of the high reactivity of the aldehydes, the bisulfite addition compounds are best decomposed with saturated sodium bicarbonate solution. The aldehyde is separated from the resultant mixture either by decantation in the case of the water-insoluble compounds or by ether extraction in the case of the low-molecular weight members as above.

By Methyl Nicotinium *p*-Toluenesulfonate Hydrazones. These hydrazones, like the oximes, lend themselves very readily to hydrolysis with hydrochloric acid. Yields of over 85% of the aldehyde can be recovered. Sulfuric acid can be used in place of hydrochloric acid.

By α-Methyl-*p*-Tolyl Hydrazones (148). This reaction serves to separate aromatic aldehydes from aliphatic and aromatic ketones.

For every 0.005 mole of the aldehyde dissolved in 5 ml ethyl alcohol add 1g α-methyl-p-tolyl hydrazine dissolved in 15 ml ethyl alcohol at 20°. Allow to stand for 24 hours and then filter off the hydrazone. Wash the latter with water and recrystallize. For the recovery of the aldehyde heat the hydrazone with concentrated HCl for 30 minutes at boiling temperature, using 10 ml alcohol and 10 ml 12 molar HCl for every 0.002 mole of the hydrazone. Then cool to room temperature, add 30 ml water and steam distil the aldehyde. Extract the distillate with ether three times. Dry the extract and distil off the ether. About 75% of the aldehyde can be recovered in this way.

STROH suggests that it might be possible to differentiate between meta and ortho and para substituted aldehydes by this method.

Quantitative Determination of Aldehydes.

Most of the methods for the determination of the carbonyl group are limited in their application to certain compounds. They include gravimetric, volumetric, and gasometric procedures.

Titrimetric Procedure. The method of SCHÖNIGER, LIEB, and GASSNER (138) depends upon the conversion of the carbonyl compound into the corresponding substituted phenylhydrazone. The excess of the reagent is then reduced to the diamino compound and the excess of the reducing agent, titanium trichloride, is titrated with ferric ammonium sulfate.

Reagents. Phenylhydrazines. The reagents are 4-nitrophenylhydrazine (m. pt. 156°), 2,4-dinitrophenylhydrazine (m. pt. 198°), or 2,4,6-trinitrophenylhydrazine (m. pt. 182°). The quantity of the solid phenylhydrazine (from 0.15 to 0.25 g, depending upon which compound is used) to form an approximately 0.01 molar solution is dissolved in 100 ml of 2 molar HCl.

Preparation of more than this quantity is not recommended since the solutions are stable for only about a week.

Titanium trichloride. Boil 500 ml of 10% HCl (3 m) to remove dissolved hydrogen. Then add about 280 ml of 20% titanium trichloride solution and dilute with boiled distilled water to 1000 ml. The final solution should be kept under an atmosphere of nitrogen.

Ferric ammonium sulfate. This should be a 0.05 normal solution and should be standardized in the usual way iodometrically.

Ammonium thiocyanate. A 10% solution is used as an indicator.

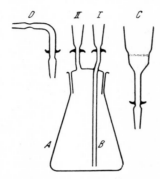

Fig. 155. Schöniger, Lieb, and Gassner Apparatus for Aldehyde Determination.

Hydrochloric-hydrofluoric acid. To 150 ml 12 m HCl add 10 ml 40% H_2F_2 and keep the resulting solution in a plastic bottle.

Hydrochloric acid, 2 m. Use as wash liquid.

Solvents. Use solvents which are miscible with water such as methyl alcohol, ethyl alcohol, dioxane, tetrahydrofurane, or pyridine.

Apparatus.

The apparatus, Fig. 155, is made of Jena Geräte glass or Pyrex. The titration flask A has a capacity of 100 ml and is fitted with a ground stopper which in turn is fitted with two standard taper joints I and II. On one of these is fused a capillary tube so that it extends to within 3 or 4 mm of the bottom of the flask. The fritted glass crucible O (G 4 porosity) is fitted with a similar standard taper joint. The angle tube D serves to connect the apparatus with a water suction pump or as an inlet for nitrogen during the titration. If the preferred magnetic stirrer cannot be used, the capillary B can be bent somewhat so that the introduction of the nitrogen serves to stir the solution.

Procedure.

Weigh out 2 to 5 mg of solid test substance in a weighing tube and place tube and substance into a 25- to 50-ml Erlenmeyer flask. Add 2 ml of a suitable water-miscible solvent and warm, if necessary, to achieve complete

solution. Weigh out fluid test substances in a capillary according to the
PREGL procedure (118) and then crush the capillary in the flask after adding
the solvent. Rinse off the glass rod used for the crushing with the minimum
quantity of $2\,m$ HCl. Add 5 ml of the phenylhydrazine reagent, using a
calibrated pipet. Allow the mixture to stand for 12 hours or, better, over-
night, at low temperature. When working with substances of completely
unknown composition, it is advisable to allow several samples to react
with the phenylhydrazine solution for varying lengths of time.

After the quantitative conversion to the hydrazone, draw off the excess
nitrophenylhydrazine solution by the use of the flask described above.
First clean the flask with chromic-sulfuric acid solution, wash with distilled
water and dry. Lubricate the stopper joint with a very thin layer of grease.
Place the filter crucible C in the joint I and the angle tube D in joint II.
Connect the angle tube to the water suction pump. Then pour the reaction
mixture into the filter crucible. Rinse the reaction flask and the crucible
with the minimum (3 to 5 ml) of $2\,m$ HCl.

Replace the glass filter crucible with the angle tube and connect this
with a cylinder of nitrogen. Close the reducing valve of this cylinder until
the bubbles rising in the flask are just still countable. Then add 2 ml of the
hydrochloric-hydrofluoric acid mixture and, after the nitrogen has passed
through the solution for five minutes, 1 ml of the titanium trichloride reagent from a calibrated pipet. While the nitrogen is still passing continually
through the reaction mixture, boil the latter for ten minutes to bring
about complete reduction of the excess nitrophenylhydrazine. Then cool
in running water and add 2 ml of the ammonium thiocyanate indicator
solution for the final titration.

If a magnetic stirrer is used, introduce the stirrer bar and titrate the
non-oxidized titanium trichloride (with continuous introduction of nitrogen)
with the ferric ammonium sulfate to the first permanent rose color. For
convenience place the tip of the microburet in joint II. This must be wide
enough to still permit the escape of the nitrogen.

Carry out a blank in the same manner and with the same quantities of
reagents for every series of determinations.

% carbonyl $= 100\ FN\ (A{-}B)\,/\,$mg of sample

$A =$ ml of ferric ammonium sulfate used in titation

$B =$ ml of ferric ammonium sulfate in blank

For 4-nitrophenylhydrazine $F = 4.669$; log F $= 66926$

For 2,4-dinitrophenylhydrazine $F = 2.335$; log F $= 36823$

For 2,4,6-trinitrophenylhydrazine $F = 1.556$; log F $= 19214$

$N =$ normality of ferric ammonium sulfate.

Gravimetric Procedure. MA, LOGAN, and MAZELLA (97) recommend
gravimetric determination of the carbonyl group as the 2,4-dinitrophenyl-
hydrazine when only occasional determinations are required.

Reagent.

Weigh out 1 g pure oxalic acid and 0.2 g pure 2,4-dinitrophenylhydrazine into a 100-ml volumetric flask. Fill to the mark with methyl alcohol and shake the mixture vigorously. On standing, the insoluble solids will settle out. Use the clear supernatant liquid. It is not necessary to filter the solution but it is not advisable to prepare a larger volume of stock solution since it will deteriorate on exposure to air.

Apparatus.

Use a test tube, 23-mm inner diameter and 100 mm long, with a capacity of about 35 ml as the reaction tube. Prepare a filterstick from tubing, 4-mm outer diameter, 2-mm bore, by making a capillary constriction about 10 mm from one end. Fill this end with asbestos fibers or, better, with a tiny roll of filter paper with the end of this protruding 1 mm from the end of the filterstick. Place reaction tube and filterstick in a 50-ml beaker. Always weigh the three pieces together.

Weighing the Sample. Place the clean and dry reaction tube, filterstick, and beaker on the left-hand pan of the balance. Use a second beaker and test tube as counterpoise and add lead shot to the counterpoise until the two loads are balanced with the rider of the balance resting between 0 and 5 mg on the beam. Introduce solid samples directly into the reaction tube. Place semisolids and oils in a microboat which has been preweighed with the beaker and drop the boat into the reaction tube after the weighing. Weigh out low boiling liquids in a micro weighing bottle with a ground-in stopper. The handle of the stopper should be provided with a loop through which a wire hook can be inserted to disengage the stopper from the weighing bottle after the latter has been dropped into the reaction tube and immersed in the solvent. The sample should weigh between 5 and 15 mg (corresponding to between 0.05 and 0.15 millimole of the carbonyl compound) and should be weighed accurately to $\pm$ 0.01 mg.

Precipitation, Filtration and Drying. Remove the beaker containing the sample, filterstick, and reaction tube from the balance and introduce 4 ml of methyl alcohol to dissolve the sample. Add a 20-ml aliquot of the 2,4-dinitrophenylhydrazine reagent by means of a pipet. Mix the solutions thoroughly. Fifteen minutes after the appearance of the precipitate, remove the reaction tube from the beaker and place it in an ice water bath for an hour or until the precipitate settles on the bottom. Wipe the outside of the reaction tube and return it to the beaker. By means of the rubber tubing connect the filterstick to a siphon which leads to the filtrate receiver. The receiver consists of a test tube of 35-ml capacity fitted with a 2-hole rubber stopper with one hole carrying a glass tube joined to the suction line. Place the filterstick inside the reaction tube so that the filter mat is just above the precipitate. Draw the supernatant liquid off and wash the precipitate with small amounts of methyl alcohol until free of the reagent. When the liquid passing through the siphon becomes colorless the washing is completed. Then dry the precipitate, filterstick, reaction tube, and beaker at 75° and weigh to ± 0.01 mg.

Procedure for Volatile Aldehydes. This procedure is a modification of the one described by HUNTER and POTTER (69) for the determination

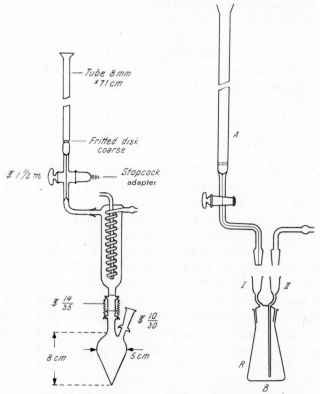

Fig. 156. Apparatus for Determination of Volatile Aldehydes.

of amino acids by oxidation to the aldehydes and recovery and determination of the latter. It is therefore primarily intended for volatile aldehydes.

Reagents.

Sodium bisulfite, reagent grade: 1% solution freshly prepared.

Iodine, standard solution: 0.1 n and 0.02 n solutions in water, standardized.

Soluble starch indicator: 0.5% solution protected from deterioration with elemental mercury.

Sodium thiosulfate, standard solution: 0.02 n freshly prepared from 0.1 n reagent by dilution.

Sodium carbonate: 1 molar solution.

Sulfuric acid: 0.5 molar.

Apparatus.

The apparatus used by HUNTER and POTTER is shown in Fig. 156 *A*. However, since this was designed to permit prior oxidation of amino acids it can be simplified as shown in Fig. 156 *B*. In this way the absorption tube can be combined with the titration vessel. This is a combination of the apparatus of SCHÖNIGER, LIEB, and GASSNER and that of HUNTER and POTTER.

Procedure.

Fit the absorption tube *A* of the apparatus into joint *I* (Fig. 156 *B*) and the angle tube into joint *II*. Connect the angle tube to a cylinder of compressed nitrogen. Introduce 25 ml of the sodium bisulfite solution into the absorption tube, while allowing a stream of nitrogen to flow through the apparatus. Place the reaction flask *R* in a heating bath and heat to a temperature of 100 to 105°. The nitrogen should pass through the apparatus at a rate of about 80 to 90 ml per minute to transfer the volatile aldehydes into the sodium bisulfite. About 45 minutes of heating should suffice. At the end of the heating period, disconnect the absorption tube and quantitatively transfer the contents to a 50-ml volumetric flask. Add water to make the volume up to the mark.

Pipet 10 ml of the bisulfite solution into a 125-ml flask, add a few drops of starch indicator solution, and titrate with 0.1 *n* iodine solution until just short of the end point. Bring to the exact end point by addition of 0.02 *n* iodine from a 10-ml buret. Add 10 ml of 0.02 *n* iodine and then 5 ml of Na_2CO_3. Place the solution in the dark for from 20 to 30 minutes. Add 10 ml of 0.5 *m* H_2SO_4, stopper the flask lightly and allow it to stand for ten minutes in the dark. Treat a blank sample of bisulfite in the same manner as the sample. Run all procedures in duplicate. At the end of ten minutes titrate the unreacted iodine with 0.02 *n* sodium thiosulfate.

Millimoles of aldehyde $= 1.25 \, N \, (V - V')$

$N =$ Normality of thiosulfate

$V =$ Volume of thiosulfate used to titrate blank

$V' =$ Volume of thiosulfate used to titrate unreacted iodine in unknown.

Indirect Determination. A procedure which can be employed if the micro DUMAS apparatus of PREGL is available is the indirect method. This consists of carrying out a preliminary test to determine which phenylhydrazone is best and most completely formed and then converting the aldehyde to this hydrazone. The latter is purified and a determination of total nitrogen is carried out according to the PREGL procedure. If the substance itself contains nitrogen, obviously a determination of the nitrogen content must be carried out also on the original test substance. The carbonyl content of the test substance can then be calculated from the results of these determinations.

Carbohydrates.

Generic Test.

The generic test for carbohydrates consists of two parts. The first part is the MOLISCH test; three supplementary tests constitute the second part. The MOLISCH test is applied first. If the result is positive, the supplementary tests are carried out. The latter are necessary to exclude compounds of other genera which also give positive MOLISCH reactions.

Dip one end of a capillary (1-mm bore, 100-mm length) into a 1% solution or suspension of the test substance until a droplet about 0.5 mm long has risen into the capillary, Fig. 157. If too much is taken, remove

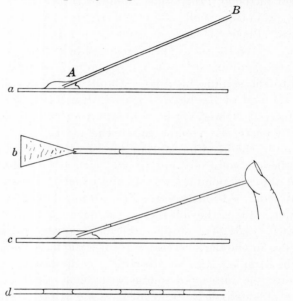

Fig. 157. Performance of MOLISCH Test for Carbohydrates.

the excess by inserting the point of a triangular piece of filter paper into, or touching a piece of porous tile to this end of the capillary. Then incline the capillary toward the other end and allow the droplet to flow a short distance toward the middle of the tube. Place the finger over the end of the tube which has not been used as yet and dip the filling end into the MOLISCH reagent solution (a drop on the slide will do). When the pressure of the finger is released, the reagent (1 to 2 mm) will rise into the tube. Allow both drops to slide to the middle of the capillary. Now close the filling end with the finger and dip the other end into concentrated sulfuric acid to a depth of 1 cm. Remove the finger from the tube end and allow the acid to fill 1 cm of the tube. Then close the end again with the finger. Allow all drops to slide to the middle of the capillary. Wipe off the end through which the sulfuric acid had been filled and seal in the flame. Centrifuge all droplets to this end. This brings the sulfuric acid on the bottom, with the reagent next, and then the test solution. Thus the reagent and the test solution are mixed but the proper contact between acid layer and reagent-substance layer is secured. In the presence of carbohydrates a red ring forms at the acid-reagent interface. Then mix the solution with a glass thread, whereupon a violet color appears throughout the liquid when the test is positive. On diluting a violet precipitate may form. Cut off the sealed end and blow the liquid out into the depression of a spot plate. Add escess ammonia. A yellow-red color results in positive tests.

If the results of the above test are negative, omit the supplementary tests described below and proceed directly to the test for acids (page 182).

Notes.

1) The reagent is a 10% solution of α-naphthol in chloroform. The original MOLISCH test (100) used an alcoholic solution of α-naphthol. Roos (130) recommended the use of chloroform in place of the alcohol to avoid interferences from impurities in the latter.

2) The composition of the colored compound formed has not been definitely determined. MOLISCH explained the reaction on the basis of the formation of furfural by the action of the acid on the carbohydrate and the condensation of the furfural with the α-naphthol. Later work has shown that some carbohydrates which react positively do not form furfural under the conditions of the test.

3) In using filter paper for the removal of excess liquid from the capillary, great care must be taken that no fibers of the paper remain in the tube since the delicacy of the test is so great that such fibers may give a positive result despite the absence of carbohydrates in the test substance.

4) DEVOR (36) claims certain advantages in the use of a sulfonated α-naphthol in this test. First, the reagent is soluble in water; second, the color is more definite and the ring test is not necessary; third, the aqueous solution of sulfonated α-naphthol does not darken in light; and fourth, water-insoluble materials such as cotton dissolve as the sulfuric acid is added. The reagent is prepared by DEVOR as follows. Add 28 to 30 ml concentrated sulfuric acid to a small beaker containing 15 g of purified α-naphthol. Warm the mixture slightly (the reaction is exothermic) and stir continuously until the sulfonated product forms a pasty mass. After allowing it to stand several hours (usually over night) break up all large lumps, add 25 ml of distilled water and stir the hot mixture until solution is obtained. Set the resulting hot solution aside in a cold place (refrigerator) for 16 hours or longer. After crystallization is complete remove as much as possible of the dark liquid by filtering with suction through a coarse fritted glass filter. Mix the nearly white crystals with 1 or 2 ml of cold distilled water while still on the filter and draw off the washings as completely as possible. Do not dry. Dissolve 10 g of these crystals in 100 ml water to use as the reagent. Store the solution but avoid exposure to bright light.

Supplementary Tests.

1) Dissolve a little of the test substance in a drop of water on a slide and test with litmus silk or a narrow triangular strip of litmus paper. If the solution is distinctly acid, the substance is not a carbohydrate.

2) Place a few micrograms of the test substance in the depression of
a spot plate, add (from a capillary pipet) a few drops of water, and then
mix with 1 μl concentrated sulfuric acid. If a color other than a yellow
or brown to black appears, the sample is not a carbohydrate.

3) Add one drop (from a capillary pipet) of a 0.1% FeCl$_3$ solution to
a large drop of a 1% aqueous solution of the carbohydrate, or, if it is very
insoluble, to its cold saturated solution. Unless the solution remains colorless or, at the most, shows a pale yellow or orange-yellow coloration, the
compound is not a carbohydrate.

Sectional Tests.

The carbohydrates are divided into two divisions according to their
solubility in water at 20°. The procedure is the capillary method of solubility determination described on page 152. Mix about 0.5 mg of the test
substance in a capillary with 5 μl of water. If the substance dissolves,
it belongs to Division I. If it does not dissolve or if it gives an opalescent
suspension, it is in Division II.

Division I is further divided according to the speed of osazone formation
(*see* the test below).

Classification Tests for Carbohydrates.

Osazone Precipitation. The conditions under which this reaction
is carried out must be rigidly adhered to, the errors in measurement not
to exceed 1%. Use a capillary of at least 1-mm bore and 120-mm length.
Draw 7 mm of reagent into the middle of the capillary through one end
and then 3 mm of the 25% aqueous solution of the test substance at the
other. Seal the reagent end of the capillary, join the two droplets by
centrifuging and then mix by means of a glass thread. Seal the open end
of the capillary and centrifuge the droplets back to the reagent end. Because of the heating of the carbohydrate end during the sealing, some
charring takes place. The solutions must not come into contact with this
charred residue. Then place the sealed tube in a beaker of boiling water,
noting the exact time of immersion and observing the tube for the formation
of a precipitate. Note the time required for the appearance of a precipitate.
The precipitate may be transferred to a slide for study of its appearance
under the microscope (64, 115). (*See* also references on page 177). The
melting point of the precipitate can also be determined after washing
and recrystallizing from 50% alcohol.

Notes.

1) The reagent is prepared by dissolving 1 g phenylhydrazine hydrochloride
and 1.5 g of sodium acetate in 7 ml water and warming to dissolve. The phenylhydrazine salt should be perfectly white and dry.

2) When taking the melting point of the osazones, raise the temperature of the bath or block quickly, that is, about one degree in two or three seconds.

3) MULLIKEN and HUNTRESS divide Division I of the carbohydrates into three sections according to the speed of the osazone formation as follows:

Section A.   The above test gives a white precipitate in less than one minute:

d-Mannose

Section B.   The above test gives a yellow or orange-yellow precipitate from the hot solution in 20 minutes or less:

d-Glucose	*l*-Xylose
d-Galactose	*d*-Fructose
l-Arabinose	Rhamnose

Section C.   No precipitate is formed in the above test from the hot solution within 20 minutes:

Raffinose	Maltose
α-Methylglucoside	Lactose
"Dextrin"	Sucrose

Fehling's Test.   This test may be carried out in a microcone, in a capillary, or on a slide.   Since the time of precipitate formation is of some importance and since the solution must be boiled, one of the first two should be used, preferably the capillary.   Use a tube with a bore of 0.5 mm. Draw in about 2 mm of the reagent (made by mixing FEHLING's A and FEHLING's B solutions on a slide) and 10 mm of the 1% sugar solution and seal one end of the capillary.   After centrifuging to this end, seal the open end and centrifuge the liquids back and forth several times to mix them thoroughly.   If no precipitate appears, heat the capillary on the water bath for two minutes.   Centrifuge again and observe any precipitate.

Notes.

A precipitate of cuprous oxide is obtained with all carbohydrates in Sections A and B and with maltose and lactose of Section C.   Inulin, raffinose, sucrose, and gum arabic require boiling for about two minutes and then give only a slightly yellowish turbidity.   Glycogen, starch, and cellulose give no precipitate even after boiling for two minutes.   .

Red Tetrazolium Test.   As can be noted, FEHLING's solution will be reduced by simple aldehydes as well as sugars.   A more sensitive test for reducing sugars and one which distinguishes more sharply between α-ketoses and simple aldehydes is the so-called red tetrazolium test.   Add 100 µl of a 0.5% aqueous solution of the reagent to a drop of a solution containing a few hundredths of a milligram of the test substance in a microcone and follow this by one drop of a 10% sodium hydroxide solution. Put the cone into a hot water bath and note the order in which the colors appear.

Notes.

1) The reagent is 2,3,5-triphenyltetrazolium chloride.   A fresh solution should be used each time and the excess acidified and discarded.

2) The reaction results in the reduction of the reagent from a nearly colorless, water-soluble substance to a water-insoluble, intensely colored compound, a diformazon:

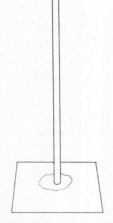

Red tetrazolium   RT-Diformazon

Aniline Acetate Test.   Add 2 to 3 mg of the test substance to 50 µl of 3 m HCl (1 volume of concentrated acid to 3 volumes of water) in a microcone. Boil for exactly one minute. Insert a cylindrical roll of freshly prepared aniline test paper in the upper end of the microcone and continue boiling for no more than one minute. A pink or reddish coloration of the paper is obtained with carbohydrates which give much furfural.

Notes.

1) The paper is prepared by wetting a piece of filter paper with a mixture of 5 ml aniline and 10 ml 50% acetic acid and pressing out the excess liquid with another piece of filter paper. The paper must be used while still moist and must be freshly prepared for each test.

2) The time must be noted exactly. Starch will give a positive test if the heating continues for more than one minute.

Phloroglucinol Test.   Place a few micrograms of the sugar in a capillary by pushing the end of the tube into the solid and then gently rubbing the tube with a file so that the solid falls farther into the tube. Allow 10 mm of the reagent to rise in the tube. Seal both ends and place the tube in a cold water bath. Heat the bath to boiling. During the heating observe any changes in the color of the solution. When the solution becomes dark and turbid, remove the tube from the bath and cut off both ends. Allow the contents to flow out onto a piece of filter paper by holding the capillary vertically on a piece of moist filter paper (*see* Fig. 158). Keep the end of the capillary in one spot. Place a large drop of cold alcohol on this spot to wash the precipitate. Observe the color of the latter.

Fig. 158. Transfer of the Contents of a Capillary to Filter Paper.

Notes.

1) The reagent is prepared by shaking an excess of powdered phloroglucinol with 6 m HCl until the solution is saturated.

2) The color of the precipitate obtained may vary from yellow-orange to a very dark purple. See tables for the characteristic color of each carbohydrate giving the test.

Oxidation to Mucic and Saccharic Acids. To about 5 mg of the carbohydrate in a centrifuge cone add 20 to 30 μl dilute nitric acid. Evaporate the solution on a steam bath until oxidation is complete and the liquid becomes viscous. Use an air jet if necessary. Add 20 μl water. Centrifuge the liquid and decant into a second centrifuge cone. Wash the precipitate thoroughly with hot water, dry, and determine its melting point. Heat the filtrate on a boiling water bath and neutralize with potassium carbonate. Acidify again with acetic acid and concentrate to a syrup. After cooling add more acetic acid. Potassium acid saccharate will precipitate if any saccharic acid has been formed. Filter it off by centrifuging and recrystallize from hot water. The silver salt may be prepared by dissolving the potassium salt in water, neutralizing with ammonia, and adding silver nitrate solution. The silver content may be determined by the use of a spring scale or a SALVIONI balance with platinum foil dishes; (*see* under Acids below).

Note.

The carbohydrates which give mucic or saccharic acid are noted in the tables.

Final identification of the carbohydrate may be accomplished by means of (1) a derivative such as the phenylhydrazone or substituted phenylhydrazone, (2) certain color or precipitation reactions, or (3) by microscopic identification. Directions for the preparation of derivatives may be obtained from, e. g., VAN DER HAAR (154). Unfortunately, the melting points of these derivatives which consist chiefly of the phenylhydrazones, the osazones, and the osotriazoles, lie so close in most cases that the derivative is of little value. Furthermore, many of the sugars give the same osazone. It has been shown in an extensive and intensive study by DEHN, BALLARD and JACKSON (30) that many color and precipitation reactions are not at all characteristic for one carbohydrate. In some instances the tests were characteristic of impurities in the material tested. These authors recommend that identification of the carbohydrate be based upon the results of a number of the tests rather than on one.

The crystalline form and the optical constants of the osazones and other derivatives are described by WAGENAAR (160), MORRIS (102), WEBSTER (161), BENEDICT (15), FISCHER and PAULUS (49), and HASSID and McREADY (63). The tables of VOGEL and GEORG (156) list the physical constants of nearly every known sugar and its derivatives.

Crystallization Test.

Following the work of DENIGES (33) and others, QUENSE and DEHN (120) have developed a method for identifying sugars which may be crystallized; this method appears to have great possibilities. It is based upon the recognition of the crystal habit of the sugar after the latter has been crys-

TABLE 13
Optical Properties of Sugars

Sugar	Crystal System	Elongation	Extinction	Interference Color
l-Arabinose	Orthorhombic bisphenoidal	—	Parallel to slightly inclined	1st and 2nd order
d-Arabinose	Orthorhombic	—	Parallel	2nd order
Cellobiose	Monoclinic sphenoidal	—	Approx. 16°	Low 1st order
Fructose	Orthorhombic bisphenoidal	—	Parallel	Low 1st order
Fucose	Orthorhombic	—	Parallel and approx. 25°	1st and 2nd order
Galactose	Orthorhombic	—	Parallel	Low 1st order
α-*d*-Glucose	Orthorhombic bisphenoidal	—	Parallel	1st and 2nd order
β-Glucose	No data	—	Parallel	2nd and 3rd order
α-*d*-Lactose	Monoclinic sphenoidal	—	Parallel	Low 1st order
β-Lactose	Monoclinic sphenoidal	—	Approx. 10°	1st and 2nd order
Maltose	No data	—	Parallel to slightly inclined	Low 1st order
d-Mannose	Orthorhombic bisphenoidal	±	Parallel to slightly inclined	1st and 2nd order
Melibiose	Monoclinic	+	Parallel	1st and 2nd order
Raffinose	Orthorhombic bisphenoidal	+	Parallel	Low 1st order
l-Rhamnose	Monoclinic sphenoidal	+	Parallel	Low 1st order
l-Sorbose	Orthorhombic bisphenoidal	+	Parallel	Low 1st order
Sucrose	Monoclinic sphenoidal	+	Parallel and approx. 22.5°	2nd and 3rd order
Xylose	Orthorhombic bisphenoidal	+	Approx. 6°	2nd and 3rd order
Gentiobiose	No data	+	Parallel to approx. 7°	Low 1st order
d-Lyxose	Monoclinic	—	Parallel to slightly inclined	1st and 2nd order
Trehalose	Orthorhombic	—	Parallel	1st order gray

tallized out of its solution by the addition of some other substance such as alcohol, acetone, acetonitrile, or 1,4-dioxane. The method is as follows.

A few drops of a saturated aqueous solution of the unknown sugar in a small vial are treated with sufficient acetone, alcohol, acetonitrile, or 1,4-dioxane to cause crystallization. If the precipitating liquids are not added too rapidly, the sugar solutions usually become opalescent before crystallization. When these opalescent liquids are observed under the microscope, the crystals can be studied during growth. Varying speeds of crystallization and the formation of colloidal suspensions may render such observation impossible. If immediate crystallization does not occur, insufficient sugar has been used and another trial may be necessary. Should a syrup precipitate, crystallization can frequently be effected by scratching the slide (*see* DENIGÈS, *loc. cit.*). Comparison of a representative field with either photomicrographs or preparations of known sugars leads to identification of the sugar. Further confirmation can be obtained by a study of the optical properties. Table 13 (120) gives the crystal habit and optical properties of the sugars. Although the authors of the paper include photomicrographs of the crystals obtained with various sugars and have even extended their scheme to mixtures of sugars (120 a), the same objection may be raised to these as to photomicrographs of inorganic crystals, namely, that all the characteristic forms do not appear on one photomicrograph. It is therefore advisable for the analyst to carry out precipitations of as large a number of sugars as possible to familiarize himself with the appearance of the crystal forms. It is also necessary to carry out a number of such crystallizations in order to become so familiar with the crystal forms that it is possible to identify them immediately and even in mixtures.

BAILEY (7) has suggested a scheme for the examination of crystals of sugars for identification; it is based on crystal form and properties. He does not give the values for the optical constants for the various sugars.

Degradative Procedures.

Carbohydrates may be reduced to the alcohols, oxidized to acids, or, in the case of the polysaccharides, hydrolyzed to the monosaccharides.

Hydrolysis. Hydrolysis is most easily carried out. Place 200 µl of an approximately 3% to 5% solution of the test substance in a microcone and add 400 µl 1.5 *m* HCl. Heat on the water bath for 15 minutes. Cool, neutralize by addition of an equal volume of sodium hydroxide of the same normality as the acid.

Oxidation. Oxidation is best carried out in an acid medium. Alkaline oxidation usually results in some isomerization or even decomposition of the carbon chain with valueless fragments. The oxidants used are bromine water, nitric acid, and periodic acid. The degree of oxidation increases in that order. The bromine water oxidation combined with subsequent treatment constitutes the *Ruff* degradation, one of the most useful reactions in the study of carbohydrates. It gives first a glyconic acid, that is, a monocarboxylic acid, from aldoses only. Thus it serves to differentiate between aldoses and ketoses. Nitric acid will oxidize not only the aldehyde group but also the terminal hydroxy group of a carbohydrate. It will therefore produce a dicarboxylic acid. Periodic acid attacks the carbonyl group and the hydroxy group adjacent to it and the products are a carbonate ion and an aldose of one less carbon. The reactions are carried out as follows.

Oxidation with Bromine Water: To a solution of 10 mg of the sugar in 100 µl water at room temperature add bromine water drop by drop until the color persists. Allow to stand for five minutes and then add several more drops of the bromine water again until the color persists. Place on the water bath and heat to drive off excess bromine. Neutralize the hot solution with calcium carbonate, adding an excess. Heat again on the boiling water bath. Cool the solution, add three drops of a 10% ferric ammonium sulfate solution and then 2 to 4 ml of 3% hydrogen peroxide. Heat the solution to destroy excess hydrogen peroxide, centrifuge, and decant to remove calcium carbonate. The supernatant liquid will contain the carbohydrate product.

Oxidation with Nitric Acid: The procedure for this reaction is described above under Classification Tests. Dilute nitric acid is preferred over the concentrated since the formation of oxalic acid is thereby minimized. The yield of, for example, mucic acid varies considerably, from 38% from lactose to 75 to 79% from galactose.

Oxidation with Periodic Acid: The oxidizing agent is a solution of 0.5 g periodic acid in 20 ml of water to which is added 80 ml of glacial acetic acid. The solution should be kept in a dark, well-stoppered bottle. To about 10 mg of the test substance add 10 ml of the oxidizing reagent in a small glass-stoppered flask such as a 25-ml volumetric flask. Stopper and allow to stand for one-half hour at room temperature. Transfer the solution to a beaker and boil to expel carbon dioxide. The aldose product will be found in the solution. The reaction is quantitative.

Reduction to Alcohol. The reduction is effected with sodium amalgam. Dissolve the carbohydrate in 10 times as much water in a microcone and add small portions of sodium amalgam until about 1.5 times the theoretical amount has been added. Centrifuge and decant after all reaction has ceased. The aqueous layer contains the alcohol which can be identified or determined by, e. g., the acylation procedure given below.

Chemical Separation of Carbohydrates.

The procedure for rate of osazone formation given under the classification tests for carbohydrates (page 174) can be used to separate some of this group of compounds. Filtration of any precipitate should, of course, be carried out with the hot solution and at the time intervals specified.

Some carbohydrates will form metallic salts. For example, sucrose will form a sparingly soluble calcium or strontium compound from which the sugar can be released by treatment of the suspension with carbon dioxide.

In other cases the carbohydrate can be converted into another type of compound by specific action of bacteria or enzymes. Lactose, for example, can be converted to lactic acid by *Bacillus lacticus*.

Quantitative Analysis of Carbohydrates.

The reducing power of certain sugars can be determined by the use of alkaline oxidizing agents such as FEHLING's reagent, but the methods are all empirical and give little or no information on the identity of the carbohydrate. The details can be found in texts on physiological analysis.

The carbonyl content of the test substance can be determined by precipitation of the hydrazone or osazone and determination of the nitrogen content of the latter as described under Aldehydes.

Hydroxyl by Acylation. A most useful value is that of the hydroxyl content. This is determined by acylation to form either the acetyl or benzoyl esters. The method of PETERSEN, HEDBERG and CHRISTENSEN (112) for the determination of hydroxyl content has been modified by CHRISTENSEN and CLARKE (27) for the inclusion of sugars and glycosides.

The reaction tube is a melting point tube, 3 mm in diameter and 60 mm in length, made from a soft-glass test tube. Introduce 2 to 4 mg of the test substance into the weighed reaction tube by means of a medicine dropper with a fine, drawn-out capillary tip. In the case of solids use the filling method employed in the RAST molecular weight determination (page 136). Centrifuge the tube and weigh again. Using the same technique, add approximately 20 to 25 mg (4 to 5 drops) of pure acetic anhydride from a second, similar medicine dropper, centrifuge and weigh again. In order to ensure the quantitative conversion of the sugar to the ester, a ratio of a least 2 moles of anhydride per equivalent of hydroxyl should be maintained. Add 8 to 12 drops of pure pyridine and centrifuge again. Insert a small glass rod in the tube, seal, and then shake well to ensure complete mixing, if necessary by centrifuging back and forth several times. Set aside for 24 hours. At the same time run a blank to determine the volume of standard base required to neutralize the acid derived from 1 mg of acetic anhydride. Place the reaction tube in a 50-ml Erlenmeyer flask, add 5 ml of water, and then break the tube by means of a heavy stirring rod. Titrate the released acid with 0.04 m NaOH. The percent hydroxyl can then be calculated as follows:

% OH = 1700 (mval anhydride used — mval acid found)/mg sample

where: mval acid found = ml NaOH × normality NaOH

mval anhydride = mg anhydride × ratio × normality

ratio = ml of base required to neutralize acid derived from 1 mg anhydride.

Notes.

1) Pure redistilled acetic anhydride must be used to obtain best results. Erratic results will be obtained if acetic acid is present in the anhydride.

2) Avoid too great an excess of the anhydride but do not use less than 100% excess.

Acids.

Generic Test.

The test for acids consists of two parts. The first is the titration in water, the second the titration in alcohol. The first part is carried out with every test substance, regardless of its solubility or whether it is a liquid or a solid. The second part is applied only to those solid compounds which are insoluble in water and which do not titrate as acids in the first part.

Titration in Water.   Weigh out about 5 mg of test substance either on a SALVIONI or a good analytical balance (14). If a liquid of which the

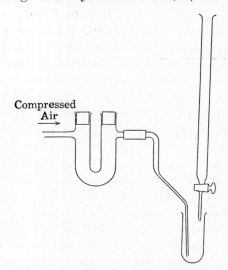

Fig. 159. Titration of Acids.

specific gravity is known, a definite volume can be taken in a capillary as an alternative. Dissolve the sample in 2 ml water in a 7- to 10-ml micro-beaker. Add one drop of phenolphthalein indicator solution. Dip a fine capillary, connected through a soda-lime tube to a source of compressed air, into the solution (Fig. 159). Care must be taken not to have the air bubble through too rapidly as spattering might otherwise occur. Place the capillary to one side so that the rising stream of bubbles produces thorough mixing. The carbon dioxide-free air forms a cover over the liquid surface and prevents the absorption of carbon dioxide from the atmosphere. Dip the tip of a 10-ml (divided into 0,05 ml) buret into the beaker (but not into the solution) opposite the air inlet capillary. Add the 0.02 n NaOH dropwise at such a rate that the color due to one drop is dissipated before the next drop is added. The end point is reached when the color persists for more than one minute.

Titration in Alcohol. If less than 0.5 ml of alkali was required in the titration in water and if the solid did not go into solution, repeat the titration, using 2 ml of alcohol in place of the water, and two or three drops of phenolphthalein. Ignore any precipitate. Use previously neutralized alcohol or run a blank on the alcohol.

If more than 0.5 ml of the 0.02 n NaOH is used in either titration and the end point is sharp (that is, if one drop of alkali causes a permanent change of color) and the color changes suddenly from colorless to red, the substance is classified as an acid in the tables.

Notes.

1) If the sample is a solid, it should be ground to a fine powder.

2) The indicator is made up by dissolving one part by weight of phenolphthalein in 300 parts of 50% alcohol.

Divisional Test.

This genus comprises two divisions: acids solid at ordinary temperatures and acids liquid at ordinary temperatures. Allocation is made by inspection.

Sectional Tests.

Each of the divisions is divided into two sections. Section A consists of all acid species soluble in 50 parts by weight of water at 20°; Section B includes the species insoluble in 50 parts of water at 20°. The determination of solubility is carried out by the capillary tube method described on page 152. MULLIKEN and HUNTRESS list the various degree of solubility as follows:

Volume of water for complete solution	Designation
5 parts	Very soluble (V. sol.)
5 to 20 parts	Easily soluble (Eas. sol.)
20 to 50 parts	Soluble
50 to 150 parts	Difficultly soluble (Dif. sol.)
150 to 250 parts	Very difficultly soluble (V. dif. sol.)
More than 250 parts	Insoluble (Insol.)

The designations are, of course, only approximate.

Classification Tests.

Neutralization Equivalent. The neutralization equivalent is determined by carring out the titration as described above but the sample, however, is weighed out carefully and the alkali must be carefully standardized. Calculate the neutralization equivalent by the equation:

Neutralization equivalent =

$$\frac{1000 \times \text{grams of sample}}{\text{ml of alkali neutralized} \times \text{normality of alkali}}$$

Notes.

1) The alkali should be prepared and standardized as described in texts on quantitative microanalysis. The presence of much carbonate in the alkali should be avoided.

2) The end point may not be sharp when titrating weak monobasic acids such as the higher fatty carboxylic acids. It may be improved by using the salts and titrating them in a mixture of cosolvents instead of in water. PALIT (111) uses a 1:1 mixture of ethylene or propylene glycol and isopropyl alcohol, although that author states that the ratio may vary over a wide range. He titrates the salt with hydrochloric or, preferably, perchloric acid. From 100 to 200 times as much solvent is used as salt and a Beckman glass electrode is used with a Beckman pH meter.

A method for the determination of the neutralization equivalents of organic acids by electrolysis of their salts is described by DITTMER and GUSTAVSON (38). The basic ions are electrodialyzed through a sintered glass membrane above which stands negatively charged mercury. The base amalgam reacts with an excess of standard acid which is placed above the mercury. The amount of base present in the sample is determined by the titration of the excess standard acid with standard base. A microbalance and a fairly good microburet are required. The authors state that five checks and a blank can be carried out in less than one and a half hours.

Test for α-Hydroxy Acids. Place a very small droplet (1 mm) of 10% aqueous solution of crystallized ferric chloride in the depression of a spot plate. Place a similar drop in an adjacent depression. Add a large drop of 0.1% cold aqueous solution of the test substance (acid) to the first reagent drop and stir the two together with a glass thread. To the other reagent drop add a large drop of 0.1% tartaric acid. Compare the two test drops.

Note.

α-Hydroxy acids will produce a yellow color like that of the standard tartaric acid but perhaps more intense. If the color of the solution is paler than that of the tartaric acid or if it has a reddish or orange color, the unknown may or may not be an α-hydroxy acid. The comparison may also be made in coloroscopic capillaries, liquid columns of the same length being used.

Acids Losing Carbon Dioxide at 200°. Prepare a capillary as shown in Fig. 160, about 70 mm long and with a slight taper like that of a melting point tube. Introduce 1 mg of the sample and bring it to the sealed end by tapping the capillary or rubbing it with a file. Push a plug of cotton about half way down the tube. This serves to remove any substance adhering to the walls of the open end of the tube. Draw out the latter end into a finer capillary, Fig. 160C. Heat the portion of the tube just above the fine capillary at the point indicated by the arrow. Quickly insert the fine tip into a clear saturated solution of barium hydroxide.

Allow 5 to 10 mm of this solution to be drawn into the tube by the contraction of the heated air. Then seal the end of the fine capillary, holding
the tube inclined in the flame so that the gases from the flame do not come
into contact with the solution. Place the end of the capillary containing
the acid into a heating block (see page 69) and heat the sample cautiously.
If the sample melts, do not allow it to "boil" (too rapid evolution of carbon
dioxide). Observe the barium hydroxide solution continuously during the
heating. A precipitate may form and then redissolve as the bicarbonate
and thus escape notice.

Acids having two or more carboxyl groups attached to the same carbon
atom decompose into carbon dioxide and an acid of fewer carbon atoms
when heated above the melting point which is below 200° in all cases.

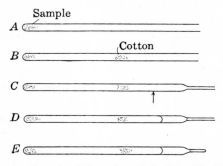

Fig. 160. Test for Liberation of Carbon Dioxide.

Baeyer's Test for Unsaturated Acids. Dissolve a few micrograms
of the test substance in a drop of 1,5 m Na_2CO_3 solution in a depression
of a spot plate. From a capillary pipet add a 1% $KMnO_4$ solution, drop
by drop, stirring with a glass thread after each addition. If the color of
permanganate is bleached and a brown precipitate of manganese dioxide
appears, the acid may be unsaturated.

Note.
   All easily oxidizable substances give this test. However, if properly carried out,
it is superior to the bromine test for unsaturation. For example, acetone, which
would decolorize bromine solutions, can be used as a solvent in the BAEYER test.
On the other hand, aldehydes and alcohols will give a positive test but will not decolorize bromine solutions.

Formation of Esters. Place or draw a few micrograms of the dry
acid into a capillary. Add about 5 μl of a mixture of 1 volume of concentrated sulfuric acid and two volumes of methyl or ethyl alcohol. Seal
the tube at both ends and heat it in a steam bath for several minutes.
Cool the tube, cut it open, and blow the contents out into a drop of water
on a slide or watch glass. Warm the solution and note the odor.

Notes.

1) The EMIL FISCHER method of preparing the ester, described above, is easily carried out and often gives high yields but there are limits to the reaction. Some combinations of acids and alcohols react very slowly or reach a state of equilibrium at a point where little or no ester has been formed.

$$R-\overset{\displaystyle O}{\overset{\|}{C}}-OH + H-O-R \rightleftharpoons R-\overset{\displaystyle O}{\overset{\|}{C}}-OR + H_2O$$

2) The OH group of the water comes from the acid and not from the alcohol.

3) Perception of the true, characteristic odor is best achieved by holding the watch glass some distance away so that only low concentrations of the vapor reach the nose and then gradually bringing it nearer.

4) A comparison of the odor of the ester obtained should be made with that obtained in a control test with a sample of the acid known to be pure.

Preparation of Silver Salts.

Neutralize a few milligrams of the acid by the addition of silica-free ammonia and boil off the excess ammonia. When the solution is again at room temperature add an excess of 0.1 m AgNO$_3$. Centrifuge the mixture and decant the clear liquid. Wash the precipitate with water until the washings no longer give a test for nitrate with diphenylamine (page 274). Then wash the residue with alcohol and, finally, ether, and put it in a desiccator in a dark place. The silver content can be determined by the use of a spring (JOLLY) balance, a SALVIONI balance, or a sensitive analytical balance. Since only a residue determination is involved, it is not necessary to know the actual weights of the sample or the residue but merely the ratio of the two. Hence the spring or SALVIONI balance need not be calibrated for this determination. Place the salt on a platinum foil dish and hang it on the balance. Note the position on the scale and then remove and heat the dish and contents high above a flame, gradually lowering the dish and finally igniting it in the flame. Cool in a desiccator and weigh again. Calculate the percentage of silver from the ratio of the two pointer positions.

Notes.

1) DENIGÈS (31) prepares the silver salt for microscopic examination by placing several drops of the acid in the bottom of a gas chamber (see page 72), a droplet of ammoniacal AgNO$_3$ solution on the cover, and allowing it to stand. For less volatile acids a droplet of the 5% to 10% aqueous solution of the acid is added to a drop of the silver reagent.

2) Because some of the silver salts are explosive, a preliminary ignition test as described on page 27 should be run on a small sample.

3) If the acid contains sulfur or halogen, the residue of the ignition may not be pure metallic silver. In case of doubt, make certain of the complete reduction of the silver by heating the platinum foil dish in a stream of hydrogen and then weighing again, repeating until constant weight is obtained.

Classification by Means of Indicators.

Although the procedure was intended as a classification procedure similar to the solubility classifications and included not only acids but bases and neutral compounds, the indicator

TABLE 14

Acidity Scale, Strength Types, and Indicator Reagents

Colors shown by Indicator Reagents for Acids		Strength Type of Acid	Acidity Scale		Strength Type of Base	Colors shown by Indicator Reagent for Bases	
A-I (Detector)	A-II (Classifier)	Examples	pK_a of Acid	pK_b of Base	Examples	B-II (Classifier)	B-I (Detector)
		Strong			*Feeble*		
		(As)	—2	16	(Bf) (N)		
	Salmon-						Purple
	red		—1	15			
		Ex.: RSO_3H			Ex.: RSO_3^-		
		CCl_3COOH	0	14	CCl_3COO^-		
		$Ar_2NH_2^+$	1	13	Ar_2NH^-		
Yellow			**2**	**12**		Yellow	
		Intermediate			*Weak*		
		(Ai)	3	11	(Bw)		
	Yellow		4	10			
		Ex.: RCOOH	5	9	Ex.: $RCOO^-$		
		$ArNH_3^+$	6	8	$ArNH_2$		
	Dichro-					Dichro-	
	matic		**7**	**7**		matic	
	Zone					Zone	
		Weak	**8**	**6**	*Intermediate*		
		(Aw)			(Bi)		
Green			9	5			Yellow
		Ex.: ArOH			Ex.: ArO^-		
		RNH_3^+	11	3	RNH_2		
	Blue-		**12**	**2**		Blue-	
	violet					violet	
		Feeble	13	1	*Strong*		
		(Af) (N)			(Bs)		
			14	0			
Purple		Ex.: ROH	15	—1	Ex.; RO^-		
		$(NH_2)_2C=$	16	—2	$(NH_2)_2C=$		
		$=NH_2^+$			$=NH$		

method of DAVIDSON and PERLMAN (29) will be described here under the acids. The action of the test substance to certain acid-base indicators is used as the basis for the classification. The reagents are as follows:

A-I: 25 ml 0.1% Alizarin Yellow R in methyl alcohol, 25 ml 0.1% bromothymol blue in methyl alcohol, 25 ml 2 *m* KOH in methyl alcohol, 425 ml methyl alcohol, 500 ml pyridine.

A-II: 25 ml Bromothymol blue in methyl alcohol, 25 ml thymol blue in methyl alcohol, 37.5 ml 0.1% bromocresol purple in methyl alcohol, 25 ml 2 *m* KOH in methyl alcohol, 887.5 ml methyl alcohol.

B-I: 25 ml 0.1% Benzeneazodiphenylamine in glacial acetic acid, 4.5 ml HCl, 970.5 ml glacial acetic acid.

B-II: 25 ml 0.1% Bromothymol blue in methyl alcohol, 37.5 ml 0.1% bromocresol purple in methyl alcohol, 4.5 ml 12 m HCl, 933 ml methyl alcohol.

DAVIDSON and PERLMAN recommend that 30 mg of the test substance be added to 1 ml of the indicator reagent. These quantities can be reduced, of course, with due provision for observation of the color of the resultant solution.

Grind the sample against the wall of the reaction vessel, if necessary, with a stirring rod to bring about solution. In any case add a second portion of the test substance. Use the A-I and B-I reagents first and use the A-II and B-II only if changes are observed with the first reagents. A drop of water may be added in the case of water soluble substances which are insoluble in the reagents.

As far as carboxylic acids are concerned, some will fall into the strong acid group as will their anhydrides, Most, however, are in the intermediate acid classification. The method does not permit differentiation between such compounds as carboxylic acids and phenols. Some of the latter, particularly the polyphenols, fall into the intermediate acid group, the rest into the weak acid group.

Reference will be made to this procedure later, particularly when the higher orders are discussed where the method shows its greatest advantages.

Derivatives of Acids.

Preparation of Acid Chlorides and Their Conversion to Amides, Anilides, p-Toluidides, etc.

A) Thionyl Chloride Procedure. Place a few milligrams of the acid into a reflux tube and add an equal quantity of thionyl chloride. Seal the tube and heat it in a water bath for one hour. Cool and cut off at the tip and then at the taper. Transfer the contents into a microcone. For conversion into the amide, add excess ammonia and stir thoroughly. Warm until the largest part of the precipitate has dissolved. When it has been warmed to below the boiling point and most of the precipitate has dissolved, decant and recrystallize the residue from water or dilute alcohol. To convert the chloride into the anilide or p-toluidide, add aniline or p-toluidine dissolved in 300 μl of benzene to the contents of the reflux tube. Heat briefly with stirring. Centrifuge and decant the clear benzene layer into a second microcone. Wash with water, acid, base, and water again, each time drawing off the lower (aqueous) layer. Mix thoroughly at each washing. Then take some of the benzene layer into a capillary, blow it out on a slide or cover slip and allow the benzene to evaporate. Take the melting point of the residue. Evaporate the remainder of the benzene layer in the centrifuge cone to dryness and recrystallize the residue to a constant melting point.

B) Phosphorus Pentachloride Procedure. To several milligrams of the acid or its sodium salt in a microcone add 1.5 times as much phosphorus pentachloride. Stir with a glass thread or sealed capillary and, when thoroughly mixed, centrifuge. Transfer the liquid in a capillary to another microcone and add excess ammonia. Heat until almost all of the crystals dissolve and then treat further as under *(A)*. For anilides and toluidides treat the decanted liquid as under *(A)*.

C) Phosphorus Trichloride Procedure. To a few milligrams of the acid in a microcone, add 1.5 times as much phosphorus trichloride, keeping the cone dipped in ice water. Stir, then warm to 40° to 50° in a metal block, removing and stirring occasionally to aid the evolution of HCl gas. When no more HCl is given off, proceed as in *(B)* from the point at which ammonia is added.

The methyl esters of the acids are easily prepared from the chlorides by merely substituting methyl alcohol for the ammonia in the above procedures.

Notes.

1) The choice of reagent to be used in the conversion of the acids into their chlorides depends upon the ease with which the acid reacts and upon the volatility of the acid chloride.

$$R\text{---}CO \cdot OH + SOCl_2 \rightarrow R\text{---}CO \cdot Cl + SO_2 + HCl$$
$$R\text{---}CO \cdot OH + PCl_5 \rightarrow R\text{---}CO \cdot Cl + POCl_3$$
$$R\text{---}CO \cdot OH + PCl_3 \rightarrow R\text{---}CO \cdot Cl + H_3PO_3$$

Thionyl chloride is preferred whenever it can be used because the by-products of the reaction are gaseous and pass off. Phosphorus pentachloride is used when a more inactive acid is encountered. The reaction with this reagent, however, is too violent for acids such as the lower members of the aliphatic series and hence phosphorus trichloride must be included among the reagents to be used.

2) It is not necessary or advisable to isolate the acid chlorides of simple carboxylic acids. The chlorides of sulfonic acids, however, are often solids which can be recrystallized from non-aqueous solvents and identified.

3) Not all acids yield chlorides by these methods. Dibasic acids may give anhydrides instead when treated with thionyl chloride. Some aromatic acids with a negative constituent in the para position may not react all at. With phosphorus pentachloride, nitro- or aminosulfonic acids may have these groups replaced by chlorine when the acid chloride is formed.

4) If the sample is an aqueous solution of the acid, neutralize it first with sodium hydroxide and evaporate to dryness. Use this sodium salt in the test.

5) The reactions with ammonia, alcohol, and amines are as follows:

$$R\text{---}CO \cdot Cl + HNH_2 \rightarrow R\text{---}CO \cdot NH_2 + HCl$$
$$R\text{---}CO \cdot Cl + HOR' \rightarrow R\text{---}CO \cdot OR' + HCl$$
$$R\text{---}CO \cdot Cl + HNH \langle \hexagon \rangle \rightarrow R\text{---}CO \cdot NH \langle \hexagon \rangle + HCl.$$

Partition Constants of Volatile Aliphatic Acids. (146) Prepare a capillary pipet by drawing out a 4- to 5-mm bore glass tube to a capillary of about 1-mm bore and about 15 cm long. Leaving about 4 cm of the wider tube attached to the capillary, cut off the remainder and fire-polish the end. Make a mark on the capillary 12 cm (or the 150 µl point) from its end by scratching with a file. Prepare several extraction tubes by sealing one end of glass tubes 15-cm long and 4 mm in bore. Prepare a 0.3 molar solution of the acid in water. Introduce 120 mm of this solution into the extraction tube from a BENEDETTI-PICHLER-HYBBINETTE or similar buret. Then introduce 150 µl ethyl ether. Seal the open end of the tube and centrifuge the contents back and forth several times. Then cut the tube open close to the surface of the ether. Dip the capillary pipet down into the aqueous layer in the extraction tube, keeping the upper end of the pipet closed with the finger. Since even with this precaution some of the ether layer will enter the pipet, blow a bubble or two of air carefully through the pipet to displace any ether solution. Then draw the aqueous layer into the pipet and withdraw the required volume. Transfer this sample to a microbeaker and titrate it with 0.3 n NaOH, using phenolphthalein as indicator. Using the same pipet, titrate an equal volume of the original acid solution. The ratio

$$\frac{\text{volume of alkali used for extracted sample}}{\text{volume of alkali used for original sample}} \times 100$$

is the partition constant.

Notes.

1) The following table gives the values of this constant for some of the acids.

Acid	Partition Constant
Formic	64.3
Acetic	48.7
Propionic	33.7
Butyric	14.5
n-Valeric	5.0

2) DERMER and DERMER (34) recommend the use of water-saturated ether.

3) The advantages of the extraction method over the DUCLAUX method for the identification of organic acids are enumerated in the papers of BEHRENS (10) and WERKMAN (110, 162).

p-Nitrobenzyl Esters of Acids. Place 3 to 6 mg of p-nitrobenzyl bromide in a reflux tube. Add 10 µl of 95% alcohol and 5 µl of distilled water. To this suspension add 3 to 6 mg of the sodium salt of the acid if monobasic, 2 to 4 mg if dibasic. Cool quickly with shaking. If no crystallization occurs, reheat and add water in small quantities until separation of the solid occurs on cooling. Centrifuge and decant and then wash the crystals twice with alcohol of the same strength as the mother liquor and twice with water. Recrystallize from hot alcohol to constant melting point.

1) As the reaction proceeds, the ester may precipitate. If this occurs, add more alcohol.

2) The solution of the salt should be just acid if it has been prepared from the free acid by neutralization. If the dry salt is used add one drop of 6 m HCl to the solution from a capillary pipet.

3) The reaction is

$$R \cdot C \overset{O}{\underset{O-Na}{\Big\langle}} + BrCH_2 \langle \rangle NO_2 \rightarrow R \cdot C \overset{O}{\underset{O-CH_2}{\Big\langle}} \langle \rangle NO_2 + NaBr$$

Phenacyl Esters of Acids. Dissolve 4 mg of the acid in 50 µl of water and 50 µl of 0.5 m Na_2CO_3. Add 50 µl of alcohol. Place 10 mg of phenacyl bromide (or the corresponding quantity of the substituted phenacyl bromide) into a reflux tube and add the acid mixture. Seal and reflux for one hour for monobasic acids and two hours for dibasic acids. Cool and transfer the contents of the tube to a microcone. Centrifuge, decant, and wash the residue in the reflux tube into the microcone with 50% alcohol or the mother liquor. Centrifuge again, decant, and wash the crystals with 50% alcohol. Recrystallize from 95% alcohol by dissolving and adding water to start crystallization.

Notes.

The reaction is

$$X \langle \rangle CO \cdot CH_2Br + Na \cdot O \cdot CO \cdot R \rightarrow X \langle \rangle CO \cdot CH_2 \cdot O \cdot CO \cdot R + NaBr$$

Crystalline Metallic Salts of Acids. The metallic salts of some organic acids have crystalline forms sufficiently characteristic to be used as a means of identifying the acid. The most complete description of these metallic salts is found in BEHRENS-KLEY (13). KLEIN and WENZEL (80) have carefully reviewed these tests and recommend the following salts for the identification of some of the lower fatty acids.

Formic: Cerous salt. Neutralize the free acid with magnesium oxide and add 20% cerous nitrate solution to the test drop under a cover glass and allow to stand. Heating to 50 or 60° will speed up crystallization.

Acetic: Copper salt. Use the sodium, potassium, or ammonium salt of the acid and saturate the solution with copper carbonate. *See also* BARLOT and BRENET (8) and KRÜGER and TSCHIRCH (85) regarding the sodium-uranyl acetate test.

Propionic: Mercurous salt. Add solid mercurous nitrate to a solution of the salt of the acid.

Butyric: Silver salt.   Add silver nitrate to the solution of the acid.

n-Valeric: Mercurous salt.   Like propionic.

Isovaleric: Mercurous salt. Like propionic.

n-Caproic: Copper salt.   Add copper acetate to saturate the solution of the sodium salt of the acid or add copper carbonate to the free acid.

Isocaproic: Copper salt.   Like the normal acid.

Heptylic: Copper salt. Add copper carbonate to the solutions of the salts.

Other tests involving the metallic salts of the acids or using the appearance of the crystalline products as a test are those described by WAGE-NAAR (159) (distinction between maleic and fumaric acids), VAN NIEUWEN-BURG and BROBBEL (155) (detection of maleic acid by brucine), DENIGÈS (32) (cholesterin as reagent for lower fatty acids), ROSENTHALER (129) (precipitation of organic acids by inorganic salts), VORLÄNDER (158) (behavior of salts of organic acids on melting), McLENNAN (98) (microscopic structure and optical properties of soaps), and BRYANT and MITCHELL (23) (optical properties of the *p*-bromanilides of some lower fatty acids).

KLEIN and WERNER (82) and FISCHER and STAUDER (50) have described the appearance of sublimates of some acids when sublimed under the microscope.

Other derivatives which can readily be prepared by micromethods are the diamides of 4,4'-diaminodiphenylmethane (121), 2-alkylbenzimidazoles (21, 116), and the *s*-benzylthiouronium salts (39).

Optical Properties of Aliphatic Dicarboxylic Acids. The principal optical and crystallographic properties of some of the aliphatic dicarboxylic acids have been determined and tabulated by CASTLE (26).   The values for these are found in Table 15.

Degradative Procedures for Acids.

Reduction affords the best means for study of the structure of an acid. Oxidation sufficiently strong to affect the acid usually results in complete rupture of the molecule to form carbon dioxide and water.   Decarboxylation with soda-lime will give the hydrocarbon with one less carbon but this is usually more difficult to identify than the alcohol obtained from the reduction except when certain other functional groups are present.

The reduction can be carried out best with lithium-aluminium hydride as described below in the LIEB and SCHÖNIGER procedure for determination of active hydrogen (p. 195).   The resulting alcohol is, of course, left in the reaction flask and can be separated from the solvent and other residual material by distillation.

Another degradative procedure is the distillation of the calcium salts of the acids with production of a ketone.   The ease of separation of the products and the chemical activity of ketones make this procedure attractive.

TABLE 15

Optical Properties of the Crystals of Dicarboxylic Acids

Acid	Habit	Crystal System	Extinction	Elongation	Optic sign.	Refractive Indices		
Oxalic Anhydrous	Thick tablets	Orthorhombic	Parallel	plus	minus	1.431	1.540	1.636
Oxalic Dihydrate	Tabular to equant	Monoclinic	Parallel on common orientation XX ∥ b 22°	plus	minus	1.417	1.505	1.550
Malonic	Lath-shaped to acicular	Triclinic		plus	plus	1.448	1.448	1.578
Succinic	Tabular	Monoclinic	Parallel on common orientation	plus	minus	1.448	1.531	1.610
Glutaric	Acicular	Monoclinic	YY ∥ 6, Z ∧ c = 8°	plus	plus	1.451	1.502	1.585
Adipic	Tabular to lath-shaped	Monoclinic	YY ∥ b, Z ∧ c = 40°	plus	plus	1.464	1.506	1.592
Pimelic	Tabular to lamellar	Monoclinic	YY ∥ b, Z ∧ c = 2°	plus	plus	1.458	1.492	1.579
Suberic	Lamellar	Monoclinic			plus	1.469	1.507	1.587
Azelic	Tabular	Monoclinic			plus	1.466	1.495	1.582
Sebacic	Tabular	Monoclinic			plus	1.470	1.507	1.589

Chemical Separation of Acids.

Acids can readily be separated from other materials by their ability to form non-volatile, water soluble salts with strong bases, as discussed under Neutralization Equivalent, page 183. After adding an excess of base such as sodium hydroxide, the aqueous layer is decanted from any other phase which may be present. An equivalent quantity of sulfuric acid is added to this aqueous solution and the organic acid is then extracted with ether. In some cases it might be preferable to precipitate a slightly soluble salt of the organic acid by treating the solution of the sodium salt with a solution of silver nitrate or the like as described above.

Acids can also be isolated from mixtures by the use of ion-exchangers. The technique and procedures are described under that heading on page 84.

Quantitative Analysis of Acids.

Four general types of procedures have been suggested for the determination of the carboxyl group. These are: (1) simple titration, (2) conversion to salt and determination of the metal content of the salt by residue determination or carbonate titration, (3) determination of active hydrogen, and, finally, (4) by decarboxylation of carboxyl groups attached to aromatic rings and determination of the released carbon dioxide.

Titration of Carboxyl Group. This is carried out as in the determination of neutralization equivalent, p. 183. While the latter suffices for corroborative evidence, it is open to a number of sources of error and difficulty. The end point may not be sharp or it may be considerably removed from the stoichiometric point. It is therefore recommended that unknown acids be first titrated using a pH meter and plotting the pH against the volume of alkali. In the case of water insoluble acids, an indicator must be used if the sample is dissolved in alcohol or, the sample can be dissolved in excess standard base and the excess of the base back-titrated. *See* also Note 2 under Neutralization Equivalent above, p. 184. An excellent discussion of acid-base titrations in non-aqueous solvents is that of FRITZ (55).

Conversion to Salt. The presence of other functional groups in an acid molecule will, of course, often change the strength of the acid. If the acid is weakened, it is advisable to use a procedure other than titration. The acid is precipitated as its barium or calcium salt by the addition of a solution of barium or calcium hydroxide. The precipitate is washed with water and alcohol and then dried at 100°. The metal content is determined in one of two rather simple ways.

In the first weigh out a sample of 3 to 5 mg in a micro platinum combustion boat, treat with an excess of concentrated sulfuric acid and ignite in a PREGL micromuffle, Fig. 161. The residue is either barium or calcium sulfate. A second treatment with sulfuric acid is required if the residue is not pure white but shows black specks of unoxidized carbon.

The second procedure is based on that of SIGGIA and MAISCH (143). Weigh out a 3- to 5-mg sample of the barium or calcium salt in a platinum combustion boat and ignite until it is perfectly white. Drop the boat into 3 ml of 0.02 n HCl in a 10-ml Erlenmeyer flask. As soon as the ignition residue has dissolved, titrate the excess acid with standard alkali. Then make the solution barely acid with HCl, boil to expel the carbon dioxide,

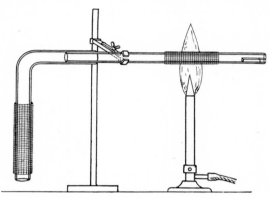

Fig. 161. Micromuffle of PREGL.

and titrate to the end point with methyl red as the indicator. The percent carboxylic acid is calculated according to the equation

$$\% \text{ carboxylic acid salt} = \frac{C \times \text{N NaOH} \times \text{mol. wt. salt} \times 100}{S \times 1000 \times V}$$

where: V = valence of cation on salt $\times$ number of cation atoms per molecule of salt

S = grams of sample

$C = A - B$ = milliliters of alkali equivalent to carboxylic acid salt

A = mililiters of alkali needed to titrate all standard acid used in analysis

B = milliliters of alkali used in titration of sample.

Determination of Active Hydrogen. Lieb and Schöniger Method (94). The third procedure for the determination of the carboxyl group is based upon the determination of active hydrogen by means of lithium aluminum hydride. All substances which contain active hydrogen react with this reagent to give free hydrogen which can be measured volumetrically. Complete dehydration of the test substance and reagents is required in view of the sensitivity of the reagent to moisture and care must be taken to avoid temperatures much above 30° to avoid decomposition of the reagent.

Reagents.

Lithium-aluminum hydride: Powder the lithium-aluminum hydride before use and keep it in a brown bottle sealed with paraffin. After removing a sample, seal the bottle again.

Di-*n*-propyl ether: The commercially available product is carefully dried over calcium chloride or, better, over calcium hydride. Di-isopropyl ether is less suited because of its lower solvency for lithium-aluminum hydride.

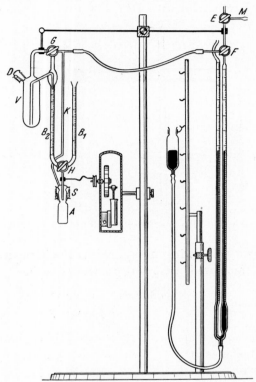

Fig. 162.   Determination of Active Hydrogen according to LIEB and SCHÖNIGER.

Hydrogen: In cylinder.

Vaseline, pure, and vaseline-lanolin, 1 : 1: The outer portions of the plug of stopcock *H*, Fig. 162, are lubricated with a very thin layer of vaseline alone. The other stopcocks are lubricated with the vaseline-lanolin mixture. Also the ground joint of the reagent vessel should be lubricated only at the upper end.

Apparatus.

The apparatus employed is essentially that of SOLTYS (140) except that the gas buret is enclosed in a glass outer jacket which can be filled with water, Fig. 162. In the case of liquid test substances the reaction vessel shown in Fig. 163 is used as described below.

Determination of Blank. Lead an even stream of hydrogen through the apparatus to establishment of the zero point (about 50 ml per minute). The hydrogen from a cylinder of the compressed gas passes through a valve flask which contains mercury to a height of 6 cm to ensure the proper pressure for filling the buret. From this valve lead the hydrogen through a gas washing bottle containing concentrated sulfuric acid through a U-tube filled with magnesium perchlorate (caution!) and thence through stopcock *M* into the buret.

Clean the reaction flask with chromic-sulfuric acid and dry for ten minutes in a drying block at 120°. By means of a small spoon place 28 to 30 mg of the powdered lithium-aluminium hydride in the vessel while it is still warm. Connect the warm reaction vessel to the apparatus and attach the safety

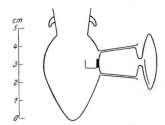

Fig. 163. Reaction Vessel for Active Hydrogen Determination.

springs. Dip the vessel for a short time into a vessel of cold water to bring it to room temperature and then place in a 1-liter beaker of water at room temperature. Fill the glass jacket around the gas buret also with water at room temperature. Shake the vessel (mechanically) for ten minutes. The entire apparatus must be filled at the same temperature. Then fill the solvent buret B_2 from the reservoir V by means of the hydrogen and bring the mercury level in the gas buret to its zero point. To test the apparatus for leaks, lower the leveling bulb about 10 cm and fix it at this position. After ten minutes raise the bulb again. If the zero point has not changed, the apparatus is tight. Then lower the mercury bulb again about 5 cm and allow about 0.5 ml of solvent to pass into the reaction flask by rotating the stopcock *H* counterclockwise. Shake for 15 minutes. At the end of this time a reduced pressure must exist in the apparatus. If more then 15 minutes is required for carrying out the determination, use this same time for the blank experiment. The temperature of the cooling water for the reaction flask and the burets must remain constant and always controlled.

After ending the shaking, raise the gas buret again so that the mercury level in each arm of the buret is exactly the same and read the gas volume. For calculating the blank, deduct the volume of solvent added from the gas volume read. The blank is due to the vapor pressure of the solvent, the small amount of hydrogen from the reaction of the hydride on the solvent, and the slight decomposition of the hydride. It is necessary to carry out several blank determinations before each series of determinations on test substances. The average blank found by LIEB and SCHÖNIGER was 0.8 to 1 ml at temperatures of 19° to 21°.

Determination with Test Substance. The determination of reactive groups in carbon compounds is carried out in the same way as for the blank. Just before adding the solvent, however, introduce a sample of 3 to 5 mg into the still-warm reaction vessel by means of a weighing tube.

Weigh out liquid substances in a capillary as described by PREGL. Place the sealed capillary in the reaction flask shown in Fig. 163 and crush it by means of a 2-cm long glass rod. Leave the rod in the vessel. The glass spoon fastened into the plug of the side stopper contains the hydride. After the solvent has been added as described above, turn this plug to allow the hydride to drop into the solution. The remaining procedure is the same as that for solid substances.

Determination of Active Hydrogen according to Subba Rao, Shah, and Pansare (149). The authors use the simple ROTH apparatus (132) with some modifications. The reagents are the same as for the previously described method.

Place the accurately weighed sample of test substance (3 to 5 mg) at the bottom of the long limb B of the dry reaction vessel. Place about 30 mg of well-powdered lithium-aluminum hydride in the short limb A and add about 1 ml of dry n-propyl ether. Attach the reaction flask to the apparatus as shown in Fig. 164.

Pass previously purified and dried hydrogen through the apparatus for about five minutes while keeping stopcock Hb open to the air. Then close stopcock Ha and turn stopcock Hb to connect the system to the gas buret. Immerse the reaction vessel in a water bath which is at the same temperature as that of the water circulating in the jacket surrounding the gas buret. Release the excess pressure developed in the system from the moisture in the solvent and the surroundings by suddenly opening and closing stopcock Hb. Repeat this operation at short intervals until no further increase of pressure in the system is observed for five minutes. After noting the temperature of the bath, the atmospheric pressure, and the height of the mercury column in the gas buret, remove the water bath and add the lithium-aluminum hydride solution to the substance by tilting the reaction vessel through about 60 to 70 degrees. Shake the reaction vessel well. Lower the mercury bulb to reduce the excess pressure produced by the evolution of hydrogen and then place the reaction vessel again in the water bath. After ascertaining that no more hydrogen is being evolved, read the volume accurately after bringing the system to atmospheric pressure by adjusting the mercury levels to about the same height.

Decarboxylation of Aromatic and Aromatic-Type Heterocyclic Acids. HUBACHER (68) has shown that carboxyl groups attached to an aromatic ring will readily lose carbon dioxide when treated with quinoline in the presence of a catalyst. BEROZA (16) has adapted this procedure to a micro scale and has been able to apply it also to aromatic-type heterocyclic acids.

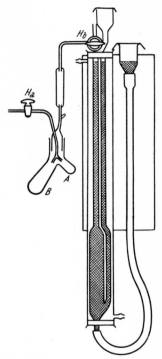

Fig. 164. Determination of Active Hydrogen according to SUBBA RAO, SHAH, and PANSARE.

Reagents.

Quinoline, synthetic, redistilled before use. Use only the fraction distilling between 236° and 237° at atmospheric pressure.

Basic cupric carbonate

Ascarite

Anhydrone (magnesium perchlorate)

Concentrated sulfuric acid

Diethylene glycol

Glass wool and KRÖNIG's cement

All reagents must be pure.

Apparatus: The apparatus is shown in Fig. 165. A small reaction flask *A* is attached with springs to a section of glass tubing *B* fitted with ground joints. *B* connects with a bubbler *C* which contains about 2 ml of 18 *m*

H_2SO_4. This in turn is sealed to tube D which contains Anhydrone. During the determination a micro absorption tube F is attached to D by means of the usual impregnated rubber tubing E which has been lubricated with a minimum of glycerol. The first three-fourths of the absorption tube are filled with Ascarite and the last fourth with Anhydrone. The two layers are separated by glass wool. Joints c, d and e are sealed with KRÖNIG cement. The reaction flask A is constructed with a heating jacket G so that a constant temperature can be maintained through the boiling of a liquid in the 100-ml boiling flask H. This constant temperature is the boiling

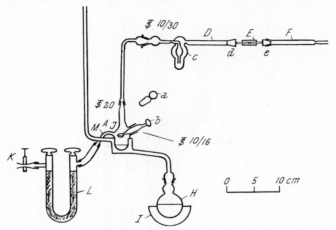

Fig. 165. Apparatus of BEROZA.

point of the heating liquid. A voltage regulator controls the input to the electrical heating mantle I to keep the liquid refluxing halfway up the tube J. By covering the heating jacket H and the tube connecting it to the flask H with glass wool, loss of heat will be reduced and a uniform temperature maintained in the jacket. Once the voltage regulator is set, no further attention is required.

Nitrogen is conducted through pressure tubing, fitted with a pressure clamp, to a U-tube L. The first half of this is filled with Ascarite and the second half with Anhydrone. After the nitrogen passes through this U-tube it is dry and free of carbon dioxide. It is then led to the inlet tube M of the reaction flask by means of a rubber tube. When the stopper a is inserted, the flow of nitrogen through the system may be observed by watching the bubbler C. A small platinum combustion boat which fits into the cup of the spoon B is used to introduce the sample and the catalyst.

A semimicrobalance sensitive to 0.02 mg, wiping flannels and chamois, and a medicine dropper are also required.

Procedure: Assemble the apparatus except for tube F. Introduce about 0.8 to 1 ml of quinoline with a medicine dropper into the reaction flask through the $^{10}/_{16}$ joint. Close the orifice with a stopper and cautiously open screw clamp K until the bubbler C shows a nitrogen flow of about three bubbles per second. Turn on the electrical heater and adjust the voltage regulator so that the liquid refluxes about half way up the tube J. BEROZA used diethylene glycol (b. pt. 245°) to maintain the temperature in the heating jacket, but states that any other liquid boiling at about the same temperature may be used. After about 30 minutes all the carbon dioxide in the quinoline and the system will be flushed out. Attach tube F. Meanwhile weigh out 5 to 10 mg of the test substance (enough to give 1 to 3 mg of carbon dioxide) and about 1 to 1.5 mg of the catalyst into the platinum boat. Place this in the cup of the spoon. Set the latter aside and remove tube F with the flannel wiping cloths and weigh. Wipe out the inlet tube and the outside of the absorption tube in the manner employed in combustion analyses. Place the tube directly on the balance and weigh after ten minutes. Connect it again to the rubber tube E and speed up the flow of nitrogen to about four bubbles per second. Remove stopper a and introduce the spoon containing the sample and the catalyst in its place. Then cut down the flow of nitrogen to about two bubbles per second and invert the spoon to drop the boat into the flask.

Two hours after the addition of the sample pull the absorption tube almost out and stop the flow of nitrogen through the system. Weigh the absorption tube as described above. In the meantime stopper the open end of tube E with a glass rod. Then return the absorption tube to its former position and again pass nitrogen through the system at a rate of two bubbles per second. Repeat the weighing of the absorption tube at one hour intervals until its weight is constant. The amount of evolved carbon dioxide is, of course, equal to the difference between the initial and final weights of the absorption tube. When the analysis is complete, the products of the reaction may be removed from the reaction flask by means of a dropping pipet which reaches to the bottom of the flask and rinsing the flask with a suitable solvent. Any adhering catalyst can be removed by means of fine steel wool held on the end of a wooden stick with fine wire. Before starting the next determination, wipe out tube B with acetone on a cotton swab and then with a dry cotton swab to remove any quinoline. Clean the platinum boat in hot nitric acid, rinsing with water and acetone, and drying.

$$\% - COOH = 102.3 \ (W_1 - W_2)/S$$

$W_1 =$ weight of carbon dioxide developed in the analysis

$W_2 =$ weight of carbon dioxide due to catalyst

$S \ \ =$ weight of the sample

All of the above weights are in milligrams.

The basic cupric carbonate catalyst develops the theoretical amount of carbon dioxide (19.9% of its weight) in all analyses.

Phenols.

Generic Tests.

The test for the phenols consists of two parts: the ferric chloride test and the alkali test. The former is applied to all samples, solid or liquid. The alkali test is applied only to solids which do not give a coloration with the ferric chloride.

Ferric Chloride Test. Prepare the reagent by diluting 3 drops of a 10% FeCl$_3$ solution with 1 ml of water. Dissolve a few micrograms of the test substance in a small drop of water in the depression of a spot plate. Take up a very small volume of the reagent in a platinum wire loop or at the end of a glass thread or loop and stir it into the test drop. Repeat the addition of the ferric chloride three times. Note any coloration. If no color develops, prepare a solution of the substance in alcohol and repeat the test.

Alkali Test. Employ this only for substances which gave a negative ferric chloride test. This is essentially a test of the solubility of the substance in water and in 5% sodium hydroxide solution. The procedure is the same as that for the determination of the solubility by the capillary method described on page 152. First determine the solubility of the test substance in ten parts of cold water. If it is soluble and no color was observed in the ferric chloride test, it is not a phenol. If it does not dissolve appreciably in cold water, determine the solubility in 20 parts of 5% sodium hydroxide. If it does not dissolve completely, add ten parts more of water. If the substance dissolves completely in either the undiluted or the diluted alkali, it must be regarded as belonging to this genus. The production of a pronounced color in the alkali solution is also an indication that the substance is a phenol.

Notes.

1) Not all phenols give colors with ferric chloride, hence it is necessary to carry out the second part of this test, the alkali-solubility determination.

2) The colors may last for hours or they may be very fleeting. A slight excess of reagent may destroy the color. At other times, an excess may be necessary. Add the reagent, therefore, in small increments.

3) RASCHIG (123) explained the color formed by the ferric chloride and the phenol as being due to a simple ferric salt. The later work of WESP and BRODE (163), however, indicates that a complex $[\text{Fe}(\text{OC}_6\text{H}_3)_6]\equiv$ is formed.

4) The addition of water after testing for the solubility of the test substance in 5% alkali is necessary since the sodium salts of some phenols are less soluble in alkali than in water.

5. The ease with which some liquid esters are saponified by even 5% alkali makes it necessary to restrict the alkali test to the solids which give no positive ferric chloride test.

Classification Tests for Phenols.

Ferric Chloride Test. In order to secure the most characteristic color from each phenol, the ferric chloride test is carried out again, but this time a 2.5% solution of ferric chloride is used. Add it dropwise as before, ceasing the addition when a color of sufficient depth is obtained. If a set of standards is available, compare the color with that of a standard. Allow the test to stand for five minutes and then compare again with the standard and again after 15 minutes.

Note.
The concentration of the phenol solution should be about 1% in water.

Phthalein Fusion Test. Using the same technique as in filling a melting point tube, introduce a crystal of phenol (approximately 5 µg) and an equal bulk of phthalic anhydride into a capillary 50 to 60 mm long and 1 to 1.5 mm in bore, sealed at one end. Add a droplet of 18 m H_2SO_4 by means of a capillary pipet. Centrifuge the acid to the solid. Heat the tube in a sulfuric acid (melting point) bath at 160° for three minutes. After cooling introduce two drops of water by means of a capillary pipet, centrifuge to the sealed end, and mix by means of a glass thread. Cut off the sealed end and blow the liquid out on a slide. Add enough 5% sodium hydroxide solution to make the solution alkaline. The bright and characteristic colors of the phthaleins are obtained. Should sodium sulfate crystallize out when the solution is made alkaline, add a drop or two of water to dissolve it.

Note.
Phthalic anhydride will condense with phenols to give phthaleins, the colors of which are characteristic of the phenol.

Derivatives of Phenols.

2,4-Dinitrophenyl Ethers. To 3 to 6 mg of the phenol in a reflux tube add 2 to 7 µl 0.01 m NaOH and 20 µl of water. Dissolve 6 to 10 mg of the 2,4-dinitrochlorobenzene in 150 µl 95% ethyl alcohol and add this to the contents of the reflux tube. More alcohol may be added if a solid separates out. The mixture will become colored, usually red, at this point. Seal the tube and heat in a water bath until the color disappears and a heavy precipitate of salt appears. Cut the tube open and add a volume of water equal to that of the contents of the tube to precipitate the ether. Centrifuge and decant. Wash the residue with water and recrystallize the product from ethyl alcohol.

Note.

$$R \cdot O \cdot Na + Cl \langle \rangle NO_2 \rightarrow R \cdot O \langle \rangle NO_2 + NaCl$$
$$ NO_2 NO_2$$

p-**Nitrobenzyl Ethers.** To 2 to 3 mg of the phenol in a reflux tube add an equal quantity of *p*-nitrobenzyl bromide. To this add 50 μl of 0.2 *m* alcoholic potassium hydroxide solution. Seal the tube and heat in a water bath for one hour. Cut off the conical end of the tube. Invert the bottom part of the tube into a microcone and centrifuge the contents into the cone. If necessary, rinse out the reflux tube with alcohol. Add water to dissolve any potassium bromide which may precipitate and alcohol, if necessary, to keep the ether in solution while hot. Cool, centrifuge, and remove the liquid with a capillary pipet. Recrystallize the solid from alcohol, adding water if necessary to start crystallization.

Notes.

$$R \cdot O \cdot Na + BrCH_2 \langle \rangle NO_2 \rightarrow ROCH_2 \langle \rangle NO_2 + NaBr$$

An excess of the phenol is recommended.

α-**Naphthyl Urethans.** Dry a microcone thoroughly by holding it in the flame for a few moments. Stopper it and allow to cool. To 3-6 mg of the phenol in this microcone add a slight excess of α-naphthyl isocyanate. Place the microcone in the heating block and heat at a temperature of about 100° for several minutes. In some instances it may be necessary to boil the solution over a free flame. Allow the cone to cool and start crystallization by scratching the wall with a glass needle. If no crystallization takes place, reheat the solution until crystals appear on cooling. Some phenols, such as resorcinol, α-naphthol, and β-naphthol, require the addition of trimethyl or triethylamine as a catalyst. Extract the urethan by adding 200 to 300 μl of ligroin and heating the solution to 110° in the block. Siphon off the clear solution through a capillary siphon into a second microcone. If necessary, the ligroin solution can be concentrated by heating in the block and blowing a stream of air over the cone mouth. Recrystallize from ligroin.

Note.

$$\text{N}{=}\text{C}{=}\text{O} \qquad\qquad \text{NH}{-}\text{CO}{-}\text{OR}$$
$$\langle\langle \rangle\rangle + HOR \longrightarrow \langle\langle \rangle\rangle$$

For other urethan reactions *see* SAH and coworkers. (134)

Aryloxyacetic Acids. In the presence of alkali, phenols react readily with chloroacetic acid to give salts of aryloxyacetic acids:

$$R \cdot O \cdot Na + Cl \cdot CH_2 \cdot CO \cdot ONa \rightarrow R \cdot O \cdot CH_2 \cdot CO \cdot ONa + NaCl$$

The addition of mineral acid releases the free aryloxyacetic acid. These acids are easily titrated and therefore the neutralization equivalent as well as the melting point may be used for identification. NAMETKIN, MEL'NIKOV, BASKAKOV, and BOKAREV (104) prepare the amides and anilides also. They treat the sodium salt of the phenol with the corresponding quantity of chloracetamide or chloracetanilide instead of the chloroacetic acid and reflux for an hour. The mixture is filtered while hot and the melting point then determined on the product crystallizing on cooling. Data for 154 phenols are given in the original paper.

Treat 2 to 3 mg of the phenol in a microcone with 7 to 10 µl of 33% sodium hydroxide solution. Add 5 to 6 µl of a 50% aqueous chloroacetic acid solution. Stopper loosely and heat in a water bath for one hour. Cool, dilute to twice the volume with water, and stir. Acidify the solution with 12 m HCl until acid to moist Congo red paper. Add approximately 200 µl of ether and, placing the thumb over the mouth of the microcone, shake vigorously. Centrifuge and pipet off the ether into another microcone. Add dilute sodium carbonate solution and water if necessary to dissolve the aryloxyacetic acid. Stir thoroughly, centrifuge, and pipet off the ether. Acidify the sodium carbonate solution, centrifuge, and decant the supernatant liquid. Recrystallize the residue from hot water. Take up the crystals and the mother liquor in a wide capillary and transfer to a slide with a cavity (culture slide). Filter off the mother liquor with a fine-tipped capillary, drain the remainder of the liquid with a triangular piece of filter paper and determine the melting point.

Notes.

1) In the presence of alkali, phenols react readily with chloroacetic acid to give aryloxyacetic acids:

$$R—O—Na + Cl—CH_2 \cdot CO—ONa \rightarrow R—O—CH_2CO—O—Na + NaCl$$

2) Since these aryloxyacetic acids are easily titrated, the neutralization equivalent as well as the melting point can be determined in identifying them.

p-Nitrobenzoyl and 3,5-Dinitrobenzoyl Esters of Hydroxyl Compounds. Phenols, alcohols, amines, and mercaptans react with substituted benzoyl chlorides as follows:

Procedure A. Dissolve 3 to 6 mg of the test substance in 30 to 60 µl of dry pyridine in a microcone. Quickly add an equal weight or slight excess of *p*-nitrobenzoyl chloride or 3,5-dinitrobenzoyl chloride and cool under the tap if necessary. Dilute the mixture with approximately 600 µl of water and stir until precipitation occurs. If no precipitate appears after a reasonable time, set the tube aside for ten minutes and then stir again. Centrifuge out the precipitate, discard the supernatant liquid, and wash the residue with 600 µl of water, 600 µl of 0.15 *m* Na₂CO₃, and finally again with 600 µl of water. Recrystallize the product from a suitable solvent to a constant melting point.

Procedure B. Proceed as in *(A)* but, after the reaction has taken place, dissolve the mixture as far as possible in 500 µl of ether and extract the pyridine by mixing with 500 µl of water three times and removing the water layer each time. Wash the ether layer twice with 50 µl of 1.5 *m* Na₂CO₃ solution and twice with 50 µl of water. Evaporate the ether and allow the residue to stand in an evacuated vacuum desiccator to remove all volatile substances as completely as possible. Recrystallize the residue from a suitable solvent to a constant melting point.

Notes.

1) The reagents will gradually hydrolyze if exposed to moist air. If they are kept covered with petrolic ether, the decomposition is retarded.

2) An excess of the reagent is preferred to an excess of the phenol because the former is more readily removed.

3. It has been found that the use of the sodium compound or the presence of sodium ion increases the efficiency of the conversion of the hydroxy compound (alcohol or phenol) to the ester. HOLLEY and HOLLEY (67) add anhydrous potassium carbonate to the pyridine solution of the hydroxy compound before adding the 3,5-dinitrobenzoyl chloride. To make even more certain of the conversion of the hydroxy compound, DUNBAR and FERRIN (40) add small pieces of sodium to the alcohol or phenol. Their greatest problem was the limitation of the quantity of sodium added to less than that required for the full reaction with the hydroxy compound because of the violence of the reaction between elementary sodium and the acid chloride. Their suggestion that solid alcohols and phenols be first dissolved in an inert solvent such as ether leads to the possibility of using a sodium dispersion in an inert medium. *See* also page 94. The sodium dispersions are commercially available in media such as toluene, xylene, light naphtha, etc. Since the amount of sodium added in this form can easily be controlled, the metallic compound of the alcohol or phenol can easily be formed and the reaction carried out with a much greater yield of the ester. After addition of the acid chloride to the sodium compound (careful cooling is required at all times to prevent charring of the test substance) it is merely necessary to add water whereupon the esters separate as solids. After decantation the crystalline residue is washed with 0,2 *m* Na₂CO₃ solution and recrystallized several times from acetone or ethyl alcohol. When using the latter, care must be taken to prevent transesterification.

4) *See* under Alcohols (page 229) for literature references on the optical properties of the esters.

ROSENTHALER (127) has described the crystal precipitates obtained upon the addition of certain inorganic salts to phenols. He has also described (127) a reaction of phenols with *n*-nitrobenzenediazonium salt. WILDI (166) describes a test with silver nitrate for ortho and para dihydric phenols.

Degradative Procedures.

The simplest degradative reaction for phenols is the reduction to the hydrocarbon or substituted hydrocarbon by means of a zinc dust distillation. The procedure of EMICH (44, 45) is as follows.

Draw out a Pyrex glass tube of 5-mm bore to a capillary of from 1- to 2-mm bore (Fig. 166). At *a*, a distance of 15 mm from the point at which the capillary is joined to the wider tube, constrict the wider tube to about

Fig. 166. Zinc Dust Distillation according to EMICH.

half the bore. Introduce a plug of ignited asbestos at *b*. Fill in a 10-mm layer of zinc dust, followed by a 5-mm layer of zinc dust mixed with test substance. Seal the tube at *a*, but leave the portion to the left attached to use for clamping the tube. Heat first the zinc dust layer and then the mixture with a small flame to dull red heat. The product will sublime or distill into the capillary. Cut off the capillary after cooling it in an ice bath, if necessary, and remove the product for either a boiling point or melting point determination. *See* also KÖGL and POSTOWSKY (84).

Oxidation will produce the hydroxy acid of the homologues of phenol. *See* below for oxidation of side chains of cyclic hydrocarbons, page 237.

Chemical Separation of Phenols

The acidic nature of phenols makes it possible to prepare the sodium or potassium salts by simple neutralization, using the reagents of DAVIDSON and PERLMAN (29). These salts are water-soluble and can be separated from the other components by decantation. Care must be taken to exclude carbon dioxide since the phenols are but weak acids and the salts are hydrolyzed to a considerable degree in aqueous solution. In fact, in many cases the free phenols can be released from the salts by bubbling carbon dioxide through the aqueous solution of the salts. This reaction can be used in reverse, that is, phenols can be separated from carboxy sulfonic acids by dissolving these latter in sodium carbonate in which the phenol is insoluble.

Quantitative Determination of Phenols.

Phenols may be determined quantitatively by making use of the ease of bromination, by the reaction with active hydrogen, and by means of the coupling reaction with diazonium compounds. The micromethods for the first two will be described. The third method requires considerable in the way of precautionary measures, such as the maintainance of low temperatures, to prevent the decomposition of the reagents.

Determination by Bromination. The general procedure is the same as that used for hydrocarbons, *see* below, page 238. A blank must be run on the reagents and the volume of thiosulfate solution used for the blank deducted from that used in the determination. The number of bromine atoms that will substitute on one molecule of a pure phenol under examination of the content of phenol in a mixture can be calculated from the following.

$$\% \text{ phenol} = \frac{100\,V\,N\,M}{2000\,B\,S} = V\,N\,M/20\,B\,S$$

V = volume of thiosulfate standard solution in milliliters
N = normality of thiosulfate
M = molecular weight of phenol
S = weight of the sample in grams
B = number of bromine atoms that will substitute on one molecule of the phenol.

Determination by Hydrogenation. The determination is carried out in exactly the same manner as for carboxyl described on page 195.

Esters.

Generic Test.

The saponification of esters constitutes the test for this group. In carrying out this saponification a diethylene glycol solution of the alkali is used instead of an alcoholic solution (137). Prepare a distillation tube by blowing a bulb about 6 to 7 mm in diameter at the end of a Pyrex tube of 4- to 5-mm bore and about 100 mm long, Fig. 167. Fill this bulb half full with ignited asbestos and introduce about 30 μl of the diethylene glycol solution of KOH directly into the bulb with a capillary pipet. Then introduce 10 μl of the ester in the same way. Take care that no liquid touches any part of the walls of the tube except the bulb. Wipe off the outside of the capillary pipet before introducing it into the distillation tube. If the liquids do not soak into the asbestos, brief centrifuging will bring this about. Place the tube in the metal heating block and cautiously heat the block until a condensate appears where the tube emerges from the block. Then increase the rate of heating until a definite ring of condensate has formed. Continue heating until the ring is 1 or 2 cm from the block. Sometimes no definite ring forms, only a larger number of drops. Collect the condensate in a capillary pipet. Should the condensate be turbid, seal the end of the pipet and centrifuge the contents. Cut the capillary at the interface and transfer the alcohol to a capillary containing a drying agent such as calcium oxide or anhydrous copper sulfate. After the alcohol has been dried, take it up in a boiling point capillary and determine the boiling point (*see* page 115 and note 3). Identify the acid part of the ester by adding a drop of water and a drop of alcohol to the residue in the distillation tube. After stirring and centrifuging, transfer the liquid to a centrifuge cone by means of a capillary pipet. Add a drop of phenolphthalein solution and acidify the solution

Fig. 167. Distillation Tube.

with sulfuric acid. Centrifuge to remove the potassium sulfate and siphon off the clear liquid for identification of the acid as described under Acids above.

Notes.

1) The 1 *m* KOH reagent is prepared by dissolving 60 g of pure KOH in 250 ml of technical diethylene glycol in a 500-ml flask and heating to no more than 130° to bring about complete solution. The hot solution is poured into 750 ml of diethylene glycol.

2) REDEMANN and LUCAS (124), who first suggested the diethylene glycol reagent, determined the reaction times of various esters and found that all reactions are complete within two minutes when carried out on a macro scale; hence, by the time the first distillate appears, the reaction is complete.

3) In all cases the distillate must be dried. Since there is always water in the reagents even if it is not added in making up the alkali, some water will distil with the alcohol. With water-insoluble alcohols this is not serious because the combined water-alcohol condensate in the capillary pipet can be separated into its components by centrifuging as described. With water-soluble alcohols some help is obtained from the fact that they boil at temperatures below the boiling point of water. Thus the first condensate is the alcohol, which, with care, can be collected without the water.

4) ROSENTHALER (126) carries out the saponification on a microscope slide and uses alcoholic potassium hydroxide.

5) BUCKLES and THELEN (24) have suggested the use of the hydroxamic acid test for esters in place of the saponification. This is a color reaction which depends upon the formation of a complex

$$\left[\begin{array}{c} \text{O} \\ \nearrow \quad \searrow \\ \text{R---C} \qquad \text{Fe} \\ \diagdown \quad \diagup \\ \text{NH---O} \end{array} \right]_3$$

which has a magenta color. BUCKLES and THELEN found it necessary to use three different procedures and even then some esters gave negative tests, some carboxylic acids and anhydrides, some aldehydes, etc., gave positive tests.

Derivatives of Esters.

Saponification Equivalent.   Weigh out 0.15 to 0.2 g of the glycol-
potassium hydroxide reagent on a microbalance or good analytical balance
in a glass-stoppered weighing bottle, 10 mm in diameter and 20 mm in
height.   Introduce 6 to 10 mg of the ester from a capillary pipet directly
over the reagent in the bottle and weigh the bottle again.   Then close the
stopper tightly and heat the bottle in a metal block (Fig. 168) to 60° or 70°.

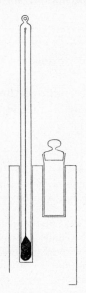

Fig. 168. Heating Block.

Open the stopper momentarily and close tightly again and heat the bottle
to 130°, holding it at this temperature for two minutes.   Allow it to cool,
occassionally lifting the stopper momentarily to prevent formation of a
partial vacuum when the bottle is cold.   When it reaches room temperature,
remove the stopper and rinse it off into the bottle.   Wash the contents of the
latter into a 10-ml Erlenmeyer flask.   The volume of the liquid must not
exceed 2 ml.   Titrate with 0.02 n acid using phenolphthalein as indicator.
Run a blank on the reagent to determine the milliequivalents b of potassium
hydroxide per gram of the reagent.

$$\text{Saponification equivalent} = S/b\ R\ V\ N$$

S = weight of sample in milligrams
b = milliequivalents of potassium hydroxide per gram of reagent
R = grams of reagent
V = volume of hydrochloric acid in milliliters
N = normality of acid

Note.

Care must be taken throughout the determination to prevent the loss of easily volatilized esters. Keep the bottle closed as much as possible.

Examination of the Saponification Products. *Neutral.* The distillate from the generic saponification test will contain the volatile products. For water-soluble substances, the distillation tube will act like an EMICH fractionation tube and the distillate will be practically pure. After suitable drying with calcium oxide or anhydrous copper sulfate, it is taken up in a boiling point capillary and the boiling point determined. Further confirmatory tests can then be carried out as follows.

Methyl Alcohol. Place the droplet in a 0.5-ml porcelain crucible. Heat a helix of fine copper wire, from 0.5 to 1 mm in diameter and 5 mm long, to bright red heat in the flame, allow it to cool until the red glow has just disappeared, and then drop it into the crucible. Quickly place a slide carrying a drop of methone solution (see page 160) on its under side over the crucible. The formaldehyde formed by the oxidation of the methyl alcohol causes the formation of formaldimethone which crystallizes in fine needles on the slide.

Ethyl Alcohol. Place the droplet in a microcone. Add a drop of potassium hydroxide solution, then iodine-potassium iodide solution to make the solution yellow, and then just enough alkali to decolorize it. A yellow powder can be seen at low magnifications but a high-power objective shows yellow hexagons and other forms reminiscent of snow-stars. This test is, of course, not specific for ethyl alcohol but should be used in conjunction with the boiling point.

Acetone and Isopropyl Alcohol. Carry out the iodoform test described above and determine the boiling point. *See* also the reactions of ketones.

Insoluble Products. When the distillate appears in the form of little droplets, a water-insoluble product is condensing as well as water. Take up the droplets in a fine-tipped capillary pipet, seal the tip, and centrifuge. Cut the tube at the interface and take up the alcohol in a boiling point capillary. Determine the boiling point. Sometimes it will be necessary to aid the separation of the alcohol and water mixture by the addition of a salt such as potassium carbonate. If the boiling point indicates an unsaturated alcohol such as allyl alcohol, test with bromine as described on page 235. If the distillate has a phenolic odor, test with bromine water and with ferric chloride as described above under Phenols.

Non-Volatile Products. Non-volatile products such as glycerol and the glycols remain behind with the salts of the acids in the residue from the distillation. They can be recovered by extracting the residue with, for example, ether, and recovering and identifying the extracted substance by the usual procedure of carrying out the generic tests, etc.

Acid Products of the Saponification. For the identification of the acid portion of the ester use the titrated solution from the determination of the saponification equivalent. Add 1 n H_2SO_4 just equivalent to the alkali consumed during the saponification. Shake thoroughly.

Insoluble Solid Acids. If a precipitate appears which is insoluble even on addition of more water (potassium sulfate may be precipitated if the solution is too concentrated) transfer the solution to a microcone and centrifuge. Decant the supernatant liquid and recrystallize the precipitate and identify as described under Acids above.

Acids Volatile with Steam. If the solution remains clear upon acidifying or after addition of more water, transfer the solution to an EMICH distilling flask (Fig. 38, page 36) and distil off almost all of the liquid. Remove the distillate as it forms in the knee of the flask as soon as a volume of several tenths of a milliliter has been collected, using a capillary pipet. For the identification of the acid use the partition method, page 190.

Acids Not Volatile with Steam. Transfer the residue from the EMICH flask to a microcone and evaporate to dryness. Extract the residue with ether or other solvent. Recrystallize the extracted acid and identify as described under Acids above.

DERMER and KING (35) describe a method for preparing the N-benzyl amides directly from the ester as a means of identifying the acid portion. The method can readily be adapted to microquantities by the use of a reflux tube.

LASKOWSKI and ADAMS (91) use the mixed fusion procedure of KOFLER to identify esters such as the 2,4,6-trinitrobenzoates.

Degradative Procedures.

Saponification is the most effective and informative degradative reaction for esters. It serves not only to identify the ester but to clarify the manner in which the acid and alcohol portions constitute the complete molecule.

When reduced by lithium aluminium hydride, the acid portion is converted to the corresponding alcohol. This reaction is especially valuable when dealing with the esters of the lower alcohols and the higher acids. Care must be taken to avoid too great an excess of the hydride. The procedure is described above under Acids.

Chemical Separation of Esters.

Esters are, in general, quite inert but some of the simpler ones as well as those of substituted acids are sufficiently active to be hydrolyzed or otherwise affected by strong mineral acid or base. With mixtures it is best, therefore, to rely upon the greater chemical activity of other possible components and to remove these. In the case of the more reactive esters, the substances usually found with them are the corresponding free acids and alcohols (from, e. g. bacterial action) and possibly the oxidation products (aldehydes) of the latter. The esters can be removed from such mixtures after successive treatment with acid and base and, possibly, bisulfite, by extraction, and fractional distillation. The acids which may be found in the mixture may also serve as a guide in the identification of the esters.

Quantitative Determination of Esters.

The most general method for the determination of esters is the procedure for the determination of the saponification equivalent. The possibility of studying the structure of certain hydroxy compounds such as the carbohydrates by acetylating or benzoylating them makes the determination of the acyl group very valuable and important. Hence, a number of methods have been developed for this purpose. The ease of hydrolysis of such acyl compounds varies considerably, however. If the original substance is somewhat complex, by-products of the hydrolysis aside from the acyl and the hydroxy portions may be acidic and volatile. The procedures described below are designed to permit only acetyl or benzoyl groups to be released as free acids and to provide for the more difficultly hydrolyzable or saponifiable substances. The method of KUHN and ROTH (88) uses p-toluenesulfonic acid for acid hydrolysis and methyl alcohol solution of NaOH for the alkaline saponification. These authors also use chromic-sulfuric acid for hydrolysis, but since this will also convert C-methylated groups into acetic acid, WIESENBERGER (165) proposed a combination of saponification and oxidation which would eliminate the interference of such C-methylated groups.

Determination of Acetyl or Benzoyl Group according to Kuhn and Roth.

Reagents.

$1 n$ NaOH in methyl alcohol. Dissolve 4 g NaOH (pellet form) in 50 ml water and 50 ml methyl alcohol. The methyl alcohol is best freed from residual acid by refluxing over solid KOH for 15 minutes and then distilling.

p-Toluenesulfonic acid. Pure, 25 % solution in water.

Metaphosphoric acid. Prepare by mixing phosphorus pentoxide with a few drops of water.

Barium chloride, crystals.

$0.01 n$ NaOH and $0.01 n$ HCl, standardized.

Phenolphthalein, 1% solution.

Apparatus.

The apparatus used is shown in Fig. 169. The U-tube and bubble counter is that used in microcombustion analysis. The bubble counter is filled to the proper height with 50 % sodium or potassium hydroxide, the U-tube with Ascarite or soda-lime. The saponification flask is made of Pyrex or Jena glass and has a capacity of 45 ml. The 2-mm bore inlet tube entering the flask through the ground joint A reaches close to the bottom of the flask. The central neck of the flask, B, is 80 mm long and the ground joint is fitted with a funnel which reaches just below the juncture with the flask. The funnel has an interior ground joint into which a glass plug S is fitted. The funnel should have a capacity of about 8 ml when the plug is in place and the 2 ml and 7 ml levels should be marked. Ground joint O is attached at an angle of 50° to the horizontal. This is 65 mm long and 5 mm in bore and fits vacuum tight into joints at the ends of a condenser of vitreous silica. As seen from the figure, this condenser can be fitted to the saponification flask in two positions, one to serve for refluxing and the other for

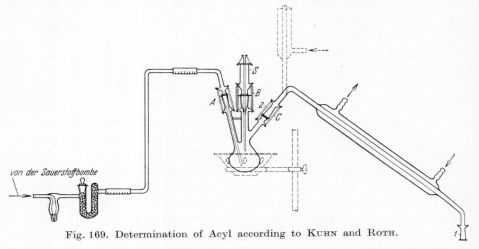

von der Sauerstoffbombe

Fig. 169. Determination of Acyl according to KUHN and ROTH.

distilling. During the saponification the flask is immersed in a 1-liter beaker containing boiling water so that the water reaches to the point where the necks are attached to the flask. The silica condenser is 36 cm long overall.

Procedure. Carefully clean the apparatus with chromic-sulfuric acid if it is new or used only infrequently. Rinse all glass parts of the apparatus thoroughly with distilled water prior to each determination and dry. Clean the condenser in the same way but do not dry it.

Attach the condenser before introducing the sample. Weigh out sufficient test substance in a long-handled weighing tube (Fig. 170) to require about 3 to 6 ml of the standard acid in the final titration. Pulverize difficultly soluble substances first in an agate mortar. If the test substance had to be quantitatively dried, weigh it out in a combustion boat and drop boat and sample into the saponification flask, holding the latter inclined. Weigh out liquids as described on page 188 and introduce the capillary tip first into the reagent already in the flask. Break the capillary by pressing on the handle with a glass rod. Rinse off the glass rod with 1 ml of water and quickly insert the funnel and fasten the springs.

Connect the bubble counter with a cylinder of oxygen or nitrogen by means of rubber tubing. Adjust the gas velocity with the needle valve of the cylinder to about 50 bubbles per minute. In acid hydrolysis add 1 ml of the 25 % p-toluenesulfonic acid, in alkaline saponification add 4 ml of the 1 n methyl alcohol solution of sodium hydroxide. Clamp the flask to a support stand, wet the joint C with water and attach the condenser tightly in the reflux position. Secure the condenser with a second clamp. Wet the gas inlet and funnel joints with the metaphosphoric acid and set firmly in place. Secure all ground joints with the springs. Add 1 to 2 ml of water to the stoppered funnel. Immerse the flask in a boiling water bath and allow the reaction to proceed for the required time. This may range from 15 minutes to several hours, depending upon the complexity of the test substance.

Fig. 170. Charging Tubes, nat. size.

At the conclusion of the reaction remove the water bath and allow the flask to cool. Rinse the condenser with 4 to 6 ml water from a wash bottle into the flask after removing the glass stopper from the funnel. Replace the stopper, remove the condenser and clean this carefully with 100 to 200 ml water. Return it to the flask in the distilling position and fasten it firmly and tightly into place. If the methyl alcohol solution was used, distil off 5 ml of the contents of the flask, rinse the condenser again as before and again connect to the flask.

If p-toluenesulfonic acid has been used, add 0.5 ml 1 n NaOH from a pipet to the funnel. If the alkali was used, add 1 ml 6.5 m H$_2$SO$_4$ (100 ml conc. H$_2$SO$_4$ diluted with 200 ml water). By carefully lifting the stopper, allow the acid or base to flow into the flask and rinse with 2 to 3 ml water. Add water to the 7-ml mark in the funnel after replacing the stopper. Add a few boiling stones to the solution in the flask. Distil at a rate of 5 to 6 ml every 5 minutes, collecting the distillate in a 25-ml Pyrex or Jena graduated cylinder. When the volume of the residue in the flask approaches 2 to 3 ml, lift the stopper of the funnel to allow the water in the latter to drop to the 2-ml mark without interrupting the distillation. Repeat this addition of 5 ml of water until the distillation is complete. When 20 ml of the distillate has been collected, remove any adhering drop by touching with the cylinder and at the same time place the silica flask under the end of the condenser. Place the funnel which had been in the cylinder in the silica flask and pour

the contents of the cylinder into the flask. Without rinsing, place the funnel
and cylinder under the condenser and remove the silica flask for the titration.
Be careful not to lose any drops of distillate during this exchange. While
the distillation is continuing, add 2 or 3 crystals of barium chloride to the
silica flask, boil the solution for several seconds to remove carbon dioxide
and observe if any turbidity appears in the solution. Such a turbidity would
be caused by sulfuric or sulfonic acid carried over by entrainment and the
presence of these acids would naturally cause error. In such a case the determination must be repeated. If the solution remains clear, add 4 to 5 drops
of phenolphthalein and titrate. Test all other distillates in the same way with
the barium chloride. If less than 4 ml of the alkali are required for the titration, titrate the next 10 ml of distillate. If the amount of acetic acid is
found to be larger, collect three 5-ml distillates for the titration. If the indicator changes color upon the addition of the first drop of the base, the analysis is complete.

$$\% \text{ Acetyl} = V\,F_1/S$$
$$\% \text{ Benzoyl} = V\,F_2/S$$

$F_1 = $ milligrams CH_3CO equivalent to 1 ml standardized NaOH
$F_2 = $ milligrams C_5H_6CO equivalent to 1 ml standardized NaOH
$V = $ ml of 0.01 n NaOH used in titrations
$S = $ weight of sample in milligrams

Determination of Acetyl according to Wiesenberger. The oxidation procedure proposed by Kuhn and L'Orsa (87) and modified by
Kuhn and Roth (88) for micro-quantities for the determination of C-methylated groups also serves to hydrolyze acyl groups. To avoid confusion between
the acetic acid originating in acetyl groups and that originating in other
C-methylated groups, Wiesenberger (165) suggested using the usual
p-toluenesulfonic acid hydrolysis or alkaline saponification first and passing
the volatile products through chromic-sulfuric acid oxidation solution to
destroy all acidic compounds other than the acetic acid derived from the
original acetyl group in the test substance.

Reagents.

Even the purest reagents will give a small blank. Before beginning an
extended purification of freshly prepared solutions it is advisable to carry
out a blank determination for every procedure. Only if the results of these
are too high (usually they lie between 0.1 and 0.15 ml of 0.01 n NaOH),
should any purification of the individual solutions be carried out.

For the sulfuric and chromic-sulfuric acid solutions this is best and most
efficiently accomplished by boiling them for some time under reflux and
then distilling off the low boiling acid components. The water distilled off
is replaced by equal volumes of freshly distilled water to maintain the
same concentration of the reagents.

The same procedure is used in the preparation of the p-toluenesulfonic acid but, after the boiling under reflux, the distillation is carried out several times with freshly distilled alcohol. The original volume is finally restored by adding alcohol to the residue in the flask. The alcohol used for this purpose should be boiled under reflux over sodium carbonate and then distilled.

Prepare the p-toluenesulfonic acid solution in small lots that are used up in a few days. Since the blank value rises again with solutions more than a few days old, longer periods of storage are not recommended.

The methyl alcohol used for the alkali solutions is freed of acids by boiling over KOH and then distilling.

De-ionized water prepared by the use of ion-exchange resins is preferred over distilled water since the latter does not meet the high requirements of purity for this procedure.

Apparatus.

The apparatus consists of (a) the saponification flask *1*, with refluxing insert *2*, (b) the connector with the washer *3* for the chromic-sulfuric acid with the double condensation chambers, and (c) the condenser *5* and the flask for the collection of the distillate *6*. The tube *4* serves as a connection with a water suction pump when *3* is to be washed out. Clean out the apparatus thoroughly with chromic-sulfuric acid. This is most essential for proper performance of the determination. If the apparatus is in constant use, repeat the cleaning every week. Thoroughly rinse out with tap water. In particular leave all ground joints which come into contact with the distillate in running water for at least ten minutes. Rinse with purest distilled water. Dry the saponification flask before use.

Assemble the apparatus as shown in Fig. 171 for the saponification as well as for the chromic-sulfuric acid oxidation. Clamp the condenser of the apparatus to a support stand and attach all other parts to the condenser by means of the springs on the joints. Weigh out the test substance in a long-handled weighing tube as in the previous procedure. Introduce this in a horizontal position into the dry saponification flask and raise to the vertical position so that the substance drops into the flask. Weigh back the tube to determine the weight of sample used. The sample should come to rest as far as possible on the bottom of the flask. Weigh out hygroscopic substances in thin-walled platinum boats after drying and drop boat and sample into the flask. Add two or three platinum tetrahedra to prevent bumping. Use only sulfuric acid for cleaning these tetrahedra, never nitric or hydrochloric acid.

Acid Hydrolysis. For this only the flask and insert *2* are needed at the beginning. Connect the water inlet and outlets, the reaction flask containing the sample, etc. and seal the joints with water. Add 2 ml of 6 m H_2SO_4 through the funnel by lifting the stopper and lower the flask into a previously heated bath so that the two liquid levels are the same. Carry out the reaction at 160° to 170°. About 30 minutes will be required. In the meantime add 2 ml of chromic-sulfuric acid (4 parts of $5\,n$ chromic acid and 1 part concentrated sulfuric acid) into the washer and heat this to 135° to 140°. At the conclusion of the hydrolysis, lift the flask out of the heating bath, allow 2 ml of water to flow from the ground-in funnel into the flask and connect the flask to the remainder of the apparatus.

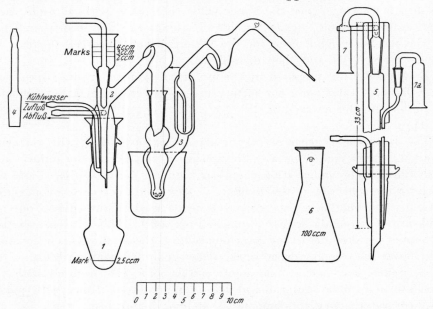

Fig. 171. WIESENBERGER's Apparatus for the Determination of Acetyl.

After draining the cooling water from the reflux condenser, start the distillation by carefully heating the contents of the flask, using a low Bunsen flame shielded by a chimney. The tip of the flame must not touch the bottom of the flask. Adjust the rate of distillation so that about 1 ml of distillate per minute is obtained. Collect this in a freshly steamed-out silica receiving flask (receiver) which has been rinsed with distilled water. To control the amount of liquid distilled, mark the distillation flask at the 2.5 ml point and always carry out the distillation to this point. In addition, note the expected final volume on the receiver. First distil to the 2.5-ml mark. Then allow 2 ml of water again to flow in and again distil off the same volume of water. Add the water by first removing the burner to allow the chromic-sulfuric acid to return to the point shown by the arrow in Fig. 171. Then open the ground-in stopper by carefully turning it and allow a slow, uniform entry of the water. This procedure will require but 20 seconds and hardly interrupt the distillation. Immediately replace the burner under the distillation flask and repeat the entire procedure until the distillate reaches the marked point of 26 ml on the receiver. If the distillation is carried out properly, it should be completed in 30 to 35 minutes. During the distillation make certain that the temperature of the heating bath remains within the prescribed limits. Distil off each time a volume corresponding to the volume of water added. Never empty the funnel completely.

Alkaline Saponification. The apparatus and the sample are prepared as above. Use 2 ml of a 1 m NaOH in methyl alcohol and add this directly to the flask prior to the connection with the reflux condenser. Boil the solution 20 minutes (temperature of heating bath 130° to 140°) to saponify the test substance. Remove the heating bath, add 2 ml of water from the ground-in funnel, drain the water from the reflux condenser and heat the contents of the flask to boiling by means of a small flame. The methyl alcohol vapors do not condense but go out into the atmosphere. Repeat the boiling off the methyl alcohol twice, adding water previously each time and then evaporating to the 2.5-ml mark. Then connect the previously prepared distillation apparatus and slowly add 2 ml of the 6 m H_2SO_4 through the ground-in funnel. The last drop of the acid seals the stopper. Then fill water into the funnel immediately. Carry out the distillation as above. The methyl alcohol solution of sodium hydroxide has a high solvent power and is preferred as a saponification agent. In a few cases it is necessary to use more strongly concentrated alkali solutions. Otherwise the procedure is the same. The amount of sulfuric acid which must be added is, of course, determined by the concentration of the alkali used.

Determination of Acetyl by Transesterification. Wash out the apparatus shown in Fig. 171 with distilled water and then rinse with the same ethyl alcohol as used in the determination and assemble it while moist with the alcohol. Use the saponification flask after drying it. Introduce the sample as described above. Add 2 ml of the solution of 50 mg p-toluenesulfonic acid in 1 ml ethyl alcohol through the ground-in funnel and boil under reflux for ten minutes. Dip the flask in the heating bath (95° to 100°) so that the levels of the liquids are the same. After this preliminary heating, drain the cooling water from the condenser without interrupting the heating and distil off the alcohol-ester mixture for the first time. The distillation takes place at constant temperature and requires about ten minutes. Turn on the flow of water through the condenser again and allow 1 ml ethyl alcohol to flow into the flask from the ground-in funnel. Heat the contents of the flask again for ten minutes under reflux. Then carry out the final distillation of the alcohol-ester mixture with the heating bath temperature at 105° to 110°. In all, a total of 10 ml of alcohol should be distilled off. Take care, however, to leave about 1 ml of liquid in the flask at all times during the distillation. Every milliliter distilled off should be replaced immediately from the ground-in funnel. Collect the distillate in a 100-ml Jena Erlenmeyer flask which fits on the joint of the condenser 5. Use 1 ml of a 0.5 n NaOH for the saponification of the ester. At the conclusion of the distillation, loosen the ground joint between 2 and 5, rinse the condenser 5 with 1 to 2 ml alcohol and stopper it with the soda-lime tube 7. Bring the distillate to a gentle boil under reflux for 15 minutes to complete the saponification. Place the flask in a beaker of water to cool it and rinse out the condenser and deaerating tube with 10 ml distilled water. Disconnect the flask from the condenser and begin the evaporation of the alcohol by holding the flask by means of a tongs over a free flame and continually swirling it until the contents boil. As long as the liquid is kept in continual rotatory motion, losses through spraying will not occur. In 3 to 5 minutes the alcohol will be evaporated and the solution concentrated to 3 to 5 ml.

If desired, the alkaline sodium acetate solution can be converted into an acetic acid solution by the use of a cation exchange resin (*see* page 84) and titrated as usual with a 0.02 n HCl.

For other procedures for acyl determination see ELEK and HARTE (42), ALICINO (2), CLARKE and CHRISTENSEN (28), BRADBURY (19), and SCHÖ-NIGER, LIEB, and EL DIN IBRAHIM (139).

Acid Anhydrides and Lactones.

There is no separate generic test for these classes of compounds. Substances which do not react readily enough with an alkali to give positive results in the generic tests for acids or phenols, but which give a saponification equivalent of less than 500 in the test for esters and which yield the potassium salt as the only product of the saponification are placed in this class.

ROTH (133) states that anhydrides and lactones can in many cases be titrated by the technique described below. To distinguish between the two classes of compounds he suggests the ZEREWITINOFF reaction with GRIGNARD reagent or the conversion of the anhydride to the 2,4-dichloro-anilide.

Titration of Anhydrides and Lactones.

Weigh out the sample of test substance into a 100-ml Erlenmeyer flask of vitreous silica. The latter should be fitted with a ground-in stopper which can be replaced, if necessary, by a condenser. Dissolve the sample in methyl or ethyl alcohol as above in the determination of neutralization equivalent of acids and add a 50 to 80% excess of 0.01 n NaOH. Carefully heat the solution to boiling. If the substance goes completely into solution, back-titrate the excess base with 0.01 n acid using phenolphthalein as indicator. To make certain that the hydrolysis of the anhydride or lactone was complete, titrate a second sample of the test substance but only after the solution has been boiled for ten minutes under reflux.

2,4-Dichloroanilides of Anhydrides.

The anhydride is treated in an inert solvent with 2,4-dichloroaniline to form one molecule of the dichloroanilide and one molecule of the acid:

$$CH_3 \cdot CO$$
$$O + C_6H_3Cl_2NH_2 \longrightarrow C_6H_3Cl_2NH \cdot CO \cdot CH_3CH_3 + HCO \cdot OH$$
$$CH_3 \cdot CO$$

It is possible, of course, to titrate the acid after removal of the excess reagent or to determine the latter iodometrically without separating it. The latter procedure is preferred for micro quantities.

Reagents.

0.02 n Bromide-bromate solution. Weigh out 0.504 g of sodium bromate and 2.38 g potassium bromide into a 1-liter volumetric flask, dissolve in doubly distilled water and then make up to the mark.

0.02 n Sodium thiosulfate solution.

2,4-Dichloroaniline standard solution. Dissolve 1 g 2,4-dichloroaniline in 100 ml glacial acetic acid.

Acetic acid, glacial; 2 n hydrochloric acid; starch indicator solution, 1%.

Procedure. Weigh out 5 to 8 mg of the test substance into a test tube. Add 2 ml glacial acetic acid. In the case of liquid test substances weigh out the sample in capillary tubes and crush the capillary in the acetic acid with a glass rod and rinse off the rod with 0.3 to 0.5 ml glacial acetic acid. Add 2 ml of the 2,4-dichloroaniline standard solution by means of a precision pipet and stopper the test tube with a cork. After two hours rinse the solution quantitatively with 16 ml glacial acetic acid into a 250-ml titration flask (with a ground-in stopper). Add 20 ml distilled water, 5 ml 2 m HCl, and, from a buret, axactly 15.0 ml of the 0.02 n-bromide-bromate solution. Allow the closed flask to stand for five minutes, add a few milligrams of potassium iodide from the fine tip of a spatula and 8 to 10 drops of the starch indicator. Swirl the contents of the flask and titrate in the usual way with the 0.02 n sodium thiosulfate solution until the starch-iodide color is dissipated.

Carry out a blank determination under exactly the same conditions. According to the equation given above, one molecule of anhydride (or 2,4-dichloroaniline) requires two atoms of bromine.

$$\% \ C_2O_3 = 72.02 \ (A - B)/S$$

$A =$ ml 0.02 n sodium thiosulfate used in determination
$B =$ ml 0.02 n sodium thiosulfate used in blank
$S =$ mg sample

SMITH, BRYANT, and MITCHELL (144) use the KARL FISCHER reagent to determine the water required to hydrolyze a sample of anhydride in the presence of a catalyst.

Degradative Procedures.

The fragmentation of anhydrides is accomplished by hydrolysis, ammonolysis, or alcoholysis. All of the reactions of monocarboxylic acid anhydrides result in the formation of at least one molecule of the free acid or its salt and this can be identified as described under Acids. The salt is usually formed more easily than the free acid. Ammonolysis or alcoholysis produces an amide or ester as well as the free acid. The latter reactions are somewhat different, however, in the case of cyclic anhydrides. In such cases half the original anhydride group is converted to the carboxyl group and the other half to the acyl group, forming a mixed derivative. Thus, for example, succinic anhydride upon treatment with ammonia will give but one product, ammonium succinamate or, with alcohol, ethyl hydrogen succinate.

Aromatic anhydrides will react with an aromatic hydrocarbon in the presence of aluminum chloride in a type of FRIEDEL-CRAFTS reaction to form one molecule of an aryl ketone and one molecule of the acid. These can be separated by the formation of a metallic salt of the acid. The PERKIN reaction of an aromatic aldehyde and an aliphatic anhydride to form an unsaturated acid can be employed in some cases.

Chemical Separation.

The anhydrides can be separated from compounds other than acids by first hydrolyzing or saponifying to the acids or salts and then using the procedures outlined for acids.

Quantitative Determination.

The bromide-bromate titration of the dichloroanilides described above can be used to measure the anhydride directly. Conversion to a salt permits determination by one of the residue determinations described under Acids. The procedures for determination of active hydrogen serve also for the quantitative measurement of anhydrides.

Ketones.

Generic Test.

The generic test for ketones consists of two parts. The first is conducted at room temperature and the second, which is applied only if negative tests are obtained in the first part, at 80°.

The reaction is that with phenylhydrazine to form phenylhydrazones:

$$R-\underset{\underset{H(R')}{|}}{\overset{\overset{O}{||}}{C}} + \underset{\underset{H}{|}}{\overset{\overset{H}{|}}{N}}-N\langle\bigcirc\rangle \rightarrow R-\underset{\underset{H(R')}{|}}{\overset{\overset{O\ H}{|\ \ |}}{C}}-N-N\langle\bigcirc\rangle \rightarrow$$

$$R-\underset{\underset{H(R')}{|}}{C}=\overset{\overset{H}{|}}{N}-N\langle\bigcirc\rangle + H_2O$$

I) Draw about 0.5 μl of the phenylhydrazine reagent into a capillary tube of 1-mm bore and allow it to slide to the middle of the tube. Draw about five times as much of the test substance in at the other end of the capillary. Seal the first end and centrifuge the reagent and sample to this end. A precipitate or turbidity appears within five minutes if the test is positive.

II) If the contents of the tube remain clear, place the tube in a water bath which is kept at 80°. Observe the contents of the capillary for 15 minutes. If an opacity or precipitate appears within that time, the test is positive.

Notes.

1) The reagent is prepared by mixing 1 ml of pure phenylhydrazine, 7.5 ml of 95% ethyl alcohol, and 2.5 ml of glacial acid and diluting with distilled water to a total volume of 25 ml.

2) Some esters and anhydrides also react with the reagent to form acyl derivatives.

3) The acetic acid catalyzes the reaction but strong acids such as hydrochloric may prevent the reaction. Certain salts of phenylhydrazine such as the oxalate, sulfate, and phosphate are insoluble in water.

4) Ketones of low molecular weight react almost immediately but those of higher molecular weight may require a considerable time. The conditions of the test and the reagent are set to include all the ketones of this genus. WU (167), who determined the conditions and limitations of the test, notes that the ketones which will not react positively in this test have a carbonyl group that is joined to (1) two alkyl radicals larger than hexyl; (2) any aryl radical and an alkyl larger than $C_{11}H_{25}$; (3) any two tertiary alkyl radicals; (4) any carbocyclic radical containing two substituents in ortho position to its point of attachment to the carbonyl group. Isocyclic ketones having an *esocyclic* carbonyl lying immediately between two ortho substituents also do not react.

Derivatives of Ketones.

Oxidation of Ketones. Place 3 to 6 mg of the ketone in a reflux tube. Add the calculated volume of the oxidizing solution. Seal the tube and heat in a water bath until the solution turns green. Open the tube cautiously; first cut off the fine tip and then cut the tube at the wider portion. Transfer the contents to an EMICH distilling flask (Fig. 38, page 36) by inserting the open end of the reflux tube into the neck of the inverted flask so that the end of the tube is beyond the opening of the side tube of the flask. Then, holding the flask and the tube securely, bring the hand down sharply so that the flask is in the upright position and the tube is inverted. Avoid getting any of the solution on the side walls of the flask. Using a boiling capillary or two, distil off most of the liquid, removing the distillate with a capillary pipet as often as a sufficiently large drop forms. Allow the flask and contents to cool, open the stopper, and wash down the walls with a small amount of water from a capillary pipet. Repeat the distillation. The acids in the distillate may be identified by the partition method (page 190), by the formation of the silver salts (page 186), or by the formation of characteristic metallic salts (page 191).

Note.

The oxidizing solution is prepared by adding 8 ml 18 m H_2SO_4 to 60 ml of water and dissolving in this solution 10 g of commercial chromic anhydride crystals. This solution is equivalent to two milliequivalents of oxygen per milliliter.

Ketones in general resist the usual oxidizing agents but not a strong oxidant such as hot nitric acid or chromic-sulfuric acid. Methyl ketones can be oxidized selectively to acids by sodium hypochlorite (73, 153). The result of the oxidation is the breaking of the molecule at the carbonyl group and the formation of a mixture of acids:

$$CH_3 \cdot CO \cdot C_2H_5 \nearrow 2\, CH_3CO \cdot OH$$
$$\searrow HCO \cdot OH + C_2H_5CO \cdot OH$$

Other Derivatives of Ketones.   The phenylhydrazones, substituted phenylhydrazones, and semicarbazones and other derivatives are prepared by the corresponding procedures under Aldehydes. See also FISCHER (46) and FISCHER and MOOR (48).

HOFMANN, METZLER, and LECHER (66) describe the crystalline products obtained by the reaction of ketones and perchloric acid.

Degradative Procedures.

The oxidation of ketones described above results in the formation of two acids, thus complicating the identification of the degradative products. It may therefore be preferable to resort to reduction. This is accomplished most easily and readily by the use of lithium-aluminum hydride. The procedures given on pages 195 and 198 describe the method and apparatus for such reduction. The products are, of course, the secondary alcohols. It should be kept in mind, however, that reduction of ketones may also take place by the process known as bimolecular reduction. In the case of acetone, for example, when reduced by magnesium, a considerable amount of pinacol is formed by the reaction of two molecules of the ketone.

Chemical Separation of Ketones.

The additive power of the carbonyl group in ketones is lower compared to aldehydes and therefore reactions such as bisulfite addition cannot be used for the general separation of this group of compounds.

TREIBS and RÖHNERT (151) have used phenylhydrazine-p-sulfonic acid (p-hydrazinobenzenesulfonic acid) as a means of separating ketones from aldehydes. Prepare the reagent by buffering a solution of the reagent in 50% alcohol with an equal weight of sodium acetate. Treat the ketone with an excess of the reagent and heat under reflux for two hours. Cool, add an equal volume of water, and extract the excess reagent with ether. To recover the ketone, hydrolyze the condensation product in the water layer by heating with dilute sulfuric acid for one hour. Extract the ketone from the cooled solution with ether, shake with sodium bicarbonate solution to remove any acid, and dry the residue with anhydrous sodium sulfate after evaporation of the ether.

For separation of ketones from compounds other than aldehydes, the oximes and the semicarbazones are most frequently employed. The procedures described under Aldehydes are followed.

Quantitative Determination of Ketones.

Since ketones condense readily with the substituted phenylhydrazines, these compounds can be used as with aldehydes for the determination of the carbonyl group. The procedures are described under Aldehydes.

Alcohols.

Generic Test.

The compounds which comprise this group consist of the following:

A) Compounds which have given negative results in all of the previous generic tests and which are completely soluble in less than 50 parts of water at 20°.

B) Compounds which have given negative results in all of the previous generic tests, which are insoluble in 50 parts of water at 20°, which are liquid at 75°, and which give positive results in the sodium test described below.

The lower alcohols (up to about 3 carbon atoms) usually contain moisture and would therefore give a positive test with sodium in any event. Hence, the substance is classified as an alcohol if the sample is soluble in 50 parts of water. The generic test for alcohols, therefore, consists of two parts: (I) the determination of the solubility and, (II) the sodium test for those substances which do not show the required solubility.

I) The solubility is determined by the capillary method described on page 152. If the substance is not soluble in the required degree, its reactivity with sodium is determined.

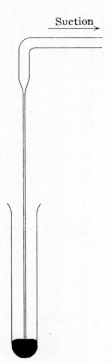

Fig. 172. Filling a Capillary with Sodium.

II) Sodium Test. Prepare the reagent by melting some sodium in a hard glass test tube. Draw out a glass tube into a thin-walled capillary of about 0.5-mm bore and about 150 mm long. Without cutting the capillary from the wide tube, dip the capillary into the molten sodium and apply suction carefully, Fig. 172. The sodium will rise in the capillary. Allow it to cool and congeal, as it will almost immediately. Cut short pieces of the filled capillary for the test just before use to ensure a clean surface of the sodium.

Carry out the test by placing a drop of the test substance on a slide. Lay a piece of sodium capillary on the slide so that the fresh-cut end is in the center of the drop. Place the entire set-up under a lens or low-power microscope. If the substance is an alcohol, bubbles of hydrogen will issue from the capillary. If no evolution of hydrogen takes place, put the slide on a metal block and heat to 75° and observe again.

Note.

Normally sodium does not replace the hydrogen attached to carbon but some functional groups may activitate the hydrogen adjacent to them. For example, acetylenes or monosubstituted acetylenes, acetoacetic ester, acetone, and acetophenone will all react with sodium with the displacement of hydrogen. Judgment must, therefore, be used when carrying out the test. The evolution of hydrogen should continue for some time after **starting**.

Classification Tests for Alcohols.

Iodoform Test. Place about 0.1 mg of the test substance in a micro-cone and add a drop or two of 10% potassium hydroxide solution. Warm the solution and then add potassium iodide-iodine reagent until the solution becomes yellow. Add more potassium hydroxide until the solution becomes colorless once more. The reagents can best be added by placing drops on a slide and transferring small quantities to the test drop by means of a platinum hook or glass thread. Allow the test to stand for two minutes, then examine for a precipitate. If no precipitate has formed, place the cone in a metal block or water bath and heat to 60° for just one minute. If no precipitate appears, set aside for two minutes and then observe again.

Notes.

1) The reaction involves oxidation, halogenation, and cleavage:

$$R—CH—CH_3 + KOI \rightarrow R—C—CH_3 \ , \ R—C—CH_3 + KOI \rightarrow R—C—CI_3 \ ,$$
$$\ \ \ |\qquad\qquad\qquad\qquad\ \ \|\qquad\qquad\quad\ \ \|\qquad\qquad\qquad\qquad\ \|$$
$$\ \ OH\qquad\qquad\qquad\qquad\ O\qquad\qquad\quad\ \ O\qquad\qquad\qquad\qquad\ O$$

$$R—C—CI_3 + KOH \rightarrow RCO \cdot O^- + K^+ + CHI_3$$
$$\quad\ \|$$
$$\quad\ O$$

2) Prepare the potassium iodide-iodine reagent by rubbing 1 part of iodine, 5 parts of potassium iodide, and 15 parts of water together in a mortar.

3) The precipitate will appear amorphous but when it is examined under a micro-scope, yellow hexagons and stars resembling snow crystals can be observed.

4) This test will give a positive result with compounds containing the CH_3CO—, CH_2ICO—, or the CHI_2CO— group joined to a hydrogen atom or to a carbon atom which does not carry active hydrogen atoms, or with compounds which will react with the reagent to give any of the above groups. Typical compounds giving the test are acetaldehyde, ethyl alcohol, methyl ketones, and secondary alcohols which undergo oxidation to methyl ketones. For a review of the iodoform test see FUSON and BULL (57).

5) A method for carrying out the test on a slide is described by SCHAEFFER (136).

Distinction Between Liquid Saturated Primary, Secondary, and Tertiary Monohydric Alcohols.

A) *Lucas Test.* The reaction involves the replacement of the hydroxyl group with chloride:

$$ROH + HCl \longrightarrow RCl + H_2O$$

Draw 2 to 3 mm of the test substance into one end of a capillary. Draw six times as much zinc chloride-hydrochloric acid reagent into the other end. Seal both ends and centrifuge the liquids back and forth twice. Examine the contents for turbidity. After one hour examine the capillary again. If a turbidity appears at either time, centrifuge the capillary and examine for the presence of two layers. Normal alcohols will show no turbidity even after standing for one hour. Secondary alcohols will become turbid after a time, and two layers appear upon centrifuging. Tertiary alcohols will give an immediate turbidity which may separate into two layers even without centrifuging.

Notes.

1) Prepare the reagent by dissolving 13.6 g anhydrous zinc chloride in 10.5 g 12 *m* hydrochloric acid with cooling.

2) Impurities in the primary alcohols may cause some cloudiness, but no second layer will separate; hence the formation of this second layer is required for a positive test. Primary alcohols will be changed to chlorides by this reagent but only upon prolonged heating at 130 to 150°.

3) For the behavior of insoluble alcohols see the original paper of LUCAS (95).

B) *Oxidation Test.* RITTER (125) has used the relative ease of oxidation as a basis for the distinction between primary, secondary, and tertiary aliphatic alcohols. Fit a microcone with a stopper carrying a glass rod which reaches to the bottom of the cone. Introduce 150 µl glacial acetic acid into the cone and then one drop, from a capillary pipet, of the test substance. Also from a capillary pipet add, a drop at a time, a saturated, filtered solution of potassium permanganate in water, stoppering and shaking between additions. This is best accomplished by holding the top of the centrifuge cone tightly between the thumb and forefinger of the left hand and pulling the forefinger of the right hand over the bottom of the cone so as to make it snap. If no decolorization of the permanganate takes place, the alcohol is tertiary. If decolorization does take place, continue the addition of the permanganate until a pink color persists. Then add a drop of concentrated sulfuric acid and continue the addition of permanganate with shaking. If the color is not discharged under these conditions, the alcohol is primary. If decolorization proceeds again after the addition of the sulfuric acid, followed by a final permanent pink color, the alcohol is secondary.

Notes.

1) This method has been found reliable for all aliphatic alcohols through the amyl group.

2) The distinctive behavior of the alcohols depends not only upon the relative ease of oxidation but also upon the quantity of oxidant consumed in the oxidation. Primary alcohols are most readily oxidized, secondary alcohols are next in order, and tertiary alcohols are most resistant to oxidation. But while each molecule of a primary alcohol is oxidized (finally) to one molecule of an acid, the secondary alcohols are oxidized to two molecules of acid for every molecule of original alcohol and hence will consume more of the oxidant.

3) It is advisable to run a blank test on the glacial acetic acid used since some samples of this acid contain substances oxidizable with the permanganate.

Derivatives of Alcohols.

α-Naphthyl Urethans. Add a slight excess of α-naphthyl isocyanate to 3 to 6 mg of the anhydrous test substance in a dry microcone. Stir and allow to stand for several minutes. If no precipitate appears after this time, warm the cone gently and allow it to cool again. Repeat this process until a precipitate forms. Decant if a liquid remains with the solid and extract the solid with boiling ligroin by adding 200 to 500 µl of ligroin and heating the cone in a metal block or in a boiling water bath. Transfer the hot ligroin in a capillary pipet to another microcone. If the carbamate does not separate out when this solution cools, concentrate it by heating the cone and blowing air over the surface of the solution. Recrystallize from ligroin.

Notes.

1) The reaction is as follows:

$$C_{10}H_7N{=}C{=}O + ROH \rightarrow C_{10}H_7NHCO \cdot OR$$

2) Water hydrolyzes the urethans to give arylamines which combine with excess reagent to form di-α-naphthylurea:

$$C_{10}H_7NHCO \cdot OR + H_2O \rightarrow C_{10}OH_7NHCO \cdot OH \rightarrow C_{10}H_7NH_2 + CO_2$$
$$C_{10}H_7N{=}C{=}O + C_{10}H_7NH_2 \rightarrow C_{10}H_7NHCONHC_{10}H_7$$

The method is therefore best suited for water-insoluble alcohols. A trace of water which may produce the above urea is not serious because the urea can be removed in the treatment with ligroin in which the urea is insoluble.

Acid Esters of 3-Nitrophthalic Acid.

To about 2 mg of 3-nitrophthalic anhydride in a centrifuge cone add enough of the dry alcohol to moisten the reagent. Avoid an excess. Heat the cone in the metal block until the contents liquify. Keep them at this temperature for five to ten minutes. Cool in ice and start crystallization by scratching with a glass thread. Dissolve the ester in the smallest amount of boiling benzene. If a residue remains, centrifuge it off and decant the supernatant liquid. Add an equal volume of ligroin to the clear liquid and allow crystallization to take place slowly.

Notes.

1) The reaction is as follows:

2) This reagent has the advantage of reacting with the alkyl esters of ethylene glycol and diethylene glycol as well as with the simple alcohols.

3) Since the products are half-esters, they are acidic enough to be titrated and the neutralization equivalent can be be determined.

p-Nitrobenzoates and 3,5-Dinitrobenzoates.

These derivatives of alcohols are prepared in the same manner as for the phenols. *See* page 205 for the procedure. In the case of alcohols the preparation of the sodium derivatives as a preliminary step as described in Note 3 on page 206 seems particularly advantageous.

ARMSTRONG and COPENHAVER (6) suggest the use of excess alcohol with the alcohols of few carbon atoms but a 10% excess of the acid chloride with the higher alcohols.

DEWEY and WITT (37) have described the optical properties of the phenyl urethans. ALBER (1) describes microprocedures for the FISCHER and TAFEL test for glycerine, the GLÄSER and MORAWSKI reaction for diethylene glycol, and the ROSE reaction for *d*-mannite.

The reaction of the alcohols with acetyl chloride has been carried out on a microscale by FOULKE and SCHNEIDER (52, 53), and a test for triaryl carbinols is described by MORTON and PEAKES (103).

For *n*-propyl and higher alcohols BAIR and SUTER (17) suggest *s*-benzyl-thiouronium chloride as a reagent in a procedure readily adaptable to micro quantities. The preparation of the triphenylmethyl ethers of polyhydric alcohols by the method of SEIKEL and HUNTRESS (140) is also very simple.

Degradative Procedures for Alcohols.

The oxidation of the alcohol presents the greatest possibility of obtaining fragments which are easily and readily identifiable. As pointed out above in the discussion of the RITTER method for distinguishing between primary, secondary, and tertiary alcohols, the effect of oxidizing agents varies. This in itself is of advantage in a diagnostic study. On the other hand, the indifference of the tertiary compounds calls for the use of a very vigorous oxidizing agent, hot nitric acid, which will break up the original compound into a considerable number of fragments, which might be difficult to relate to the alcohol when the latter is a simple aliphatic monohydric compound. If an aldehyde or acid results from the oxidation with permanganate, the test substance must have been a primary alcohol; if a ketone is obtained, it must have been a secondary alcohol. The reactivity of the products makes the identification easy.

Polyhydric alcohols offer a number of possibilities as far as cleavage or oxidation products are concerned. The use of other, more selective, oxidants such as lead tetracetate in acetic acid solution or periodic acid in aqueous solution will give aldehydes, ketones, or both with glycol. Periodic acid in particular gives a quantitative reaction, and the amount of acid used as well as the nature of the products is employed for determination of the structure of the original material. Oxidation of unsaturated alcohols may be directed to the multiple bond or to the alcohol group by choice of oxidant and conditions. For example, oxidation of allyl alcohol by dilute permanganate will give glycerol, while protection of the double bond by bromine will result in the formation of acrolein and acrylic acid.

Chemical Separation of Alcohols.

Alkoxides such as sodium ethoxide are formed by the interaction of the alcohol with the metal. The latter must be in a certain form depending upon its activity. Sodium or potassium are best added in the form of metal dispersions in an inert solvent such as toluene; barium and calcium in the form of their oxides will react with the primary and secondary alcohols at about 130°. Aluminum alkoxides are formed by heating the alcohol with aluminum amalgam. These alkoxides are usually soluble in the respective alcohol and the excess of the latter must be evaporated to obtain the metallic compound. It must be kept in mind that, as pointed out above in the discussion of the generic test, compounds other than alcohols will react with metals.

Some alcohols will enter into the composition of compounds as *alcohol of solvation*. Glycerol has been reported as forming a compound $CaCl_2 \cdot 3 C_3H_5 (OH)_3$. Such compounds, again, are not limited to alcohols but they may be of use in separations. *See* PFEIFFER (113) and GREEN-BAUM (60) for more complete lists.

Quantitative Determination of Alcohols.

The determination of the hydroxyl content may be made by the acylation procedure of CHRISTENSEN and CLARKE described on page 181. *See* also OGG, PORTER, and WILLITS (108) for a semimicro method for the determination of the hydroxyl content of some alcohols.

A number of the simpler alcohols, particularly the more volatile ones, can be determined by the ZEISEL method which consists of the conversion into the corresponding alkyl iodide and the reaction of the latter with silver nitrate. Many modifications of the original PREGL microprocedure have been described. The method of KIRSTEN and EHRLICH-ROGOZINSKY (78) attempts to overcome the difficulties met with in the older procedures.

Zeisel Method for the Determination of Alcohol. The ZEISEL method for the determination of the RO-group depends upon the following reactions:

$$R—O—H + HI \rightarrow RI + H_2O$$
$$RI + Br_2 \rightarrow RBr + IBr$$
$$IBr + 3 H_2O + 2 Br_2 \rightarrow HIO_3 + 5 HBr$$
$$HIO_3 + 5 HI \rightarrow 3 I_2 + 3 H_2O$$

Reagents.

Reaction mixture: Reflux 2 g red phosphorus, 60 g phenol, 100 g hydriodic acid (sp. gr. 1.7), and 5 ml propionic acid for 30 minutes in a slow stream of nitrogen. Then turn off the water in the condenser and reduce the heat so that the solution is boiling only gently. Continue this for 15 minutes. Pour the solution into a Pyrex bottle with a cap stopper which should be lubricated with the silicon grease.

Alkoxy-free silicone grease: Suspend 100 g Dow Corning high vacuum silicone grease in 200 ml petrolic ether. Add 100 g hydriodic acid (sp. gr. 1.96) and agitate the solution strongly for three hours. Then heat for ten hours in a boiling water bath to drive off all the petrolic ether and any alkyl iodide. Wash the residue of grease very thoroughly with 10% potassium iodide solution and then with water and dry at 120°. Most commercial greases are sufficiently pure to use without treatment.

Bromine: Free from iodine.

Potassium bicarbonate: 15 g potassium bicarbonate in 50 ml water.

Acetic acid-acetate: 10 g potassium acetate dissolved in 100 ml glacial acetic acid.

Sodium acetate: 40 g sodium acetate trihydrate dissolved in water and the solution made up to 100 ml.

Formic acid: 99–100%.

Potassium iodide: 20 g potassium iodide and one pellet of potassium hydroxide dissolved in 200 ml water. Keep in dark bottle.

Sodium thiosulfate: Standardized solution.

Starch solution: Indicator.

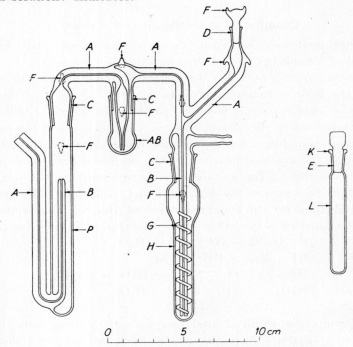

Fig. 173. Distilling Unit for Alkoxy Determination.

Apparatus.

The apparatus is shown in Figs. 173 and 174.

Procedure. Weigh out the sample of the test substance and introduce it into tube *L*. In the case of liquids weigh them out in sealed capillaries and place into tube *L*, tip downwards. Add 2 ml of the reaction mixture and break the tip of the capillary with a glass rod. When determining propoxyl and butoxyl groups introduce a few glass beads with the capillary and stopper the tube. Upon agitating the tube, for example, by holding it against a square-cut rubber stopper rotating at the end of a stirrer, the glass beads will crush the capillary and completely release the sample. The stopper of the tube should be lubricated slightly with the silicone grease. Fix the stopper with clamp *M* and place the tube in a boiling water bath for 30 minutes. Then cool it under the water tap. Charge the absorption tube of the distilling apparatus with 5 ml of acetic acid acetate and

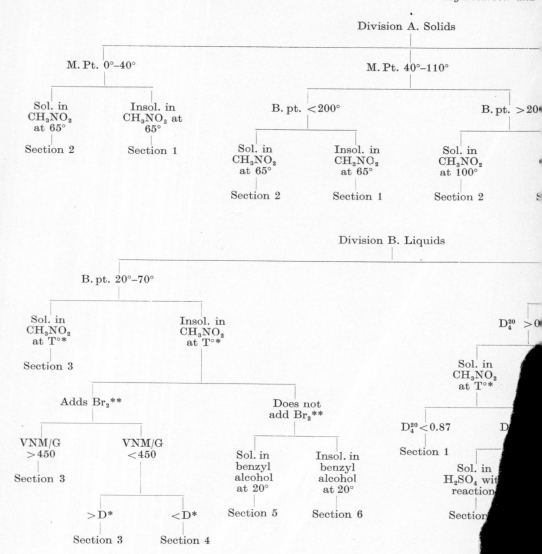

Division A. Solids

M. Pt. 0°–40°

Sol. in CH₃NO₂ at 65°

Section 2

Insol. in CH₃NO₂ at 65°

Section 1

M. Pt. 40°–110°

B. pt. <200°

Sol. in CH₃NO₂ at 65°

Section 2

Insol. in CH₃NO₂ at 65°

Section 1

B. pt. >20

Sol. in CH₃NO₂ at 100°

Section 2

Division B. Liquids

B. pt. 20°–70°

Sol. in CH₃NO₂ at T°*

Section 3

Insol. in CH₃NO₂ at T°*

Adds Br₂**

VNM/G >450

Section 3

VNM/G <450

>D*

Section 3

<D*

Section 4

Does not add Br₂**

Sol. in benzyl alcohol at 20°

Section 5

Insol. in benzyl alcohol at 20°

Section 6

D₄²⁰ >0

Sol. in CH₃NO₂ at T°*

D₄²⁰ <0.87

Section 1

Sol. in H₂SO₄ wit reaction

Section

D

* Temperature at which solubility in indicated solvent is to be determined and density dividing line between Section 3 and 4 as shown in Table 17.
** Addition of bromine is indicated by the bromide-bromate titration.

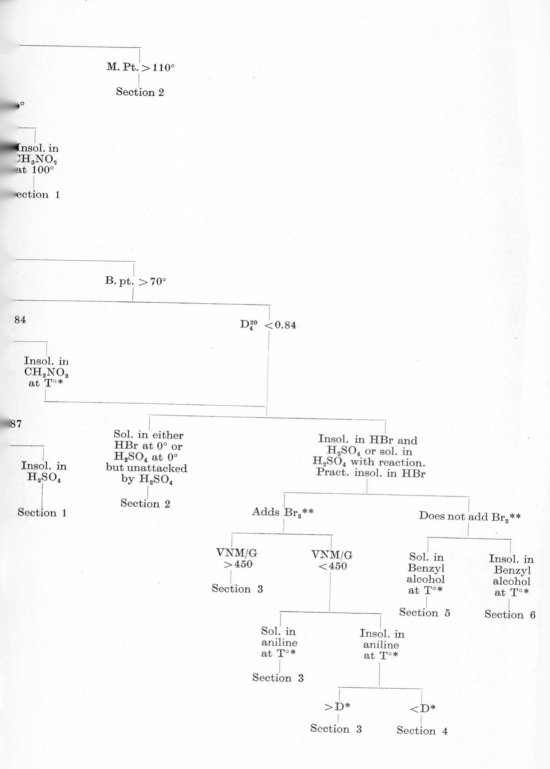

M. Pt. > 110°

Section 2

°

Insol. in
CH₃NO₂
at 100°

Section 1

B. pt. > 70°

84

D_4^{20} < 0.84

Insol. in
CH₂NO₂
at T°*

87

Insol. in
H₂SO₄

Section 1

Sol. in either
HBr at 0° or
H₂SO₄ at 0°
but unattacked
by H₂SO₄

Section 2

Insol. in HBr and
H₂SO₄ or sol. in
H₂SO₄ with reaction.
Pract. insol. in HBr

Adds Br₂**

Does not add Br₂**

VNM/G
> 450

Section 3

VNM/G
< 450

Sol. in
Benzyl
alcohol
at T°*

Section 5

Insol. in
Benzyl
alcohol
at T°*

Section 6

Sol. in
aniline
at T°*

Section 3

Insol. in
aniline
at T°*

> D*

Section 3

< D*

Section 4

10 drops of bromine and charge the scrubber with 1 ml of potassium bicarbonate solution. Connect the distillation flask P to the closed stopcock Q. Lubricate joint R of the distillation apparatus with one drop of water. Quickly open tube L, invert it over the inner tube of the flask P, drop the stopper in after it and immediately attach the flask to joint R. Open stopcock Q and bring the solution to a boil and keep it boiling gently for 15 minutes. Then remove the absorption tube from the apparatus, wash the inlet tube B with water and transfer the contents of the tube and the washings to a 100-ml ERLENMEYER flask. Add 2 ml of sodium

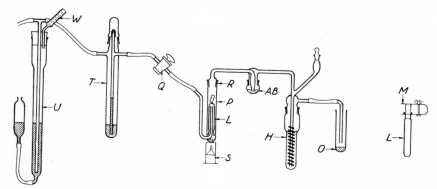

Fig. 174. Distilling Train for Alkoxy Determination.

acetate followed by 10 drops of formic acid. Shake vigorously for two minutes and then add 3 ml potassium iodide. Titrate the solution with sodium thiosulfate, adding 2 ml of starch indicator near the end point.

For other procedures and discussions of the applicability of the method *see* also PREGL-ROTH (119), FURTER (56), LIEB (93), KÜSTER and MAAG (90), ELEK (41), FRIEDRICH (54), SAMSEL and MCHARD (135), HOFFMAN and WOLFRAM (65), and STEYERMARK (147).

Hydrocarbons and Ethers.

If the compound consists only of carbon, hydrogen, and oxygen and has given negative results with all the preceding tests, it is placed in this group.

Because there is no test for the group as a whole, it is divided into sections and divisions. The two divisions are the solids and the liquids. The solids are divided into two sections: the non-aromatics and the (chiefly) aromatics. The liquids are separated into six sections: aromatics; acyclic ethers; polyalkenes, alkynes, cyclenes, and terpenes; alkenes; naphthenes; and alkanes.

The test for oxygenated compounds (page 93) can be used for classifying the substance as a hydrocarbon or an ether.

Sectional Tests.

The section to which a substance belongs is determined by a series of sectional tests consisting of the determination of the melting point, boiling point, density (range), solubility in a number of solvents, and the bromide-bromate number. These tests are performed in the sequence given in Table 16.

Boiling or Melting Point. These are determined as described in Chapter IV, pages 110 and 115.

Determination of Density Range. In classifying the hydrocarbon according to the above scheme it is not necessary to know the exact value of the density but only whether it lies within one range or another. Therefore, if the sample is compared to a few standards whose densities

TABLE 17
Standards for the Density Tests

Substance	Sp. Gr at 20°	B. pt.
Octane	0.706	125°
Diethyl ether	0.708	35.5°
Decane (*n*)	0.730	173°
Methyl isobutyl ketone	0.801	118°
Decyl alcohol (*n*)	0.830	231°
Acrolein	0.841	52.5°
Amyl isopropionate	0.870	160°

lie at the boundaries of these ranges, it is easy to determine in which range the density of the test substance is to be found. This comparison is carried out by the schlieren method. The unknown is used as fluid sample and the standards as static samples. The standards must be substances in which the unknown is soluble, which do not have too low a boiling point, and which are not too rare or expensive. Since we are concerned here with hydrocarbons, substances as much like these in character are used as standards to ensure mutual solubility. Table 17 lists a number of substances which meet these requirements.

The cell shown in Fig. 141 is used. The fluid sample is introduced from a capillary pipet with its outlet bent at right angles to the pipet proper so that the fluid sample issues horizontally if its density and that of the static sample are the same. One of the above liquids is introduced into the cell and the test substance is allowed to flow out into it. If the resulting schlieren ascends, the test substance has obviously a lower density than the standard. In this event a standard of lower density is employed next. If, however, the schlieren are descending, the test substance has a density higher than that of the standard and a standard of higher density is employed in the next test. In this way a standard in which the schlieren ascend and an adjacent standard in which the schlieren descend can be found and the range of density of the test substance can thus be fixed.

Determination of Solubility. The solubility of the test substance in the following solvents must next be determined to place it in its proper section:

> Nitromethane at 65°
> Nitromethane at 100°
> Hydrobromic acid ($D = 1.48$) at 0°
> Sulfuric acid at 0°

Further solvents and temperatures are given in Table 18.

TABLE 18

Conditions for Classification According to Solubility and Density as a Function of the Boiling Point of the Hydrocarbon

Boiling Point of Hydrocarbon in the Range: °C	Use the Following Solvents at the Indicated Temperatures			For Density Boundary between Sections 3 and 4 Use the Following Values: g/ml at 20°C
	Nitromethane °C	Aniline °C	Benzyl Alcohol °C	
20– 40	0	—	20	0.70
40– 70	15	—	20	0.73
70–130	0	0	30	0.78
130–160	10	15	50	0.80
160–190	25	15	50	0.80
190–220	40	30	70	0.83
220–250	55	30	70	0.83
250–280	70	45	70	0.83
< 280	85	60	70	0.83

The classification into the proper section is made by making the density and solubility tests called for by Table 16 together with the determination of the bromide—bromate number as described below.

The organic solvents should be pure and dry. The capillary method of determining the solubility (page 152) is employed. Use an equal volume of solvent; if hydrobromic acid is used, twice as much is taken as test substance. Take a sample of the test substance of about 5 µl if a liquid, and 3 mg if a solid. Before and after mixing place the capillary in a bath which is about ten degrees warmer than the temperature at which the solubility determination is to be made. If a turbidity or two distinct layers appear on cooling to the desired temperature, the substance is classed as insoluble.

Classification Tests.

Bromine Test for Unsaturation. Dissolve about 0.2 mg of the hydrocarbon in 2 µl of carbon tetrachloride in a deep-well slide and place a cover glass over the cell. Add the bromine-carbon tetrachloride solution dropwise from a capillary pipet to the solution of the hydro-carbon, pushing the cover glass aside to allow the entrance of the pipet tip. If the solution becomes colorless, add more bromine until a yellow color remains. Then remove the cover glass and blow a stream of moist air from a capillary (blowing with the mouth into a capillary held horizontally over the well of the slide serves the purpose) over the solution. A white cloud (hydrated hydrogen bromide) indicates substitution rather than addition.

If no decolorization of the first two drops of the reagent has taken place, put the slide on a warmed metal block, heat the solutions to gentle boiling and repeat the test.

Notes.

1) The reagent is prepared by dissolving 4 ml of bromine in 100 ml of carbon tetrachloride.

2) Carbon tetrachloride has been found to be the best solvent for this test because, although it dissolves bromine and most organic substances readily, hydrogen bromide is practically insoluble in it.

3) Alkenes and alkynes add bromine as follows:

$$\text{>C=C<} + Br_2 \rightarrow \text{>C=C<} \\ \qquad\qquad\qquad\quad \text{Br Br}$$

$$CH \equiv CH + Br_2 \rightarrow CHBr = CHBr$$
$$CHBr = CHBr + Br_2 \rightarrow CHBr_2 - CHBr_2$$

Alkenes with electronegative groups attached to each of the unsaturated carbon atoms react slowly with bromine (e. g. cinnamic acid).

Other compounds will react with bromine reagent but will form substitution products, as, for example,

$$\text{OH} \qquad\qquad\qquad \text{OH}$$
$$\bighexagon + 3\,Br_2 \rightarrow \text{Br}-\bighexagon-\text{Br} + 3\,HBr$$
$$\qquad\qquad\qquad\qquad\qquad \text{Br}$$

This substitution reaction can be distinguished from the addition of bromine by the evolution of hydrogen bromide which results from the former. It is detected by the formation of a cloud of hydrobromic acid when moist air is blown over the reaction mixture. A positive test for unsaturation, therefore, is the decolorization of the bromine reagent without the evolution of hydrogen bromide.

Colorations with Aluminum Chloride.

Dip a Pyrex capillary tube with a bore of about 1 mm into powdered anhydrous aluminum chloride so that some of the latter is pushed into the tube. Wipe off the excess salt on the outside of the capillary. Holding the tube inclined, heat the end which contains the aluminum chloride cautiously, starting at the very tip so that the salt sublimes into the capillary. When all has sublimed away from the end, heat the latter to the softening point and pinch it shut with forceps. Then hold the tube high over the burner to sublime the aluminum chloride farther into the tube but slowly so that it deposits again in a thin layer. After cooling, cut off the sealed end and dip the other end into a solution of the test substance in chloroform (0.5 g of the hydrocarbon in 2.5 ml of chloroform). Allow the drop to slide down the tube to the aluminum chloride. Observe the color of the latter against a white background immediately and again 20 minutes later.

Notes.

1) The FRIEDEL and CRAFTS reaction of an aromatic hydrocarbon and an alkyl chloride takes place as follows:

$$3 \ C_6H_6 + CHCl_3 \xrightarrow{\text{AlCl}_3} (C_6H_5)_3CH + 3 \ HCl$$

The colors obtained in this test are due to the formation of chloro compounds as secondary products as, for example, in the reaction with benzene, triphenylchloromethane:

$$5 \ C_6H_6 + 2 \ CHCl_3 \xrightarrow{\text{AlCl}_3} (C_6H_5)_3C \cdot Cl + (C_6H_5)_2CH_2 + 5 \ HCl$$

These chloro compounds combine with aluminum chloride to form carbonium salts:

2) Some of the colors obtainable in this test are orange to red-orange: benzene and its liquid homologs and aryl halides; yellow-orange: di- and triphenylmethane; yellow to green: anthracene; blue to blue-green: naphthalene; purple: phenanthrene; blue: biphenyl.

Oxidation of Side Chains. The permanganate oxidation of the side chain can be used for confirmatory identification. Since an excess of the permanganate will oxidize and destroy the benzoic acid or other acid formed, it is important that not much more than the theoretical amount of the reagent be employed. A reflux tube is used. The bulb is about 10 mm in diameter and the wide portion of the tube has a bore of 6 mm and is 50 to 60 mm long. Introduce 10 µl of the test substance and the calculated amount of a saturated potassium permanganate solution into the tube, and seal it. Heat the tube in a steam bath for two to eight hours with frequent shaking. After the color of the permanganate has disappeared, cool the tube and cut off the sealed tip. Cut off the conical portion of the tube and insert the narrow end into the open end of the rest of the reflux tube. Centrifuge the two together. Wash the funnel-shaped piece once into the tube. Transfer the liquid into a microcone by inverting the reflux tube into the cone and centrifuging in this position.

Usually, merely shaking the two with the hand (as one does a clinical thermometer) suffices to transfer the liquid. After centrifuging the mixture in the cone, transfer the supernatant liquid into a second microcone by siphoning through a capillary siphon. Concentrate it in this second cone to about 0.3 ml on the water bath and use an air jet. If a precipitate appears at this point, filter it off. Acidify the clear liquid with hydrochloric acid. Separate the precipitate by centrifuging, wash with water, and finally recrystallize from alcohol. Take the melting point of the product.

Notes.

1) The reaction is exemplified by the following:

$$2\,C_6H_5CH_3 + 4\,KMnO_4 \rightarrow 2\,C_6H_5CO \cdot OH + 4\,MnO_2 + 4\,KOH$$

2) The saturated solution of potassium permanganate contains about 65.8 g per liter at 20°. This is equivalent to 0.01 g available oxygen per milliliter.

Cuprous Chloride Test for Triple Bonds. Pass the gaseous test substance through a very fine-tipped capillary or add a very small drop of the liquid test substance to the cuprous chloride solution in the microcone. Stir, and then draw up the liquid and the precipitate into a wide capillary tube. Hold the capillary in a vertical position and touch the end to the center of a square of filter paper. Allow the contents of the tube to flow out. Observe the color of the precipitate.

Notes.

1) Prepare the cuprous chloride solution freshly before each test. Dissolve 1 g of a mixture of 32 g anhydrous copper sulfate, 13 g sodium chloride, and 10 g sodium bisulfite in 20 ml of water and bring to a boil. After the cuprous chloride has settled, decant the clear liquid and wash once by decantation. Dissolve the residue in 3 ml of 12 *m* ammonia and dilute to 35 ml with distilled water.

2) Compounds containing the group —C≡CH will form metallic derivatives with cuprous copper and silver:

$$HC \equiv CH + 2\,Cu(NH_3)_2OH \rightarrow CuC \equiv CCu + 4\,NH_3 + 2\,H_2O$$

From a basic solution of mercuric salts such as NESSLER's solution, analogous mercuric compounds are obtained:

$$2\,(H\!-\!C\equiv CH) + 2\,K_2HgI_4 + 4\,KOH \longrightarrow 4\,Hg\!\!\bigvee_{\substack{\\ C\equiv C}}^{\substack{C\equiv C \\ \\}}\!\!Hg + 8\,KI + 4\,H_2O$$

3) *Caution!* The dried metallic compounds are very dangerous. Dispose of them immediately in a safe manner.

Bromide-Bromate Titration. Measure half a milliliter of the 0.5 *n* bromide-bromate solution accurately from a pipet (1 ml in $^1/_{10}$) into a 10- or 15-ml glass-stoppered weighing bottle. Run in about 5 μl of the hydrocarbon from a calibrated capillary pipet. Add 0.5 ml of 10% sulfuric acid immediately. If the solution is colorless after vigorous shaking, add more bromide-bromate solution in 0.1- or

0.2-ml aliquots (noting the exact volume used) until the solution remains yellow after shaking for two minutes. Keep the bottle tightly stoppered during the shaking. Then add 0.5 ml of potassium iodide (15% solution) and titrate the liberated iodine with $0.02\,n$ sodium thiosulfate solution using starch as indicator.

From the results of the above experiment it is possible to determine (a) whether the test substance is unsaturated or not, (b) in which section it is to be placed, and (c) the bromide-bromate number. If less than 0.04 ml of the bromide-bromate solution has reacted, the hydrocarbon is saturated. The section is determined by the value of VNM/G, in which V is the volume in milliliters of the bromide-bromate solution which has reacted, N is the normality of the bromide-bromate solution, M is the average molecular weight of the compounds of Division B, Section 3, which boil at the same temperature as the test substance, and G is the specific gravity of the hydrocarbon. When the bromide-bromate titration is carried out on a microscale as described above, these VNM/G values must be multiplied by 100 to obtain the values given in the tables. If the value of this constant is greater than 450, more than three atoms of bromine per molecule have been added; if less, fewer than three atoms. The bromide-bromate number is the number of centigrams of bromine added by one gram of the hydrocarbon.

Notes.

1) The bromine is formed as follows:
$$KBrO_3 + 5\,KBr + H_2SO_4 \longrightarrow 3\,K_2SO_4 + 3\,H_2O + 3\,Br_2$$

2) The reagent is prepared by dissolving 14 g of pure potassium bromate and 50 g of pure potassium bromide in water and diluting to 1000 ml. It may be standardized against aniline.

3) ROSSMANN (131) describes a micromethod for the determination of active and inactive double bonds in heavy greases and oils. BOESEKEN and POLS (18) determine the unsaturation by the bromination of the compound using several milligrams of test substance. LUCAS and PRESSMAN (96) suggest the use of mercuric sulfate as a catalyst for the bromination of triple-bonded hydrocarbons. *See* also below in discussion of quantitative determinations of hydrocarbons.

Solubility and Color Reactions with Sulfuric Acid.

A) Carry out the test just as described above under Determination of Solubility. Use sulfuric acid which has been cooled in ice water. Immerse the capillary in ice water after mixing. If the solution becomes clear and remains clear for two minutes, the substance is probably an aliphatic ether. Cut the capillary open and dilute the solution with ice water. If the original substance separates out again, the compound is an aliphatic ether of Division B, Section 2.

B) To a few cubic millimeters of the test substance in a capillary add an equal volume of sulfuric acid $(D = 1.84)$. Immerse in ice water after mixing. If solution does not take place, allow the capillary to attain room temperature and mix again by centrifuging back and forth. If the hydrocarbon has a density between 0.84 and 0.87 and complete solution occurs in this test, it is not an aromatic and does not belong in Division B, Section 1.

Notes.

1) Ethers and unsaturated hydrocarbons react with concentrated sulfuric acid in the cold to give soluble compounds:

$$R\!-\!O\!-\!R' + H_2SO_4 \longrightarrow \left[R\!\overset{\overset{\displaystyle H}{|}}{-}O\!-\!R' \right]^+ + HSO_4^-$$

$$CH_2\!=\!CH_2 + HOSO_2OH \longrightarrow CH_3CH_2OSO_2OH \text{ (Alkylsulfonic acid)}$$

The reaction with ethers is reversible:

$$\overset{R}{\underset{R'}{>}}\overset{H}{O}\!-\!O\!-\!\overset{\overset{\displaystyle O}{||}}{\underset{\underset{\displaystyle O}{||}}{S}}\!-\!OH \overset{H_2O}{\longrightarrow} R\!-\!O\!-\!R' + H_2SO_4$$

With ethylene, however, an alcohol is obtained:

$$CH_3CH_2OSO_2OH \overset{H_2O}{\longrightarrow} CH_3CH_2OH + HOSO_2OH$$

The nature of the product often helps in determining the nature of the multiple bond. Acetylenes dissolve completely in the acid and yield oils of pleasant odor different from the original, when the solution is diluted. Conjugated diolefines react vigorously in the cold giving a red interface between acid and test substance. Upon warming a thick red paste forms which upon dilution leaves a heavy red oil in suspension. Olefines of the diallyl type are attacked far less, frequently giving only unstable colored emulsions and a light yellow oil upon dilution.

2) Mere color formation does not necessarily mean that the test substance is soluble.

3) See also GILLESPIE (59).

Derivatives of Hydrocarbons and Ethers.

3,5-Dinitrobenzoates of Symmetrical Aliphatic Ethers. The method is restricted to symmetrical aliphatic ethers and is not suitable for aromatic or mixed aliphatic ethers. Mix 0.5 to 0.8 mg of finely powdered anhydrous zinc chloride in a reflux tube with 2.5 mg of 3,5-dinitrobenzoyl chloride. Add 5 to 10 µl of the perfectly dry test substance. Seal the tube and reflux for an hour, shaking the tube frequently to return the condensed liquid to the bulb of the tube. After cooling, cut the tube open and transfer the contents to a microcone. Rinse the reflux with 50 µl 0.75 m sodium carbonate solution. Add the rinse solution to the reaction mixture. Heat the microcone to 90° in a water bath, stirring for one minute. After allowing the cone to stand at room temperature for five minutes, centrifuge and decant. Wash the residue with 25 µl 0.75 m carbonate solution and then with two 25 µl portions of water. Decant as much of the liquid as possible, moving the tip of the capillary pipet used for the decantation around in the crystal mass. Add 50 µl of carbon tetrachloride to the residue and boil for three minutes. Centrifuge and siphon the solution while hot into another microcone. Evaporate the carbon tetrachloride (air stream, page 17) and recrystallize the residue from 10 to 15 μl of carbon tetrachloride.

Note.

Zinc chloride catalyzes the cleavage of aliphatic ethers and one of the radicals reacts with 3,5-dinitrobenzoyl chloride to form the ester:

$$R—O—R + Cl—C—O\bigcirc\!\!\!\!\!\begin{smallmatrix}NO_2\\ \\NO_2\end{smallmatrix} \longrightarrow R—C—O\bigcirc\!\!\!\!\!\begin{smallmatrix}NO_2\\ \\NO_2\end{smallmatrix} + RCl$$

Acetamino and Benzamino Derivatives of Alkyl Benzenes.

Nitration. To 20 μl of a nitration mixture consisting of 4 drops of concentrated sulfuric acid and 3 drops of concentrated nitric acid in a microcone, add 12 μl of the hydrocarbon test substance. Stir for two minutes without warming, then hold the cone in a simmering water bath or in a metal block to heat it to 60°. Stir the mixture occasionally. After half an hour, add a few drops of water and centrifuge. Remove the supernatant liquid and wash the droplet of nitro compound with water until the washings show no acid reaction.

Reduction. The reduction of the nitro compound can be carried out either with tin and hydrochloric acid or, preferably, with sodium amalgam. Place a drop of the nitro compound in a crucible of about 0.5-ml capacity. Add to this a piece of sodium amalgam large enough to cover the sample. Add a drop of alcohol. At short intervals, as the reaction proceeds, add 2 or 3 drops (from a capillary pipet) of 6 *m* HCl. At first the mixture will become red-brown and then yellow. When the yellow color disappears, the reaction is complete. Transfer the material to a microcone, centrifuge, and decant the aqueous layer to a second cone. Wash the remaining amalgam with alcohol and add the washings to the first filtrate. Evaporate this to dryness. Extract the residue with water. The free amine can be prepared from the hydrochloride by the addition of dilute alkali and converted to the acetyl or benzoyl derivative by one of the methods described on page 264.

Note.

The amine formed from the hydrocarbon need not, of course, be converted to the acyl derivatives mentioned but can be treated further to even more reactive forms such as azobenzene, etc. *See*, e. g., VOGEL, WATLING, and WATLING (157).

2,4,7-Trinitrofluorenone Complexes.

The complexes or adducts formed by polynuclear aromatic hydrocarbons with 2,4,7-trinitrofluorenone (109) are colored, sharp-melting, and do not decompose upon heating to the melting point. The ratio of hydrocarbon to reagent is 1:1 in the complexes. Some substituted benzenes also form these products (92).

Reagent.

The 2,4,7-trinitrofluorenone is prepared by mixing 200 ml of red, fuming nitric acid (sp. gr. 1.59) in the cold with 100 ml of 96 % sulfuric acid. To this add portionwise, with shaking after each addition, 10 g of pure powdered fluorenone. Reflux the mixture for two hours and then pour onto ice. Filter the precipitate, dry, and recrystallize from acetic acid. The product should melt at 175—176°.

Procedure. Dissolve equimolecular quantities of the pure 2,4,7-trinitro-fluorenone and the hydrocarbon separately in absolute ethyl alcohol or ethyl alcohol-benzene mixture to form nearly saturated solutions. Heat the two solutions and mix. A coloration develops in the solution and the complex usually precipitates immediately. Filter, dry, and determine the melting point. Recrystallize from absolute alcohol, alcohol-benzene, or benzene alone.

2,4-Dinitrobenzenesulfenyl Derivatives of Aromatic Hydrocarbons and Olefins.

The reaction with the aromatics is a modified FRIEDEL-CRAFTS procedure using 2,4-dinitrobenzenesulfenyl chloride with aluminum chloride.

Procedure for Olefins (77). Glacial acetic acid has proven itself to be the best solvent. Dissolve 10 mg of the reagent and 10 to 15 mg of the olefin in 250 µl of glacial acetic acid. Heat on the steam bath for 15 minutes. Place the microcone in a refrigerator or immerse it in crushed ice. If a precipitate forms, filter this off and recrystallize it from ethyl alcohol. If no precipitate forms, drop small pieces of ice into the mixture in the micro-cone and filter off the precipitated product. Recrystallize from ethyl alcohol. Determine the melting point.

Procedure for Aromatic Hydrocarbons (25). Purify the solvent, ethylene chloride, by distillation until the distillate is clear. Dissolve 10 mg of the 2,4-dinitrobenzenesulfenyl chloride in 150 µl of this solvent which has been cooled to 5° in an ice bath. Add approximately 10 mg anhydrous aluminum chloride and shake for one minute. To this mixture add 15 to 20 mg of the hydrocarbon. If the latter is solid, dissolve it first in a minimum of ethylene chloride before adding to the reagent. Hydrogen chloride will be evolved and the temperature will rise as the reaction proceeds. Add 50 µl ethyl alcohol *slowly* and keep the temperature below 30°. Proper temperature control will result in a transparent or reddish brown solution. Wash twice with water or dilute hydrochloric acid to remove the aluminum compounds. Concentrate the layer with the organic products to about 50 µl in an air stream or by distilling the solvent. To the resultant solution add an equal volume of absolute alcohol. On cooling, the sulfide will usually precipitate but occasionally the ethylene chloride must be replaced entirely by the alcohol before precipitation takes place. Recrystallize from absolute alcohol or alcohol-benzene mixture. Determine the melting point.

Most aromatic hydrocarbons also form complexes with picric acid (109), but these are not actually picrates. A number of difficulties are met with in the use of these as derivatives. In many cases the hydrocarbon is so insoluble that it precipitates before the complex or it is precipitated in excess on the complex. The melting points of the adducts are undesirably close for distinction between possibilities.

Alkane-choleic Acids. Desoxycholic acid forms addition products with a very large number of organic compounds. The fact that the usually inert paraffins form such compounds with this reagent makes it valuable in the identification of this group.

The addition compounds are formed rather simply by the mixing of 10 µl of the hydrocarbon with a filtered solution (if $C = 8$ or more: 20 µl, if $C =$ fewer than 8: 100 µl of 10 g of desoxycholic acid in 50 ml of acetone-free methyl alcohol. Allow the mixture to stand at room temperature for 15 minutes. If no precipitate forms, chill the solution in ice water for one half hour and filter in the cold. Dry under suction for one half hour to remove any excess solvent or hydrocarbon. Do not dry in an oven.

No actual melting points are obtained but liquefaction occurs at definite temperatures which can be used for the identification of the hydrocarbon.

The method of HUNTRESS and coworkers (70, 71, 72) which employs chlorosulfonic acid as a reagent for the characterization of aromatic ethers and alkylbenzenes is simple and can readily be adapted to micro samples. A micro reflux tube can be used for the preparation of aroylbenzoic acids from aromatic hydrocarbons by adaptation of the method of UNDERWOOD and WALSH (152).

Degradative Procedures for Hydrocarbons and Ethers.

The alkanes do not lend themselves to the ordinary degradative reactions. To establish their constitution and structure it is therefore necessary to resort to the preparation of derivatives and degradation of these derivatives. Other lines of attack include the physical methods such as infrared spectroscopy.

Alkenes can be subjected to cleavage at the double bond by either ozonolysis or oxidation by permanganate. The former is preferable and more reliable. The ozone gas is passed through a solution of the alkene in an inert solvent such as carbon tetrachloride or chloroform. The solution is in a flask fitted with a reflux condenser. After the reaction the solvent is distilled off and the residue is treated with water immediately and without prior purification in the presence of a reducing agent such as zinc. The products will be the aldehyde and the ketone corresponding to the two fragments of the original hydrocarbon with the cleavage point at the multiple bond. The permanganate oxidation carries the reaction to the carboxylic acid and the ketone as the products of the two fragments.

Alkynes will also react with ozone but will give ketoacids as the product. Dienes react like the alkenes to give aldehydes and ketones.

Cyclic aliphatic hydrocarbons behave like the open chain compounds.

In the case of aromatic hydrocarbons, the degradation takes place more easily in view of the greater reactivity of these compounds. The oxidation and other reactions are described above.

There is only one cleavage reaction for ethers and that is the use of an acid such as hydriodic or hydrobromic at a higher temperature; *see* under Quantitative Determination of Alcohols, p. 231. The epoxide compounds can be converted to the corresponding chlorohydin by the procedure of KERCHOV and SIGGIA, p. 250.

Chemical Separation of Hydrocarbons and Ethers.

Some of the methods described above can be used for the separation of ethers from hydrocarbons, as, e. g., the treatment with sulfuric acid. They can also be used for the separation of some hydrocarbons from other types. Thus, alkynes can be precipitated as metallic salts, some aromatics as bromo compounds, etc. The adducts or molecular compounds, of which some can be used as derivatives, as described above, can also be used for the separation of hydrocarbons from other types of compounds and of various types of hydrocarbons from others.

Urea Adducts. The use of urea for separating straight-chain hydrocarbons from branched-chain has been described by ZIMMERSCHIED, DINERSTEIN, WELTKAMP, and MARSCHNER (169). These complexes contain eleven moles of urea for every mole of hydrocarbon. Halogen, sulfur, and oxygen derivatives of hydrocarbons from entirely similar compounds if the linearity of the carbon chain is preserved. If the chain consists of 20 or more carbon atoms and a single methyl branch, it will also complex. Add the hydrocarbon, dissolved, in 9 volumes of mixed decahydronaphthalenes to fifteen times as much urea and one and a half times as much methyl alcohol. Stir the suspension at $25°$ for 45 minutes. Filter with suction or by centrifuging, wash three times with 30 times as much isopentane as original hydrocarbon and then decompose the complex by adding 20 times as much water. Take up the liberated hydrocarbon in ten volumes of ether and evaporate the separated ether layer (and any residual isopentane) to recover the hydrocarbon.

2,4,7-Trinitrofluorenone Adducts. These can also be decomposed to the original hydrocarbon quantitatively by chromatographic separation, by reduction with tin and hydrochloric acid, or by catalytic reduction. In the first procedure the benzene solution of the adduct is passed over a short column of activated alumina. The hydrocarbon is eluted much more rapidly than the trinitrofluorenone. The latter remains behind on the alumina, while the hydrocarbon can be recovered by evaporation of the benzene from the eluate. For reduction with tin, dissolve 10 to 15 mg of the adduct in 700 μl glacial acetic acid in a reflux tube. Add 40 to 60 mg tin and 125 μl 12 m HCl. Reflux for 20 minutes or until all of the tin is dissolved and the solution turns light red in color. Open the tube with the usual precautions and add crushed ice to the contents. Transfer to a microcone, centrifuge, and decant. Dry the solid residue and dissolve it in benzene. Treat the solution with activated carbon, centrifuge, decant again, and evaporate the clear liquid to recover the hydrocarbon. The reduction can also be carried out catalytically using ADAMS' platinum oxide as the catalyst at room temperature.

Quantitative Determination of Hydrocarbons.

Determination of Unsaturation. *Bromination.* The bromide-bromate titration as performed in the sectional test described on page 238 can also be used to determine the unsaturation. The number of moles of bromine absorbed by one mole of the test substance is calculated as follows:

$$V N M / 2000 S.$$

V = milliliters of the thiosulfate solution
N = normality of thiosulfate solution
M = molecular weight of test substance
S = weight of sample in grams

A blank should be run on the reagents alone and used for correcting the bromate consumption in the titration. Since the reaction of the bromine is not entirely additive but also to some small degree substitutive, the blank will minimize error from this source.

Iodine monochloride has also been used for the halogenation of unsaturated compounds (114). The test substance is treated in a special iodine flask with a calculated volume of ICl from an automatic buret. After reaction in the dark, the excess ICl is titrated with sodium thiosulfate solution.

Determination of Unsaturation. *Hydrogenation.* A number of procedures for the hydrogenation of unsaturated compounds has been described. The determination is more reliable in general than that involving halogenation since errors from substitution and conjugation are avoided. The hydrogen absorbed is measured either volumetrically or manometrically. A method which combines a number of very desirable features with simplicity of apparatus and operation is that of OGG and COOPER (107).

Reagents.

Hydrogen. This must be purified before use by passage through a purifying train. This consists of a (preferably electrically heated) micro

combustion furnace holding a quartz combustion tube containing platinum
star contact catalysts and a semi-micro PRATER (117) absorption tube
containing indicating Drierite. The hydrogen is then passed through
two more PRATER tubes, the first containing about an inch (2.5 cm) of
the solvent used in the reaction vessel (acetic acid) and the second filled
with glass wool to remove entrained solvent.

Acetic acid, redistilled.

Palladium catalyst. Dissolve 1 g palladium chloride in 25 ml distilled
water and add a suspension of 6 g activated carbon in 50 ml water. Transfer

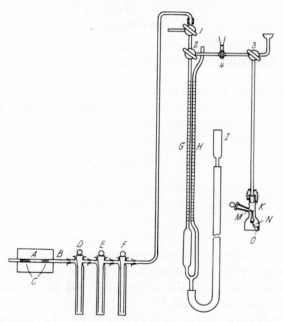

Fig. 175. Hydrogenation Apparatus of OGG and COOPER.

the mixture to a pressure vessel and hydrogenate under 35 lbs (2.4 atm.)
pressure for one half hour in a pressure vessel such as the PAAR apparatus.
Then transfer the suspension to a BÜCHNER funnel, draw off the liquid,
and wash the catalyst with water until the washings are free of hydrochloric acid. Dry the catalyst at room temperature in a vacuum oven for
16 to 20 hours and then store in a desiccator over phosphorus pentoxide.

Apparatus.

The apparatus, Fig. 175, is similar to the active hydrogen apparatus
of SOLTYS with modifications to facilitate use. All the 7/15 standard taper
joints in the hydrogen train are sealed with DE KHOTINSKY cement. The
purification train is attached to stopcock 1 of the apparatus by means
of glass tubing with a Tygon tubing connector. Buret *G* and manometer

H have parallel and coinciding graduations with 0.02-ml intervals from 0 to 7 ml. Mercury is leveled in *G* and *H* by raising or lowering bulb *I* with a rack and pinion device. The reaction unit is connected to the buret by the 12/2 ball joint *J* and held in place by two steel springs. Side arm and stopper *M* are made from 10/12 ground joints. The stopper, which extends into the neck of the flask, has a groove near the tip and perpendicular to its long axis. Sample cup *N* is hung on the stopper and dropped by turning *M*. Cup *N* is made by drilling a hole in an aluminum rod about 6 mm in diameter and 8 mm long so that its volume is about 0.1 ml. The nichrome wire handle is attached through two holes drilled on opposite sides of the cup. The stirring bar *O* is made by sealing fine iron filings in a glass tube about 3 mm in outside diameter and about 15 mm long. The cup attached to stopcock *3* facilitates cleaning the tube leading to the reaction vessel. Stopper *M* and joint *L* are greased carefully before each determination, and the stopcocks and ball joint are lubricated frequently to avoid loss of hydrogen. A thermometer, 0–100°, is hung between buret and reaction vessel. All temperature readings are made to the nearest 0.1°.

Procedure. Start the hydrogen from a cylinder through the purification train and through stopcock *1*, venting it to the atmosphere. Adjust the hydrogen pressure to approximately 1 pound (50 mm Hg) and the flow to 25 to 35 ml per minute. Start the combustion furnace and, when it has reached the operating temperature, stop the flow of hydrogen by turning stopcock *1*.

Place 4 ml of acetic acid, about 20 mg of the catalyst, and the stirring rod into the reaction flask. Weigh a sample of the test substance equivalent to 3 to 5 ml of hydrogen into the aluminum cup. Suspend the cup from the stopper in the reaction vessel by grasping the wire handle with forceps and lowering the cup into the vessel and hooking it in the groove of stopper *M*. Attach the reaction vessel *K* to the apparatus and hold it in place with the springs. Fill the buret with mercury to stopcock 2 and then turn this to close the buret.

Loosen stopper *M* and sweep the reaction unit with hydrogen by turning stopcocks *1*, *2*, and *3* to allow the hydrogen to flow through the unit at a rate of 25 to 35 ml per minute. After 15 minutes seat *M* firmly, turn stopcock 2 to connect the buret with the purification train and fill the buret with hydrogen. Give stopcock *1* a $^1/_8$ turn to close all openings and then turn stopcock 2 so that the buret is connected with the reaction unit. Place the hydrogen in the buret under positive pressure by raising the leveling bulb and release the excess pressure by momentarily opening stopcock *3*. Stir the acetic acid and the catalyst for five minutes after the gas volume ceases to diminish. Move the magnetic stirrer under the reaction flask and allow the apparatus to equilibrate for 15 minutes before reading and recording volume, temperature, and pressure.

Drop the cup containing the sample into the flask by turning stopper M and stir the reaction mixture vigorously for 15 minutes after the manometer reading indicates that no more hydrogen is being absorbed (about 30 minutes). The mercury levels in the buret and manometer should not differ by more than 1 cm during the determination. Remove the stirrer and, after a period of 15 minutes for equilibration, read and record the final volume (ml), temperature (C), and pressure (mm Hg).

The weight in grams of test substance that will react with 1 mole of hydrogen is given by

$$22\,400\; S/(V_i^\circ - V_f^\circ)$$

where:

initial volume of hydrogen, S. T. P., $= V^\circ_i = 273\,(V_t + V_i)\,(P_i - P_{si})/760\,T_i$
final volume of hydrogen, S. T. P., $= V^\circ_f = 273\,(V_t + V_f)\,(P_f - P_{sf})/760\,T_f$

T_i: $273 + t_i$ and T_f: $273 + t_f$

S: weight of sample in grams

V_t: total gas volume of apparatus to the zero mark of the buret

V_i and V_f: initial and final buret readings

P_i and P_f: initial and final barometric readings

t_i and t_f: initial and final temperatures

P_{si} and P_{sf}: vapor tensions of solvent at t_i and t_f

Other methods for determination of unsaturation by hydrogenation are those of HYDE and SCHERP (74), KUHN and MÖLLER (86), JOHNS and SEIFERLE (75), and ZAUGG and LAUER (168).

Determination of Acetylenic Unsaturation. The ability of the acetylenes to form metallic salts mentioned above can be utilized for the determination of this type of compound. Either the silver or the copper compounds may be used. The former gives more accurate and precise results.

Reagents.

Silver nitrate solution, 0.1 n, standardized

Ammonium thiocyanate solution, 0.1 n, standardized

Ammonium hydroxyde, 15 m

Ammonium hydroxide, 1 m

Ferric alum solution, saturated, for indicator

Nitric acid, 16 m

Sodium hydroxide, 6 m

Procedure. Pipet exactly 5.00 ml of the standard silver nitrate solution into a 50-ml glass-stoppered flask. Add 0.6 ml of the 6 m NaOH and then enough 15 m ammonia to redissolve the precipitate and 0.4 ml in excess. Weigh out a 6- to 8-mg sample of the test substance in a capillary and drop this into the flask. Break the capillary as described above with a glass rod or pieces of glass rod after stoppering the flask. Shake the flask for five minutes. Transfer the contents quantitatively to a 15-ml centrifuge tube, rinsing the flask three times with 1 ml portions of 1 m NH_3, adding the washings to the centrifuge tube. Centrifuge and decant the supernatant liquid very carefully into a 50-ml Erlenmeyer flask, using a pipet dipped below the surface of the liquid in the centrifuge tube to avoid transferring any of the solid with the liquid. Wash the residue in the centrifuge tube three times with 2-ml portions of 1 m NH_3, adding the washings to the centrifugate. In view of the explosive nature of the silver compound, destroy the residue in the centrifuge tube immediately by dissolving in dilute nitric acid and washing the solution down the sink. Rinse out the apparatus in which the solid had been kept with dilute nitric acid and water to make certain that all of the silver salt has been destroyed.

Neutralize the centrifugate with concentrated nitric acid and add a slight excess. Titrate with the standard ammonium thiocyanate solution using the ferric alum indicator.

Calculation: Since only one of the acetylenic hydrogens is involved in this determination the total number of such hydrogens is calculated as follows:

$$\text{Number of acetylenic hydrogen atoms per molecule} = \frac{(5.00-V)NM}{S} + 1$$

where

$V =$ milliliters of standard ammonium thiocyanate solution
$N =$ normality of standard ammonium thiocyanate solution
$M =$ molecular weight of test substance
$S =$ weight of sample in milligrams

Another method for the preparation of the silver compound is described by ALTIERI (5).

Ethers.

A) Symmetrical Aliphatic Ethers. Such ethers with low-carbon alkyl groups can be determined by the alkoxy determination procedure as used for alcohols, p. 231. In the case of unsymmetrical ethers, certain modifications are necessary to separate and distinguish between, e. g., methyl and ethyl groups. *See* the references on p. 233.

B) Vinyl Ethers. They can be determined by conversion into the corresponding iodoacetal and measurement of the iodine consumed. The method is an adaptation of the one by SIGGIA and EDSBERG (142).

Reagents.
Iodine solution, aqueous, 0.1 n, standardized
Sodium thiosulfate solution, 0.1 n, standardized
Methyl alcohol.

Procedure. Weigh out a 6- to 8-mg sample of the test substance in a capillary and drop it into a 100-ml glass-stoppered flask containing 10 ml methyl alcohol. Break the capillary as usual by the use of a glass rod or pieces of a glass rod and shaking. Carefully pipet exactly 10.00 ml of the standard iodine solution into the flask, stopper tightly, and shake. Allow the flask and contents to stand for ten minutes, shaking frequently if the test substance is very volatile. Then open the bottle and titrate the excess iodine with the standard thiosulfate solution using the disappearance of the iodine color as the end point.

The number of iodine atoms absorbed per molecule of ether is equal to the following

$$\frac{(v_1 - v_2)\, M\, N}{2\, S}$$

where $v_1 =$ milliliters of thiosulfate required for 10.00 ml of standard iodine solution

$v_2 =$ milliliters of thiosulfate used for the sample

$M =$ molecular weight of test substance

$N =$ normality of thiosulfate solution

$S =$ weight of sample in milligrams

C) Cyclic Ethers of the Epoxide Type. These can be determined by the chlorhydrin reaction method of KERCHOV modified by SIGGIA (76, 141).

Reagents.

Hydrochloric acid and calcium chloride reagent. Dissolve 810 g $CaCl_2 \cdot 2\,H_2O$ in 600 ml of water and 95 ml of concentrated HCl.

Sodium hydroxide solution, 0.1 n, standardized

Phenolphthalein indicator.

Procedure. Place 1 ml of the reagent in a 5-ml glass-stoppered Erlenmeyer flask and introduce the weighed 3- to 8-mg sample in a capillary in the usual way. Stopper and break the capillary by shaking with pieces of glass rod in the flask. Continue the shaking for three minutes. In the case of very volatile compounds such as ethylene oxide, cool the flask and contents by dipping in ice water before breaking the capillary. When the reaction is complete, open the flask and rinse off the stopper into the flask and also rinse off the inner walls of the flask. Titrate the contents with the sodium hydroxide solution to the phenolphthalein end point.

The number of epoxy oxygen atoms in one molecule of test substance is equal to the following

$$\frac{(v_1 - v_2)\, M\, N}{S}$$

where $v_1 =$ ml 0.1 n NaOH required by 1.00 ml reagent

$v_2 =$ ml 0.1 n NaOH used for sample

$M =$ molecular weight of test substance

$S =$ weight of sample in milligrams

$N =$ normality of NaOH

Chapter VII.

Compounds of Order II.

This order consists of compounds which contain nitrogen in addition to carbon, hydrogen, and possibly oxygen. It can be divided into two sub-orders, namely, the colored and the colorless compounds. Inasmuch as the former is quite small, no separate tables for them have been included in the present volume. The order, however, is divided into three genera. The division is based upon the results of titrations which place the substance into one of the following: Genus 1, acidic species; Genus 2, basic species; and Genus 3, neutral species. The titrations and divisions are summarized in Table 19.

TABLE 19

Compounds of Order II

Titration in Alcohol with 0.1 n Alkali using Thymol Blue (Test 1-A)

Species consuming *more* than 1.00 ml of 0.1 *n* alkali: titrate in water with 0.1 *n* alkali and phenolphthalein (Test 1 B)		Species consuming *less* than 1.00 ml of 0.1 *n* alkali: titrate in alcohol with 0.1 *n* *acid* and Thymol Blue (Test 2)	
Species consuming *more* than 1 ml of 0.1 *n* alkali: Acidic Species Genus 1	Species consuming *less* than 1.00 ml of 0.1 *n* alkali or 0.1 *n* acid: Neutral Species Genus 3		Species consuming *more* than 1.00 ml of 0.1 *n* acid: Basic Species Genus 2

Titration of Compounds of Order II. The titration set-up is the same as that used for the titration of acids (page 182). Care must be taken naturally to regulate the stream of air bubbles so that very volatile compounds will not be carried out by the air. Some difficulty may be experienced with substances which are insoluble prior to their reaction with acid or base. In such instances the color change of the indicator may take place and then be reversed as more of the substance goes into solution and reacts with the excess of acid or base. Titrate slowly in such cases. The constantly changing cushion of air will ensure that the fading of the color is not due to absorption of carbon dioxide or ammonia from the laboratory atmosphere. The only precaution necessary is to avoid too great an excess of base which may destroy the indicator.

A) Dissolve 2 to 3 mg of the test substance (weighed out on an analytical balance) in 1 ml of alcohol in a microbeaker. Add 0.05 ml of 0.02 *n* sodium hydroxide, drop by drop. If a color develops, add 2 drops (from a capillary pipet) of thymol blue indicator solution. Continue the addition of alkali until a clear blue solution is obtained in which the color persists for sixty seconds or more.

B) If more than 0.1 ml of 0.02 *n* sodium hydroxyde was used in the fore-going titration, titrate another 2 to 3 mg of the test substance, using water as the solvent in place of the alcohol and phenolphthalein in place of the thymol blue.

1) If more than 0.1 ml of 0.02 *n* sodium hydroxide is used to bring about a permanent color change, the compound is placed in the acidic series, Genus 1.

2) If less than 0.1 ml of 0.02 *n* sodium hydroxide is used, the compound is placed in the neutral series, Genus 3.

C) If less than 0.5 ml of 0.02 *n* sodium hydroxide is used in A, titrate another 2 to 3 mg as in A but with 0.02 *n* hydrochloric acid instead of the sodium hydroxide until the solution remains pink for one minute or more.

3) If more than 0.1 ml of 0.02 *n* hydrochloric acid is required, the com-pound is placed in the basic series, Genus 2.

4) If less than 0.1 ml of 0.02 *n* hydrochloric acid is used, the compound is placed in the neutral series, Genus 3.

Notes.

1) The alcohol used in this test must, of course, be neutral. If the ordinary 95% alcohol is not too acidic or alkaline, it can be neutralized by the cautious addition of acid or base.

2) If the end point is sharp, the neutralization equivalent can be obtained just as with other acids.

3) The DAVIDSON and PERLMAN indicator classification is of considerably more value with compounds of the higher orders. The following groupings of nitrogen compounds can be made according to this classification. It should be kept in mind that this classification is on the basis of the indicator system given on page 186, not upon the titration grouping according to the generic test.

Strong acids (As): polynitrophenols and their complexes.

Intermediate acids (Ai): salts of weak bases, weak bases–weak acids, and weak bases–intermediate acids; nitrogenous carboxylic acids; nitrophenols; dinitro-methanes; cyanophenols; some cyclic ureides; and some amino acids.

Weak acids (Aw): salts of intermediate bases and of intermediate bases and weak acids, acylaminophenols, oximes (except aliphatic ketoximes), imides, primary and secondary nitro compounds, some aromatic derivatives of nitromethane, ureides, some amino acids.

Strong bases (Bs): alkylguanidines.

Intermediate bases (Bi): salts of weak acids and of intermediate bases and weak acids, amidines, arylguanidines, alkylhydrazines, monoalkylamines, dialkylamines, and trialkylamines.

Weak bases (Bw): salts of intermediate acids, of weak bases and weak acids, and of weak bases and intermediate acids; betaines; arylhydrazines; azomethines; aliphatic ketoximes; monoarylamines; arylalkylamines; aryldialkylamines; hetero-cyclic amines (benzenoid type).

Ampholytes (Am): BwAi: salts of intermediate acids and weak bases, primary salts of aromatic diamines, aromatic aminocarboxylic acids, heterocyclic amino-carboxylic acids, aliphatic aminodicarboxylic acids. BwAw: salts of intermediate acids and intermediate bases and of weak acids and weak bases, primary salts of mixed diamines and of some aliphatic diamines, aliphatic aminocarboxylic acids, and aminophenols.

Nitrogen neutrals (Nn): salts of nitrogenous acids, guanidinium and quarternary ammonium salts of strong acids, hydrazine derivatives of carbonyl compounds, aliphatic ketoximes, hydrazo compounds, di- and triarylamines, alkyl nitrites and nitrates, N-nitrosodialkylamines, nitro and nitroso compounds, azo and azoxy compounds, ureas, urethanes, amides, nitriles, and pyrroles.

Genus 1.

Acidic Species.

Classification Reactions.

Millon's Test for Proteins.   Add a tiny particle (a few micrograms) of the test substance to a small drop (2 mm in diameter) of the reagent on a microscope slide.   Observe any color which may develop against a white background.   If necessary, warm the drop by placing the slide on a heated metal block or covered water bath.

Notes.
   1) Prepare the reagent by adding 50 ml of 15 m HNO_3 (D = 1.405) to 68 g of mercury in a 250-ml beaker and allow the mercury to dissolve without heating. Then dilute the solution with 92 ml of water. Stir in 2.7 ml more of the nitric acid until any precipitate which may form is completely dissolved. *See* also DENIGÈS (11).
   2) A red color or precipitate is specific for tyrosine because the reagent will give a positive test for certain types of substances containing phenolic groups, and tyrosine is the only proteolytic amino acid of this type. Only those proteins which give tyrosine on hydrolysis will give a positive reaction in this test.

Mulder's Reaction.   Add a tiny crystal (a few micrograms) of the test substance to a small drop of 15 m HNO_3 on a microscope slide. Observe the color against a white background.   If necessary, warm the slide by placing it on a water bath. Then invert the slide over the mouth of a bottle of concentrated ammonia.   Observe the color again against a white background.

Note.
   A positive test is the appearance of an orange-red color in the acid and an orange color when the ammonia is added. Since the test is positive for tyrosine or tryptophan, proteins containing them will give the test.

Murexide Reaction for Certain Purine Derivatives.   Add 1 to 2 μg (or less) of the test substance to a very small drop (2 to 3 mm in diameter) of 6 m HCl on a *thin* porcelain crucible cover and then a very small crystal (just visible) of potassium chlorate. Heat the cover on a water bath.   If no color develops after evaporation, continue heating cautiousy over a free flame.   Avoid charring.   A pink or brown color which turns purple-red on addition of a drop of ammonium hydroxide is a positive result.

Note.

The test is given by purine derivatives; for example, uric acid gives

$$
\begin{array}{ccccccc}
\text{HN} & \rule[0.4ex]{2em}{0.4pt} & \text{C}{=}\text{O} & & \text{O}{=}\text{C} & \rule[0.4ex]{2em}{0.4pt} & \text{NH} \\
| & & | & & | & & | \\
\text{C}{=}\text{O} & & \text{C} \rule[0.4ex]{2em}{0.4pt} {=} \text{N} \rule[0.4ex]{1.5em}{0.4pt} \text{C} & & \text{C}{=}\text{O} \\
\| & & | & & & & \| \\
\text{HN} & \rule[0.4ex]{2em}{0.4pt} & \text{C--O}\cdot\text{NH}_4{}^+ & ^-\text{O--C} & \rule[0.4ex]{2em}{0.4pt} & \text{NH}
\end{array}
$$

Adamkiewicz–Hopkins–Cole Reaction. Place 3 to 4 μl of the reagent in a microcone. Add a few micrograms of the protein. Add 5 to 6 μl of concentrated H_2SO_4, by means of a capillary pipet, to the bottom of the cone under the reagent. After allowing the liquids to stand for a few minutes, mix the two layers. If no color is visible at the interface before mixing or in the mixed solution, draw up the liquid into a coloriscopic capillary (*see* page 11) and examine under a microscope or a lens.

Notes.

1) The reagent is prepared by placing 10 g of powdered magnesium in a large flask, covering it with distilled water, and then slowly treating it with 250 ml of a cold saturated solution of oxalic acid. The flask should be cooled in running water during this addition because much heat is developed. When the reaction is complete, the solution is filtered and the filtrate is acidified with acetic acid and diluted to 100 ml.

2) A positive test is the appearance of a violet color at the interface of the two solutions. The mixing of the solutions when drawing them up into a coloriscopic capillary may produce a violet color. The test is positive for tryptophan or a protein containing it.

Derivatives of Amino Acids.

The derivatives of the amino acids can be either those of the carboxyl group or of the amino group. Among the former are found the metallic salts, but the latter group is more numerous and more easily prepared and characterized. Among these are the acetyl, benzoyl, 3,5-dinitrobenzoyl, picrate, benzene sulfonyl, and *p*-toluene sulfonyl compounds. The preparation of these is described under Amines on pages 264 ff.

Another excellent derivative of the amino acids is the 2,4-dinitrofluorobenzene compound. This is prepared as described below under Degradative Procedures.

LACOURT, SOMMEREYNS, FRANCOTTE, and DELANDE (31) prepare the eutectics of the amino acids with various other amines and dibasic acids and obtain the melting points of these for the identification according to the method of KOFLER.

Microscopic Tests for Amino Acids. A) The amino acids will give crystalline precipitates with a number of reagents. Picrolonic acid (1-*p*-nitrophenyl-3-methyl-4-nitropyrazolone-5) gives crystalline salts not only with all the naturally ocurring monoamino acids except proline and oxy-proline (29) but also with many synthetic amino acids. Although the crystal habits of the various amino acid picrolonates are insufficiently characteristic to use them for indentification, the refractive indices can be used for this purpose. The picrolonates are prepared by warming a few crystals of the amino acid and a little picrolonic acid in a few drops of water on a slide until dissolved. On cooling, the salt crystallizes out directly. The refractive index can be measured by the immersion method. The properties of the picrolonates of the various amino acids are listed in Table 20.

TABLE 20
Properties of Picrolonates of Amino Acids

Amino Acid	Type of Crystal	Extinction	Elongation	Refractive Index	
				N_1	N_2
ine nine	Anisotropic	Parallel	Negative	1.716	1.580
ype a	Anisotropic	Parallel	Positive	1.716	1.580
ype b	Isotropic	—	—	1.578	—
ype c rtic acid	Anisotropic	Parallel	Positive	—	—
ype a	Anisotropic	Parallel	Positive	< 1.527	Between 1.527 and 1.512
ype b	Anisotropic	Parallel	Negative	> 1.740	> 1.740
eine	Anisotropic	Parallel	Negative	> 1.740	> 1.740
ine omotyrosine	Anisotropic	Parallel	Positive	1.600	1.548
ype a	Anisotropic	Parallel	Positive	> 1.740	Between 1.616 and 1.549
ype b	Anisotropic	Oblique (App. 44°)	Negative	< 1.549	> 1.580
lorotyrosine	Anisotropic	Parallel	Positive	Between 1.740 and 1.698	Between 1.633 and 1.618
lotyrosine	Anisotropic	Parallel	Positive	—	—
amic acid	Anisotropic	Parallel	Negative	1.574	1.596
ine	Anisotropic	Parallel	Positive	1.616	1.531
dine	Anisotropic	Parallel	Positive	1.616	1.557
oxyproline	Anisotropic	Parallel	Positive	1.658	1.493
oxyvaline	Anisotropic	Parallel	Positive	app. 1.56	app. 1.54
ucine rine	Anisotropic	Parallel	Positive	1.610	1.520
pe a	Anisotropic	Parallel	—	> 1.740	app. 1.70
pe b	Anisotropic	Parallel	Positive	1.608	1.520
pe c	Anisotropic	Parallel	Positive	1.660	1.529
ine	Anisotropic	Parallel	Positive	1.617	1.527
ne	Anisotropic	Parallel	Positive	1.645	1.520
ionine	Anisotropic	Parallel	Positive	app. 1.62	1.494
ucine	Anisotropic	Parallel	Negative	Between 1.740 and 1.658	Between 1.740 and 1.658

TABLE 20 *(continued)*

Amino Acid	Type of Crystal	Extinction	Elongation	Refractive Index	
				N_1	N_2
Norvaline					
Type a	Anisotropic	Parallel	Positive	—	—
Type b	Anisotropic	Parallel	Negative	1.684	> 1."
Phenylalanine					
Type a	Anisotropic	Parallel	—	—	—
Type b	Anisotropic	along shortest diagonal	—	> 1.74	> 1."
Proline	Anisotropic	Parallel	—	1.530	1.(
Serine					
Type a	Anisotropic	Oblique 35–40°	Positive	1.567	1.!
Type b	Anisotropic	Parallel	Positive		
Tryptophan	Isotropic	—	—	1.712	—
Tyrosine	Anisotropic	Oblique 35–37°	Positive	1.596	1.!
Valine	Anisotropic	Parallel	Negative	1.549	> 1."
dl-α-Amino-*n*-valeric acid	Anisotropic	Parallel	Negative	1.685	> 1.!

N_1 is, in elongated crystals, the index when the crystal is oriented so that the incident b of polarized light vibrates parallel or approximately parallel to the long axis or diagonal. In absence of an outstanding direction in the crystal forms, the indices are arbitrarily assigned.

In some cases the crystals are soluble in the immersion media and hence no refractive in measurements can be obtained.

The reader is referred to the original publication for a detailed description of the crystal f(of the salts.

Notes.

The data in Table 20 and the method of preparing the salts were described by KIRK and his coworkers (29).

B) Another type of compound of the amino acids which gives crystalline products which can be examined for their optical properties is the nitro-indandion derivative (33). This is prepared by adding the amino acid to an equivalent amount of a hot, saturated aqueous solution of 2-nitroin-dandion-1,3. Keep the mixture in a boiling water bath for about five min-utes. If the derivative does not crystallize upon cooling the solution, use another solvent such as alcohol. After crystallization, filter off the precipi-tate, dry, and recrystallize from water or other solvent several times. Wash the crystals with either acetone or alcohol, according to their solubility. The properties of the derivatives are listed in Table 21. Photomicrographs of the crystalline forms are given in the original paper.

WERNER (50) and BROWN (6) have studied the appearance of sublimates and the sublimation temperatures cf amino acids. TAKAYAMA (44) gives some data on the properties of *d*- and *l*-glutamic acid hydrochlorides.

Surmatis and Willard (43) began a study of microscopic tests for amino acids in which they tried out the alkaloid reagents and salts of the heavy metals. Denigès (12) also described a test for glycocoll with phosphotungstic acid.

Degradative Procedures for Acidic Nitrogen Compounds.

In the study of the constitution and structure of proteins and peptides it is necessary to learn the sequence and the identity of the amino acids which make up the molecule. The procedures are based upon the fact that the two ends of the chain form active groups which are different from each other and from the other parts of the chain. The end which contains the free α-amino group is called the N-terminal residue, the other, which contains the free α-carboxy group, is called the C-terminal residue. By removing these groups, one after the other, and identifying them and then repeating the procedure with the newly formed terminal groups, the desired information on the sequence and identity of the amino acids which constitute the links in the chain can be obtained. Actually, complete stepwise removal of each link is never carried out. It is usually sufficient to subject the chain to partial hydrolysis and then to identify the dipeptides, tripeptides, etc., which result, as above.

Hydrolysis. Proteins and peptides can be hydrolyzed into the constituent amino acids or polypeptides by refluxing with 6 m HCl or 4.5 m H_2SO_4. All proteins give 10 to 18 products. Alkaline hydrolysis is not recommended since it can lead to extensive racemization of most of the products. Enzymatic hydrolysis is slow and never complete but it is not as destructive to sensitive amino acids as acid or alkaline hydrolysis. With the exception of the enzymatic method, hydrolysis will usually result in a more ore less complete breaking up of the entire protein or polypeptide. For determination of the sequence of the links in the chain, partial hydrolysis must be employed. This usually involves conversion of the terminal residue into a labeled compound which can be separately identified.

Enzymatic hydrolysis is the most successful method of determining the C-terminal residue. The terminal residue is removed selectively by the enzyme carboxy-peptidase. This cleaves only peptide linkages adjacent to free α-carboxyl groups in polypeptide chains. After removal of the first terminal residue, the treatment can be repeated to remove the new C-terminal group and so on.

The two best procedures for the removal and identification of the N-terminal residue are those of Sanger (41) and Edman (15).

Sanger Procedure. The procedure consists of reacting the free amino group of the peptide with 2,4-dinitrofluorobenzene. To a mixture of the sample of the test substance with twice the amount of sodium bicarbonate dissolved in 2 to 3 times the weight of sample of water, add twice the weight of 2,4-dinitrofluorobenzene dissolved in 2 to 3 times as much ethyl alcohol. Allow to react at room temperature for two hours with occasional mixing. Then extract excess reagent with ether and hydrolyze the product with 6 m HCl to obtain the derivative of the N-terminal residue by crystallization.

Edman Procedure. The advantage of the EDMAN procedure is that after removal of the first N-terminal residue the remainder of the molecule is left intact and the analysis can be repeated for the next link in the chain.

TABLE 21

Properties of Nitroir

Nitroindandionate of	Crystal Habit	System	Optical Sign	Elongation
d-l-Alanine	Parallelogram plates	Monoclinic	—	+
d-Arginine (di-derivative)	Small rosettes	—		
l-Aspartic acid	Yellow needles and rods	Orthorhombic	+	±
l-Cysteine	Rectangular tablets	Orthorhombic	—	+
d-Glutamic Acid	Yellow rectangular plates	Orthorhombic	—	—
Glycine	Yellow needles and rods	Monoclinic	+	+
l-Histidine (di-derivative)	Tan rectangular plates	Monoclinic	—	—
l-Hydroxyproline	Broken prisms	Orthorhombic	+	—
3,5-Diiodo-l-tyrosine	Thin plates and radiating needles	Orthorhombic	+	
d-Isoleucine	Yellow, thin elongated needles	Orthorhombic	—?	—
l-Leucine	Yellow rectangular plates	Orthorhombic	—	—
d-Lysine	Broken prisms and tablets	Orthorhombic	+	+
d-l-Methionine	Needles and thin plates	Orthorhombic	+?	+
β-Phenylalanine	Needles	—		
l-Proline	Thin rectangular plates	Orthorhombic	+	—
d-l-Serine	Yellow rods and needles	Monoclinic	+	+
d-l-Tryptophane	Small rectangular plates	—		
d-l-Valine	Square and rectangular tablets	Orthorhombic	—	+

The reaction of an amine with an isocyanate (*see* page 267) is used to prepare a phenylthiocarbamyl peptide. This is then hydrolyzed in nitromethane solution saturated with HCl to release a phenylthiohydantoin. The remainder of the protein can then be treated further with the reagent.

Chemical Separation of Acidic Nitrogen Compounds.

The group as a whole can, of course, be separated by the neutralization with alkali and precipitation from non-aqueous solvents. Within the group the various peptides and amino acids can be separated from each other by making use of the fact that their lowest solubility is at the isoelectric point and that this differs for the various members of the group. By careful adjustment of the pH of the solution it is possible to achieve a satisfactory separation of the individual members from each other. Table 22 gives the values for the pH at the isoelectric points for the more common amino acids. The procedure of separation usually consists of the slow salting out of the amino acid or peptide with, e. g., ammonium sulfate, in a solution buffered to the required pH. The ammonium sulfate is placed

TABLE 21

ndionates of Amino Acids

Axial Dispersion	Refractive Indices			Extinction Angle in Degrees
Strong v > r	1.478	1.738	> 1.870	40
—	—	—	—	—
Strong r > v	1.631	1.683	> 1.870	Parallel
Strong v > r	1.513	1.748	> 1.870	Parallel
Strong v > r	1.449	1.689	> 1.870	Parallel
Strong v > r	1.636	1.717	> 1.870	10
Strong v > r	1.636	1.758	?	15
Strong v > r	1.461	1.621	1.802	Parallel
Strong v > r	1.766	1.786	> 1.870	Parallel
	1.450	1.652	1.771	Parallel
Strong r > v	1.449	1.645	1.758	Parallel
Strong r > v	1.517	1.522	1.781	Parallel
Strong v > r	1.622	1.667	?	Parallel
—	—	—	—	—
Strong r > v	1.524	1.678	> 1.870	Parallel
Strong r > v	1.626	1.705	1.802	5
—	—	—	—	—
Strong v > r	1.467	1.678	> 1.870	Parallel

in a plastic container such as a cellophane bag and hung into a solution of the peptide or amino acid. The precipitate, which consists of the peptide together with ammonium sulfate, must be dialyzed against distilled water to remove the ammonium salt. This can be carried out in apparatus such as that of WOOD (53) or BAER (1). The latter employs electrodialysis. Other apparatus for this purpose is described by TAYLOR, PARPART and BALLANTINE (45), and KEYS (21).

Another method of separating the amino acids or the fragments of the hydrolysis of peptides and protein is the EMIL FISCHER procedure of esterifying these first and then fractionally distilling the esters. The favorable

17*

spread between the boiling points of these esters facilitates such fractionation. The hydrolysis is carried out as described above under Degradative Procedures.

Some of the amino acids can be precipitated as salts of heavy metals. Tryptophan, for example, is precipitated with mercuric sulfate. Basic amino acids can be precipitated with phosphotungstic acid.

Reference is also made to electrophoretic methods which have been successfully used for the identification and isolation of proteins from complex mixtures.

TABLE 22

Isoelectric Points of Amino Acids

Amino Acid	Isoelectric Point	Amino Acid	Isoelectric Point
Glycine	5.97	Cysteine	5.05
Alanine	6.00	Cystine	4.8
Valine	5.96	Methionine	5.74
Leucine	6.02	Serine	5.68
Isoleucine	5.98	Aspartic acid	2.77
Proline	6.30	Glutamic acid	3.22
Phenylalanine	5.48	Lysine	9.74
Tyrosine	5.66	Arginine	10.76
Tryptophan	5.89		

Beginning with the work of MARTIN and SYNGE (34 a) (*see* also page 81) chromatographic methods have been widely used as a means of separating and identifying the amino acids. Starch columns were first used and then paper strip chromatography. *See*, for example, HELMER (22), PATTON and FOREMAN (36), and ROCKLAND and DUNN (38). UNDERWOOD and ROCKLAND (47) discuss the factors affecting the separation and sequence of amino acids in paper chromatography.

DUNN and DRELL (14) present a scheme for the qualitative identification of amino acids in mixtures containing from two to five components, which includes separation on the basis of some of the reactions given above and also others.

Ion exchange resins can also be used for the separation of the amino acids. *See*, for example, WINTERS and KUNIN (52) for a description of the use of these resins in protein hydrolyzate fractionation. The new ion-exchange resin papers present the possibility of combining the action of both procedures.

Quantitative Determination of Amino Acids.

The neutralization equivalent of amino acids can be determined according to GRASSMANN and HEYDE (19) but the simplest method is that of VAN SLYKE (48) or, better, that of KAINZ, HUBER, and KASLER (24) which has a wider application than that of VAN SLYKE. The details of the method are given under Amines p. 270.

Genus 2.

<h1 style="text-align:center">Basic Species.</h1>

<h3 style="text-align:center">Classification Reactions.</h3>

Specific Test for Ammonia. This test is carried out in a gas chamber consisting of a microscope slide (preferably one with a concave depression) as a base, a glass ring about 10 mm high and 10 mm in diameter, and a 2.5-cm (1-inch) watch glass as a cover, Fig. 176.

Place a small drop of water on the underside of the watch glass and a large drop of acetone or ether on the upper side. The evaporation of the

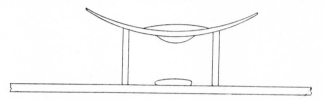

Fig. 176. Distillation of Ammonia.

latter liquid keeps the watch glass cool. Place the drop of the solution of the test substance in the depression of the slide, the glass ring around it, and the watch glass on the ring. After warming the slide gently for a few minutes, take off the watch glass and touch the underside to a clean slide so that the drop of distillate is transferred to the slide. Test this drop for ammonia as follows: add formalin (40% aqueous formaldehyde) drop by drop from a capillary until sufficient has been added to react with most of the ammonia but not all. An excess of ammonia must be present after the addition of the formalin. Warm the solution gently at first and then more rapidly until an edge crust forms on the drop. Then add a crystal of potassium ferrocyanide and a small drop of dilute hydrochloric acid. Avoid an excess of the acid. If ammonia is present in the original sample, rhomboidal and hexagonal plates of the ferrocyanide of hexamethylenetetramine appear.

Notes.

1) ROSENTHALER (39) recommends the iodine-potassium iodide reagent.

2) For a discussion of the hexamethylenetetramine reaction *see* CHAMOT and MASON (8).

Test for Salts of the Ammonium Type. This test should be carried out before the generic tests because ammonium salts are not listed in the table. Use the same procedure and apparatus as in the foregoing test, but add 15 µl water and 0.15 mg of finely divided magnesium oxide to 0.1 mg of the substance. Set the complete gas chamber on a metal block and heat the latter until the drop being distilled begins to decrease in size. Test the drop of distillate as described in the foregoing test or by means of any of the ammonia reagents such as chloroplatinic acid or NESSLER's reagent. If ammonia is present, the acid with which it was combined must be identified in the residue.

Notes.

1) This test should be carried out only if the substance has a rather high and unsharp melting point and is quite soluble in water.

2) According to WACEK and LÖFFLER (49) the gas chamber can be used for the separation of volatile primary, secondary, and tertiary amines and ammonia. They use bases of increasing strength to liberate the amines.

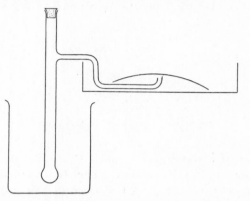

Fig. 177. Test for Primary Amines with Nitrous Acid.

Detection of Primary Amines with Nitrous Acid. In this test the presence of primary amines is established by collecting the gas evolved when the sample is treated with nitrous acid and comparing its volume with that of the gas obtained in a blank experiment.

Set up a small distilling flask as shown in Fig. 177. Stopper the flask with a small cork, place the side arm in the Petri dish, and fill the latter with alkaline permanganate solution. Invert a 5-cm watch glass over the opening of the side arm in such a way that a small bubble (approximately 10 mm in diameter) of air is trapped under the glass. This can be done by holding the watch glass in an inclined position and lowering it into the Petri dish until only part of the edge projects above the liquid. When the proper amount of air remains, bring the watch glass to a horizontal position under the liquid surface and place it over the side arm. Bring the air bubble over the mouth of the side arm. The presence of the bubble is necessary later to prevent the sucking back of the permanganate solution due to the contraction of the gases in the distilling flask because of the initial absorption of the oxides of nitrogen. Mark the circumference of the air bubble on the watch glass with a glass-marking pencil.

Remove the cork from the flask and immerse the bulb and part of the neck in a beaker of ice water. Place the sample of test substance (0.5 mg) and 0.1 ml of ice-cold 6 m HCl in the bulb. Then add 0.02 ml of ice-cold 3 m NaNO$_2$ solution. Stopper the flask quickly and allow it to stand for one or two minutes. Heat the water in the beaker *slowly* to boiling. Do not continue the boiling too long. Allow the flask and contents to cool, keeping the outlet of the side arm open to the gas bubble at all times to prevent the sucking back of the permanganate solution. After cooling mark the outline of the gas bubble with a glass-marking pencil. Run a blank experiment the same way, starting with an air bubble of the same diameter as the one used in the test. Compare the diameter of the bubble obtained in the blank with the diameter of the bubble obtained in the test. If the latter is larger, the test substance was a primary amine.

Notes.

1) The permanganate solution is prepared by dissolving 5 g of potassium permanganate and 2.5 g of potassium hydroxide in 100 ml of water.

2) Both primary amines and amides give this test. The aliphatic primary amines give nitrogen and an alcohol:

$$R\text{---}N\begin{array}{c}H\\[4pt]\\[4pt]H\end{array} + HO\text{---}N\text{=}O \longrightarrow ROH + N_2$$

Aromatic primary amines give an intermediate diazonium compound:

$$C_6H_5NH_2\text{---}HCl + HO\text{---}N\text{=}O \longrightarrow C_6H_5\text{---}N\text{=}N\text{---}Cl + 2\,H_2O$$

This is stable only at low temperatures and in excess acid. On heating it decomposes into nitrogen and a phenol:

$$C_6H_5\text{---}N\text{=}N\text{---}Cl + H_2O \longrightarrow C_6H_5OH + N_2 + HCl$$

Carbylamine Reaction for Primary Amines.

Place about 30 µg of the test substance in a microcone and add a drop of alcoholic potassium hydroxide and a small drop of chloroform from a capillary pipet. Warm on the water bath. If the odor of carbylamine is not noticed at once, cool and heat to boiling again.

Notes.

1) Directions for this test are from EMICH (17).

2) A piece of potassium hydroxide about the size of a pea is dissolved in 1 ml of alcohol. This is used as the reagent.

3) The reaction is as follows:

$$R\text{---}N\begin{array}{c}H\\H\end{array} + \begin{array}{c}Cl\quad Cl\\C\\Cl\quad H\end{array} + 3\,KOH \longrightarrow R\text{---}N\text{≡}C + 3\,KCl + 3\,H_2O$$

4) The test is so sensitive that it will detect primary amines present as impurities in secondary or tertiary amines.

Rimini Test for Primary Aliphatic Amines. Place 1 drop (1 mm in a capillary) of the amine in the depression of spot plate. Add 20 times as much (20 mm in the capillary) water from an adjacent depression of the spot plate. Then add 1 drop of pure acetone and 1 drop of 1 % sodium nitroprusside solution, both from a capillary pipet. A violet-red color is a positive test.

Simon Test for Secondary Aliphatic Amines. Place one drop (from a capillary pipet) of the test substance in a depression of a spot plate and add 12 times as much water and 1 drop of 1 % sodium nitroprusside solution. In an adjacent depression place 1 to 2 drops of ethyl alcohol. Heat the end of a piece of fine copper wire red hot and dip immediately into the alcohol. Repeat the heating and immersion of the wire. Add 1 drop of the resulting solution to the test drop. A blue color fading to green and yellow is a positive test.

Derivates of Amines.

Acylation of Amines. Direct Acylation. To 3 to 6 mg of the test substance in a microcone add twice as much acetic anhydride. Heat the mixture in a metal block at 100° or on a water bath for one minute. After cooling, dissolve the product in a hot solvent (water, dilute alcohol, or 95 % alcohol, as recommended for the particular derivative). Cool the tube with ice and scratch the sides until precipitation occurs. After centrifuging and decanting the supernatant liquid, rinse the precipitate sparingly with the solvent. Take a melting point and, if necessary, recrystallize the product.

Notes.

1) $R-NH_2 + (CH_3CO)_2O \longrightarrow RNHCO-CH_3 + CH_3CO-OH$

$$\begin{matrix} R \\ \\ R \end{matrix}\!\!\!> NH + (CH_3CO)_2O \longrightarrow \begin{matrix} R \\ \\ R \end{matrix}\!\!\!> NCO-CH_3 + CH_3CO-OH$$

2) A trace of sulfuric acid will catalyze the reaction.

Acylation of Amines. Schotten-Baumann Reaction. Place 3 to 6 mg of the test substance in a reflux tube. Add a slight excess of 3 m NaOH (MULLIKEN and HUNTRESS recommend potassium hydroxide for a better yield) and then 4 to 7 μl benzoyl chloride. Seal the tube and allow it to stand for half an hour with occasional centrifuging of the contents back and forth. Then open the tube. If the odor of the chloride is still noticeable, seal it again and allow it to stand again for half an hour with centrifuging as before. If a precipitate appears when the reaction is complete, centrifuge it out. If there is no precipitate, acidify the reaction mixture with hydrochloric acid. Wash the precipitate with water and extract with cold ether, discarding the extract. The chief difficulty in this preparation lies in the purification of the product. The principal impurity is benzoic acid which should have been removed by the ether extraction. However, the derivative in some cases is also soluble in ether, and hence the separation is not very efficient. In such cases the benzoic acid can be removed by sublimation. Place the residue from the cold ether extraction on a cover slip. Set the cover slip on a metal block, lay pieces of glass rod, 1 to 2 mm in diameter, on either side of the residue, and place a clean slide on the rods. Heat the cover slip to 90° to 100°. When no more sublimate forms on a clean portion of the slide, remove the cover slip to a melting point apparatus and determine the melting point.

Notes.

1)
$$RNH_2 + R'-\overset{O}{\underset{Cl}{C}} + NaOH \longrightarrow RNH-\overset{O}{\underset{R'}{C}} + NaCl + H_2O$$

2) If the contents of the tube become warm, cool the tube under the tap.

Acylation of Amines. Acylation in Pyridine.

First Procedure. Dissolve 3 to 6 mg of the test substance in 30 to 60 μl of dry pyridine in a microcone. Quickly add an equal quantity or slight excess of the reagent and cool under the tap if necessary. Dilute the mixture with approximately 600 μl water and stir until precipitation occurs. If no precipitate appears after a reasonable time, set the cone aside for ten minutes and then stir again. Centrifuge the precipitate out, discard the supernatant liquid, and wash the precipitate with 600 μl of water, 600 μl of 0.15 m sodium carbonate solution and finally again with 600 μl water. Recrystallize the product from a suitable solvent to a constant melting point.

Second Procedure. Proceed as in the first method but, after the reaction has taken place, dissolve the mixture as far as possible in 500 μl of ether and extract the pyridine three times by mixing with 500 μl water each time and removing the water layer. Wash the ether layer twice with 50 μl 0.15 m sodium carbonate solution and twice with 50 μl water, drawing off the lower layer in a capillary pipet each time. Evaporate the ether and allow the residue to stand in an evacuated vacuum desiccator to remove all volatile substances as completely as possible. Recrystallize the residue from a suitable solvent to a constant melting point.

Notes.

1) The reaction is:

2) This procedure is used when the product of the acylation is easily saponified.

3) The reagent may be either *p*-nitrobenzoyl chloride or 3,5-dinitrobenzoyl chloride. *See* also p. 205.

Picramides from Primary and Secondary Amines.   Mix 3 to 6 mg of the amine, 50 µl ethyl alcohol, and 330 µl 2% alcoholic solution of picryl chloride in a microcone   After allowing the mixture to stand for a few minutes, heat to boiling.   If necessary, add water to produce a slight turbidity to induce crystallization.   After centrifuging briefly to concentrate the solid in the lower end of the microcone (but not enough to pack it down), remove the larger part of the supernatant liquid.   Stir up the precipitate with the remaining liquid and transfer the slurry to a microscope slide.   Draw off the liquid with a piece of filter paper or a capillary pipet and wash the solid with alcohol.   Take a melting point.

Notes.
1) The reactions are:

2) The methylamine derivative hydrolyzes very readily. The hydrochloride should therefore be used in place of the free amine.   Mix 3 to 6 mg of the hydrochloride, dissolved in 15 to 20 µl alcohol, with 100 µl 2% alcoholic picryl chloride.   Then add 3 to 6 mg of powdered potassium hydroxide and mix until the color becomes uniform. After centrifuging decant the supernatant liquid into another microcone and treat with 12 m HCl until the brown liquid turns yellow.   Centrifuge again, remove the supernatant liquid, and evaporate it to dryness or to the formation of crystals.   Wash the solid with alcohol, dry, and determine the melting point.

3) The methyl aniline derivative may also present difficulty in either of these procedures.   A modification of Turpin's (46) method makes it possible to prepare it. Dissolve 5 mg of picryl chloride in sufficient boiling alcohol to dissolve it.   Then add 3 mg of methyl aniline and 3 mg of anhydrous sodium acetate.   Place the micro-cone in the water bath or metal heating block and heat until half the alcohol has been evaporated.   Then place the cone in a vacuum desiccator until crystallization takes place.

Aryl Sulfonyl Derivatives of Primary and Secondary Amines. Behrens (3) suggested that benzene sulfonyl chloride (Hinsberg reagent) be used for the micro separation of primary, secondary, and tertiary amines. Quaternary amines can be removed by distilling the mixture with not too concentrated alkali.   The quaternary amines are not volatile and, if the alkali is not too concentrated, they will not be decomposed by this treatment.   The tertiary amines do not react with the Hinsberg reagent.

Add 5 to 9 µl of benzene sulfonyl chloride to 3 to 6 mg of the amine mixture and stir until reaction takes place. Cool the mixture under the tap or in ice water if necessary. Then add 12 to 24 µl of 4 m KOH potassium hydroxide and heat the mixture slowly to very gentle boiling in a heating block to remove the excess reagent, stirring while heating. Centrifuge.

A) If the material dissolves completely in the potassium hydroxide, the test substance is a primary amine. Centrifuge off any insoluble material and acidify the clear liquid with 12 m HCl. Centrifuge out the resulting precipitate. The supernatant liquid contains any tertiary amines which may be present. The precipitate is extracted with ether and recrystallized from ether or benzene.

B) If the derivative does not dissolve in the potassium hydroxide or if a large residue remains after the treatment with the alkali, the original test substance is or contains a secondary amine. Centrifuge off the residue and extract it with ether. Recrystallize from ether or benzene. The sulfonamides can also be converted to benzene sulfonic acid and the hydrochloride of the amine by heating in a sealed capillary with concentrated hydrochloric acid at 160°.

Notes.

1) The reaction of the reagent with primary amines is:

$$\text{C}_6\text{H}_5\text{—SO}_2\text{Cl} + \text{H}_2\text{NR} \longrightarrow \underset{\text{Soluble in alkali}}{\text{C}_6\text{H}_5\text{—SO}_2\text{—N(H)—R}} \xrightarrow{\text{KOH}} \left(\text{C}_6\text{H}_5\text{—SO}_2\text{—N—R}\right)^- \text{K}^+$$

With secondary amines the following reaction takes place:

$$\text{C}_6\text{H}_5\text{—SO}_2\text{Cl} + \text{HNR}_2 \longrightarrow \underset{\text{Insoluble in alkali}}{\text{C}_6\text{H}_5\text{—SO}_2\text{—N(R)—R}}$$

2) The amines can be recovered by hydrolysis of the benzenesulfonamides with hydrochloric acid. A separation of the primary, secondary, and tertiary amines can thus be made with this reagent.

3) Other sulfonyl chlorides can be used as the reagent, p-toluenesulfonyl chloride being particularly recommended.

Isocyanates and Isothiocyanates of Primary and Secondary Amines.

Dissolve 3 to 6 mg of the amine in 3 µl 95% alcohol in a reflux tube. Add 3 to 6 µl of the reagent. Heat for 5 to 10 minutes. Cool and, if necessary, scratch the walls of the tube after cutting open. Filter by transferring the contents to a microcone and centrifuging and decanting. Recrystallize the product from boiling alcohol.

Note.

The reactions are:

$$\text{R—N=C=O} + \text{R'NH}_2 \longrightarrow \text{RNH—CO—NHR'}$$
$$\text{R—N=C=S} + \text{R'NH}_2 \longrightarrow \text{RNH—CS—NHR'}$$

Salts of Amines.

Picrates. The method for the preparation of the picrates varies according to the amine. Two examples will illustrate the technique. Dissolve 2 to 3 mg of quinoline in alcohol and add an equal volume of a saturated alcoholic solution of picric acid. Centrifuge the precipitate which forms immediately, remove the supernatant liquid, and wash the residue with five times the original volume of liquid. Dry at 60° and determine the melting point. In the case of substances such as urea, dissolve 3 to 6 mg of the test substance in water and then add an equal volume of a saturated solution of picric acid and a small drop of dilute hydrochloric acid. A precipitate forms in about ten minutes. Centrifuge it out, remove the supernatant liquid, and wash the residue with very little water.

Note.

Amines will form salts which can be used for identification with a number of acids, particularly picric, picrolonic, chloroplatinic, and chloroauric acids. The metallic content of the salts of the last two can be determined by simple ignition, thus affording another means of identification. DUNBAR and KNUTESON (13) give photomicrographs of amine picrates.

3,5-Dinitrobenzoates. Dissolve 2 mg of 3,5-dinitrobenzoic acid in 25 to 50 µl of absolute alcohol. Mix this solution with an equal volume of a solution containing 0.00001 mole of the amine in absolute alcohol. Pass a stream of dry air over the surface of the solution until the latter is completely evaporated. Recrystallize the solid from absolute alcohol or other anhydrous solvent such as benzene.

Note.

The manipulations of this method must be carried out as quickly as possible and the substances must be shielded from moisture at all times because they are very easily hydrolyzed.

p-Toluene Sulfonates. Add 3 to 6 mg of the monoamine or 2 to 4 mg of the diamine to 20 µl of a 2.5 *m* *p*-toluene sulfonic acid solution. Heat the mixture to gentle boiling on a metal block until the solution becomes clear. Add 1 to 2 mg of decolorizing carbon and boil the solution gently again for a few minutes. While the solution is still hot, centrifuge and transfer the hot liquid to another microcone. Cool the filtrate in ice water to crystallize out the salt. If no solid separates, evaporate the solution to some extent. Recrystallize the solid from hot water and dry in air at 110°.

Notes.

1) The *p*-toluene sulfonic acid reagent is prepared by dissolving 47.55 g of the acid in distilled water and bringing the volume up to 100 ml.

2) An example of how the microprocedure results in a product with the lowest melting point reported in the literature for the product is presented by the *p*-toluene sulfonates. For the aniline salt the following melting points have been reported

in the literature: 238.4°, 235° to 236°, 230° to 231°, 223°, and 216°. GARCIA and SCHNEIDER (18) obtained a product melting at 215° to 218°. Similar results were obtained in several other cases. This may be a case of polymorphism.

Other salts of amines have been prepared and used for the identification of the bases either by characteristic crystal habit or by the optical properties of the salts. BEHRENS (2) describes the double salts of magnesium and amine phosphates and uranyl acetates and ferrocyanides. BOLLAND (4) lists a large number of reactions of amines with inorganic reagents. LANGLEY and ALBRECHT (32) use the flavianates for the identification of some bases and give some optical constants. PLEIN and DEWEY (37) identify 22 primary amines by means of the optical properties of the diliturates of the bases.

The reaction of BROWN and CAMPBELL (7) for the preparation of the β-naphthylthioureas of amines can be carried out on a micro scale in a capillary tube.

Degradative Procedures.

Amines may be degraded into smaller molecules by exhaustive methylation to quaternary ammonium salts, followed by the HOFMANN elimination. After treatment with methyl iodide, the quaternary iodide is converted to the hydroxide by treatment with silver oxide. When this hydroxide is heated to 125° or higher, the products will be a tertiary amine (e. g. trimethylamine if the original compound was a primary amine), an unsaturated hydrocarbon, and water. The ring structure of cyclic amines will be broken by this procedure and one molecule of an unsaturated tertiary amine will be the only product.

A newer, somewhat more reliable, procedure involves the use of hydrogen peroxide. For example, a tertiary amine when treated with hydrogen peroxide will be converted to a tertiary amine oxide. When this is heated to 140° or higher, it will decompose to an alkene and a dialkylhydroxylamine. This in turn can be exhaustively methylated with methyl iodide and then treated with silver oxide to give another tertiary amine oxide, etc. Thus, all of the original alkyl groups in the amine can be identified as the corresponding alkene.

Diazotization and subsequent conversion of the diazonium salt to the phenol etc. can also be used as a degradative procedure for aromatic amines.

Chemical Separation.

Amines can be separated from other, non-basic, compounds by converting them into salts of mineral acids. These are usually water-soluble and can be separated by extraction. Treatment with a strong base such as NaOH will release the free organic base.

The classes of amines, primary, secondary, and tertiary, can be separated from each other by means of the HINSBERG reaction, p. 266.

As mentioned above, WACEK and LÖFFLER (49) describe the use of fixed bases of increasing strength to liberate ammonia and the classes of volatile amines in sequence and thus achieve separation.

Quantitative Determination.

The KJELDAHL procedure can be used for the determination of aminoid nitrogen but is not, of course, restricted to amines. If the nature of the nitrogen compound has been established as an amine, the determination can be carried out with excellent results.

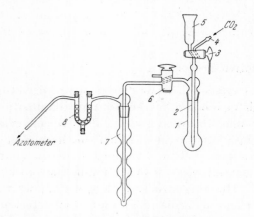 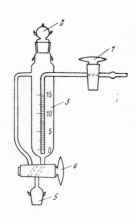

Fig. 178. Apparatus of KAINZ, HUBER, and KASLER for the Determination of Primary Amine.

Fig. 179. Preparation Pipet of KAINZ, HUBER, and KASLER.

Compounds containing the primary amino group can be determined by reaction with nitrous acid and measurement of the liberated nitrogen (VAN SLYKE method), or by determination of the nitrite used for diazotization or nitrosation.

The lithium aluminum hydride method of LIEB and SCHÖNIGER (34) p. 195 for the determination of active hydrogen can also be used in the determination of amines.

Determination of Primary Amino Groups with Nitrosylbromide. The difficulty in obtaining correct results with some types of compounds when using the VAN SLYKE method of deamination with nitrous acid led KAINZ, HUBER, and KASLER (24) to the use of nitrosyl bromide in glacial acetic acid solution.

Reagents. Nitrosyl bromide solution. Add 3 ml bromine (HOOD) to 15 ml glacial acetic acid and then 2 g solid sodium nitrite. Transfer the resulting black-brown solution to the dried preparation pipet described below.

Bromate-sulfuric acid. Prepare immediately before use by mixing 5 ml of 7.5% sodium bromate with 5 ml 9 m sulfuric acid with cooling.

Formic acid-sodium formate solution. Equal volumes of formic acid and 20% sodium formate solution.

Absolute ethyl alcohol.

Carbon dioxide. From Kipp or solid carbon dioxide generator.

Apparatus. The apparatus (Fig. 178) consists of a reaction tube (*1*), an inlet tube (*2*), a special three-way stopcock (*3*), an inlet tube for the carbon dioxide (*4*), a dropping funnel (*5*), an inlet stopcock (*6*), a washer (*7*), and a U-tube (*8*). In addition, a separate preparation pipet (Fig. 179) and a PREGL micro azotometer are required. The latter should be fitted with the usual three-way stopcock to permit purging of air prior to the determination. The ground joint of the preparation pipet fits into the dropping funnel of the rest of the apparatus. All stopcocks are lubricated with silicone grease. The connection of the carbon dioxide inlet tube with the source of carbon dioxide is made with polyvinyl chloride tubing.

Procedure. Connect the preparation pipet containing the nitrosyl bromide with the rest of the apparatus, place several milliliters of the formic acid-sodium formate solution in the reaction tube and pass carbon dioxyde through the nitrosyl bromide solution for 30 minutes. Wash the apparatus (with the exception of the preparation pipet) by dipping the outlet of the azotometer stopcock in a dish of water and applying suction at the carbon dioxide inlet (*4*) at the first stopcock. Dry the apparatus by introducing 4 ml of absolute alcohol in the reaction tube, opening stopcock (*6*) to the atmosphere, and turning the carbon dioxide on full stream. Repeat this last operation with acetone and finally draw air through the reaction tube.

Fill the washer (*7*) with bromate-sulfuric acid. Wet the beads in the U-tube with either saturated sodium thiosulfate solution or the formic acid-sodium formate solution. Introduce 2 to 3 mg of the test substance into the reaction tube and pass carbon dioxide through the inlet tube (*4*) until microbubbles are obtained in the azotometer (about ten minutes). Allow about 2 ml of the nitrosyl bromide-acetic acid solution to enter the reaction tube and then pass carbon dioxide at the rate of one bubble per second. After 20 to 25 minutes, microbubbles will again appear in the azotometer. At times it may be necessary to extend this time to fifty minutes.

At the end of the determination draw water through the apparatus as described above. This makes it possible to carry out several determinations without error from residual bromine fumes.

Run a blank in the same manner as the determination and subtract any volume of nitrogen found from the results of the determinations on test substances.

Determination of Amines by Acetylation. Amines can also be quantitatively acetylated and the procedure is the same as that used for hydroxylated compounds by OGG, PORTER, and WILLITS (35). These authors suggested that their method might be employed for amines, and SIGGIA (42) reports that checks on such compounds have shown the procedure to operate well for primary as well as secondary amines.

Reagents. Acetic anhydride reagent. One volume of reagent-grade acetic anhydride mixed with 3 volumes reagent-grade pyridine.

n-Butanol.

Mixed indicator solution. One part 0.1% aqueous cresol red neutralized with sodium hydroxide and 3 parts 0.1% thymol blue neutralized with sodium hydroxide.

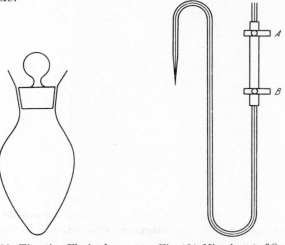

Fig. 180. Titration Flask of OGG, PORTER, and WILLITS.

Fig. 181. Microburet of OGG, PORTER, and WILLITS.

Alcoholic sodium hydroxide standard solutions, approximately 0.1 *n*. Prepare the solution from saturated aqueous sodium hydroxide and aldehyde-free ethanol made by alkaline aluminum reduction. Using the mixed indicator, standardize the alcoholic solutions to ± 2 parts per 1000 against either potassium acid phthalate or a standard acid of approximately the same normality.

Apparatus. Titration flask. This is a pear-shaped flask with ground-in stopper and a capacity of 50 ml, Fig. 180.

Buret. This is an **S**-shaped capillary buret of 1-mm bore with a mercury column in contact with the solution, Fig. 181. The buret is filled and the reagent expelled by releasing and applying pressure by means of the two clamps to tubing which serves as the mercury well of the buret. Two hair lines are placed on the buret at the points which would allow the delivery of approximately 0.4 ml.

Procedure. Weigh a sample of the test substance directly into the dry reaction flask. The sample should have an amine content equivalent to approximately 2 ml of the standard sodium hydroxide. Draw the acetic anhydride-pyridine reagent into the buret to a point below the lower mark. Wipe off the tip of the buret with a cloth and then with the tips of the fingers to "grease" it to prevent creeping of the solution up the tip and to ensure more uniform removal of the reagent. Touch the inner wall of a beaker against the buret tip and bring the mercury meniscus to the lower mark by carefully closing the screw clamp A. Replace the beaker with the reaction flask held so that the buret tip touches its inner wall. Rotate the flask slowly while allowing the reagent to flow from the buret by tightening A and then B until the meniscus is at the upper mark. Immediately connect the flask to a water-cooled condenser and seal the glass joint with a few drops of pyridine. Place the flask and condenser on a steam bath with the tip of the flask extending approximately 1.25 cm through the ring which fits most tightly. Acetylate for 30 minutes, then add 3 ml of distilled water through the condenser and hydrolyze by heating for two minutes longer if no carboxyl groups are present or 30 minutes longer if there are.

Add 1 ml of pyridine to the cup of the neck of the flask and disconnect the flask so that the pyridine flows over and rinses the condenser tip. Insert a stopper loosely, and immediately cool the flask to room temperature under running water. Add 3 ml of n-butanol to the cup and loosen the stopper so that it and the walls of the flask are rinsed. Add three drops of the mixed indicator and shield the flask from the air with a rubber dam, held in place with a rubber band to prevent absorption of carbon dioxide near the end of the titration. Insert the buret tip through a pinhole in the dam and titrate the excess of the acetic acid and any acid in the sample with the 0.1 n alcoholic sodium hydroxide until the solution changes to gray, volume A.

Run a blank determination on the same volume of the acetic anhydride-pyridine solution, volume B.

Determine any free acid in the test substance by dissolving a sample in ethanol previously neutralized against the mixed indicator and titrating in the same way as in the acetylation. From this titration calculate the volume of the 0.1 n sodium hydroxide equivalent to the free acid in a 1-mg sample of the test substance, volume C.

The per cent amino or imino content is calculated from

$$100 f N (B - A + C S)/S$$

where N = normality of standard sodium hydroxide,

$\quad S$ = weight of sample in milligrams,

$\quad B$ = volume of standard solution required for blank, and

$\quad f$ = 16.026 for NH_2 and 15.018 for NH.

Microtitration of Amines.   KEEN and FRITZ (25) have described a method for the titration of amines in non-aqueous solvents using perchloric acid.

Reagents. Diphenylguanidine. Commercial grade recrystallized from toluene, then from 95% ethyl alcohol, and finally from toluene again.

Methyl violet, concentrated: saturated benzene solution.

Methyl violet, dilute: 30 mg dissolved in 100 ml benzene.

Perchloric acid, 0.01 n. Dissolve 0.85 ml 72% perchloric acid in 1 liter of reagent-grade glacial acetic acid. Prepare 0.001 n perchloric acid by dilution of the 0.01 n with acetic acid. Standardize against diphenylguanidine in chlorobenzene or potassium acid phthalate.

Solvents, reagent-grade.

Apparatus. A microburet that can easily be read to 0.01 ml. A Koch buret is recommended for Procedure C.

Procedures. Procedure A. Dissolve a sample of the test substance containing 0.03 to 0.08 milliequivalents of amine in 5 to 10 ml of the desired solvent. Add two to three drops of methyl violet indicator (saturated benzene solution) and titrate the solution to a clear blue (disappearance of violet tinge) with 0.01 n perchloric acid. Near the end point add the titrant in 0.01-ml increments.

Procedure B. Dissolve the sample in about 1 ml of the desired solvent in a 5 ml beaker. Add one drop of the indicator and titrate the solution with 0.01 n perchloric acid to a blue color. A small magnetic stirrer (*see* p. 20) may be used to provide the necessary agitation. Near the end point add the titrant in about 0.005-ml increments.

Procedure C. Dissolve the sample in 1 ml of benzene and carry out the titration in a 15-ml centrifuge tube. Add one drop of the dilute methyl violet indicator and titrate with 0.001 n perchloric acid to the first permanent blue color. For best accuracy add the titrant in increments of 0.002 to 0.005 ml near the end point. An indicator blank is required and must be subtracted from the buret reading. The titrant should be standardized against a solution of diphenylguanidine in about 50 ml of chlorbenzene diluted to one liter with benzene.

The relative accuracy and precision of the above procedures are given as: A. 0.3%, B. 0.5%, and C. 1 to 2%.

Avoid touching the buret or the acetic acid solutions with the hands since the coefficient of expansion of acetic acid is quite high and a considerable error can be introduced by slight increases in temperature.

Genus 3.

Neutral Species.

Classification Tests.

Test for the Nitro Group. Dissolve 0.1 to 0.2 mg or less of the compound in 10 µl of 50% hot ethanol in a microcone and add 5 to 6 drops (from a capillary) of 0.1 n calcium chloride solution and a pinch of zinc dust. Heat the mixture on a water bath until a reaction takes place and keep it hot until the reaction ceases. Then bring it to a boil. After allowing it to stand for two to three minutes, centrifuge and siphon off the supernatant liquid through a capillary into a second cone containing 10% silver nitrate in concentrated ammonia. The appearance of a silver mirror or an immediate gray or black precipitate indicates a nitro compound. Disregard a white or light yellow precipitate.

Notes.

1) A blank experiment should be run, the zinc dust being omitted, to determine whether the test substance will reduce ammonical silver nitrate without previous reduction. If the more specific test for hydroxylamine described in Note 3 on page 278 is used, this blank test is unnecessary.

2) With a mild reducing agent such as zinc dust and water, the reduction of a nitro compound proceeds only to the hydroxylamine stage:

$$RNO_2 + 2 H \rightarrow R\!-\!N\!=\!O + H_2O$$
$$R\!-\!N\!=\!O + 2 H \rightarrow R\!-\!NHOH + H_2O$$
$$R\!-\!NH\!-\!OH + Ag_2O \rightarrow R\!-\!N\!=\!O + H_2O + 2 Ag \downarrow.$$

3) The solution of the sample should be neutral. If necessary, neutralize first with ammonia.

4) HEARON and GUSTAVSON (21) describe a test for the nitro group carried out on a semimicro scale. It consists of the oxidation of ferrous hydroxide by the nitro compound, which gives a precipitate of brown ferric hydroxide. Color reactions for nitro compounds are given by BOST and NICHOLSON (5), KULIKOW and PANOWA (30), and KIRCHHOF (28). DAVIES and HARTSHORNE (10) identify aromatic nitro compounds by optical and crystallographic methods.

For the reduction of nitro compounds to amines see under Acetamino and Benzamino Derivatives of Alkyl Benzenes, p. 241.

Diphenylamine Test for Nitrates, Nitrites, Aliphatic Nitro Compounds, and Nitrosoamines. Place a drop of the diphenylamine reagent on a freshly cleaned slide. Dip a glass thread into the sample of test substance and then into the drop of the reagent and stir it around. In the case of solids, dipping the glass thread into the powdered solid will usually suffice to cause sufficient material to adhere for a test but the thread should be examined before dipping into the reagent to make certain that some test substance was taken up. Observe the drop against a white background. If a blue color develops in one minute, the test is positive.

Notes.

1) The reagent is made by mixing four volumes of pure concentrated sulfuric acid with one volume of water. While this is still warm, dissolve 0.2 g of pure diphenylamine in each 100 ml of the acid.

2) A spot plate should not be used because it is more difficult to get perfectly clean than a slide.

3) A positive test is obtained from all compounds which yield nitric or nitrous acid when acted upon by concentrated sulfuric acid. In addition, other oxidizing agents,

both organic and anorganic, will give the same color reaction (16). GREBBER and KARABINOS (20) investigated the applicability of the test to aliphatic nitro compounds and found it limited.

4) According to KEHRMANN and ST. MICEWICZ (26) the color is due to a quinonoid immonium salt of N,N'-diphenylbenzidine:

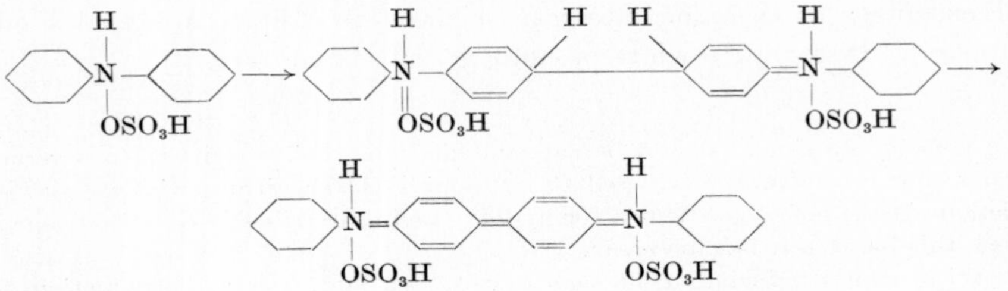

Biuret Reaction.

Biuret Reaction. Dissolve the sample of test substance in water in a microcone (0.1 mg in 2 μl) and add 5 drops of 10% sodium hydroxide solution from a capillary. Boil if necessary to bring the sample into solution and then cool. Next add 3% copper sulfate solution drop by drop from a capillary pipet. Stir and centrifuge. Draw up the clear liquid in a coloroscopic capillary (page 11) and observe the color of the solution by axial illumination. A red to violet-blue solution shows the presence of a protein, albumose, or peptone.

Notes.

1) A blank experiment is advisable to make certain that impurities in the sodium hydroxide and the copper sulfate do not produce a color like that described for a positive test.

2) The test is a general one for proteins, albumoses, and peptones, but acid imides with the group —CO—NH—CO— also give a color.

3) In the case of biuret the color is due to the compound

$$K_2Cu\,(NH_2 \cdot CO \cdot NH \cdot CO \cdot NH_2)_2$$

Hydrolysis of Nitriles, Amides, Anilides, Etc.

Procedure A. With Hydrochloric Acid. Introduce 0.5 to 1 mg of the test substance into a capillary either by pushing the end of the tube into the powder, if a solid, or by dipping it into the substance if a liquid. Dip the same end into 6 n HCl in a watch glass until a 10-mm column has risen in the tube. Seal both ends of the capillary and heat for one half hour on the water bath. If a solid appears on cooling, centrifuge to one end of the capillary and cut this end off just above the solid layer. Recrystallize the solid from water. Should no solid appear, cut the tube open at both ends and blow the liquid out on a slide. Evaporate to dryness (note the odor of the vapors) and take up the residue in 5 μl of 10% sodium hydroxide. Draw up the solution in a capillary pipet. Seal the end of the pipet and centrifuge the contents. If the liquid does not separate into two layers, extract it with ether or distil in an EMICH distillation tube.

Note.

The reactions are:
$$RCN + HCl + 2 H_2O \rightarrow RCOOH + NH_4Cl$$
$$RCONH_2 + H_2O + HCl \rightarrow RCOOH + NH_4Cl$$
$$RCONHR' + H_2O + HCl \rightarrow RCOOH + R'NH_2 \cdot HCl.$$

Procedure B. With Sulfuric Acid. Heat the sample of test substance in a capillary as in (A) but use $9 m$ H_2SO_4. After the heating, blow the contents out upon a slide into 5 to 10 µl of water. If a precipitate forms, remove the liquid by means of a capillary pipet with a very fine tip. If no precipitate forms, stir and scratch the cooled slide to induce crystallization. If desired, the basic product of the hydrolysis can be recovered in this method as well as in (A) by making the filtrate alkaline and extracting with ether.

Procedure C. With Potassium Hydroxide. The same procedure as in (A) and (B) is followed except that 20% alcoholic potassium hydroxide is used instead of the acids. Centrifuge the contents back and forth occasionally during the heating. After the heating, cut the capillary at both ends and blow the contents out on a slide. Allow the alcohol to evaporate. Wash out the capillary with $6 m$ HCl onto the residue on the slide. If necessary, add more HCl to make the solution acid. Dilute with water and remove the liquid with a capillary pipet. Wash the precipitate with water and recrystallize. The basic product of the hydrolysis can be recovered as in (B).

Notes.

1) The reactions are:
$$RCN + H_2O + KOH \rightarrow RCOOK + NH_3$$
$$RCONH_2 + KOH \rightarrow RCOOK + NH_3$$
$$RCONHR' + KOH \rightarrow RCOOK + RNH_2$$

2) A diethylene glycol solution of the potassium hydroxide is recommended by ROVIRA and PALFRAY (40) for the hydrolysis in place of the alcoholic. The diethylene glycol is extracted from the reaction mixture afterwards with ether and the hydrolysis products are recovered from the aqueous solution by acidifying with hydrochloric acid.

Hydrolysis of Carbonyl Condensation Products.

To 5 to 6 mg of the test substance in a reflux tube add 90 µl $12 m$ HCl. Seal the tube and heat in a boiling water bath for 30 minutes (in some cases 15 minutes will suffice). Cool the tube, open the tip, and add two volumes of water. Centrifuge and decant the clear liquid. Evaporate the latter to dryness on the water bath and dissolve the residue in 350 µl water. To 70 µl of this solution add 150 µl of TOLLEN's reagent, *see* page 158.

Notes.

1) A blank experiment should be run with the TOLLENs reagent and the original substance to make certain that the latter does not reduce the reagent before hydrolysis.

2) The products of the hydrolysis are the carbonyl compound and the hydroxylamine, hydrazine, or semicarbazide from which the sample had been formed.

3) For a more specific test for hydroxylamine add 5 mg of sodium acetate and a small drop of benzoyl chloride to the final solution obtained by dissolving the residue of the evaporation in water. Stir for one minute and then add four drops of 10 % ferric chloride solution and four drops 12 m HCl (or just enough to clear the solution). The appearance of a red-violet or purple color is a positive test for hydroxylamine.

$$C_6H_5CO \cdot Cl + H_2NOH \rightarrow C_6H_5CONHOH + HCl$$

Howells and Little (23) carry out the Hoesch reaction on a semimicro scale for the identification of nitriles. The optical constants of benzamide, its homologs, and some aliphatic amides have been listed by Willard and Maresh (51).

The α-iminoalkylmercaptoacetic acid hydrochlorides of nitriles can be prepared by the method of Condo, Hinkel, Fassero, and Shriner (9) on a microscale by using proportionate quantities of test substance and reagent

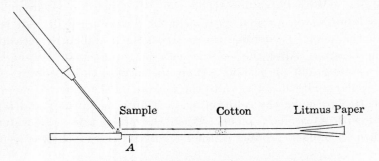

Fig. 182. Test for Liberation of Ammonia, nat. size.

and carrying out the reaction in a capillary tube open at one end. The tube can be placed in a 3-inch (7.5-cm) test tube which can be connected to a source of hydrogen chloride.

Tests for Compounds Easily Decomposed by Alkali to Yield Ammonia or Amines. Alkali Treatment of Original Compound. Use a capillary of the size and shape shown in Fig. 182. Introduce 0.1 mg or less of the test substance into end A of the tube. Before introducing the sample, fit a cotton plug in the middle of the tube and insert a piece of moist red litmus in the wide end. The sample can be introduced easily by placing it on the end of a microscope slide; hold the end A of the capillary horizontally against the edge of the slide and push the solid into the tube with a needle or glass thread. Introduce 1 mg of powdered potassium hydroxide in the same way. Draw 3.5 µl alcohol into the same end and allow the droplet of the resulting solution to slide down the tube for a distance of 2 to 3 mm. Seal end A of the tube cautiously in the microflame. Observe the litmus paper during the sealing. If no change of color occurs, dip the sealed end of the capillary into hot water and observe the paper again.

Derivatives of Neutral Species.

Nitro compounds can be reduced to amines and these converted into derivatives as described under Hydrocarbons, p. 241.

Side-chains of aromatic nitro compounds can be oxidized to carboxyl group by the permanganate method described under Hydrocarbons, p. 237.

Degradative Procedures for Neutral Species.

As described above, all of the neutral species compounds with the exception of the nitro compounds can be hydrolyzed readily by acid or base. Nitro compounds would require preliminary reduction followed by the hydrolysis.

Quantitative Determination of Neutral Species.

Procedures which have been described for other types of compounds can be used for the quantitative determination of nitro compounds, isocyanates, and hydrazines.

The lithium-aluminum hydride reduction method of LIEB and SCHÖ-NIGER (p. 195) is stated by these authors to be applicable to nitro compounds, although they do not give any examples.

The method of ROTH described below, p. 293, for the determination of isothiocyanates is also applicable to isocyanates.

Hydrazines can be determined by oxidation with bromine to free nitrogen, the alkyl bromide, and other products. The quantity of bromine required is measured as an index of the hydrazine content. The bromide-bromate procedure is described under Hydrocarbons, p. 238.

Chapter VIII.

Compounds of the Higher Orders.

In addition to carbon, hydrogen, and possibly oxygen, the compounds of the higher orders contain elements other than nitrogen. The number of compounds in which these other elements constitute or are part of the functional group or groups is relatively small. The first step in the identification, after the elementary analysis shows the presence of such an element, should therefore be the performance of the generic tests of Order I and II. In the event that these prove to be negative, the compound should be sought in the groups described below.

Halogen Compounds.
Classification Test.

Decomposition by Alkali. Perform the decomposition as described on p. 278 in the last chapter for ammonia.

A) After noting any color change of the litmus paper, cut off the sealed end of the capillary and blow the contents out on a slide. Rinse the tube with 3 m HNO$_3$ onto the residue on the slide. If a clear solution does not result, draw the liquid up in a capillary pipet, seal the tip, and centrifuge. Cut off and discard the portion of the tube containing the precipitate. Make the clear solution acid with nitric acid and add 0.1 m AgNO$_3$.

B) If a precipitate is obtained in the above test with silver nitrate, perform the following test. Introduce a few micrograms of the test substance into a capillary. Add about 5 μl water or alcohol plus a few drops of 6 m HNO$_3$ and a few drops of aqueous or alcoholic silver nitrate. If a precipitate forms, either in the cold or on warming, blow the contents of the tube out on a slide and, after making certain that the precipitate is not soluble in 6 m HNO$_3$, invert the slide over the mouth of a bottle of ammonia.

Notes.

1) Blanks should be run with both of these tests to ensure the purity of the reagents.

2) The rate of the reaction of the silver nitrate and the test substance is an index of the reactivity of the halogen atom. This reactivity depends, first, upon which halogen is involved, and, secondly, upon the radical to which it is attached. The order of reactivity of the halogens in compounds is iodine, bromine, chlorine, and fluorine, in the order of decreasing activity.

The following divisions of halogen-containing substances can be made on the basis of their speed of reaction with silver nitrate solution:

Immediate precipitate in the cold with aqueous silver nitrate:

> Hydrogen halide salt of an amine
> Oxonium salts
> Chlorides of low molecular weight acids.

Immediate precipitate in the cold with alcoholic silver nitrate:

> Chlorides of high molecular weight acids
> α-Halogen acid esters
> Tertiary alkyl chlorides
> Allyl chlorides
> Ethylene bromide
> Alkyl iodides.

Precipitate with hot alcoholic silver nitrate:

> Primary and secondary alkyl chlorides
> Alkyl dibromides
> Aromatic compounds with halogen in the side chain.

Derivatives of Halogen Compounds.

Amides, Anilides, etc. from Acyl Halides. These compounds are prepared as described under Acids, p. 188. Obviously, treatment with the sulfonyl chloride, etc., is eliminated.

Alkyl Mercuric Halides. The alkyl halides can be used in the preparation of a GRIGNARD reagent. This in turn can be converted into a number of compounds which will serve to identify the original halide. Dissolve 10 to 15 μl of the alkyl chloride, bromide, or iodide in 200 μl anhydrous ether in a microcone. Add about 20 mg activated magnesium and allow the solution to stand loosely stoppered for a time until the reaction is complete. The time can be considerably reduced by touching a platinum wire to the magnesium in the solution. This will start the reaction and, whenever it seems too slow, touching a new spot on the magnesium with the wire will speed it up again. Then centrifuge and decant the clear solution into another microcone containing about 50 mg (excess) of mercuric chloride, bromide, or iodide, depending upon which halogen was present in the original test substance. Stir to mix thoroughly and then evaporate the ether by warming the cone in a metal block. Add 250 µl of 95% alcohol to the residue and bring to a boil. Centrifuge and decant the supernatant liquid into another cone. Dilute with 100 µl water. Reheat to dissolve the product, and allow the solution to cool slowly.

Notes.

1) The reaction is as follows:

$$RX + Mg \rightarrow R \cdot MgX$$
$$RMgX + HgX_2 \rightarrow R \cdot HgX + MgX_2$$

2) Since the test depends upon the formation of a GRIGNARD compound, it is limited in practice to primary bromides and iodides. The tables do include some secondary and aryl bromides.

3. The magnesium can be activated by very brief immersion in a solution of mercuric chloride. The addition of a crystal of iodine to the original solution will also initiate the reaction.

3,5-Dinitrobenzoate Esters from Alkyl Iodides.

Place 1.5 µl of the test substance in a dry reflux tube and add 30 µl of 95% alcohol followed by 8 to 10 mg of the dry powdered silver dinitrobenzoate. Draw out the open end of the reflux tube to a very fine hair capillary and reflux the contents of the tube at 100° for half an hour. At the end of this time cut the tube open and siphon the contents out onto a 0.5-inch (1-cm) watch glass. Using an air stream, evaporate the alcohol. Extract the residue three times with 50 µl of ether, centrifuge the combined extracts in a microcone, decant and evaporate the ether solution. Wash the residue with a drop of 1% Na_2CO_3 solution and then with water. Recrystallize the product from the minimum amount of boiling 75% alcohol.

Notes.

1) The reagent is prepared freshly before use. Dissolve exactly 1.06 g of finely powdered 3,5-dinitrobenzoic acid in a mixture of 20 ml of water and 5 to 6 ml 6 m NH_3. Boil off the excess ammonia and slowly add 50 ml of 0.1 m $AgNO_3$. Filter off the precipitate with suction, wash with water, alcohol, and finally ether. Dry in the air.

2) The reaction is as follows:

3) See also JURAČEK and VEČERA (12).

s-Alkylisothiouronium Compounds. The procedure of BROWN and
CAMPBELL (5) has been converted into a microprocedure by JURAČEK and
VEČERA (12). The substituted thiourea is easily prepared and can then be
converted into either the 3,5-dinitrobenzoate or the picrate.

Heat 5 to 10 mg of the alkyl halide in a reflux tube with 250 µl of a 2%
acetone solution of thiourea on a steam bath. Iodides will require one
hour heating, bromides two hours, and chlorides in the presence of 5 mg
of sodium iodide, three hours. Upon completion of the reaction distil off
the solvent and dissolve the residue in 100 µl water.

For the picrate add 50 to 100 µl of a saturated alcoholic solution of
picric acid. Heat on the boiling water bath for five minutes and then cool
with ice. Recrystallize the derivative which separates from an alcohol-
water mixture.

The 3,5-dinitrobenzoate is prepared similarly by adding an equivalent
quantity of the sodium salt of 3,5-dinitrobenzoic acid to the aqueous solution
of the substituted thiourea.

2,4-Dinitrophenyl Sulfides and Sulfones. BOST, STARNES, and WOOD
(2) make use of the ease of reaction between a variety of halogen compounds and 2,4-dinitrothiophenol for the preparation of thioethers and
the conversion of these by oxidation to sulfones.

In a microcone dissolve 40 mg of 2,4-dinitrothiophenol in 400 µl amyl
alcohol and add 40 µl 28% potassium hydroxide. To the deep-red solution
add 10 mg of the test substance. If no immediate reaction takes place, warm
the solution to 70° for ten to thirty minutes on the water bath. Then cool and
dilute with several volumes of ice water. Centrifuge and decant. Recrystallize the product from ethyl alcohol, 1-butanol, dioxane, benzene, or
acetone.

Notes.
1) The synthesis of the reagent is described in the original paper.
2) In the case of chlorine compounds add the reagent, the solvent, the potassium
hydroxide, 25 mg potassium iodide, and the test substance in that order, stirring
thoroughly between additions.
3) The thioethers can be oxidized to sulfones by fuming nitric acid, 30% hydrogen
peroxide in acetic acid, or by permanganate in acetic acid.

Aryl halides can be identified by nitration. The procedure is described
under Hydrocarbons, p. 241. They may also be converted to sulfonyl
chlorides and then to the sulfonamides by the procedure of HUNTRESS and
CARTEN (11) with reduction of the quantities. The procedure of DREW and
STURTEVANT (9) for the identification of alkyl halides by the formation of
alkyl triiodophenyl ethers can also be carried out with milligram samples.

Alkyl dihalides can be identified by the use of 6-nitro-2-mercaptobenzo-
thiazole by the method of CUTTER and KREUCHUNAS (7).

Degradative Procedures for Halogen Compounds.

Aside from the test with silver nitrate described above under Classification Test, which may indicate the type of halogen compound under examination, the degradative procedures are those for the other functional group or groups in the molecule. These are described under the various genera in Orders I and II.

Chemical Separation of Halogen Compounds.

No satisfactory chemical separation reactions are available for halogen compounds. In general, they are quite inert and stable and any reactions they do enter into result in products from which the original material cannot be recovered.

Quantitative Determination of Halogen Compounds.

Many methods for the determination of halogen in organic compounds have been described. All involve the decomposition by combustion of the test substance and the conversion of the organic halogen into an inorganic ionic form. SCHÖNIGER (18) has developed a microtechnique based upon the method of MIKL and PECH (15) which is simple, rapid, and can be applied to the determination of sulfur and phosphorus as well.

The substance is wrapped in a piece of ash-free filter paper and burned in a flask filled with oxygen. The combustion products are absorbed and the halogen content is determined volumetrically.

Reagents.

For Determination of Chlorine.

Potassium hydroxide solution, 2 n.

Hydrogen peroxide, 30%, reagent grade.

Sulfuric acid, reagent grade, 2 n.

Mercuric hydroxycyanide solution, saturated, neutralized against mixed indicator (*below*), in brown bottle.

Mixed indicator solution. Methyl red, 0.1% solution in methyl alcohol, and methylene blue, 0.1% solution in methyl alcohol. The two solutions are mixed in such proportions that they give a violet color in acid solutions, green in alkaline solutions, and gray at the equivalence point. The proportion must be determined anew every time fresh indicator solutions are made up.

For Determination of Iodine.

Potassium hydroxide solution, 2 n.

Bromine-glacial acetic acid solution. Dissolve 100 g potassium acetate in

1000 ml glacial acetic acid (reagent grade) and add 4 ml reagent-grade bromine to this solution.

Formic, acid, approximately 98%, reagent grade.

Sulfuric acid, 2 n reagent grade.

Potassium iodide, reagent grade.

Sodium thiosulfate solution, 0.02 n, standardized.

Starch indicator solution according to BALLCZO and MONDL (1). To 70 ml water add 0.1 to 0.2 g salicylic acid (reagent grade) and bring to a boil. After

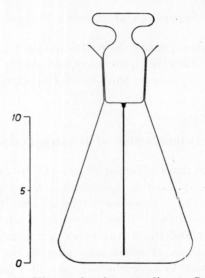

Fig. 183. Microcombustion according to SCHÖNIGER.

cooling saturate this solution with potassium chloride, reagent grade. Dissolve 1 g amylum solubile, reagent grade, in 20 ml water by boiling and add this to the potassium chloride-salicylic acid solution. Allow to stand for 24 hours and then filter if necessary.

For Determination of Bromine.

Buffer solution. Dissolve 20 g sodium dihydrogen phosphate in 100 ml distilled water.

Sodium chloride solution. Dissolve 300 g sodium chloride, reagent grade, in 1000 ml distilled water.

Hypochlorite solution. Pass enough chlorine through a 1.1 m NaOH solution until the solution becomes about 1 n to chlorine as determined by weighing.

Sodium formate solution, about 50%.

Sulfuric acid, about 3 m.

Sodium thiosulfate solution, 0.02 n, standardized.

Starch indicator solution, as *above*.

For Determination of Fluorine.

Hydrochloric acid, 0.01 n.

Bromthymol blue indicator solution, 1% in water.

Murexide solution. Dissolve about 0.5 g murexide in about 50 ml distilled water. The indicator is not stable and must be prepared fresh daily.

Cerous chloride solution, 0.01 n. Dissolve 1.24 g $CeCl_3 \cdot 7\ H_2O$, reagent grade, in 1000 ml distilled water.

Methyl alcohol, reagent grade.

Apparatus. The oxidation is carried out in a 250- to 300-ml Pyrex or Jena Geräte glass, Erlenmeyer flask with ground-in stopper. Preferably

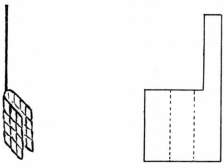

Fig. 184. Basket for Sample.   Fig. 185. Paper for Sample.

the flask should have a funnel-shaped neck projecting above the ground-in portion as in iodine flasks. A platinum wire, 100 mm long and 0.5 to 0.7 mm in diameter, is fused into the stopper at one end, Fig. 183. The

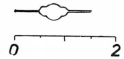

Fig. 186. Capillary for Weighing Liquids.

other end carries a platinum wire gauze, Fig. 184, for holding the sample. MARTIN and DEVERAUX (14) have designed a modification of the flask to permit electrical ignition of the sample.

The paper used for holding the sample, Fig. 185, should be the ash-free type.

Procedure. Depending upon halogen content, weigh out 4 to 8 mg of the test substance in a platinum boat. Empty this onto the filter paper so that it forms the smallest possible heap. Weigh back the boat to obtain the exact weight of the sample. Liquids with boiling points above 100° are weighed in capillaries as usual except that the capillaries should be enlarged somewhat in the center, Fig. 186. Liquids with low boiling points and high vapor pressures cannot be analyzed by this method.

Fold the filter paper along the dotted lines shown in Fig. 185 and clamp the platinum gauze around it so that the *ignition strip* projects to the bottom. In the case of liquids roll the capillary into the paper in a similar manner, but just before the combustion crush the capillary into the paper. If the test substance is a very volatile solid, it is best to wrap the sample in a second piece of paper. After introducing the proper absorption solution into the flask, pass oxygen from a cylinder into the flask to displace the air. Ignite the paper at the ignition strip and place the stopper quickly into the flask. Hold the flask in one hand and press the stopper into the joint with the other so that the expansion of the gas in the flask due to the combustion does not force out the stopper. As soon as the combustion is complete, the absorption of the products (principally the carbon dioxide from the burning of the paper) will produce a negative pressure in the flask which will keep the stopper tightly closed. SCHÖNIGER recommends that the flask be held inclined during the combustion so that the pieces of filter paper breaking off the main portion will fall on the dry walls of the flask and thus be able to burn up completely. Shake the contents of the flask repeatedly to hasten absorption of the combustion products. This should be complete in ten minutes. Place some distilled water around the neck of the flask around the stopper and then withdraw the latter. The reduced pressure within the flask will draw the water into the flask and thus rinse off the stopper. Rinse off the platinum gauze and the walls of the flask with distilled water.

Determination of Chlorine. The absorption solution used for chlorine determination consists of 10 ml distilled water, 1 ml 2 m KOH solution, and about 3 drops of hydrogen peroxide.

After the combustion boil the alkaline solution to destroy the excess hydrogen peroxide and then acidify with 3 ml 2 n H_2SO_4. Boil again for two minutes and then cool quickly by holding the flask under the tap. Almost neutralize the excess sulfuric acid with 2 m KOH using the mixed indicator and, after rinsing the walls of the flask, complete the neutralization with the 0.01 n standard acid. Add 10 ml of the neutral mercuric hydroxy cyanide solution and titrate with 0.01 n H_2SO_4. Calculate the chloride content from the following:

$$\% \, Cl = \frac{100 f N V}{S}$$

where V = ml of sulfuric acid used in titration
   f = atomic weight of chlorine
   N = normality of acid
   S = weight of sample in milligrams

Determination of Iodine. The absorption solution for the iodine determination is the same as that for chlorine except that the hydrogen peroxide is omitted. After the combustion and absorption add 10 ml of the bromine-glacial acetic acid solution. Reduce the excess bromine with formic acid and wait about three minutes. Then add 4 ml 2 n H_2SO_4 and a few centigrams of potassium iodide and titrate with sodium thiosulfate solution using the stabilized starch indicator. Calculate the iodine content from the following:

$$\% \ I = \frac{100 \, f \, N V}{S}$$

where V = ml of sodium thiosulfate solution

f = 42.31

N = normality of thiosulfate solution

S = weight of sample in milligrams

Determination of Bromine. The absorption solution for the bromine determination consists of 5 ml of the buffer solution, 20 ml of the sodium chloride solution, and 10 ml of the hypochlorite solution. After the combustion and absorption bring the contents of the flask to a boil. Add 5 ml of the sodium formate solution to destroy the excess hypochlorite and again boil briefly. Blow air from a pump or atomizer bulb into the flask to displace the chlorine. Cool the flask under the tap, add 20 ml 3 m H_2SO_4, about 0.2 g potassium iodide and dilute to 100 ml with distilled water. Titrate with the 0.02 n sodium thiosulfate. Calculate the bromine content from the following:

$$\% \ Br = \frac{100 \, f \, N V}{S}$$

where V = ml of sodium thiosulfate solution

f = 26.64

N = normality of thiosulfate solution

S = weight of sample in milligrams

Determination of Fluorine: The absorption liquid in the determination of fluorine consists of a few milliliters of distilled water only. After the combustion and absorption, acidify the solution with about 5 ml of 0.01 n HCl, boil to expel the carbon dioxide, and neutralize with the 0.01 n NaOH using bromthymol blue as indicator. When the color changes to green, add just enough more acid so that the solution becomes and remains yellow (pH 5 to 6). Avoid an excess of acid. Add an equal volume of methyl alcohol and five drops of the murexide solution. Titrate with the 0.01 n cerous chloride solution until the indicator color changes from violet to orange. Calculate the fluorine content by the following:

$$\% \ F = \frac{100 \, f \, N V}{S}$$

where V = ml of cerous chloride solution

f = 19.00

N = normality of cerous chloride

S = weight of sample in milligrams

It is essential that the indicator error be determined and subtracted from the volume of titrant used.

Sulfur Compounds.

Classification Test.

Alkali Fusion Test for Valence of Sulfur. Mix 1 mg of the test substance and 10 mg powdered sodium hydroxide in a porcelain microcrucible of about 0.5-ml capacity. Place the crucible in a silica triangle and this in turn inside a larger porcelain crucible (10-ml) as shown in Fig. 187. Heat the outer crucible until the mixture in the microcrucible melts. Stir the melt with a nickel wire and heat one to two minutes longer. Cool the crucible and take up the melt with water, heating if necessary on a water bath. Transfer the solution to a microcone by means of a pipet.

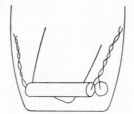

Fig. 187. Alkali Fusion Test.

Before proceeding with the tests, prepare the following items. First, make a filter paper cap for the microcone by holding a circle of filter paper about twice the diameter of the microcone over the mouth of the cone and folding down the edges over the rim so that the cap fits tightly. Then put this aside. Secondly, fit a loop made from a glass thread or capillary sealed at one end as shown in Fig. 188 into a cork which in turn fits into the microcone. Such a cork can be cut out of a larger one with a cork borer which has a diameter about 1 mm larger than the internal diameter of the cone. The handle of the glass loop should fit loosely enough in the cork so that, when the latter is pushed into the microcone, the loop can be raised or lowered easily.

When these two preparations have been made, acidify the solution in the microcone with 9 m H_2SO_4. Place the filter paper cap quickly over the cone and put a drop (from a capillary pipet) of lead acetate solution in the center of the paper cap. If no hydrogen sulfide is given off as shown by the failure of the lead acetate to blacken, remove the cap and carry out the test for sulfur dioxide as follows. Place a drop of the sulfur dioxide test reagent in the glass loop by dipping the loop into the reagent and withdrawing it quickly again. Pull the loop as close to the cork as possible and insert the cork with the loop into the microcone. Push the loop down close to the solution. If the solution in the loop becomes colorless and turbid within five minutes, sulfur dioxide has been evolved from the solution of the melt.

Notes.

1) The sulfur dioxide reagent is prepared by mixing 100 ml of 0.1 m HCl, 30 ml 0.5 m BaCl$_2$ solution, and 10 ml of 0.02 m (0.1 n) KMnO$_4$ solution.

2) Typical reactions are as follows:

$$RSH + NaOH \rightarrow NaSH + H_2O$$
$$R \cdot SO_3Na + NaOH \rightarrow ROH + Na_2SO_3$$

If the sulfur present in the compound is bivalent, sodium sulfide is formed. If it is tetra- or hexavalent, sodium sulfite is the product. Salts of sulfuric acid and alkyl sulfates do not decompose to give sulfur dioxide in this test.

GARNER (10) describes tests for twenty substituted naphthalene sulfonic acids. WHITMORE and GEBHART (21) found that benzoylation of substituted sulfonic acids yields readily isolated products with characteristic crystalline forms. DENIGÈS (8) describes a test for sulfonalides, together with a discussion of the crystalline forms of sulfonanilides. CASTLE, WITT, and POE (6) list the optical crystallographic properties of some sulfonamides and their derivatives.

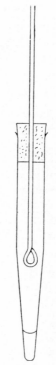

Fig. 188. Testing for Gas Liberated from a Reaction Mixture, nat. size.

Derivatives of Sulfur Compounds.

2,4-Dinitrophenyl Sulfides from Thiols. Use a reflux tube with a bulb 1 cm in diameter. Fill the bulb half full with absolute alcohol. Add 3 mg of 2,4-dinitrochlorobenzene, 1 µl of the thiol test substance, and 1 µl of 10% aqueous sodium hydroxide. Seal the tube and heat in the water bath for ten minutes. Cut be tube open and transfer the contents to a microcone. Heat the solution again and centrifuge while hot. Decant the supernatant liquid into another microcone and allow it to cool. Recrystallize from absolute alcohol the product which separates on cooling.

Notes.

1) The reaction is as follows:

$$RSNa + Cl\langle\bigcirc\rangle NO_2 \rightarrow RS\langle\bigcirc\rangle NO_2 + NaCl$$
$$\qquad\quad NO_2 \qquad\qquad\quad NO_2$$

2) The sulfide can be oxidized to the sulfone by means of permanganate (4).

Sulfonyl Chlorides from Sulfonic Acids and Salts. The chlorides of sulfonic acids can be prepared with phosphorus pentachloride as described under carboxylic Acids, p. 189. The amides and other derivatives can be also prepared from the sulfonyl chlorides in the same way as the carboxyl chlorides.

3,5-Dinitrobenzoyl Esters of Thiols. These are prepared from the thiol by the same method as employed for alcohols, p. 229. *See* also other alcohol derivatives.

s-**Alkylisothiouronium Compounds from Ureas.** By replacing the reagent thiourea with the sample of test substance and using ethyl or methyl iodide as the alkyl halide, the method given on p. 282 can be used for preparation of these derivatives of urea and substituted ureas.

Degradative Procedures for Sulfur Compounds.

Thiols. Thiols are oxidized by an alkaline solution of iodine to disulfides. These can be reduced back to the thiols by zinc and acid. Concentrated nitric acid oxidizes thiols to the corresponding sulfonic acids.

Thioethers. Thioethers can be oxidized to the sulfoxide by concentrated nitric acid or 30% hydrogen peroxide at room temperature. With fuming nitric acid, 30 % hydrogen peroxide in acetic acid, or potassium permanganate in acetic acid or acetone, the oxidation continues to the sulfone. The lower sulfoxides are soluble in water. With cyanogen bromide the thioethers can be cleaved to give one molecule of alkyl isothiocyanate and one molecule of alkyl bromide. Passing chlorine through an acetic acid solution of the thioether cleaves this to one molecule of alkyl sulfonyl chloride and one molecule of alkyl chloride.

Sulfonic Acids. Desulfonation of aromatic sulfonic acids can be carried out in reflux tubes with dilute hydrochloric acid. The hydrocarbon will be one of the products. Fusion with potassium or sodium hydroxide in a microcrucible will produce the phenol. In view of the volatility of the phenols, the crucible should either be covered or the fusion should be carried out in a sealed tube.

Chemical Separation of Sulfur Compounds.

Thiols. Thiols form salts with heavy metals which are only slightly soluble in water. For example, mercuric oxide reacts with thiols to form compounds of the type $(RS)_2Hg$. The mercuric oxide is used in the form of a suspension in alcohol. Treatment of the mercuric compound with strong acid results in the reformation of the thiol.

Thioethers. Thioethers are soluble in concentrated sulfuric acid, probably forming sulfonium ion compounds. Mercuric or palladous chloride reacts with thioethers to form coordination compounds which are in many cases crystalline. The reaction of thioethers with alkyl halides in ethyl ether or boiling alcohol results in the formation of sulfonium salts, trialkyl sulfonium halides.

Sulfonic Acids. Sulfonic acids are strong acids and can be neutralized with a base such as sodium hydroxide to form water soluble salts.

Quantitative Determination of Sulfur Compounds.

Thiols. The oxidation by iodine mentioned above under Degradative Procedures has been employed for the determination of thiols (13). Since this cannot always be used because of the presence of other substances which would also react with the iodine, the method of ROTH (16) using an organic cupric salt which is easily soluble in organic solvents is preferred.

The determination is based upon the formation of copper mercaptide and a disulfide:

$$2\ Cu^{++} + 4\ RSH \longrightarrow 2\ CuSR + RSSR + 4\ H^{+}.$$

The thiol is treated with cupric butylphthalate in a suitable inert solvent. After addition of potassium iodide and starch the excess reagent is quickly determined by titration of the released iodine with sodium thiosulfate.

Reagents.

Cupric butylphthalate is prepared as follows. Add 74 g dry, finely pulverized phthalic anhydride to 50 ml butanol in a 500-ml Erlenmeyer flask. Heat with stirring to 105°. As soon as this temperature is reached, remove the burner and continue stirring. The temperature will continue to rise to about 120° and in a few minutes the mixture will become clear. Cool and pour into 1500 ml of a 0.3 *m* NaOH solution. If the resulting solution is not acidic, make it acid with acetic acid. Filter into a 4-l beaker and slowly add a clear solution of 65 g copper sulfate pentahydrate in 500 ml water to the butylphthalate solution with vigorous stirring. Collect the precipitated cupric butylphthalate on a Büchner funnel, wash with water, and dry in air. Grind the material in a mortar and dry further in a vacuum desiccator. Prepare the 0.02 *n* reagent for the determination by dissolving 5.1 g of the cupric butylphthalate in 50 ml glacial acetic acid and diluting with amyl or butyl alcohol or a hydrocarbon solvent to 1 liter.

Potassium iodide, reagent grade.

Sodium thiosulfate solution, 0.01 *n* or 0.02 *n*, standardized.

Starch indicator solution.

Procedure. Weigh out 5 to 10 mg of the thiol into a 100-ml glass-stoppered Erlenmeyer flask. Add 20.0 ml of the reagent. If the test substance is a liquid and has been weighed out in a capillary as usual, crush the capillary with a glass rod on the bottom of the flask under the reagent solution. After mixing the contents of the flask, stopper it and allow it to stand for five minutes. Then add 1 ml of the starch indicator solution and about 100 mg potassium iodide, stirt thoroughly again, and titrate the liberated iodine immediately with the standard thiosulfate solution until the somewhat turbid solution becomes colorless. In the same way determine the equivalent V_1 of the reagent. Calculate the content of —SH by the following:

$$\% - SH = 100 \, f \, N \, (V_1 - V_2)/S$$

where $V_1 =$ ml of thiosulfate used for 20.0 ml reagent

$\quad\quad V_2 =$ ml of thiosulfate used in determination

$\quad\quad N \; =$ normality of thiosulfate

$\quad\quad f \; \; =$ 66.14

$\quad\quad S \; \; =$ weight of sample of test substance in milligram

Disulfides and Thioethers. The oxidation of alkyl disulfides to sulfoxides can be achieved by the use of bromine as well as the other oxidizing agents listed under Degradative Procedures. ROTH (16) found that the bromide-bromate method of SIGGIA and EDSBERG (20) when applied to milligram samples did not give accurate results. He found that using excess bromine instead permitted oxidation to the sulfone rapidly and both disulfides and thioethers can be determined.

Reagents.

Acetic acid, glacial, reagent grade.

Hydrochloric acid, $2 \, m$.

Bromide-bromate solution, $0.02 \, n$. Weigh out 0.504 g sodium bromate and 2.380 g potassium bromide into a 1-l volumetric flask and dissolve in doubly-distilled water.

Potassium iodide, reagent grade.

Sodium thiosulfate solution, $0.02 \, n$, standardized.

Starch solution, 1%.

Procedure. Weigh out 5 to 8 mg of the test substance (disulfide or thioether) in a 100-ml glass-stoppered Erlenmeyer flask. Liquids are, as usual, weighed out in a capillary. Add 20 ml glacial acetic acid, 15 ml doubly distilled water and 5 ml $2 \, n$ HCl. If a liquid in a capillary was used, break this with a glass rod and rinse the latter with 1 ml of water.

Add exactly 20.0 ml of the $0.02 \, n$ bromide-bromate solution and stopper the flask immediately. Allow to stand for five minutes at room temperature and then add about 100 mg potassium iodide and about 0.5 ml starch solution and titrate the liberated iodine with $0.02 \, n$ sodium thiosulfate solution to colorless.

Determine the equivalent of the bromide-bromate solution in terms of the thiosulfate under the same conditions. Calculate the disulfide or thioether sulfur content by the following:

$$\% \text{ sulfur} = 100 \, f \, N \, (V_1 - V_2)/S$$

where V_1 = ml thiosulfate used for reagent alone
V_2 = ml thiosulfate used in determination
N = normality of thiosulfate solution
f = 6.413 for disulfides
8.016 for thioethers
S = weight of sample of test substance in milligram

Isothiocyanates. The reaction of amines with isothiocyanates can be utilized for the determination of the latter:

$$R-N-C-S + R'NH \longrightarrow R-NH-\overset{\overset{\displaystyle S}{\|}}{C}-NH-R'$$

The procedure of Roth (16) as modified from the macroprocedure of Siefken (19) consists of treating the test substance dissolved in monochlorobenzene with excess dibutyl (or di-isobutyl) amine. The excess amine is then titrated with acid.

Reagents. Monochlorobenzene, B. pt. 132°.

Dibutylamine solution. Pipet exactly 2.0 ml n-dibutylamine, reagent grade, into a 100-ml volumetric flask and fill to the mark with monochlorobenzene. Each milliliter of this solution is equivalent to 5.75 ml 0.02 n HCl.

Methanol, reagent grade.

Hydrochloric acid, 0.02 n, standardized.

Bromphenol blue solution, 0.1% in methanol.

Procedure. In view of the lachrymatory and toxic properties of many of the isothiocyanates these should be handled only with adequate ventilation. Liquid test substances should be weighed out as usual in capillaries.

Weigh out 5 to 10 mg of the test substance into a 250-ml glass-stoppered Erlenmeyer flask containing 4 ml of monochlorobenzene. If the sample is a liquid in a capillary, crush this with a glass rod and rinse off the latter with 0.5 to 1 ml monochlorobenzene. Swirl the contents of the flask cautiously to bring about solution. Then add exactly 2.0 ml of the dibutylamine solution and 30 ml methanol. Stopper the flask and swirl the contents carefully for several minutes so that substances with high vapor pressures are completely absorbed. Add three drops of the bromphenol blue indicator and titrate with 0.02 n HCl until the solution is almost colorless. The end point is reached when the solution is still slightly light green.

Repeat the procedure on a blank to determine the volume of the acid required for the same quantity of the dibutylamine. Calculate the isothiocyanate content by the following:

$$\% \text{ NCS} = 100\, f\,(V_1 - V_2)/S$$

where $V_1 =$ ml acid used in blank

$V_2 =$ acid used in determination

$N =$ normality of acid

$f = 58{,}08$, and

$S =$ weight of sample of test substance in milligrams.

Sulfonic Acids.   Since sulfonic acids are about as strong as sulfuric acid they can easily be titrated with standard base using phenolphthalein as indicator.   Alcoholic solutions of acid and base can be used in the case of water-insoluble sulfonic acids.

Dithiocarbamates and thiuram disulfides can be determined by the method of ROTH and BECK (17).

Thiols, sulfonic acids, and sulfonamides can be determined by the measurement of active hydrogen with lithium-aluminum hydride as described under Carboxylic Acids, p. 195.

Literature Cited.

Chapter I.

(1) KURTZ, L. T., Ind. Eng. Chem., Analyt. Ed. **14**, 191 (1942).

Chapter II.

(1) ALBER, H. K., Ind. Eng. Chem., Analyt. Ed. **13**, 656 (1941). — (2) Z. analyt. Chem. **90**, 100 (1932). — (3) AMELINK, F., Pharm. Weekblad **68**, 1086 (1931). — (4) BABCOCK, M., Analyt. Chemistry **21**, 632 (1949). — (5) BAER, E., Kolloid-Z. **46**, 176 (1928). — (6) BAILEY, A. J., Ind. Eng. Chem., Analyt. Ed. **9**, 490 (1937). — (7) ibid. **14**, 177 (1942). — (8) BARRENSCHEEN, H. K., Mikrochim. Acta **1**, 319 (1937). — (9) BECKER, C., and C. SCHÖPF, Ann. Chem. **524**, 124 (1936). — (10) BENEDETTI-PICHLER, A. A., Ind. Eng. Chem., Analyt. Ed. **2**, 309 (1930). — (11) Mikrochem. Pregl-Festschrift 6 (1929). — (12) BENEDETTI-PICHLER, A. A., and J. R. RACHELE, Mikrochem. **19**, 1 (1935/36). — (13) BENEDETTI-PICHLER, A. A., and F. SCHNEIDER, Ind. Eng. Chem., Analyt. Ed. **5**, 255 (1933). — (14) Z. analyt. Chem. **86**, 69 (1931). — (15) BERING, P., Svensk Kem. Tid. **61**, 10 (1949). — (16) BERNHAUER, K., Einführung in die organisch-chemische Laboratoriumstechnik, Berlin: Julius Springer, 1934; p. 55. — (17) ibid. 59. — (18) ibid. 93. — (19) BEROZA, M. Chemist-Analyst **41**, 18 (1952). — (20) BLANK, E. W., J. Chem. Education **12**, 43 (1935). — (21) BLOCK, R. J., E. L. DURRUM, and G. ZWEIG, A Manual of Paper Chromatography and Paper Electrophoresis, 2nd ed. New York: Academic Press, 1955. — (22) BLOUNT, B., Mikrochem. **19**, 162 (1936). — (23) BREGER, I. A., Analyt. Chemistry **20**, 980 (1948). — (24) BRIMLEY, R. C., and F. C. BARRETT, Practical Chromatography, New York: Reinhold, 1953. — (25) BROWNING, B. L., Mikrochem. **26**, 54 (1939). — (26) ibid. 55.

(27) CHAMOT, E., Mikrochem. **4**, 97 (1926). — (28) CLARKE, B. L., and H. M. HERMANCE, Ind. Eng. Chem., Analyt. Ed. **11**, 50 (1939). — (29) CLAUSEN, S. W., J. Biol. Chem. **52**, 263 (1922). — (30) COLEGRAVE, E. B., Analyst **60**, 90 (1935). — (31) CRAIG, L., Ind. Eng. Chem., Analyt. Ed. **8**, 219 (1936). — (32) ibid. **12**, 773 (1940); ibid. **16**, 413 (1944). — (33) CRAIG, L., Analyt. Chemistry **22**, 1346 (1950). — (34) CRAIG, L., and O. POST, Analyt. Chemistry **21**, 500 (1949).

(35) DAVIES, E. S., and N. H. HARTSHORNE, J. Chem. Soc. London 1830 (1934). — (36) DENIGÈS, G., Mikrochem. **3**, 33 (1925). — (37) DONAU, J., Monatsh. **32**, 31 (1911) and **36**, 381 (1915). Also Mikrochem. **27**, 189 (1939). — (38) DUFTON, A. F., Journ. Soc. Chem. Ind. **38**, 45T (1919).

(39) EDER, R., Dissertation, Zürich 1931, p. 35. — (40) EIGENBERGER, E., Mikrochem. **10**, 57 (1931). — (41) ELEK, A., Mikrochem. **19**, 129 (1936). — (42) ELLIS, G. W., Chemistry and Industry **53**, 77 (1934) and in Weygand, Organisch-chemische Ex-

perimentierkunst, Leipzig: Akademische Verlagsgesellschaft, 1938; p. 112. — (43) EMICH, F. and F. SCHNEIDER, Microchemical Laboratory Manual, New York: John Wiley, 1932; p. 34. — (44) *ibid.* p. 38. — (45) *ibid.* p. 30. — (46) *ibid.* p. 62. — (47) *ibid.* p. 64. — (48) ERDÖS, J. and B. LÁSZLÓ, Mikrochem. **27**, 211 (1939). — (49) Mikrochim. Acta **3**, 304 (1938).

(50) FABIAN, F., Mikrochim. Acta **2**, 332 (1938). — (51) FISCHER, R., Mikrochem. **15**, 247 (1935). — (52) FISCHER, R., and W. IWANOFF, Arch. Pharmaz. **1943**, 361. — (53) FRAENKEL, E., F. BIELSCHOWSKY, and S. J. THANNHAUSER, Z. physiol. Chem. **218**, 10 (1933). — (54) FRIEDRICH, A., Mikrochem., Pregl-Festschrift 103 (1939). — (55) FUHRMANN, F., Mikrochem. **23**, 167 (1937). — (56) FULTON, R. A., Ind. Eng. Chem., Anal. Ed. **9**, 437 (1937).

(57) GABRIELSON, G., and O. SAMUELSON, Acta Chem. Scand. **6**, 729, 738 (1932); Svensk Kem. Tid. **64**, 150 (1952). — (58) GARNER, W., Ind. Chemist **4**, 332 (1928). — (59) *ibid.* 287. — (60) GAWALOWSKI, A., Z. analyt. Chem. **49**, 744 (1910). — (61) GETTENS, R., Tech. Studies Field Fine Arts **2**, 107 (1933). — (62) GOODMAN, C. H., Research **7**, 168 (1954). — (63) GORBACH, G., Mikrochemisches Praktikum, Berlin: Springer-Verlag, 1956; p. 42. — (64) Mikrochem. **12**, 161 (1932). — (65) GOULD, C. W., G. HOLZMAN, and C. NIEMANN, Analyt. Chemistry **20**, 361 (1948). — (66) GREENBAUM, F. R., J. Amer. Pharm. Assoc. **18**, 784 (1929). — (67) GROSS, P. and A. H. WRIGHT, Ind. Eng. Chem. **13**, 701 (1921). — (68) GRUBHOFER, N., Chem. Ing. Techn. **22**, 209 (1950).

(69) HANDLEY, R. and E. F. HERINGTON, Chem. and Ind. **16**, 304 (1956). — (70) HARTSHORNE, N. H., Chemistry and Industry, **1933**, 367. — (71) HÄUSLER, H., Monatsh. **53/54**, 312 (1929). — (72) HECHT, F., Mikrochimica Acta **3**, 129 (1938). — (73) HEMMES, M. H., Rec. trav. chim. (II) **16**, 369 (1898). — (74) HESSE, G., Angew. Chem. **49**, 315 (1936). — (75) HETTERICH, H., Mikrochem. **10**, 379 (1932). — (76) HOFFMANN, H. and W. C. JOHNSON, J. Assoc. Off. Agr. Chemists **13**, 367 (1930). — (77) HORTVET, J., J. Assoc. Off. Agr. Chemists **6**, 481 (1923) and **8**, 559 (1925). — (78) HOUSTON, D. F. and C. P. SAYLOR, Ind. Eng. Chem., Analyt. Ed. **8**, 302 (1936).

(79) JENNERICH, Dissertation, Hamburg, (1924). — (80) JURANY, H., Mikrochem. **27**, 185 (1939). — (81) JOHNSTONE, R. E., J. Soc. Chem. Ind. **50**, 182T (1931).

(82) KATO, T., J. Pharm. Soc. Japan **60**, 228 (1940). — (83) KEMPF, R., Z. analyt. Chem. **62**, 284, 520 (1923). — (84) KEYS, A., J. Biol. Chem. **114**, 450 (1936). — (85) KIRK, P. L., Quantitative Ultramicroanalysis, New York: John Wiley, 1950; p. 109. — (86) KIRK, P. L. and R. CRAIG, Ind. Eng. Chem., Analyt. Ed. **3**, 345 (1931). — (87) KIRK, P. L. and M. DANIELSON, Analyt. Chemistry **20**, 1122 (1948). — (88) KLATT, W., Pharm. Ztg. **79**, 1157 (1934). — (89) KLEMENT, R., Z. analyt. Chem. **136**, 17 (1952). — (90) KLENK, E., Z. physiol. Chem. **242**, 200 (1936). — (91) KOFLER, W., Monatsh. **80**, 694 (1949). — (92) KOFLER, L. and W. DERNBACH, Mikrochem. **9**, 345 (1930). — (93) KÖNIG, O., W. R. CROWELL, and A. A. BENEDETTI-PICHLER, Mikrochem. **39**, 281 (1949). — (94) KUERSCHNER, K., Mikrochem. **3**, 1 (1925).

(95) LACOURT, A. and H. GURFINKEL, Bull. soc. chim. Belg. **49**, 159 (1940). — (96) LANGER, A., Mikrochim. Acta **3**, 247 (1938). — (97) LAPPIN, G. R., J. Chem. Education **25**, 657 (1948). — (98) LAQUER, F., Z. physiol. Chem. **118**, 215 (1922). — (99) LEDERER, E. and M. LEDERER, Chromatography: A Review of Principles and Applications, New York: Elsevier, 1953. — (100) LIEB, H. and W. SCHÖNIGER, Anleitung zur Darstellung organischer Präparate mit kleinen Substanzmengen, Wien: Springer-Verlag 1950; p. 82. — (101) Mikrochem. **35**, 94 (1950). — (102) MALJAROFF, K. L., Mikrochem. **6**, 103 (1928). — (103) MARBERG, C. M., J. Amer. Chem. Soc. **60**, 1509 (1938). — (104) MAYRHOFER, A., Mikrochemie der Arzneimittel und Gifte, Berlin: Urban und Schwarzenberg, 1928. — (105) MORTON, A. A., Laboratory Technique in Organic Chemistry, New York: McGraw-Hill, 1938. — (106) MORTON, A. A. and

J. F. Mahoney, Ind. Eng. Chem., Analyt. Ed. **13**, 494 (1941). — (107) Muenster, W., Mikrochem. **14**, 23 (1933).

(108) Noller, C. R., Ind. Eng. Chem., Analyt. Ed. **14**, 834 (1942).

(109) Paschke, R. F., J. R. Kerns, and D. H. Wheeler, J. Amer. Oil Chemists Soc. **31**, 5 (1954). — (110) Peakes, L. V., Mikrochem. **18**, 100 (1935). — (111) Pfann, W. G., Chem. Eng. News, **34**, 1440 (1956). — (112) Pfeiffer, P., Organische Molekül-verbindungen, Stuttgart: Enke, 1922. — (113) Pozzi-Escot, M. E., Bull. Soc. chim. France (3) **31**, 932 (1904). — (114) Pratt, C. J., Chem. and Ind. **1941**, 719. — (115) Pregl, F., Die quantitative organische Mikroanalyse, Berling: Julius Springer, 1923; p. 206. — (116) Pregl, F., Mikrochem. **2**, 76 (1924). — (117) Pregl, F., E. Fyleman, Quantitative Organic Microanalysis, Philadelphia: Blakiston, 1930; p. 222. — (118) *ibid.* 226. — (119) *ibid.* 66.

(120) Rauen, H. M., and W. Stamm, Chem. Ing. Techn. **21**, 259 (1949). — (121) Raymond, S., Analyt. Chemistry **21**, 1292 (1949). — (122) Roper, I. N., Analyt. Chemistry **21**, 1575 (1949). — (123) Rose, A., Ind. Eng. Chem. **28**, 1210 (1936). — (124) Rosenthaler, L., Apoth. Ztg. **47**, 1358 (1932) also Ber. dtsch. chem. Ges. **21**, 388, 525 (1911), and **23**, 577 (1913). — (125) Rushman, O. F., and E. M. Simpson, Journ. Oil and Colour Chemists Assoc. **37**, 319 (1954).

(126) Schoeller, A., Z. angew. Chem. **35**, 506 (1922). — (127) Schöpf, C. and E. Becker, Ann. Chem. **524**, 49 (1936). — (128) Schoorl, N., Mikrochem. **4**, 103 (1925). — (129) Schrader, S. A., and J. E. Ritzer, Ind. Eng. Chem., Analyt. Ed. **11**, 54 (1939). — (130) Schwab, F. W., and E. Wichers, J. Res. Nat. Bur. Stand. **32**, 253 (1944). — (131) Soltys, A., Mikrochem. Molisch-Festschrift 393 (1936). — (132) *ibid.* 397. — (133) Stetten, de W. and G. F. Grail, Ind. Eng. Chem., Analyt. Ed. **15**, 300 (1943). — (134) Sullivan, J. P., U. S. Bur. Mines, Tech. Paper **381** (1927). — (135) Swindells, F. E., Chemist-Analyst **22**, 18 (1933).

(136) Taylor, A., A. Parpart, and R. Ballentine, Ind. Eng. Chem., Analyt. Ed. **11**, 659 (1939). — (137) Thiessen, A., Biochem. Z. **140**, 457 (1923). — (138) Tiedcke, C., Ind. Eng. Chem., Analyt. Ed. **15**, 81 (1943). — (139) Titus, L., and V. W. Meloche, Ind. Eng. Chem., Analyt. Ed. **5**, 286 (1933). — (140) Tschesche, R., and H. B. König, Chem. Ing. Techn. **22**, 214 (1950). — (141) Tschermak-Seysenegg, A., Mikrochem. **27**, 96 (1939). — (142) Tunmann, O., Pflanzen-Mikrochemie, Berlin: Borntraeger, 1931; p. 25. — (143) Vetter, F., Mikrochem. **14**, 23 (1933).

(144) Wagenaar, M., Pharm. Weekblad **66**, 1121 (1929). — (145) Wasitzky, A., Mikrochemie **11**, 1 (1930). — (146) Werner, O., and G. Klein, Z. physiol. Chem. **143**, 141 (1925). — (147) Weygand, F., Chem. Ing. Techn. **22**, 213 (1950). — (148) Widmer, G., Helv. Chim. Acta **7**, 59 (1934). — (149) Willstaedt, H., and T. K. With, Z. physiol. Chem. **253**, 40 (1938). — (150) Wood, R. W., J. Phys. Chem. **27**, 565 (1923). — (151) Wright, G. F., Can. J. Research **17 B**, 302 (1939).

(152) Yagoda, H., Mikrochem. **18**, 299 (1935). — (153) Young, J. W., Mikrochem. **21**, 133 (1936/37).

(154) Zechmeister, L. and L. v. Cholnoky, Die chromatographische Adsorptions-analyse, 2d ed., Wien: J. Springer, 1938.

Chapter III.

(1) Barkenbus, C., and R. H. Baker, Ind. Eng. Chem., Analyt. Ed. **9**, 135 (1937). — (2) Behrens, H., and P. D. C. Kley, Mikrochemische Analyse, 4th ed., Leipzig: Leopold Voss, 1921; p. 329. — (3) Bennett, E., C. Gould, E. Swift, and C. Niemann, Analyt. Chemistry **19**, 1035 (1947). — (4) Brown, L. E., and C. L. Hoffpauir, Analyt. Chemistry **23**, 1035 (1951).

(5) DAVIDSON, D., Ind. Eng. Chem., Analyt. Ed. **12**, 40 (1940).

(6) ELEK, A., Ind. Eng. Chem., Analyt. Ed. **9**, 502 (1937). — (7) ELEK, A. and D. W. HILL, J. Amer. Chem. Soc. **55**, 2550, 3479 (1933). — (8) EMICH, F., and F. SCHNEIDER, Microchemical Laboratory Manual, New York: John Wiley, 1932; p. 116. — (9) *ibid*. 112. — (10) *ibid*. 117.

(11) FEIST, F., Ber. dtsch. chem. Ges. **35**, 1559 (1902). — (12) FOULKE, D., and F. SCHNEIDER, Ind. Eng. Chem., Analyt. Ed. **10**, 104 (1938).

(13) GARNER, W., Ind. Chemist **5**, 58 (1929). — (14) GILMAN, H., and J. E. KIRBY, J. Amer. Chem. Soc. **51**, 1575 (1929). — (15) GOERDELER, J., and H. DOMGÖRGEN, Mikrochem. **40**, 212 (1953). — (16) GRAEBE, C., Ber. dtsch. chem. Ges. **17**, 1178 (1884).

(17) HAYMAN, D., Ind. Eng. Chem., Analyt. Ed. **11**, 470 (1939). — (18) HUNSDIECKER, C., Ber. dtsch. chem. Ges. **76** B, 264 (1943).

(19) JOHNS, I. B., Laboratory Manual of Microchemistry, Minneapolis: Burgess, 1962, p. 35.

(20) KÖRBL, J., Mikrochim. Acta **1956**, 1705.

(21) MASON, C. W., and E. M. CHAMOT, Mikrochem. **4**, 145 (1926). — (22) MENVILLE R. L., and W. W. PARKER, Analyt. Chemistry **31**, 1901 (1959).

(23) PATRICK, J., and F. SCHNEIDER, Mikrochim. Acta **1960**, 970. — (24) PEPKOWITZ, L. P., Analyt. Chemistry **23**, 1716 (1951). — (25) PREGL, F., and A. VERDINO, Mikrochem. **6**, 5 (1928).

(26) ROSENTHALER, L., Z. analyt. Chem. **109**, 31 (1937).

(27) SOZZI, J., and J. B. NIEDERL, Mikrochim. Acta **1956**, 496.

(28) VAN ALPHEN, J., Rec. trav. chim. Pays-Bas **52**, 567 (1933).

(29) WIDMARK, C., Acta. Chem. Scand. **7**, 1935 (1953). — (30) WILSON, C. L., Analyst **63**, 332 (1938). — (31) WILSON, C. L., Analyst **65**, 405 (1940). (32) WILSON, D. W., and C. L. WILSON, J. Chem. Soc. London **1939**, 1956.

Chapter IV.

(1) ALBER, H. K., Z. analyt. Chem. **90**, 87 (1932). — (2) ALBER, H. K., and J. T. BRYANT, Ind. Eng. Chem., Analyt. Ed. **12**, 305 (1940). — (3) AMDUR, I., and E. V. HJORT, Ind. Eng. Chem., Analyt. Ed. **2**, 259 (1930). — (4) ANDERSON, H. H., Analyt. Chem. **20**, 1241 (1948). — (5) ARREQUINE, V., Anales soc. quim. Argentina **3**, 133 (1915). — (6) ASHTON, F., D. F. HOUSTON, and C. P. SAYLOR, Bur. Standards J. Research **11**, 233 (1933).

(7) BARGER, G., Ber. **37**, 1754 (1904). — (8) BARKER, T. V., Systematic Crystallography, London, Thomas Murphy and Co., 1930. — (9) BEHRENS, H., and P. D. C. KLEY, Mikrochemische Analyse, Leipzig, Leopold Voss, 1921, p. 258. — (10) BEHRENS, H., and P. D. C. KLEY, Organische mikrochemische Analyse, Leipzig, Leopold Voss, 1922. — (11) BEHRENS, H., and KÜSTER, Tabellen zum Gebrauch bei mikroskopischen Arbeiten, Leipzig, Leopold Voss, 1908, pp. 48, 50, 52. — (12) BENEDETTI-PICHLER, A. A., and F. SCHNEIDER, Z. analyt. Chem. **86**, 69 (1931). — (13) BENSON, S. W., Ind. Eng. Chem., Analyt. Ed. **13**, 502 (1941). — (14) BERL, E., and O. HEFTER, Ann. **478**, 235 (1930). — (15) BILES, J. A., Mikrochem. **39**, 69 (1952). — (16) BLANK, E. W., Ind. Eng. chem., Analyt. Ed. **5**, 74 (1933). — (17) *ibid*. **3**, 9 (1961). — (18) BLANK, E. W., and M. WILLARD, J. Chem. Education **10**, 109 (1933). — (19) *ibid*. **9**, 1819 (1932). — (20) BOLD'IREV, A. K., Mém. soc. russe mineral. [2] **53**, 251; C (1962). — (21) BOLLAND, A., Monatsh. **31**, 387 (1910). — (22) BRATTON, A. C., and H. L. LOCHTE, Ind. Eng. Chem., Analyt. Ed. **4**, 365 (1932). — (23) BRILL, O., and C. EVANS, J. Chem. Soc. London **93**, 1442 (1908). — (24) BURT-GERRANS, J. T., Trans. Roy. Soc. Canada, **26**, Sect. III, 175 (1932).

(25) CALEY, E. R., Ind. Eng. Chem., Analyt. Ed. **2**, 177 (1930). — (26) CAP, F., Mikrochem. **33**, 195 (1947). — (27) CASTLE, R. N., Mikrochem. **38**, 92 (1951). — (28) CASTLE, R. N., and N. F. WITT, J. Amer. Chem. Soc. **71**, 228 (1949). — (29) CASTLE, R. N., N. F. WITT, and C. F. POE, J. Amer. Chem. Soc. **68**, 64 (1946). — (30) CHAMOT, E. and C. W. MASON, Handbook of Chemical Microscopy, 2nd ed., New York: J. Wiley and Sons, 1939; p. 383. — (31) *ibid.* p. 261. — (32) *ibid.* p. 377. — (33) CLEMO, G. R., and A. McQUILLEN, J. Chem. Soc. London, **1935**, 1220. — (34) CLERICI, E., Atti Accad. Lincei Roma **31**, 1, 116 (1922) and [6] 1, 329 (1925). — (35) CLEVENGER S. F., Ind. Eng. Chem., **16**, 854 (1924). — (36) CODD, L. W., and W. T. MOORE, Scientia Pharm. **5**, 105 (1934).

(37) DANGL, F., Mikrochem. 9, 333 (1931). — (38) DAVIES, E. J., and N. H. HARTS-HORNE, J. Chem. Soc. London 1830 (1934). — (39) DeCRINIS, M., Mikrochem. Pregl-Festschrift 25 (1929). — (40) DEININGER, J., Pharm. Ztg. **78**, 362 (1933). — (41) DE JONG, W. F., Zentr. Mineral. Geol. Abt. A, **1935**, 140. — (42) DETRE, L., Deutsch. med. Wochsch. **49**, 985 (1923). — (43) DONNAY, J. P., and W. A. O'BRIEN, Ind. Eng. Chem., Analyt. Ed. **17**, 593 (1945). — (44) DUC DE CHAULNES: Johannsen, Manual of Petrographic Methods, New York: McGraw-Hill 1914, p. 238. — (45) DUNBAR, R. E., Ind. Eng. Chem., Analyt. Ed. **11**, 516 (1939). — (46) DUNBAR, R. E., and J. KNUTESON, Microchem. J. **1**, 17 (1957).

(47) EDWARDS, A. E., and C. E. OTTO, Ind. Eng. Chem., Analyt. Ed. **10**, 225 (1938). — (48) EIGENBERGER, C., Mikrochem. **26**, 264 (1939). — (49) EISENLOHR, F., and E. WÖHLISCH, Ber. dtsch. chem. Ges. **53** , 1746, 2053 (1920); Z. angew. Chem. **34**, 266 (1921). — (50) EMICH, F., Monatsh. **38**, 219 (1917). — (51) EMICH, F., and F. SCHNEI-DER, Microchemical Laboratory Manual, New York: John Wiley, 1932; p. 40.

(52) FAJANS, K., and C. A. KNORR, Ber. dtsch. chem. Ges. **59**, 249 (1926). — (53) FEN-GER-ERIKSON, K., A. KROUGH, and H. H. USSING, Biochem. J. **30**, 1264 (1936). — (54) FISCHER, E., Ber. dtsch chem. Ges. **44**, 129 (1911). — (55) FRIEDEL, W., Biochem. Z. **209**, 65 (1929). — (56) FRIEDRICH, A., Mikrochem. **6**, 97 (1928). — (57) FUCHS, L., Mikrochim. Acta **2**, 317 (1937). — (58) FULWEILER, W. H., Proc. Am. Soc. Testing Materials, Pt. I, 519 (1926).

(59) GARCIA, C., Ind. Eng. Chem., Analyt. Ed. **15**, 648 (1943). — (60) GARNER, W., Ind. Chemist **5**, 58 (1929). — (61) GICKLHORN, J., R. COLLANDER, Protoplasma **8**, 440 (1930). — (62) GICKLHORN, J., and A. NISTLER, *ibid.* **7**, 323 (1929). — (63) GILFILLAN, E. S., J. Amer. Chem. Soc. **56**, 406 (1934). — (64) GILL, A. H., and H. S. SIMMS, Ind. Eng. Chem. **13**, 547 (1921). — (65) GILMORE, E. H., M. MENAULL, and V. SCHNEIDER, Analyt. Chemistry **22**, 892 (1950). — (66) GOULD, C., G. HOLZMAN, and C. NIEMAN, Analyt. Chemistry **19**, 204 (1947). — (67) GRANICK, S., Science **80**, 272 (1934). — (68) GROTH, P., Elemente der physikalischen und chemischen Krystallographie, Munich: R. Oldenbourg, 1921.

(69) HAAS, P., Mikrochemie, Emich-Festschrift, 83 (1930). — (70) HABER, F., and J. JAENICKE, Z. anorg. Chem. **147**, 156 (1925). — (71) HANSEN-HOUBEN, Die Methoden der organischen Chemie, 3rd ed., Vol. I, Leipzig: Georg Thieme, 1925; p. 850. — (72) HARTSHORNE, N. H., and A. STUART, Crystals and the Polarizing Microscope, 2nd ed. London: Arnold and Co., 1950. — (73) HAYS, E. E., F. W. Hart, and R. G. GU-STAVSON, Ind. Eng. Chem., Analyt. Ed. **8**, 286 (1936). — (74) HOCHBERG, S., and V. K. LaMER, Ind. Eng. Chem., Analyt. Ed. **9**, 291 (1937). — (75) HOUBEN, J., J. prakt. Chemie **105**, 27 (1923). — (76) HULTQUIST, M. E., C. F. POE, and N. F. WITT, Ind. Eng. Chem., Analyt. Ed. **14**, 219 (1942).

(77) IZMAÏLOV, N. A., and Z. P. TKACHENKO, Farm. Zhur. **1938**, No. 3, 29, (78) JANÁK, F., Chem. Listy **24**, 134 (1930). — (79) JELLEY, E. E., J. Roy. Microscop. Soc. **54**, 234 (1934). — (80) JOHNS, I. B., Laboratory Manual of Microchemistry, Minneapolis: Burgess. 1942. — (81) JONES, H. C., J. Chem. Soc. London, **33**, 175 (1878).

(82) KAMM, O., Qualitative Organic Analysis, 2nd ed., New York: John Wiley, 1932; p. 130. — (82) KEENAN, G. C., and R. M. HANN, J. Phys. Chem. **31**, 1082 (1927). — (84) KIPLINGER, C. C., J. Chem. Soc. London **125**, 963 (1924). — (85) KIRK, P. L., and C. S. GIBSON, Ind. Eng. Chem., Analyt. Ed. **11**, 403 (1939). — (85) KLEIN, G., Mikrochem. Pregl-Festschrift 193 (1929). — (87) KOFLER, L., Mikrochem. **22**, 241 (1937). — (88) KOFLER, L., and H. HILBCK, Mikrochem. **9**, 317 (1939). — (89) KOFLER, L., A. KOFLER, and A. MAYRHOFER, Mikroskopische Methoden in der Mikrochemie, Vienna: E. Haim, 1936. — (90) KOFLER, L., and E. LINDPAINTNER, Mikrochem. **24**, 43 (1938). — (91) KOMÁREK, K., Chemie (Prague) **4**, 30 (1948). — (92) KSANDA, C. J., and H. E. MERWIN, Amer. Miner. **24**, 482 (1939).

(93) LAKSHMINARAYAN, S., and U. M. NAYAK, Journ. Ind. Chem. Soc. **8**, 599 (1931). — (94) LEWIS, G. N., and R. T. McDONALD, Journ. Chem. Physics **1**, 341 (1933). — (95) LINDERSTRØM-LANG, K., Nature **139**, 713 (1937). — (96) LINSER, H., Mikrochem. **9**, 253 (1930).

(97) MA, T. S., and R. T. SCHENCK, Microchem. **40**, 242 (1953). — (98) MARION, A., Ind. Eng. Chem., Analyt. Ed. **12**, 777 (1940). — (99) MASON, F. A., Chem. and Ind. **44**, 577 (1925). — (100) MAYRHOFER, A., Mikrochemie der Arzneimittel und Gifte, Berlin: Urban & Schwarzenberg, 1928. — (101) MAYRHOFER, A., Pharm. Presse **37**, 129 (1952) and Scientia Pharm. **5**, 105 (1934). — (102) McMULLEN, R. B., J. Amer. Chem. Soc. **48**, 439 (1926). — (103) MOEHRING, A., Wissenschaft u. Ind. **2**, 17 (1923). — (104) MORTON, A. A., and J. F. Mahoney, Ind. Eng. Chem., Analyt. Ed. **13**, 498 (1941). — (105) MULLER, P., Ann. chim. anal. chim. appl. [2], **14**, 340 (1932). — (106) MULLIKEN, S. P., and E. H. HUNTRESS, Identification of Pure Organic Compounds, New York: John Wiley, 1941.

(107) NASH, L. K., Analyt. Chemistry **19**, 799 (1947). — (108) NICHOLS, L., Nat. Paint Bull. **1**, 12, **1**, 14, **1**, 5 (1937). — (109) NIEDERL, J. B., D. R. KASANOF, G. K. KISCH, and D. SUBBA RAO, Mikrochem. **34**, 132 (1949) .— (110) NIEDERL, J. B., and A. M. LEVY, Science **92**, 225 (1940). — (111) NIEDERL, J. B., and W. SASCHEK, Z. analyt. Chem. **77**, 169 (1929) and Mikrochem. **11**, 237 (1932). — (112) NIETHAMMER, A., Mikrochem. **7**, 223 (1929).

(113) PEAK, D. A., and R. A. ROBINSON, J. Phys. Chem. **38**, 941 (1934). — (114) PERMAN, E. P., J. Chem. Soc. London **87**, 194 (1905). — (115) PORTER, M. W., Endeavour **10**, 188 (1951). — (116) PORTER, M. W., and R. C. SPILLER, The Barker Index of Crystals, Cambridge: Heffer and Sons, 1951. — (117) PREGL-FYLEMANN, Quantitative Organic Microanalysis, Philadelphia: Blakiston 1930; p. 206. — (118) PREGL-ROTH, Die quantitative organische Mikroanalyse, Berlin: J. Springer 1935; p. 307.

(119) RASSOW, H., Z. anorg. Chemie **114**, 117 (1920). — (120) RAST, K. Ber. dtsch. chem. Ges. **55**, 1051, 3727 (1922). — (121) RAST, K., Ber. dtsch. chem. Ges. **54**, 1979 (1921). — (122) RAY, R. C., and Y. Dayal, Trans. Faraday Soc. **32**, 741 (1936). — (123) RETGERS, Z. physik. Chem. **3**, 289 (1889). — (124) RIECHE, A., Ber. dtsch. chem. Ges. **59**, 2181 (1926). — (125) RIESENFELD, E. H., and G. M. SCHWAB, Ber. dtsch. chem. Ges. **55**, 2088 (1922). — (126) ROSENBLUM, C., Ind. Eng. Chem., Analyt. Ed. **8**, 286 (1936).

(127) SÁNCHEZ, S. A., Anales asoc. quim. Argentina **13**, 478 (1925). — (128) SAYLOR, C. P., J. Research Nat. Bur. Standards **15**, 97, 277 (1935). — (129) SCHALLY, E., Monatsh. **58**, 399 (1931). — (130) SCHLEIERMACHER, A., Ber. dtsch. chem. Ges. **24**, 944 (1891). — (131) SCHMALFUSS, H., and H. BARTHMEYER, Mikrochem. **5**, 6 (1932). — (132) SCHNEIDER, F., Paper presented at symposium of Metropolitan Microchemical Society (1955). — (133) SCHNEIDER, and ZIMMERMAN, Botanische Mikrotechnik, Jena: 1922, p. 49. — (134) SCHWARZ, K., Monatsh. **53**, 926 (1929). — (135) SHEAD, A. C., Proc. Okla. Acad. Sci. **16**, 87 (1936); also Ind. Eng. Chem., Analyt. Ed. **17**, 593 (1945). — (136) SIERRA, F., Inform. quim. anal. **1**, 73 (1947). — (137) SIGNER, R., Ann. **478**,

246 (1930). — (138) Siwoloboff, A., Ber. dtsch. chem. Ges. **19**, 795 (1886). — (139) Slawson, C. B., and A. B. Peck, Am. Mineral. **21**, 523 (1936). — (140) Smart, W. A., and F. A. Hocking, Pharm. J. **106**, 286 (1921). — (141) Smith, A., and A. W. Menzies, J. Amer. Chem. Soc. **32**, 897 (1910). — (142) Smith, D., and S. A. Ehrhardt, Ind. Eng. Chem., Analyt. Ed. **18**, 81 (1946). — (143) Smith, J. H. C., and H. W. Milner, Mikrochem. **9**, 117 (1931). — (144) Smith, P. E., Chemist-Analyst **19**, 4 (1930). — (145) Soltys, A.: Pregl-Fyleman, Quantitative Organic Microanalysis, Philadelphia: Blakiston, 1930; p. 219. — (146) Speroni, G., Ann. chim. applicata **23**, 432 (1933). — (147) Spies, J. R., J. Amer. Chem. Soc. **55**, 250 (1933). — (148) Stanciu, V., Neues Jahrb. Mineral. Geol. Referate, I, **1933**, 354. — (149) Steinbach, O. F., and A. W. Devor, J. Chem. Education **22**, 496 (1945). — (150) Struszynski, M., Przemysl Chem. **20**, 51 (1936). — (151) Sullivan, J. D., U. S. Bur. Mines, Tech. Paper 381 (1927).

(152) Terpstra, P., Natuurw. Tijdschr. **14**, 168 (1932). — (153) Thiel, A., and L. Stoll, Ber. dtsch. chem. Ges. **53**, 2033 (1920). — (154) Van Zijp, C., Pharm. Weekblad **69**, 125 (1932). — (155) von Engelhardt, W., Zentr. Mineral. Geol. **1938 A**, 212. — (156) Vorlaender, D., and U. Haberland, Ber. dtsch. chem. Ges. **58**, 2652 (1925).

(157) Walsh, W. L., Ind. Eng. Chem., Analyt. Ed. **6**, 468 (1934). — (158) Weygand, C., and W. Gruentzig, Mikrochem. **10**, 1 (1931). — (159) Wherry, E. T., J. Am. Chem. Soc. **49**, 578 (1927). — (160) Wiberley, J. S., R. K. Siegfriedt, and A. A. Benedetti-Pichler, Mikrochim. Acta **38**, 471 (1951). — (161) Winchell, A. N., Amer. Mineral. **23**, 805 (1938). — (162) Winchell, A. N., The Optical Properties of Organic Compounds, 2nd ed., New York: Academic Press, 1954. — (163) Winchell, A. N., Elements of Optical Mineralogy, New York: John Wiley, 1927. — (164) Wood, R. G., and S. H. Ayliffe, Phil. Mag. [7] **21**, 321 (1936).

(165) Yuster, S. T., and L. H. Reyerson, Ind. Eng. Chem., Analyt. Ed. **8**, 61 (1936).

(166) Zscheile, F. P., and J. W. White, Ind. Eng. Chem., Analyt. Ed. **12**, 436 (1940).

Chapter V.

(1) Burrell, H., Interchemical Review, **14**, 3 (1955).

(2) Chao-Lun Tseng, Nat. Central Univ. (Nanking) Sci. Repts., Ser. A, Phys. Sci., **1**, 5 (1930).

(3) Gardner, J. H., and F. A. Linde, Proc. Missouri Acad. Science, **3**, No. 4, 80 (1937). — (4) Gillespie, R. J., Quart. Revs. **8**, 40 (1954). — (5) Hildebrand, J., and R. Scott, The Solubility of Nonelectrolytes, 3rd ed., New York: Reinhold, 1949. — (6) Jaecker, J. A., and F. Schneider, Mikrochim. Acta **1959**, 801. — (7) Kamm, O., Qualitative Organic Analysis, 2nd ed., New York: John Wiley, 1922. — (8) Mulliken, S. P., and E. H. Huntress, Identification of Pure Organic Compounds, New York: John Wiley, 1941. — (9) Schneider, F., and D. Foulke, Ind. Eng. Chem., Analyt. Ed. **10**, 445 (1938). — (10) Shriner R. H. and R. C. Fuson, Systematic Identification of Organic Compounds, 2nd ed., New York: John Wiley, 1941. — (11) Small, P. A., J. Appl. Chem. **3**, 71 (1953).

Chapter VI.

(1) Alber, H. K., Mikrochem. **7**, 21 (1929). — (2) Alicino, J. F., Analyt. Chemistry **20**, 590 (1948). — (3) Allen, C. F., J. Amer. Chem. Soc. **52**, 2955 (1930). — (4) Allen, C. F., and J. W. Gates, J. Org. Chem. **6**, 596 (1941). — (5) Altieri, V. J., Gas Analysis

and Testing of Gaseous Material, New York, American Gas Association, Inc., 1945, p. 330. — (6) ARMSTRONG, M. D., and J. E. COPENHAVER, J. Amer. Chem. Soc. 65, 2252 (1943).

(7) BAILEY, A. J., Mikrochim. Acta 2, 35 (1937). — (8) BAIR, R. K., and C. M. SUTER, J. Amer. Chem. Soc. 64, 1978 (1942). — (9) BARLOT, J., and M.-T. BRENET, C. r. acad. sci., Paris 174, 114 (1922). — (10) BEHRENS, H., Chem. Ztg. 95, 1125 (1902). — (11) BEHRENS, H., Z. analyt. Chem. 69, 97 (1926). — (12) BEHRENS, H., and P. D. C. KLEY, Organische mikrochemische Analyse, 2nd ed., Leipzig: Leopold Voss, 1922; p. 72. — (13) Ibid. p. 66. — (14) Ibid. p. 311. — (15) BENEDETTI-PICHLER, A. A., Ind. Eng. Chem., Analyt. Ed. 11, 226 (1939). — (16) BENEDICT, H. C., Ind. Eng. Chem., Analyt. Ed. 2, 91 (1930). — (17) BEROZA, M., Analyt. Chemistry 25, 177 (1953). — (18) BOESEKEN, J., and P. POLS, Rec. trav. chim. Pays Bas 54, [4] 16, 162 (1935). — (19) BRADBURY, R. B., Analyt. Chemistry 21, 1139 (1949). — (20) BREDERICK, H., and E. FRITZSCHE, Ber. dtsch. chem. Ges. 70, 802 (1937). — (21) BROWN, E. L., and N. CAMPBELL, J. Chem. Soc. London, 1937, 1699. — (22) BRYANT, W. M. D., J. Amer. Chem. Soc. 54, 3758 (1932). — (23) BRYANT, W. M. D., and J. MITCHELL, J. Amer. Chem. Soc. 60, 2748 (1938). — (24) BUCKLES, R. E., and C. J. THELEN, Analyt. Chemistry 22, 676 (1950). — (25) BUESS, C. M., and N. KHAR-RASCH, J. Amer. Chem. Soc. 72, 3529 (1950).

(26) CASTLE, R. W., Mikrochem. 38, 92 (1951). — (27) CHRISTENSEN, B. E., and R. A. CLARKE, Ind. Eng. Chem., Analyt. Ed. 17, 265 (1945). — (28) CLARKE, R. A., and B. E. CHRISTENSEN, Ind. Eng. Chem., Analyt. Ed. 17, 334 (1945).

(29) DAVIDSON, D., and D. PERLMAN, A Guide to Qualitative Organic Analysis, Brooklyn: Brooklyn College, 1954. — (30) DEHN, W. M., K. E. BALLARD, and D. A. JACKSON, Ind. Eng. Chem., Analyt. Ed. 4, 413 (1932). — (31) DENIGÈS, G., Bull. trav. soc. pharm. Bordeaux 17, 173 (1938). — (32) DENIGÈS, G., C. r. acad. sci. Paris 196, 1504 (1933). — (33) DENIGÈS, G., Mikrochem. 3, 33 (1925). — (34) DERMER, O. C., and V. H. DERMER, J. Amer. Chem. Soc. 65, 1653 (1943). — (35) DERMER, O. C., and J. KING, J. Org. Chem. 8, 168 (1943). — (36) DEVOR, A. W., J. Amer. Chem. Soc. 72, 2008 (1950) and Analyt. Chemistry 24, 1626 (1952). — (37) DEWEY, B. T., and N. F. WITT, Ind. Eng. Chem., Analyt. Ed. 12, 459 (1940) and 14, 648 (1942). — (38) DITTMER, K. H., and R. G. GUSTAVSON, Ind. Eng. Chem., Analyt. Ed. 12, 297 (1940). — (39) DONLEAVY, J. J., J. Amer. Chem. Soc. 58, 1004 (1936). — (40) DUNBAR, R. E., and F. J. FERRIN, Chemist-Analyst 44, 77 (1955).

(41) ELEK, A., Ind. Eng. Chem., Analyt. Ed. 11, 174 (1939). — (42) ELEK, A., and R. A. HARTE, Ind. Eng. Chem., Analyt. Ed. 8, 267 (1936). — (43) EMICH, F., Lehrbuch der Mikrochemie, 2nd ed., Munich: Bergmann, 1926; p. 206. — (45) EMICH, F., and F. SCHNEIDER, Microchemical Laboratory Manual, New York: John Wiley, 1932; p. 133. — (44) EMICH, F., Mikrochemisches Praktikum, 2nd ed., München: Bergmann, 1931.

(46) FEINBERG, B. G., Amer. Chem. J. 49, 93 (1913). — (47) FISCHER, R., Mikrochem. 13, 123 (1933). — (48) FISCHER, R., and A. MOOR, Mikrochem. 15, 74 (1934). — (49) FISCHER, R., and W. PAULUS, Arch. Pharm. 273, 83 (1935). — (50) FISCHER, R., and F. STAUDER, Mikrochem. 8, 330 (1930). — (51) FOSSE, R., P. DE GRAEVE, and P. E. THOMAS, C. r. acad. sci. Paris, 200, 1450 (1935). — (52) FOULKE, D., and F. SCHNEIDER, Ind. Eng. Chem., Analyt. Ed. 10, 104 (1938). — (53) Ibid. 12, 554 (1940). — (54) FRIEDRICH, A., Mikrochem. 7, 185 (1929). — (55) FRITZ, J. S., Acid-Base Titrations in Nonaqueous Solvents, Columbus: G. Frederick Smith, 1952; p. 10. — (56) FURTER, M., Helv. Chim. Acta 21, 1144 (1938). — (57) FUSON, R. C., and B. A. BULL, Chem. Revs. 15, 275 (1934). — (58) GARCIA, C., and F. SCHNEIDER, Ind. Eng. Chem., Analyt. Ed. 14, 94 (1942). — (59) GILLESPIE, R. J., Quart. Revs. 8, 40 (1954). — (60) GREENBAUM, F., J. Amer. Pharm. Assoc. 18, 784 (1929). — (61) GRIEBEL, C.,

Z. Untersuch. Nahr. u. Genußm. **47**, 438 (1924). — (62) GRIEBEL, C., and F. WEISS, Mikrochem. **5**, 146 (1927). — (63) HOLLEY, A. D., and R. W. HOLLEY, Analyt. Chemistry **24**, 216 (1952). — (64) HASSID, W. Z., and R. M..McREADY, Ind. Eng. Chem., Analyt. Ed. **14**, 683 (1942). — (64) HAWK, P. B., and O. BERGEIM, Practical Physiological Chemistry, Philadelphia: Blakiston, 1931; p. 51. — (65) HOFFMAN, D. O., and M. L. WOLFRAM, Analyt. Chemistry **19**, 225 (1947). — (66) HOFMANN K. A., A. METZLER, and H. LECHER, Ber. dtsch. chem. Ges. **43**, 178 (1910). — (68) HUBACHER, M. H., Analyt. Chemistry **21**, 945 (1949). — (69) HUNTER, I. R., and E. T. POTTER, Analyt. Chemistry **30**, 293 (1958). — (70) HUNTRESS, E. H., and S. S. AUTENREITH, J. Amer. Chem. Soc. **63**, 3446 (1941). — (71) HUNTRESS, E. H., and F. H. CARTEN, J. Amer. Chem. Soc. **62**, 511 (1940). — (72) HUNTRESS, E. H., and R. F. PHILLIPS, Amer. Chem. Soc. **71**, 458 (1949). — (73) HURD, C. D., and C. L. THOMAS, J. Amer. Chem. Soc. **55**, 1646 (1933). — (74) HYDE, J. F., and H. W. SCHERP, J. Amer. Chem. Soc. **52**, 3359 (1930).

(75) JOHNS, I. B., and E. J. SEIFERLE, Ind. Eng. Chem., Analyt. Ed. **13**, 841 (1941). (76) KERCHOV, F. W., Z. analyt. Chem. **108**, 249 (1937). — (77) KHARASCH, N., and C. M. BUESS, J. Amer. Chem. Soc. **71**, 2724 (1949). — (78) KIRSTEN, W., and S. EHRLICH, ROGOZINSKY, Mikrochim. Acta **1955**, 786. — (79) KLEIN, G., and H. LINSER, Mikrochem. Pregl-Festschrift 204 (1929). — (80) KLEIN, G., and H. WENZEL, Mikrochem. **7**, 318 (1929); **10**, 70 (1932); and **11**, 73 (1932). — (81) KLEIN, G., and O. WERNER, Biochem. Z. **168**, 256 (1925). — (82) Z. Physiol. Chem. **143**, 141 (1925). — (83) KOFLER, L., and H. HILBCK, Mikrochem. **8**, 117 (1930). — (84) KÖGL, F., and J. J. POSTOWSKY, Ann. Chem. **440**, 32 (1924). — (85) KRUEGER, D., and E. TSCHIRCH, Mikrochem. **7**, 318 (1929). — (86) KUHN, R., and F. L'ORSA, Z. angew. Chem. **44**, 847 (1931). — (87) KUHN, R., and E. MOELLER, Z. angew. Chem. **47**, 145 (1934). — (88) KUHN, R., and H. ROTH, Ber. dtsch. chem. Ges. **66**, 1274 (1933). — (89) KURTENACKER, A., Z. analyt. Chem. **64**, 56 (1924). — (90) KÜSTER, W., and W. MAAG, Z. physiol. Chem. **127**, 190 (1923).

(91) LASKOWSKI, D., and O. ADAMS, Analyt. Chemistry **31**, 148 (1959). — (92) LASKOWSKI, D., D. GRABER, and W. McCRONE, Analyt. Chemistry **25**, 1900 (1953). — (93) LIEB, H., PREGL-ROTH, Die quantitative organische Mikroanalyse, 4th ed. 1935, Berlin: J. Springer, p. 210. — (94) LIEB, H., and W. SCHOENIGER, Mikrochem. **35**, 400 (1950). — (95) LUCAS, H. J., J. Amer. Chem. Soc. **52**, 803 (1930). — (96) LUCAS, H. S., and O. PRESSMAN, Ind. Eng. Chem., Analyt. Ed. **10**, 140 (1938).

(97) MA, T. S., J. LOGAN, and P. MAZZELLA, Microchem. J. **1**, 67 (1957). — (98) MacLENNAN, K., J. Soc. Chem. Ind. **42**, 393T (1923). — (99) MATTHIESSEN, G., and H. HAGEDORN, Mikrochem. **29**, 55 (1941). — (100) MOLISCH, H., Monatsh. **7**, 198 (1886). — (101) MORGAN, G. J., and F. M. G. NICKELTHWAIT, J. Soc. Chem. Ind. **21** 1375 (1902). — (102) MORRIS, V. H., J. Amer. Chem. Soc. **54**, 2893 (1932). — (103) MORTON, A. A., and L. V. PEAKES, Ind. Eng. Chem., Analyt. Ed. **5**, 185 (1933).

(104) NAMETKIN, S. S., N. N. MEL'NIKOV, YU. A. BASKAKOV, and K. S. BOKAREV, Zh. Anal. Khim. **5**, 7 (1950). — (105) NEUBERG, C., and A. GOTTSCHALK, Biochem. Z. **146**, 185 (1924). — (106) NEUBERG, C., and E. REINFURTH, Biochem. Z. **106**, 281 (1920).

(107) OGG, C. L., and F. COOPER, Analyt. Chemistry **21**, 1400 (1949). — (108) OGG, C. L., and W. L. PORTER, and C. O. WILLITS, Ind. Eng. Chem., Analyt. Ed. **17**, 394 (1945). — (109) ORCHIN, M., and E. O. WOOLFOLK, J. Amer. Chem. Soc. **68**, 1727 (1946). — (110) OSBURN, O. L., H. G. WOOD, and C. H. WERKMAN, Ind. Eng. Chem., Analyt. Ed. **5**, 247 (1933) and **8**, 270 (1936).

(111) PALIT, S., Ind. Eng. Chem., Analyt. Ed. **18**, 246 (1946). — (112) PETERSON, J. W., K. W. HEDBERG, and B. E. CHRISTENSEN, Ind. Eng. Chem., Analyt. Ed. **15**, 225 (1943). — (113) PFEIFFER, P., Organische Molekülverbindungen, Stuttgart:

Enke, 1932. — (114) PHILLIPS, W. M., and W. C. WAKE, Analyst **74**, 306 (1949). —
(115) PLIMMER, R. H. A., Organic and Biochemistry, New York: Longmans, Green &
Co., 1933; 256, 267, and 280. — (116) POOL, W. O., H. J. HARWOOD, and A. W.
RALSTON, J. Amer. Chem. Soc. **59**, 178 (1937). — (117) PRATER, A. N., Ind. Eng.
Chem., Analyt. Ed. **12**, 705 (1940). — (118) Pregl-FYLEMAN, Quantitative Organic
Microanalysis, Philadelphia: Blakiston, 1930; p. 70. — (119) PREGL-ROTH, Die
quantitative organische Mikroanalyse, 4th ed.; Berlin: J. Springer, 1935, p. 210.

(120) QUENSE, J. A., and W. M. DEHN, Ind. Eng. Chem., Analyt. Ed. **11**, 55 (1939);
ibid. **12**, 556 (1940). — (121) RALSTON, A. W., and M. R. McCORKLE, J. Amer. Chem.
Soc. **61**, 1604 (1939). — (122) RAMIREZ, F., and A. F. KIRBY, J. Amer. Chem. Soc.
76, 1037 (1954). — (123) RASCHIG, F., Z. angew. Chem. **20**, 2066 (1907). — (124)
REDEMANN, C. E., and H. J. LUCAS, Ind. Eng. Chem., Analyt. Ed. **9**, 521 (1937). –
(125) RITTER, F. O., J. Chem. Education **30**, 395 (1953). — (126) ROSENTHALER, L.,
Mikrochem. **18**, 50 (1935) and **19**, 17 (1935). — (127) Mikrochem. **8**, 72 (1930). —
(128) Mikrochemie **21**, 215 (1937). — (129) Z. analyt. Chem. **97**, 405 (1934) and
Mikrochem. **12**, 98 (1932). — (130) Roos, E., Z. physiol. Chem. **15**, 516 (1891). —
(131) ROSSMANN, E., Ber. dtsch. chem. Ges. **65**, 1847 (1932). — (132) ROTH, H.,
Mikrochem. **11**, 140 (1932). — (133) Mikrochim. Acta **1958**, 766.

(134) SAH *et al.*, Rec. trav. chim. Pays-Bas **58**, 453, 582, 591, 595 (1939). — (135)
SAMSEL, E., and J. McHARD, Ind. Eng. Chem., Analyt. Ed. **14**, 754 (1942). — (136)
SCHAEFFER, H. F., J. Chem. Education **19**, 15 (1942). — (137) SCHNEIDER, F., and
D. FOULKE, Ind. Eng. Chem., Analyt. Ed. **10**, 445a (1938) and **11**, 111 (1939). —
(138) SCHÖNIGER, W., H. LIEB, and K. GASSNER, Mikrochem. Acta **1953**, 435. —
(139) SCHÖNIGER, W., H. LIEB, and EL DIN IBRAHIM, Mikrochim. Acta **1954**, 96. —
(140) SEIKEL, M. K., and E. H. HUNTRESS, J. Amer. Chem. Soc. **63**, 593 (1941). —
(141) SIGGIA, S., and R. L. EDSBERG, Ind. Eng. Chem., Analyt. Ed. **20**, 762 (1948). —
(142) SIGGIA, S., Quantitative Organic Analysis via Functional Groups, New York:
John Wiley, 1949; p. 109. — (143) SIGGIA, S., and M. MAISCH, Ind. Eng. Chem.
Analyt. Ed., **20**, 235 (1948). — (144) SMITH, D. M., W. M. BRYANT, and J. MITCHELL,
J. Amer. Chem. Soc. **63**, 1700 (1942). — (145) SOLTYS, A., Mikrochem. **20**, 107 (1936).
— (146) SPATT, C., and F. SCHNEIDER, Ind. Eng. Chem., Analyt. Ed. **16**, 479 (1944). —
(147) STEYERMARK, AL, Analyt. Chemistry **20**, 368 (1948). — (148) STROH, H. H.,
Ber. dtsch. chem. Ges. **90**, 352 (1957) and **91**, 2645, 2657 (1958). — (149) SUBBA RAO,
D., G. D. SHAH, and V. S. PANSARE, Mikrochim. Acta **1954**, 81.

(150) TIEMANN, F., Ber. dtsch. chem. Ges. **32**, 716 (1899). — (151) TRIEBS, W.,
and H. RÖHNERT, Ber. dtsch. chem. Ges. **84**, 433 (1951).

(152) UNDERWOOD, H. W., and W. L. WALSH, J. Amer. Chem. Soc. **53**, 1087 (1931).

(153) VAN ARENDONK, A. M., and M. E. CUPERY, J. Amer. Chem. Soc. **53**, 3184
(1931). — (154) VAN DER HAAR, A. W., Anleitung zum Nachweis, zur Trennung und
Bestimmung der Monosaccharide und Aldehydsäuren. Berlin, 1920. — (155) VAN
NIEWENBERG, C. J., and L. M. BROBBEL, Mikrochem., Molisch-Festschrift 338 (1936).
— (156) VOGEL, H., and A. GEORG, Tabellen der Zucker und ihrer Derivate, Berlin:
J. Springer, 1931. — (157) VOGEL, A., A. WATLING, and J. WATLING, J. Chem. Education **35**, 40 (1958). — (158) VORLAENDER, D., Ber. dtsch. chem. Ges. **43**, 3120 (1910).

(159) WAGENAAR, M., Pharm. Weekblad **71**, 229 (1934). — (160) *Ibid.* **64**, 6
(1927). — (161) WEBSTER, R. W., Diagnostic Methods, 2nd ed., Philadelphia: Blakiston,
1912. — (166) WILDI, B. S., Science **113**, 188 (1951). — (163) WESP, E. F., and W. R.
BRODE, J. Amer. Chem. Soc. **56**, 1041 (1934). — (162) WERKMAN, C. H., Ind. Eng.
Chem., Analyt. Ed. **2**, 302 (1930) also Iowa State College J. Sci. **4**, 549 (1930), **5**, 1,
121 (1930). — (164) WIELAND, H., and C. SCHEUNIG, Ber. dtsch. chem. Ges. **54**, 2534
(1921). — (165) WIESENBERGER, E., Mikrochim. Acta **1954**, 127. — (167) WU, L. C.,
Doctoral Dissertation, Mass. Inst. Technology, 1931.

(168) ZAUGG, H. E., and W. M. LAUER, Analyt. Chemistry **20**, 1022 (1948). — (169) ZIMMERSCHIED, W. J., R. A. DINERSTEIN, A. W. WELTKAMP, and R. F. MARSCHNER, J. Amer. Chem. Soc. **71**, 2947 (1949).

Chapter VII.

(1) BAER, E., Kolloid-Z. **46**, 176 (1928). — (2) BEHRENS, H., Z. analyt. Chem. **41**, 268 (1902). — (3) BEHRENS, H., and P. D. C. KLEY, Organische Mikroanalyse, 2nd ed., Leipzig: Leopold Voss, 1922; p. 179. — (4) BOLLAND, A., Monatsh. **29**, 465 (1908). — (5) BOST, R. W., and F. NICHOLSON, Ind. Eng. Chem., Analyt. Ed. **7**, 190 (1935). — (6) BROWN, J. W., Trans. Roy. Soc. Can., Sect III, 173 (1932). — (7) BROWN, E. C., and N. CAMPBELL, J. Chem. Soc. London **1937**, 1699.

(8) CHAMOT, E. M., and C. MASON, Handbook of Chemical Microscopy, 2nd ed., New York: John Wiley, 1940; vol. II, p. 393. — (9) CONDO, F. E., E. T. HINKEL, A. FASSERO, and R. L. SHRINER, J. Amer. Chem. Soc., **59**, 230 (1937).

(10) DAVIES, E. S., and N. H. HARTSHORNE, J. Chem. Soc. London 1830, **1934**. — (11) DENIGÈS, C., Bull. trav. soc. pharm. Bordeaux **64**, 3 (1936). — (12) *Ibid.* **73**, 168 (1935). — (13) DUNBAR, R., and J. KNUTESON, Microchem. J. **1**, 17 (1957). — (14) DUNN, M., and W. DRELL, J. Chem. Education **28**, 480 (1951).

(15) EDMAN, P., Acta Chem. Scand. **4**, 283 (1950). — (16) EKKERT, L., Pharm. Zentralhalle **66**, 649 (1925). — (17) EMICH, F., and F. SCHNEIDER, Microchemical Laboratory Manual, New York: John Wiley, 1932; p. 179.

(18) GARCIA, C., and F. SCHNEIDER, Ind. Eng. Chem., Analyt. Ed. **14**, 94 (1942). — (19) GRASSMANN, W., and W. HEYDE, Z. physiol. Chem. **183**, 32 (1929). — (20) GREBBER, K., and J. V. KARABINOS, J. Res. Nat. Bur. Standards **49**, 163 (1952).

(21) HEARON, W. E., and R. G. GUSTAVSON, Ind. Eng. Chem., Analyt. Ed. **9**, 352 (1937). — (22) HELMER, O. M., Proc. Soc. Expt. Biol. Med. **74**, 642 (1950). — (23) HOWELLS, H., and J. LITTLE, J. Amer. Chem. Soc. **54**, 2451 (1932).

(24) KAINZ, G., H. HUBER, and F. KASLER, Mikrochim. Acta **1957**, 744. — (25) KEEN, R. T., and J. S. FRITZ, Analyt. Chemistry **24**, 564 (1952). — (26) KEHRMANN, F., and ST. MICEWICZ, Ber. dtsch. chem. Ges. **45**, 2641 (1912); and Helv. Chim. Acta **4**, 949 (1921). — (27) KEYS, A., J. Biol. Chem. **114**, 450 (1936) and Journ. Physiol. **81**, 162 (1934). — (28) KIRCHHOF, F., Chem. Ztg. **57**, 425 (1933). — (29) KIRK, P. L., and coauthors, Mikrochemie **13**, 587 (1931), **18**, 129, 137 (1935), **21**, 245 (1936), **27**, 154 (1939). — (30) KULIKOW, F. U., and S. PANOWA, J. Chem. (U. S. S. R.) **2**, 736 (1932).

(31) LACOURT, A., G. SOMMEREYNS, C. FRANCOTTE, and N. DELANDE, Nature **172**, 906 (1953). — (32) LANGLEY, W. D., and A. J. ALBRECHT, J. Biol. Chem. **108**, 729 (1935). — (33) LARSEN, J., N. WITT, and C. POE, Mikrochem. **34**, 1 (1948). — (34) LIEB, H., and W. SCHÖNIGER, Mikrochimica Acta **35**, 400 (1950).

(34 a) MARTIN, A. J. P., and R. L. M. SYNGE, Biochem. J. **35**, 1358 (1941).

(35) OGG, C. L., W. L. PORTER, and C. O. WILLITS, Ind. Eng. Chem., Analyt. Ed. **17**, 394 (1945).

(36) PATTON, A., and E. FOREMAN, Food Technol. **4**, 83 (1950). — (37) PLEIN, E. M., and B. T. DEWEY, Ind. Eng. Chem., Analyt. Ed. **15**, 534 (1943).

(38) ROCKLAND, L., and M. DUNN, J. Amer. Chem. Soc. **71**, 4121 (1949). — (39) ROSENTHALER, L., Pharm. Ztg. **74**, 93 (1929). — (40) ROVIRA, S., and L. B. PALFRAY, C. r. acad. sci., Paris **211**, 396 (1940).

(41) SANGER, F., Biochem. Journ. **39**, 507 (1945). — (42) SIGGIA, S., Quantitative Organic Analysis via Functional Groups, New York: John Wiley, 1949; p. 66. — (43) SURMATIS, J. V., and M. WILLARD, Mikrochem. **21**, 167 (1936).

(44) TAKAYAMA, Y., J. Chem. Soc. Japan **52**, 245 (1931). — (45) TAYLOR, A., H. PARPART, and R. BALLANTINE, Ind. Eng. Chem., Analyt. Ed. **11**, 659 (1939). — (46) TURPIN, G. S., J. Chem. Soc. London **1891**, I, 714.

(47) UNDERWOOD, J., and L. ROCKLAND, Analyt. Chemistry **26**, 1553 (1954).

(48) VAN SLYKE, R. D. in E. ABDERHALDEN, Handbuch der biologischen Arbeitsweisen, Abt. I, Teil 7, p. 263, Vienna: Urban and Schwarzenberg, 1925.

(49) WACEK, A., and H. LÖFFLER, Monatsh. **64**, 161 (1934) and Mikrochem. **18**, 277 (1935). — (50) WERNER, O., Mikrochem. **1**, 33 (1923). — (51) WILLARD, M. L., and C. MARESH, J. Amer. Chem. Soc. **62**, 1253 (1940). — (52) WINTERS, S. C., and R. KUNIN, Ind. Eng. Chem. **41**, 460 (1949). — (53) WOOD, R. W., J. Phys. Chem. **27**, 565 (1923).

Chapter VIII.

(1) BALLCZO, H., and G. MONDL, Mikrochem. **36/37**, 1002 (1951). — (2) BOST, R., P. K. STARNES, and E. L. WOOD, J. Amer. Chem. Soc. **73**, 1968 (1951). — (3) BOST, R., J. TURNER, and M. W. CONN, *ibid.* **55**, 4956 (1933). — (4) BOST, R., J. TURNER, and R. NORTON, J. Amer. Chem. Soc. **54**, 1985 (1932). — (5) BROWN, E. L., and N. CAMPBELL, J. Chem. Soc. London **1937**, 1699 and **1939**, 1442.

(6) CASTLE, R. N., N. F. WITT, and C. F. POE, J. Amer. Chem. Soc. **71**, 228 (1949). — (7) CUTTER, H. B., and A. KREUCHUNAS, Analyt. Chemistry **25** 198 (1953).

(8) DENIGÈS, G., Bull. trav. soc. pharm. Bordeaux **71**, 5 (1933). — (9) DREW, R. P., and J. M. STURTEVANT, J. Amer. Chem. Soc. **61**, 2666 (1939).

(10) GARNER, W., J. Soc. Dyers and Colourists **43**, 2 (1927) and **52**, 302 (1936).

(11) HUNTRESS, E. H., and F. H. CARTEN, J. Amer. Chem. Soc. **62**, 511 (1940).

(12) JURAČEK, and M. VEČERA, Chem. Listy **46**, 149 (1951) and **46**, 722 (1952).

(13) KUHN, R., L. BIRKHOFER, and F. W. QUACKENBUSH, Ber. dtsch. chem. Ges. **72**, 407 (1939).

(14) MARTIN, A. J., and H. DEVERAUX, Analyt. Chemistry **31**, 1932 (1959). — (15) MIKL, O., and J. PECH, Chem. Listy **46**, 382 (1952) and **47**, 904 (1953).

(16) ROTH, H., Mikrochim. Acta **1958**, 766. — (17) ROTH, H., and W. BECK, Mikrochim. Acta **1957**, 844.

(18) SCHÖNIGER, W., Mikrochim. Acta **1955**, 123 and **1956**, 869. — (19) SIEFKEN, W., Ann. Chem. **562**, 100 (1949). — (20) SIGGIA, S., and R. L. EDSBERG, Analyt. Chemistry **20**, 938 (1948).

(21) WHITMORE, W., and A. I. GEBHART, Ind. Eng. Chem., Analyt. Ed. **10**, 654 (1938).

Tables of
Physical Constants of Compounds and Derivatives
Classified by
Orders, Genera, Divisions, and Sections

Arrangement of Tables and Data

The tables list the names and characteristics of compounds falling into the various orders and genera.

The compounds are listed in the order of their increasing melting or boiling points since these are the first constants determined in the course of the analysis.

The headings: "Boiling Point, Melting Point, Density, Refractive Index" refer to the constants of the simple compounds.

If the boiling point has been determined at reduced pressure, the value of the latter is shown by the superscript.

Densities are given for 20° relative to water at 4° (D_4^{20}) unless otherwise noted. Refractive indices are given for 20° and for the sodium D line (n_D^{20}) unless otherwise noted.

When available the constants of the useful derivatives of the compounds are listed. The value given is the melting point of the derivative unless otherwise noted.

Notes on the Use of the Tables

The tabulation does not follow the MULLIKEN-HUNTRESS classification exactly. The number of compounds in certain groups, particularly the higher orders, is too small to warrant or require separate tables.

Many compounds are listed as derivatives of others. If such a compound is indicated by the preliminary testing, the analyst should look for it under the listing of the root compound. For example, hydrazones should be sought under aldehydes or ketones.

Since the utility of these tables depends upon the ease of locating a compound on the basis of the observed experimental evidence, the listings cannot, for example, be alphabetical. If data such as melting points are unavailable or unreliable, as in the case of the sulfonic acids, the compound must be listed as a derivative or a related compound. The sulfonic acids are thus listed under sulfonamides. Also, boiling points at reduced pressure are given in the numerical order of the values provided in the literature regardless of the relative volatilities of the substances.

Nomenclature presents a problem not easily solved by "systems". The author does not regard it as his right or obligation to choose between, e.g., 2-hydroxy biphenyl and o-phenyl phenol or between mercaptan and thiol. The customary (or literature) nomenclature is used even if it does not conform with one of the established systems.

As pointed out elsewhere, identification is based upon comparison of several properties, not just one. Hence, a few tenths of a degree difference in the melting or boiling points of two compounds will not suffice to distinguish between these compounds. Therefore, while the values given in the literature may be more exact, the tables list them only to the nearest 0.5°. Furthermore, there will not be complete agreement between some values given in these tables and those found elsewhere in the literature. A number of reasons may account for such disagreements. One is the lack of a uniform, standardized technique or method for the determination of the constants. The author has attempted to list the values which seem to have achieved widest acceptance, rather than to list all these to be found or reported.

Abbreviations Used

anh.	= anhydrous	hyd.	= hydrate
d.	= decomposes	monom.	= monomer
dim.	= dimer	subl.	= sublimes
	trim. = trimer		

Table 1–1–A. Aldehydes, Solid

311

TABLE 1–1–A. *Aldehydes, Solid*

Name	M. Pt.	B. Pt.	Oxime	Phenyl Hydrazone	p-Nitrophenyl Hydrazone	2,4-Dinitrophenyl Hydrazone	Semicarbazone	Dimethone	Dimethone Anhydride
n-Undecylaldehyde (Undecanal)	−4 / 47-48 trim.	120^{20}	72			104	103		
n-Tridecylaldehyde (Tridecanal)	14	136^{8}	80.5			108	106		
2,3,5,6-Tetramethylbenzaldehyde	20	135^{11}	125				270 d.		
n-Myristaldehyde (Tetradecanal)	22.5-23	166^{24}	82.5		95	108	106.5		
2-Ethoxybenzaldehyde	20-22	247-249	57				219		
n-Pentadecylaldehyde (Pentadecanal)	24-25	160^{14}	86		94	107	106.5		
Palmitaldehyde (Hexadecanal)	34		88		96.5	108	107		
1-Naphthaldehyde	34	292	90	80	234		221		
Phenylacetaldehyde	34	195	99	63	151	121	156	165	
4-Methoxy-1-naphthaldehyde	34	200^{11}		113					
5-Hydroxymethyl-2-furaldehyde	35-36		77	140	185	184	195 d.		
Margaraldehyde (Heptadecanal)	35-36		89.5				107-108		
Piperonal (Heliotropin)	37	263	146 syn- / 112 anti-	102	199	265 d.	230	177	220
Stearaldehyde (Octadecanal)	38		89		101	101	108		
2-Methoxybenzaldehyde (o-Anisaldehyde)	38-39	243-246 corr.	92		204	253.5	215 d.		
Veratraldehyde	44								
(3,4)-Dimethoxybenzaldehyde	44	285	94	121		261	177	173	
3-Phenylcinnamaldehyde	44	210^{14}		173		196	214		
2,4,5-Trimethylbenzaldehyde	44.5	120^{10}		127			243		
Lauraldehyde (Dodecanal)	42-43	238	76		90	106	103.5		
Furfural diacetate	52	220							
Benzylglycolic aldehyde	52	121^{4}					137		
2-Ethyl-4-hydroxybenzaldehyde	53	145^{1}							

Table 1–1–A. (Cont.)

Name	M. Pt.	B. Pt.	Oxime	Phenyl Hydrazone	p-Nitrophenyl Hydrazone	2,4-Dinitrophenyl Hydrazone	Semicarbazone	Dimethone	Dimethone Anhydride
2-(α-Furyl)-acrolein	54	95^{9}	110	132			219.5		
2,3-Dimethoxybenzaldehyde (o-Veratraldehyde)	54	137^{12}	99	138			231 d.		
9-Hydroxynonanal	54	$120^{0.1}$					125		
2,3-Diphenylpropionaldehyde	54	170^{11}							
3-Benzyloxybenzaldehyde	54	218^{20}							
Octatrienal	55			191 di-					
Phthalaldehyde	56								
2-Hydroxy-5-methylbenzaldehyde	56	217	105	149			282		
2-Phenanthraldehyde	59		175						
Paraisobutyraldehyde	59	195							
1-Hydroxy-2-naphthaldehyde	59		145						
2-Naphthaldehyde	60	150^{15}	156	205 d.	230	270	245		
4-Phenylbenzaldehyde	60		149	189 d.	197	239 d.	243 d.		
3-Methoxy-1-naphthaldehyde	60		102				200		
3-Methoxy-4-ethoxybenzaldehyde	64								
5-Methoxy-1-naphthaldehyde	66		104		246		246		
Dibenzofuran-2-aldehyde	68			162					
2,4-Dimethoxybenzaldehyde (β-Resorcylaldehyde dimethyl ether)	71	165^{10}	106						
4-Ethoxy-1-naphthaldehyde	72								
Protocatechualdehyde 3-ethyl ether	77								
3,4,5-Trimethoxybenzaldehyde	78	163^{10}	83		201		219		
3-Phenanthraldehyde	80		145				275		
Vanillin	80	285 d.	117	105	227	271 d.	230	196	227
2-Hydroxy-1-naphthaldehyde	82	192^{27}	157				240		
Stilbene-2-aldehyde	83								
2-Methoxy-1-naphthaldehyde	84	200^{11}							
Isophthalaldehyde	89		180	242					

Table 1–1–A. Aldehydes, Solid (Cont.)　　　313

Phenylglyoxal hydrate	91				309		217 d.		
2-Phenylcinnamaldehyde	94	195[17]	129 d.	152 di-			189		
Hydroxyacetaldehyde (Glycolaldehyde)	96		168 d.	125					
2,2-Dimethyl-3-hydroxypropionaldehyde	97	85[15]		162					
Benzaldehyde-2-carboxylic acid	98 hyd.		120				202		
3-Hydroxy-2-naphthaldehyde	99		207 d.	246	265	260 d.	>270		
9-Phenanthraldehyde	101		157				223		
3-Hydroxybenzaldehyde	104	240	90	130	221		198		
9-Anthraldehyde	105		187	207			219		
2,3-Dihydroxybenzaldehyde	108			167			226 d.		
1-Phenanthraldehyde	111		189						
2-Ethoxy-1-naphthaldehyde	112								
4-Hydroxybenzaldehyde	116					258			
Terephthaldehyde	116		72	177	266	280 d.	224	188	246
2,4,6-Trimethoxybenzaldehyde	118								
Pyrene-3-aldehyde	126	245	200 di-	278d. di-	281 di-				
1,2,3,4-Tetrahydrophen-anthrene-9-aldehyde	129		201						
2,4-Dihydroxybenzaldehyde (β-Resorcylaldehyde)	135		191	159 d.		286 d.	260 d.		
D,L-Glyceraldehyde, dim.	138.5		117			166	160 d.		
3,4-Dihydroxybenzaldehyde (Protocatechualdehyde)	153 d.		157	175 d.		275 d.	230 d.		
3,5-Dihydroxybenzaldehyde	156								
Hydropyruvic aldehyde (α-Resorcylic aldehyde)	160		135				223		
Diphenylglycolic aldehyde	163		124				242		
Benzaldehyde-3-carboxylic acid	175		188 d.	164			265	197	172
2-Hydroxybenzaldehyde-3-carboxylic acid	179			188				145 d.	
4-Hydroxy-1-naphthaldehyde	181		143				224		
3,4-Benzpyrene-5-aldehyde	203								

Table 1–1–A. (Cont.)

Name	M. Pt.	B. Pt.	Oxime	Phenyl Hydrazone	p-Nitro-phenyl Hydrazone	2,4-Dinitro-phenyl Hydrazone	Semi-carbazone	Dimethone	Dimethone Anhydride
3,4,5-Trihydroxybenzaldehyde (Gallaldehyde)	215 d. monohyd.		195 d.		226				
4-Hydroxybenzaldehyde-3-carboxylic acid	248		179	219					
Benzaldehyde-4-carboxylic acid	256 subl.		208	226					

TABLE 1–1–B. *Aldehydes, Liquid*

Name	B. Pt.	M. Pt.	Oxime	Phenyl Hydrazone	p-Nitro-phenyl Hydrazone	2,4-Dinitro-phenyl Hydrazone	Semi-carbazone	Dimethone	Dimethone Anhydride
Formaldehyde (Methanal) (see below "Formalin")	-21	-91							
Acetaldehyde (Ethanal)	20	-123.5	47	57	128.5	168.5	162	139	174
Methylal (Methylene dimethyl ether)	42	-104							
Propionaldehyde (Propanal)	49	-81	40		124	155	89	154	142
Glyoxal	50	15	178	180	311	328	270	186 mono- 228 di-	224 mono-
Acrolein	52	-88			150	165	171	192	162
Propynal (Propargylaldehyde)	55								
Isobutyraldehyde	64	-65.9			130	187	125	154	144
Acetaldehyde dimethylacetal	64.3								
2-Methyl-2-propenal (Methacrolein)	73.5			74		206	198		
n-Butyraldehyde (Butanal)	75	-97		93	87	123	95.5	134	141
Trimethylacetaldehyde (Pivaldehyde)	75		41		119	210	190.5		
Formaldehyde diethylacetal	87.5								
Methoxyacetaldehyde	92				115	124			
Isovaleraldehyde (3-Methylbutanal)	92.5	-51	48.5		109	123	107	154	172
α-Methylbutyraldehyde	92–93	20 trim.				120.5	103		

Table 1–1–B. Aldehydes, Liquid (Cont.)   315

Formaldehyde 40% solution in water ("Formalin")	98				181	167	169	189	171
Crotonaldehyde (2-Butenal)	102	–69	119	145	184	190	199	183	167
tert.-Butylacetaldehyde	103					147		104.5	
Acetal	103.6		52					104.5	113
n-Valeraldehyde (Pentanal)	104			56		98			
Dimethylacetaldehyde	104								
Formaldehyde trimethylene-acetal	105								
2-Butynal	104^{755}				113				
Ethoxyacetaldehyde	105					136			
2-Isopropylacrolein	107					116			
Acetaldehyde Trimethyleneacetal	109					165			
Methylisopropylacetaldehyde	114					124			
2-Ethylbutyraldehyde	117					94.5	97.5		
Methylpropylacetaldehyde	116^{737}					103	100		
2-Methyl-2-butenal	116						216	102	
n-Propoxyacetaldehyde	119^{748}								
Acrolein diethylacetal	123.5	12.6				86			
Isobutylacetaldehyde (Isocaproic aldehyde)	121^{743}					99	127		
Paraldehyde (see Acetaldehyde)	124								
Propionaldehyde diethylacetal	124								
2-Pentenal	125				123	102	180		
3-Methoxyisobutyraldehyde	129								
n-Caproic aldehyde (Hexanal)	131		51			104	106	108.5	
Ethylisopropylacetaldehyde	133.5					121			
3,3-Dimethylpentanal	134					102			
3-Methyl-2-butenal	135						223		
Cyclopentylaldehyde	136					182	124		
3-Ethyl-2-methylacrolein	137		48	58		159	207		
Tetrahydrofurfural	144^{740}						166		
5-Methylhexanal	144^{750}					134	117		
3-Furaldehyde	144^{732}			149.5		117	211		

Table 1–1–B. Aldehydes, Liquid (Cont.)

Table 1–1–B. (Cont.)

Name	B. Pt.	M. Pt.	Oxime	Phenyl Hydrazone	p-Nitrophenyl Hydrazone	2,4-Dinitrophenyl Hydrazone	Semicarbazone	Dimethone	Dimethone Anhydride
1-Cyclopentenylformaldehyde	146						208		
2-Hexenal	150				188		176		
3-Hexenal	150				139		147		
Enanthaldehyde (Heptanal)	155	-45	57		73	108	108	135	112
Ethylisobutylacetaldehyde	155						98		
Di-n-propylacetaldehyde	161						101		
Furfural	162	-36.5	75 α / 91 β	97	154	230	202	160 d.	162
Hexahydrobenzaldehyde	162		90			172	172.5		
2-Ethylhexanal-1	163					114	254 d.		
Glycolaldehyde diethylacetal	167								
n-Caprylaldehyde (Octanal)	167–170		60		80	106	98	90	101
Succinaldehyde (Butanedial)	169 d.		172 di-			280	153.5		
2-Ethyl-3-n-propylacrolein	173	-26				124			
Benzaldehyde	179			156	190 / 192	237 / 235	222	193	200
Pelargonaldehyde (Nonanal)	185		64		130	100	84	86	
5-Methylfurfural	187		112 syn- / 51 anti-	147		212	210		
Glutaraldehyde	187 d.		175 di-		169				
Phenylacetaldehyde (Phenylethanal)	193	33	98.5	58		121	153	165	126
Salicylaldehyde (2-Hydroxybenzaldehyde)	197	-7	57	142	227	252	231	172	208
3-Tolualdehyde (3-Methylbenzaldehyde)	198		60	91	157	212	204	167	206
2-Tolualdehyde (2-Methylbenzaldehyde)	200		49	101	222	193	209		215
4-Tolualdehyde (4-Methylbenzaldehyde)	204		79	112	200.5	232	234		
D-Citronellal	206		69			78	83	77	173
n-Decylaldehyde (Decanal;Caprylaldehyde)	207					104	102	92	
Phenoxyacetaldehyde	215 d.		95	86		149	145		
3,5-Dimethylbenzaldehyde	220–222	9					201		
Hydrocinnamaldehyde (3-Phenylpropionaldehyde)	224		93		122		127		
Citral-a (Geranial)	228 d.		143			108	164		
Citral-b (Nerol)	228 d.					96	171 (HCl)		

2,6-Dimethylbenzaldehyde	228^{742}	11					158		
3-Methoxybenzaldehyde (*m*-Anisaldehyde)	230	3	39	76	171		233 d.		
Cumaldehyde (4-Isopropylbenzaldehyde)	236	52 α		129	190	243	211	170	172
		111 β							
o-Methoxybenzaldehyde (*o*-Anisaldehyde)	243		92		204	253.5	215 d.		
3-Ethoxybenzaldehyde	245.5								
4-Methoxybenzaldehyde (*p*-Anisaldehyde)	248	2.5		120	160	253	210	144	243
o-Ethoxybenzaldehyde	247		57–59				219		
Cinnamaldehyde	252 d.	–7.5	64 α	168	195	255 d.	215	213	174
			138.5 β						
4-Ethoxybenzaldehyde	255	13–14					202 d.		
	249								
3.4-Diethoxybenzaldehyde	277		98					146–8	126
Diphenylacetaldehyde	315 d.		120 α				162		
			106 β						
2-Heptynal	54^{13}					74			
Cyclohexylacetaldehyde	58^{10}					125	159		
Hexadienal	65^{11}		160	102					
2-Methyl-4-methoxy-*p*-butyraldehyde	66^{55}					88			
3-Methyl-3-hydroxybutanal	67^{13}				142				
4-Hydroxybutanal	68^{8}					118			
Adipic dialdehyde	70^{3}		185 di-				206 d.		
β-Furylpropionaldehyde	70^{14}						80		
1-Cyclohexenealdehyde	70^{13}		99				213		
3,5-Dimethylhexahydrobenzaldehyde	71^{14}						171		
2-Ethyl-2-hexenal	73^{20}					125	152		
Nonanal (Pelargonic aldehyde)	78^{3}		63			106	100		
n-Octaldehyde	81^{32}		59		80		98		
Methyl-*n*-hexylacetaldehyde	83^{20}						80		
Aldol (2-Hydroxybutanal)	83^{20}		112 syn-		109		194	146	126
			51 anti-						

Table 1–1–B. Aldehydes, Liquid (Cont.)

Table 1–1–B. (Cont.)

Name	B. Pt.	M. Pt.	Oxime	Phenyl Hydrazone	p-Nitrophenyl Hydrazone	2,4-Dinitrophenyl Hydrazone	Semicarbazone	Dimethone	Dimethone Anhydride
Phenoxyacetaldehyde	83^{5}		95			138	146		
2-Ethyl-3-hexenal	84^{52}						156		
4-Octenal	84^{13}					108			
2-Isopropyl-3-hydroxypropionaldehyde	84^{10}								
2-Heptenal	85^{14}				116	126	169		
Methyl-n-butylglycolic aldehyde	87^{35}						143		
3-Phenyl-2-methylpropanal	90^{6}						123		
1,2,3,4-Tetrahydro-2-naphthaldehyde	$92^{0.5}$						197		
Vinylbenzaldehyde	93^{14}			131		100			
7-Methyloctanal	94^{120}						80		
2,4,6-Trimethylbenzaldehyde	98^{6}						188		
Methylphenylglycolic aldehyde	101^{4}						182		
Phenylglyoxal	108^{15}				309		208 d. mono- 229 d. bis-		
Ethylphenylglycolic aldehyde	110^{5}								
2,3,6-Trimethylbenzaldehyde	114^{10}		126				188		
2-Hydroxypropionaldehyde	114^{9}				127		169		
5-Hydroxymethyl-2-furfuraldehyde	$115^{0.5}$		108	140	183	184	114		
Phenylpropargyl aldehyde	116^{17}						194 d.		
Undecanal	120^{20}		72			104	103		
2-Methylcinnamaldehyde	124^{14}						208		
2-Nonenal	126^{21}				113	126	165		
2-(1-Naphthyl)-propionaldehyde	132^{2}						204		
4-Isopropylbenzaldehyde	135^{35}						211		
Tridecanal	136^{8}		80.5			108	106		
2-Phenoxybenzaldehyde	153^{1}						215		
2-n-Amylcinnamaldehyde	161^{19}		74				118		
1-Naphthaldehyde	162^{18}		98			164	219		
2,4,6-Trihydroxybenzaldehyde	d.		195 d.						

Table 1–2–A. Carbohydrates   319

TABLE 1–2–A. *Carbohydrates*

	M. Pt.	Rotation [α]D	T°C	g/100 ml water	Azoate	Phenyl Osazone	p-Nitrophenyl hydrazone
,3-Dihydroxyacetone	65 monom. 80 dim.					132	156
-Melibiose dihydrate (6-[α-D-Galactosido]-D-glucose)	82	+ 111.7 → + 129.5	20	4	280	176	
-Ribose	87	− 23.7	20	4		164	
Ribose	87	+ 20.3 → 20.7	20	4		166	
Desoxy-D-ribose	90	+ 2.88 → + 2.13	23				
ycollic aldehyde	95					179	
Fructose	102	− 132.2 → − 92.4	20	4	125	210	176
ctic aldehyde	105					154	128
L-Rhamnose (6-Desoxy-L-mannose)	105	− 8.6 → + 8.2	20	4		222	186
Altrose	105	− 32.3	20			165	
Altrose	105	+ 32.6	20	7.6		178	
D-Lyxose	106	+ 5.5 → − 14		8		164	172
affinose (2-[α-D-Galactosido)-α-D-glucoside]-β-D-fructose)	118 anh. 80 hydr.	+ 123 + 105.2	20	4	145		
-Rhamnose	122	+ 9.1	20			222	190
Tagatose	124	+ 1.0	22	1		196	
Threose	126	+ 29 → + 19.6	22			164	
-Allose	128	+ 0.58 → + 14.41	20	5		178	
-Allose	128	− 1.9	20			165	
Talose	128	+ 30 → + 20.6	21			201	
-Xylose	129					210	
-Mannose	133	+ 29.3 → + 14.2	20	4		210	194
-Mannose	132	− 17.0 → + 14.2 →	20	4		210	194
Mannose	132	+ 14.0 → − 14.0				208	
-Mannose	132					217	
-Mannoheptose	134	+ 85.05 → + 68.64	20	11		200	
-Glyceraldehyde, dim.	139					132	
sorhamnose (6-Desoxy-D-glucose)	139	+ 72.3 → 29.7	20	10		185	

	M. Pt.	Rotation [α]$_D$	Rotation T°C	Rotation g/100 ml water	Azoate	Phenyl Osazone	p-Nitro-phenyl hydrazone
α-L-Glucose	141	− 95.5 → − 51.4	20	4		208	
L-Xylose	144	− 79.3 → − 18.6	20	9.94		159	
α-D-Xylose	145	+ 93.6 → + 18.8	20	4	157	164	155
D-Fucose (6-Desoxy-D-galactose; D-Rhodeose)	145	+ 89.3 → + 75.7	22			177	
L-Fucose (6-Desoxy-L-galactose; L-Rhodeose)	145	− 152.6 → − 75.9	20	4		178	210
α-D-Glucose	146	+ 112.2 → + 52.7	20	4	266	210	188
2-Desoxy-D-glucose	148	+ 46.6	18				
β-D-Glucose	148	+ 18.7 → + 52.7	20	4		210	
Melezitose (2-[3-(α-D-Glucosido)-D-fructo-sido]-α-D-glucose)	153	+ 88.2	20	4	130		
Turanose (3-[α-D-Gluco-sido]-D-fructose)	157 anh. 60 hyd.	+ 27.3 → + 75.8	20	4		215	
β-D-Arabinose	159	− 175 → − 105		9.45		162	
β-L-Arabinose	160	+ 190.6 → + 104.5	20		262	166	186
β-D-Galacturonic acid	160	+ 55.3	20				
β-Maltose (4-[α-D-Gluco-sido]-β-D-glucose	160	+ 111.7 → + 130.4	20	4	275	205	
D,L-Fucose (6-Desoxy-D,L-galactose; D,L-Rhodeose)	161					187	
D,L-Sorbose	162					169	
L-Galactose	162	− 120 → − 73.6		10		192	
D,L-Galactose	163					206	
β-D-Glucuronic acid	163	+ 36.3	20				225
D,L-Arabinose	164					169	
L-Sorbose	165	− 43.7 → − 43.4	20	12		156	
D-Sorbose	165	+ 42.9	20	1		168	
3-(β-D-Galactosido)-D-arabinose	166	− 50.3 → + 63.1	19			242	
α-D-Galactose	167	+ 150.7 → + 80.2	20	5	276	196	154
Stachyose	167	+ 148	20				
Sucrose	169	+ 66.53	20	26	125		
D-Glucoheptulose	171	+ 67.4	20			209	
4-[β-D-Glucosido]-β-D-mannose	176	+ 15.1 → + 10.7	16			198	

Table 1–2–A. Carbohydrates (Cont.)   321

	M. Pt.	Rotation			Azoate	Phenyl Osazone	p-Nitro-phenyl hydrazone
		$[\alpha]_D$	T°C	g/100 ml water			
α-L-Rhamnohexose	180	− 80 → − 61.4	20	9.67		200	
L-Ascorbic acid	190	+ 49	18	methanol			262 di-
Gentiobiose (6-[β-D-Glu-cosido]-D-glucose)	190	+ 21.4 → + 8.7	20	5		163	
α-D-Glucoheptose	193	− 20	20			194	
α,α-Trehalose	210	+ 178.3	20	7	134		
Primeverose (6-[β-D-Xy-losido]-D-glucose)	210	+ 24.1 → − 3.3		2.5		220	
Lactose (4-[β-D-Galacto-sido]-D-glucose)	223						
α-form anh.		+ 90 → + 55.3					
	201 hyd.		20	4			
	252	+ 35 →					
β-form anh.		+ 55.3					
β-Cellobiose (4-[α-D-Glu-cosido]-β-D-glucose	225	+ 14.2 → + 34.6	20	8	273	208	
6-[β-Cellobiosido]-α-D-glucose	247	+ 15.0 → + 8.4				224	
6-[β-Lactosido]-α-D-glucose	257	+ 34.7 → + 22.6	24			233	
Starch	d.						
D,L-Methyltetrose						140	
Apiose		+ 3.8	20	3.4		156	
D,L-Gulose						157	
L-Erythrose		+ 11.5 → + 15.2 → + 30.5	24	3		164	
D-Erythrose		− 14.5	20	11		164	
D,L-Erythrose						164	
D,L-Erythrulose						164	
L-Erythrulose		+ 12	20			164	
L-Idose		+ 52.7	20	6.2		160	
D-Gulose		− 20.4 → + 61.6	20			160	
β-Methylglyceraldehyde						171	
L-Methyltetrose		− 30.5 → − 16.5	20	9.47 96% ethanol		172	
D-Rhamnose (6-Desoxy-D-mannose)		− 8.25	16.5	10		185	
D,L-Xylulose (D,L-Xylo-ketose)						210	

Table 1–3–A. Acids, Solid

TABLE 1–3–A. *Acids, Solid*

	M. Pt.	B. Pt.	Neutral Equivalent	Amide	Anilide	p-Toluidide	p-Nitrobenzyl ester	p-Bromophenacyl ester	p-Phenylphenacyl ester
Methyl hydrogen adipate	9	178^{30}	160	78.5	58.5	107		113	145
D,L-Lactic acid	17	112^{12}	90	80				91	
trans(α)-Methyl-β-ethyl-acrylic acid	24	275		87					
Undecylenic acid	24	300 d.	184						
o-Ethoxybenzoic acid	24.5–25.5		166	132				68	80
Undecanoic acid	28.5	280	186	103	71	80			
Ethyl hydrogen adipate	28		174						
Hexahydrobenzoic acid	30	233	128	185	146				
α-Ketobutyric acid	31	78^{25}		117					
n-Caproic acid (Decanoic acid)	31.5	268–270	172	108	70	78		67	
2-Hexenoic acid	32				110				
Methyl-n-butylglycolic acid	33			58				62.5	76
Erucic acid (cis-13-Docosenoic acid)	33	264^{15}	338	84	55	75		84	113
Levulinic acid	33	245	116	107 d.	102	108	61	75	73
Pivalic acid (Trimethylacetic acid)	35.5	163	102	155		119			
α-Methylhydrocinnamic acid	36.5	272	164	109	132	130			
1-Cyclohexenylcarboxylic acid	38	107^{3}		128					
Methyl-n-hexylglycolic acid	40	250^{280}		59					
5-Aceto-n-valeric acid	40								
D,L-Campholytic acid	40.5	162^{45}		103					
α-Phenylbutyric acid (D,L-α-Ethyl-phenyl acetic acid)	42	270	164	85	145				
α-Ethylpimelic acid	43	223^{17}							
Lauric acid	42	299	200	102	78	87		76	86
Tridecylic acid (Tridecanoic)	44	312	214	100	80	88		75	87
Elaidic acid	44	234^{15}	282	93				65	73
Dimethylneopentylacetic acid	45	230^{732}		71					

Table 1–3–A. Acids, Solid (Cont.)   323

Angelic acid (*trans*-2-Methyl-2-butanoic acid)	45	185	100	127	126	135	36	104	95
tert.-Butylpropiolic acid	48	110^{10}							
Hydrocinnamic acid	48	279	150	105	98				
Benzylpyruvic acid	49			180					
2-Pentynoic acid	50	100^{10}		146					
γ-Phenylbutyric acid	52	290		84					
n-Pentadecylic acid (Pentadecanoic acid)	52	212^{16}	242	102	78		40	77	92
β-Campholenic acid	53.5	245		86					
Myristic acid (Tetradecanoic)	54	202^{16}	228	103	84	93		81	90
Dimethyl oxalate	54	167^{78}	118		246	268			
Acetyllactic acid	57								
β-Acetoglutaric acid	58			141 mono-	219 di-				
sec.-*n*-Amylmalonic acid	58								
trans-Brassidic acid	60	256^{10}	338	94	78			94	86
5-Phenylpentanoic acid	60			109					
β-Cyclohexylacrylic acid	60	154^{11}		159	90				
D-Hydnocarpic	60.5		252	112					
n-Heptadecanoic acid (Margaric acid)	61	231^{16}	270	108	91	98	49	83	96
Palmitic acid (Hexadecanoic acid)	63	222^{16}		106	77	70	42.5	86	94
Tiglic Acid	64.5	198.5	100	75			64	68	
Benzoylformic acid	66			91	89				
Acetoxyacetic acid	66	145^{12}							
3,3-Dimethylacrylic acid	67			108	85				
2-Furylacetic acid	67	106^{20}							
3,3,4,4-Tetramethylpentanoic acid	67			138					
1-Cyclohexanone-4-carboxylic acid	67								
D,L-2-Phenyllactic acid	94			101					
D-Chaulmoogric acid	68.5	247^{20}	280	106	89	100			
Stearic acid (Octadecanoic acid)	70		284	109	95.5	102	67	92	
trans(α)-Crotonic acid	72	189	86	159	118	132		95	97

21*

Table 1–3–A. (Cont.)

	M. Pt.	B. Pt.	Neutral Equivalent	Amide	Anilide	p-Toluidide	p-Nitrobenzyl ester	p-Bromophenacyl ester	p-Phenylphenacyl ester
Caproylacetic acid	74 d.			100					
1-Cyclohexanone-3-carboxylic acid	75	195^{20}							
sec.-Butylmalonic acid	76			242 di-					
Phenylacetic acid	76.5	256.5	136	156	117	135	65	89	63 d.
Arachidic acid (Eicosanic acid)	77	204^{1}		108	92	96		89	86
Glycolic acid (Hydroxyacetic acid)	78		76	120	97	143	107	138	
α-Hydroxyisobutyric acid	79	212	104			132	80.5	98	
α-Methylcinnamic acid	81			128	136				
1-Cyclohexanone-2-carboxylic acid	81				101				
n-Docosanoic acid (Behenic acid)	81			111					
2-Benzoylpropionic acid	82			145	137				
Lignoceric acid (Tetracosanoic acid)	84	222^{18}						91	
β-Methyladipic acid	85			148	200				
α-Benzoylbutyric acid	85								
p-Methoxyphenylacetic acid	87			189					
Dineopentylacetic acid	88			140					
Dibenzylacetic acid	89		240	128	155	175			
o-Tolylacetic acid	90			161					
Citraconic acid	92 d.		65	185 di-	175.5 di-	170 mono-	71 di-		
Phenyl-n-propylglycolic acid	94			132					
o-Benzoylbenzoic acid	94		244						
p-Tolylacetic acid	95	159^{15}		185					
n-Heptylmalonic acid	96.5		202	112					
3-Phenyl-2-hydroxypropionic acid	97			139					
1,2,3,4-Tetrahydro-2-naphthoic acid	97								
Glutaric acid	98	302–304	66	175 di-	223 di-	218 di-	69 di-	137 di-	152
3-Phenoxypropionic acid	98			119					
α-Crotonic acid	99	212		112	99				
Phenoxyacetic acid	98	285 d.	152	101.5				148.5	

Table 1–3–A. Acids, Solid (Cont.)   325

Acid	m.p.								
2-Benzofurylacetic acid	99			164					
α-Naphthylglycolic acid	99			135					
Citric acid, monohyd.	100		70	210 tri-	192 tri-	189 tri-	102 tri-	148 tri-	146
o-Methoxybenzoic acid (o-Anisic acid)	100		152	129				113	131
l-Malic acid	100		67	156 di-	197 di-	206 di-		179 di-	
Oxalic acid, dihyd.	101		63	219 mono- / 419 d.di- / 131 d.	148 mono- / 254 di-	169 mono- / 268 di-	87 mono- / 124.5 di-		166 d.
Acetopyruvic acid	101								
n-Butylmalonic acid	101			200 di-	193 di-		204 di-		
Aleuritic acid	102								
Benzylacetic acid	103	223^{15}		113	107				
Pimelic acid	104		80	175 di-	108 mono- / 155 di-	206 di-		137 di-	
o-Toluic acid (o-Methylbenzoic acid)	104	259^{751}	136	143	125	144	91	57	94.5
Allylmalonic acid	105				91		46		
D-Campholic acid	106	255		80					
Atropic acid	106			121					
L-Campholic acid	106	250		78	134				
Azelaic acid	107	237^{15}	94	93 mono- / 175 di- / 116	107 mono- / 186 di-	201 di-	44 di-	131 di-	141
Methylneopentylglycolic acid	109								
m-Methoxybenzoic acid (m-Anisic acid)	109								
Dehydroacetic acid	109	270	168		115				
trans-4-Methylcyclohexane-carboxylic acid	111			226					
Ethylmalonic acid	111		136	214 di-	150	118	75		
m-Toluic acid (m-Methylbenzoic acid)	111	263		94	126		87	108	136.5
o-Benzoyllactic acid	112			124					
2,4,6-Triethylbenzoic acid	113			156					
o-Phenoylbenzoic acid	113			177					
α-Naphthylglycolic acid	113			151					

Table 1–3–A. (Cont.)

	M. Pt.	B. Pt.	Neutral Equivalent	Amide	Anilide	p-Toluidide	p-Nitrobenzyl ester	p-Bromophenacyl ester	p-Phenylphenacyl ester
o-Acetobenzoic acid	114			116.5	159 mono- 200 di-				
Pyrotartaric acid	115			225 di-					
2-Phenoxypropionic acid	115			132	117	115			
3-Benzoylpropionic acid	116			145	150				
Benzylmalonic acid	117 d.			225	217 di-		119.5 di-		
D,L-Tropic acid	117		166	169					
Cuminic acid (p-Isopropylbenzoic acid)	117			133					
D,L-Mandelic acid	118		152	133	151	172	123		
L-Arabonic acid	118			136	204	200			
D,L-Citramalic acid	119			140 mono-					
3-Furoic acid	121			169	126	122			
1-Cyclopentenylcarboxylic acid	121								
Cetylmalonic acid	121.5			130 d. mono- 226					
cis-1,3-Cyclopentanedicarboxylic acid	122			231 di-	165 di-				
D,L-trans-Camphenic acid	122								
Benzoic acid	122	249	122	130	160	158	89	119	167
Diethylmalonic acid	125			146 mono- 224 di-			91 di-		
1,14-Tetradecanedicarboxylic acid	126			179	163				
2,4-Dimethylbenzoic acid, anh.	127			179	141				
2-Benzoylbenzoic acid	128		226	165	195				
1,10-Decanedicarboxylic acid	128			185			100		
Maleic acid	130		58	172 mono- 260 di-	198 mono- 187 di-	142 di-	91 di-	168	168
α-Naphthylacetic acid	131		186	180	155				
2,5-Dimethylbenzoic acid	132			186	140				
trans-Cinnamic acid	133	300	148	147	153	168	117	146	182

Table 1–3–A. Acids, Solid (Cont.)   327

Sebacic acid	133	243^{15}		170 mono- / 210 di-	122 mono- / 201 di-	201 di-	73.5 di-	147 di-	140
2-Furoic acid (Pyromucic acid)	133	230	112	142	123.5	170.5	133.5	138.5	
Malonic acid	135		52	106 mono- / 170 di-	132 mono- / 230 di-	156 d. mono- / 252 di-	85.5 di-		175
Acetylsalicylic acid	135	140 d.	180	138	136		90.5		
β-Campholytic acid	135	247	73	130	104	114			
Acetone-1,3-dicarboxylic acid	135 d.								
D,L-*cis*-Camphenic acid	135		146	225 di-	212 di-	142	83		
Phenylpropiolic acid	137			99	128				
Glutaconic acid	137			167 mono- / 228 di-					
m-Ethoxybenzoic acid	137		166	139					
Methylmalonic acid	137		217	145 d. mono- / 228 di-					
cis-Cyclobutane-1,2-dicarboxylic acid	138			228 di-					
Anhydrocamphoronic acid	139				202				
Butane-1,1,4-Tricarboxylic acid	139				177				
meso-Tartaric acid	140		75	187 di-	193 mono-	93			
Furanacrylic acid	141		138	168					
β-Naphthylacetic acid	141	286	186	200					
Suberic acid (Octanedioic acid)	144		87	125 mono- / 216 di-	128 mono- / 186 di-	218 di-	85 di-	144 di-	151 di-
Asaronic acid	144			184.5	154.5				
Phthalonic	146			179 d. α / 155 d. β / 118	176 mono- / 208 di-				
2-Hydroxyphenylacetic acid	147			167.5	180	172			
Diphenylacetic acid	148		212	135 mono-	118 mono- / 152 di-	148 mono-			111
Diglycolic acid	148		67						
4-Hydroxyphenylacetic acid	148		142	175	174	189	99.5	152	122
Benzilic acid	150	228		153					

Table 1–3–A. (Cont.)

	M. Pt.	B. Pt.	Neutral Equivalent	Amide	Anilide	p-Toluidide	p-Nitrobenzyl ester	p-Bromophenacyl ester	p-Phenylphenacyl ester
Citric acid, anh.	153		64	210 d. tri- / 233	192 tri-	189 tri-	102 tri-	148 tri-	146
Phenylmalonic acid	153								148
Adipic acid	153	216^{15}	73	125 mono- / 220 di-	151 mono- / 240 di-	241	106	154.5	
Phenylpyruvic acid	154								
2,4,6-Trimethylbenzoic acid	155			188					
3-(1-Naphthyl)-propionic acid	156			104					
Tartronic acid	156 d.		60	198 di- / 138 d.					
Benzoylpyruvic	156 d.								
Cyclobutane-1,1-dicarboxylic acid	157			275 di-	214 di-				
Salicylic acid	158		138	142	136	156	98	140	148
1-Naphthoic acid	161		172	202	162			135.5	
2-Benzofurylacetic acid	163			210					
Itaconic acid	165		65	191 di-	151.5 mono-		91 di-	117 di-	
3,4-Dimethylbenzoic acid (Mesitylenic acid)	166			130	104				
Tricarballylic acid	166		58.7	205 tri-	252 tri-			138 tri-	
D,L-Phenylsuccinic acid	167		97	158 mono-α / 145 mono-β / 211 di- / 133	175 mono-α / 171 mono-β / 222 di-	175 mono-α / 168 mono-β			
Mesitylacetic acid	168								
D-Tartaric acid	169		75	171 mono- / 196 d. di- / 149 / 190 d.	180 d. mono- / 263 d. di-		163 di-	204 di-	203 d.
2,2-Diphenylpropionic acid	171								
3-Aldehydobenzoic acid	175								
Apiolic acid	175								
Allomucic acid	176 d.			175 mono- / 176					
3-Phenanthrylacetic acid	178								
Acetylenedicarboxylic acid	179			294 d. di-					

Table 1–3–A. Acids, Solid (Cont.) 329

Acid	M.P.								
p-Toluic acid	179	275	136	160	144	160	104	153	165
Veratric acid, anh.	181			164	154				
2-Naphthoic acid	184		172	192	171	192	132	152	160
p-Anisic acid (p-Methoxybenzoic acid)	184	275	152	167 228	169	186			
o-Carboxyphenylacetic acid	185								208
Succinic acid	185	235 d.	59	157 mono- 206 d. di- 236	148.5 mono- 230 di- 250	179 mono- 255 di-	88 di-	211 di-	
Coumarin-3-carboxylic acid	187 d.								
D-Camphoric acid	187.5		100	176 mono-α 182 mono-β 192 di-	204 mono-α 196 mono-β 226 di-	212 α 190 β	65.5		
Butane-1,2,3,4-tetracarboxylic acid	189			181 d. di-	187				
Hemimellitic acid	190 d.		70						
Anthroxanic acid	190			211					
α-Chrysenic acid	190			169					
L-Ascorbic acid	190 d.								
Salicyl-o-acetic acid (o-Carboxyphenoxyacetic acid)	191		98						
Coumarilic acid	192	310		159	159				
Dimethylmalonic acid	193		58	269 di-			84		
trans-Aconitic acid	194			250 tri- 189 di-	189 di-			186 tri-	
Benzylidenemalonic acid	195								
4-Ethoxybenzoic acid	198		166	202	169				
Chrysodiphenic acid	199			275 1-mono- 220 2'-mono-					
3,4-Dihydroxybenzoic acid (Protocatechuic acid)	199		154	212	166		188		
3-Hydroxybenzoic acid	200		138	170	156	163	106	176	
o-Phthalic acid	200 sealed tube		83	149 mono- 220 di-	150 mono- 253 di-	150 mono- 201 di-	155.5 di-	153 di-	167
D,L-Tartaric acid	203		75 anh. 84 mono-hyd.	226 di-	235 di-		148 di-		

Table 1–3–A. (Cont.)

	M. Pt.	B. Pt.	Neutral Equivalent	Amide	Anilide	p-Toluidide	p-Nitrobenzyl ester	p-Bromophenacyl ester	p-Phenylphenacyl ester
cis-Apocamphoric acid	204					212 mono-			
Mesaconic acid (Methylfumaric acid)	204.5		65	222 mono-α 174 mono-β 176.5 di-	202 mono-α 163 mono-β 186 di-	196 mono-α 212 di-	134 di-		
meso-Anthroic acid (Anthracene-9-carboxylic acid)	207								
Vanillic acid	207			209 d.			140 d.		
trans-o-Coumaric acid	207		164	206			152.5		
Pentamethylbenzoic acid	210			194					
p-Coumaric acid	210								
2,4-Dihydroxybenzoic acid (β-Resorcyclic acid)	213 d.		154	222	126		188		
4-Dibenzofurylacetic acid	214			212					
Mucic acid	214 d.			192 d. mono- 220 di-			310	225	149.5 d.
4-Hydroxybenzoic acid	215		138	162	196	203	180	191.5	240
Acenaphthene-5-carboxylic acid	219			198					
4-Phenylbenzoic acid	221			223					
2-Hydroxy-3-naphthoic acid	222		188	217	243	221			
4-Hydroxy-2-naphthoic acid	225			217		206			
9-Fluorenecarboxylic acid	227			251					
2,2′-Diphenic acid	227		121	193 mono- 212 di-	176 mono- 229 di-		187 di-		
Piperonylic acid	228		166	169					
Trimellitic acid	228		70						
1-Phenanthroic acid	232			284					
Benzophenone-2,4-dicarboxylic acid	235			>288 d.					
Benzene-1,2,3,4-tetracarboxylic acid	236		63.5		168 di-				

Table 1–3–A. Acids, Solid (Cont.)   331

Anthracene-1-carboxylic acid (α-Anthroic acid)	245						
9-Phenanthroic acid	251		260				
Benzene-1,2,3,5-Tetracarboxylic acid	253	63.5	233				
Gallic acid	253 d.		189	207	141	134	160
1-Acenaphthoic acid	256		228				
2-Phenanthroic acid	260		243				
Chelidonic acid	262		245				195 d.
3-Phenanthroic acid	270		234				
Pyromellitic acid	275	63.5					
Naphthelic acid	274						
Anthracene-2-carboxylic acid	281		293				
Fumaric acid	286 sealed tube	58	270	233 mono- 313 di-	151		
Muconic acid	289 d.		240 d. di-				
Anthraquinone-2-carboxylic acid	290		280	258			
9-10-Anthraquinone-1-carboxylic acid	293		280	288			
Terephthalic acid	300 sublimes	83	>225 di-	334 di-	264 di-	225 di-	
9,10-Anthraquinone-2,3-dicarboxylic acid	240–242		>340 mono-				
Isophthalic acid	348 sublimes	83	280		202.5	179	
Benzophenone-4,4'-dicarboxylic acid	<360		>300 di-				
Trimesic acid	380	70	365 d.	118 d. tri-		197 tri-sealed tube	

TABLE 1–3–B. *Acids, Liquid*

	B. Pt.	M. Pt.	Neutral Equivalent	Amide	Anilide	p-Toluidide	p-Nitrobenzyl ester	p-Bromophenacyl ester	p-Phenylphenacyl ester
Formic acid	101	8.4	46		50	53	31	140	74
Acetic acid	118	16.6	60	82	114	153	78	86	110
Acrylic acid	141	13	72	84	104	141	31	63	103
Propionic acid	141	−20.8	74	81	106	126			
Propiolic acid	144 d.	18		61	87				
Isobutyric acid	155	−46.1	88	128	105	108.5		77	89
Methacrylic acid	161	16		102					
n-Butyric acid (Butanoic acid)	162.5	−5.5	88	115	96	75	35	63	82
Vinylacetic acid	169	−35	86	73	58				
Pyruvic acid	165 d.	13.6	88	124	104	109		81	
Isocrotonic acid	169	15	86	101	101	132		68	78
Isovaleric acid	176.5	−30	102	135	109.5	106		55	71
D,L-2-Methyl-1-butanoic acid	176		102	112	110	92.5			
n-Amylpropiolic acid	180 d.	2.5	116	91		68			
3,3-Dimethylbutanoic acid	184	6.7		132	132	134			
Cyclopropanecarboxylic acid	186	17		125					
n-Valeric acid	186	−34.5	102	106	63	74		75	64
2,2-Dimethyl-1-butanoic acid	187	−15	116	103	92	83			86
Allylacetic acid	188			94					
Cyclopropylacetic acid	190^{750}	−1.5	116	132	78	113			74
D,L-2,3-Dimethylbutanoic acid	192			152					
Cyclobutanecarboxylic acid	195	−31.8	116	112	127.5	116			77
2-Ethyl-1-butanoic acid	195		116	80	95	81			64
D,L-2-Methylpentanoic acid	195		116		87	75			47
D,L-3-Methyl-1-pentanoic acid	197.5	−41.6		125					
4-Methylpentanoic acid (Isocaproic acid)	199^{752}	−33	116	120	112	63		77	70

Table 1–3–B. Acids, Liquid (Cont.)   333

Methoxyacetic acid	204			97	58	74	72	65
2-Methyl-2-ethylbutanoic acid	204		90	78	94	32	105	
n-Caproic acid (Hexanoic acid)	205.4	−3.9	116	100	95			
Ethoxyacetic acid	206–207		104	80	75			
5-Methyl-1-hexanoic acid	207^{752}			103	94			
2-Ethyl-1-pentanoic acid	209		130	104	98			
2-Methylhexanoic acid	209.6		130	73	76.5	129		
4-Methyl-1-hexanoic acid	$217–218^{754}$		130	98		85		
2,2-Dimethyl-1-hexanoic acid	218			89				
4-Methyl-4-ethylbutyric acid	221							
Heptanoic acid	223	−7.5	130	96	70	81	72	62
2-Ethyl-1-hexanoic acid	228		144	102				54
Cyclohexylacetic acid	237		128	172				
n-Caprylic acid (Octanoic acid)	237	16.3	144	110	57	70	67	67
Pelargonic acid (Nonanoic acid)	254.4	12.3	158	99	57	84	68.5	71
D-Citronellic acid	257			84				
2-Phenylpropionic acid	265			92				
4-Acetobutyric acid	275 d.	13–14		114		123		
2-Methoxypropionic acid	89^{10}			81				
2,3-Dimethylpentanoic acid	92^{15}			102				
Allylacetic acid	92^{18}			94				
3,4,4-Trimethylpentanoic acid	98^{4}			167				
3-Heptynoic acid	102^{2}			67				
2-Isopropylbutanoic acid	105^{15}	14		135				
7-Methyloctanoic acid	105^{2}			106				
2-Methylcyclopentanecarboxylic acid	107^{9}			148				
Methylneopentylacetic acid	108^{14}			123				
3-Methylhexanoic acid	112^{16}			98				
2-Ethyl-4-methylpentanoic acid	115^{20}			89				
L-Citronellic acid	$118^{0.6}$			84	76	93		
3-Ethoxypropionic acid	120^{17}			51				

Table 1–3–B. (Cont.)

	B. Pt.	M. Pt.	Neutral, Equivalent	Amide	Anilide	p-Toluidide	p-Nitro-benzyl ester	p-Bromo-phenacyl ester	p-Phenyl-phenacyl ester
D,L-Lactic acid	122^{15}	18		78.5	58.5	107		112.8	145
5-Cyclopentylpentanoic acid	$123^{4.5}$			136					
Cyclopentanecarboxylic acid	123^{7}			179					
cis-4-Methylcyclohexanecarboxylic acid	130^{13}			175					
2-Ethyl-3-hexanoic acid	132^{19}			80					
2-Octynoic acid	133^{10}			90		60			
n-Butylpropionic acid	135^{20}			68					
6-Methyloctanoic acid	149^{23}			91					
4-Phenoxybutyric acid	197^{18}			80					
Oleic acid	216^{5}	13.5	282	75	41	42.5		40	61

TABLE 1–4–A. *Phenols, Solid*

	B. Pt.	M. Pt.	Phenyl Urethan	α-Naphthyl Urethan	p-Nitro-benzoate	3,5-Dinitro-benzoate	Aryl-oxyacetic acid	2,4-Dinitro-phenyl ether
4-Propylphenol	232	22	129					
4-n-Butylphenol	248	22	115			67	81	
4-n-Amylphenol	248	23					90	
2,4-Dimethylphenol	211.5	27	103	135	102	165		
2-Ethoxyphenol	217	28						
2-Acetylphenol	215	28						
2-Methylphenol (o-Cresol)	191	31	141	141	94	138	121	90
2-Methoxyphenol (Guaiacol)	205	32	136	118	93	141		97
4-Methylphenol (p-Cresol)	202	36	115	146	98	189	135	93

Table 1–4–A. Phenols, Solid (Cont.)

2-Benzoylphenol		41			124			69
Phenol	182	42	126	132	127	146	89	
Phenyl salicylate (Salol)	173[12]	42, 39, 28.5 (three forms)	111		111			67
4-Ethylphenol	219	47	120	128	80	132	97	
2,6-Dimethylphenol	203	49	133	176.5	70	159	139.5	
Thymol	233	50	107	160		103	149	
2-Benzylphenol	312	54	117.5					
4-Methoxyphenol	243	56					110	
2-Phenylphenol	275	56						
n-Caproylresorcinol		56						
2-Cyclohexylphenol		57						
3,5-Dihydroxytoluene (Orcinol)	343 d.	58 hyd. / 107 anh.			89			
3,4-Dihydroxy-1-propylbenzene (4-Propylcatechol)	175	60						
4-sec.-Butylphenol	240	61						
3,4-Dimethylphenol	225	62.5	120	141		182	162.5	
1-Aceto-2-naphthol		64						
3,4-Dihydroxytoluene	252	65	166 bis-				58 di-	
4-n-Hexylresorcinol	333 d.	68						
3,5-Dimethylphenol	219.5	68	148				111	
2,3-Dihydroxytoluene		68				195		
2,4,6-Trimethylphenol (Mesitol)	220	70	141				139.5	
Methyl-3-hydroxybenzoate	280	70	115					
2,3-Dihydroxy-1-propylbenzene		70						
2,4,5-Trimethylphenol (Pseudocumenol)	232	71	110				132	
4,5-Dihydroxy-m-xylene		73						
Ethyl-3-hydroxybenzoate	295	74						
2,5-Dimethylphenol		75			87	137	118	
2,3-Dimethylphenol	212	75	160	172			187	

Table 1–4–A. (Cont.)

	B. Pt.	M. Pt.	Phenyl Urethan	α-Naphthyl Urethan	p-Nitrobenzoate	3,5-Dinitrobenzoate	Aryloxyacetic acid	2,4-Dinitrophenyl ether
3-Phenylphenol	>300	78						
2,3,4,6-Tetramethylphenol (Isodurenol)	230	79	178				187	131
4-Hydroxy-3-methoxybenzaldehyde (Vanillin)	285	81						
3,5-Dihydroxy-1-propylbenzene		84						
p-Benzylphenol	321	84					120	
2-Hydroxybenzyl alcohol (Saligenin)		86						
4,5-Dimethylcatechol		87						
2,5-Dihydroxy-1-propylbenzene		90						
4-tert.-Amylphenol	260	92	108	152	143	217	193.5	128
1-Naphthol (α-Naphthol)	278	94	177					
2,2′-Stilbenediol		95 α / 197 β	268					
2-Naphthylsalicylate (Betol)		95.5						
4-Acetylphenol	296	96	148.5	110			86.5	
4-tert.-Butylphenol	237	100						
2-Aceto-1-naphthol	325	102						
3,3′-Dihydroxydiphenylmethane		103						
3-Hydroxybenzaldehyde	240	104					148	
2,4-Dihydroxytoluene	267	104						
1,2-Dihydroxybenzene (Pyrocatechol)	246	105	169 bis-	160	169 di-	152 di-	217	
3,5-Dihydroxytoluene (Orcinol)	287	107 anh.	154		214	190	104	
1,2-Dihydroxynaphthalene		108						
4-Acetylphenol		109						
2,2′-Biphenol	326	110	145 bis-					
Resorcinol (1,3-Dihydroxybenzene)	276	110	164 bis-		182 bis-	201 bis-	195	194
2,2′-Dihydroxy-3,3′-dimethylbiphenyl		113						
4,4′-Dihydroxy-2,2′-dimethylbiphenyl		114						
4-Hydroxy-3-methoxybenzyl alcohol		115						
Ethyl-4-hydroxybenzoate	297	115						

Table 1–4–A. Phenols, Solid (Cont.)   337

Compound								
3-Benzoylphenol		116						
4-Hydroxybenzaldehyde	271	116						
2,6-Dihydroxytoluene		117					198	
Phloroglucinol		117		283				
2,4'-Dihydroxydiphenylmethane		117						
2,3,5,6-Tetramethylphenol	249	118						
2,6-Dihydroxytoluene	264	119						
3,4,5-Trihydroxytoluene		120						
2,2'-Dihydroxy-4,4'-dimethylbiphenyl		120						
2-Naphthol (β-Naphthol)	286	123	155	156	169	210	154	95
3,3'-Biphenol		123					153	
1,3-Dihydroxynaphthalene		124						
2,5-Dihydroxytoluene		124						
4,6-Dihydroxy-m-xylene		125	134					
Methyl-4-hydroxybenzoate		131						
2,4,5-Trihydroxytoluene		131						
4-Cyclohexylphenol		132			137	168		
Pyrogallol	309	133	173 tri-		230 tri-	205 tri-	198	
4-Hydroxybenzophenone		135						
4,5-Dimethylresorcinol		136 anh.						
1,6-Dihydroxynaphthalene		137						
1,2,4-Trihydroxybenzene		140.5						
1,8-Dihydroxynaphthalene		142						
3,4-Dihydroxyphenanthrene (Morphol)		143						
3,4-Dihydroxybiphenyl		145						
Resacetophenone		147						
p-Hydroxypropiophenone		148						
9,10-Dihydroxyphenanthrene		148						
3,4,5-Trihydroxyphenanthrene		148						
2,4-Dihydroxy-m-xylene		149						
2,5-Dihydroxy-m-xylene		149						
2,2'-Dihydroxy-5,5'-dimethylbiphenyl		153						

Table 1–4–A. (Cont.)

	B. Pt.	M. Pt.	Phenyl Urethan	α-Naphthyl Urethan	p-Nitrobenzoate	3,5-Dinitrobenzoate	Aryloxyacetic acid	2,4-Dinitrophenyl ether
3,5-Stilbenediol		155.5						
4,4'-Dihydroxy-3,3'-dimethylbiphenyl		160						
2,3-Dihydroxynaphthalene		160						
1,2-Dihydroxyanthracene		161						
4,4'-Dihydroxytriphenylmethane		161						
2,4'-Biphenol		162						
2,6-p-Toluenediol		163						
2,2'-Dihydroxy-6,6'-dimethylbiphenyl		164					118	
4-Phenylphenol		165	167.5					
1,4-Dihydroxy-2-methylnaphthalene		170 α						
		60 β						
Hydroquinone	286	171	224 di- 205 bis-		258 di-	317 bis-	250	
2,3,4-Trihydroxyacetophenone		173						
1,4-Dihydroxynaphthalene		176						
1,7-Dihydroxynaphthalene		178						
1,2-Dihydroxyphenanthrene		178						
2,5-Dihydroxyphenanthrene		180						
9,10-Dihydroxyanthracene		180						
1,9-Dihydroxyphenanthrene		184					149	
2,7-Dihydroxynaphthalene		185						
2,7-Dihydroxynaphthalene		190						
5,6-Dihydroxyacenaphthene		196						
Methylenedi-2-naphthol		200						
Methyl gallate		200						
2,8-Dihydroxyphenanthrene		202						
1,2-Dihydroxyacenaphthene		212 cis-						
		159 trans-						
2,4,6-Trihydroxytoluene		214						

Table 1–4–A. Phenols, Solid (Cont.) 339

Compound	m.p.			
2,6-Dihydroxynaphthalene	215			
2,5-Dihydroxy-p-xylene (Hydrophlorone)	217			
Phloroglucinol	217	190 tri-		
2,2'-Dihydroxy-1,1'-binaphthyl	218			
1,1'-Dihydroxy-2,2'-binaphthyl	220			
3,5-Dihydroxypyrene	220 d.			
3,6-Dihydroxyphenanthrene	221			
3,6-Dihydroxy-o-xylene	221			
1,8-Dihydroxyanthracene (Chrysazol)	225			
5,5'-Dihydroxy-2,2'-dimethylbiphenyl	229			
2,6-Dihydroxyphenanthrene	234			
1,6-Dihydroxypyrene	240 d.			
3,8-Dihydroxyphenanthrene	247			
1,5-Dihydroxynaphthalene	265			
2,7-Dihydroxyphenanthrene	265			
Phenolphthalein	265	135 bis-		
1,5-Dihydroxyanthracene	265 d.			
4,4'-Biphenol	274			
2,7-Dihydroxyanthracene	280			
2,3-Dihydroxyanthracene	282 d.			
4,4'-Dihydroxystilbene	284			
5,7,4'-Trihydroxy-3,5'-dimethoxyflavenol	288			
2,6-Dihydroxyanthracene (Flavol)	295			
Bi-α-naphthol	300		283	
3,8-Dihydroxypyrene	330			162 tri-

Table 1–4–B. Phenols, Liquid

TABLE 1–4–B. *Phenols, Liquid*

	B. Pt.	M. Pt.	Phenyl Urethan	α-Naphthyl Urethan	p-Nitrobenzoate	3,5-Dinitrobenzoate	Aryloxyacetic acid	2,4-Dinitrophenyl ether
2-Hydroxybenzaldehyde (Salicylaldehyde)	197		133	127	128			
3-Methylphenol (*m*-Cresol)	203	12	125		90	165	103	74
2-Ethylphenol	207		143		56	108	141	
3-Ethylphenol	217		137		68		77	
Methyl salicylate (Methyl-*o*-hydroxybenzoate)	224		117		128			
p-Propylphenol	232		129					
Ethyl salicylate (Ethyl-*o*-hydroxybenzoate)	234		98		107			
4-Isobutylphenol	236						124	
Carvacrol	238	1	134	116	51	83	151	
Isopropylsalicylate	240							
3-Methoxyphenol	243			128			118	
3-Ethoxyphenol	246							
Eugenol	255	16	95.5	122	81	131	81	115
Isobutylsalicylate	260							
2-Methoxy-4-propenylphenol (Isoeugenol)	267.5		118 *cis*-	149	109	158	94	130
n-Butylsalicylate	270							
Isoamylsalicylate	276							
3-Acetoxyphenol	283							

Table 1–5–A. Esters, Solid 341

TABLE 1–5–A. *Esters, Solid*

	M. Pt.	B. Pt.	Saponification Equivalent	n_D^{20}	D_4^{20}
Diethyl fumarate	0.2	218.4	86	1.44103	
Diethyl sebacate	1.3	307	129	1.43657	0.9631 D_4^{15}
Ethyl cinnamate	6.5	271	176	1.55982	1.0490
Ethyl-*p*-methoxybenzoate	7	269	180	1.5254	1.1038
Dimethyl maleate	7.6	204.5	72	1.44156	1.14513 D_4^{15}
Dimethyl adipate	8.5	107.5	87	1.42835	1.0625
Diethyl isophthalate	11.5	286^{733}	111		
Ethyl myristate	12	295	256	1.4362	0.8573 D_4^{25}
m-Tolyl acetate	12	212	150	1.4978	1.043 D^{26}
Ethyl-β-[α-furyl] acrylate	14	232	166		
Methyl pentadecylate	15.5		256	1.4390	0.8618 D_4^{25}
Dimethyl succinate	18	196	73	1.41965	1.1192
Ethyl piperonylate	18.5	286	194		
Methyl myristate	18.5		242	1.428 n_D^{45}	
Diethyl D-tartrate	18.5	280	103	1.44677	1.2028
Phenyl propionate	20	211	150		
Ethyl margarate (β-form)	20.5		298		
Benzyl benzoate	21	323	212	1.5681 n_D^{21}	1.1224 D^{19}
Di-*n*-butyl D-tartrate	22		131	+ 10.09 $[\alpha]_D^{14}$	1.0886 D_4^{18}
3,4-Dimethylphenyl acetate	22	235	164		
Isobutyl stearate	22.5		340		
	28				
Isoamyl stearate	23		354		
Ethyl palmitate α-form	24		384		
β-form	19		384		
Cetyl acetate α-form	24		284		1.1256
β-form	18.5				
Di-*n*-propyl D,L-tartrate	25	286	117		
Dimethyl sebacate	26.6		115	1.43549 n_D^{28}	0.98818 D_4^{28}
Methyl β-[α-furyl] acrylate	27	227	152		
i-Butyl stearate	27.5		340		
Ethyl D,L-mandelate	8		180		
D-Bornyl acetate	29	226	196		
Methyl margarate	29		284		
Methyl palmitate	30		270	1.4317 n_D^{45}	
i-Amyl stearate	30		354		
i-Octadecyl acetate α-form	30		312		
β-form	32				
Ethyl β-naphthoate	32	304	200		
Methyl-*p*-toluate	33	222.5	150		
Di-(β-ethoxyethyl) phthalate	33		155		
Ethyl stearate α-form	31		312		
β-form	33.5		312		
Diisopropyl D,L-tartrate	34		117		1.1166
Ethyl pyromucate (Ethyl furoate)	34	197	140	1.4797	1.1174 $D^{20.8}$

	M. Pt.	B. Pt.	Saponification Equivalent	n_D^{20}	D_4^{20}
2,4,5-Trimethylphenyl acetate	34	245	178		
Ethyl benzilate	34		256		
Methyl cinnamate	36	261	162		
Dimethyl itaconate	38	208	79	1.44413	1.12410 D_4^{18}
Methyl stearate	39		298	1.4346 n_D^{45}	
Methyl dibenzylacetate	41		254		
Dibenzyl phthalate	43		173		
Diethyl terephthalate	44	302	111		
Dicyclohexyl oxalate	47		127		
β-Phenylethyl cinnamate	47		252		
α-naphthyl acetate	48		186		
Methyl-p-methoxybenzoate	49	255	166		
Phenacyl acetate	49		178		
Di-m-tolyl carbonate	49		242		
Dibenzyl D-tartrate	50		165		
Dibenzyl succinate	51		149		
Methyl piperonylate	51	270^{777}	180		
Cetyl palmitate	51.5		480		
Ethylene glycol dilaurate	52		213		
Phenyl stearate	52		360		
Methyl D,L-mandelate	53	250	166		
Dimethyl tartronate	53		74		
Tetraethyl pyromellitate	54		91.5		
Diethyl mesotartrate	55		103		
m-Tolyl benzoate	55	314	212		
α-Naphthyl benzoate	56		248		
Cetyl stearate	56.5		508		
Diisobutyl D,L-tartrate	58	311	131		
Ethyl diphenylacetate	58		240		
Ethyl o-benzoylbenzoate	58		254		
Diethyl naphthalate	58		136		
Methyl diphenylacetate	60		226		
Di-o-tolyl carbonate	60		242		
Methyl-o-(p-toluyl) benzoate	61		254		
Dimethyl D-tartrate	61.5		89		
Ethylene glycol dimyristate	63		241		
Dicyclohexyl phthalate	66		165		
Dimethyl isophthalate	67		97		
Ethyl o-(p-toluyl) benzoate	68		268		
Phenyl benzoate	69	314	198		
Diisobutyl D-tartrate	70		131		
Ethylene glycol dipalmitate	70.5 (69)		269		
β-Naphthyl acetate	71		186		
p-Tolyl benzoate	71	316	212		
Glyceryl tribenzoate	72		135		
Ethylene glycol dibenzoate	73		135		

Table 1–5–A. Esters, Solid (Cont.)   343

	M. Pt.	B. Pt.	Saponification Equivalent	n_D^{20}	D_4^{20}
Diphenyl phthalate	74		159		
Methyl 2-hydroxy-3-naphthoate	75		202		
Methyl benzilate	75		242		
Trimethyl citrate	76		78		
Ethylene glycol di-n-stearate	76		297.5		
Methyl α-phenyl-n-butyrate	77		178		
Methyl β-naphthoate	77	290	186		
Diphenyl carbonate	78		214		
Isoeugenol acetate	79	283	206		
Methyl o-benzoylbenzoate	79		240		
Benzoin acetate	83		254		
Pentaerythritol tetraacetate	84		76		
Pyrocatechol dibenzoate	84		159		
Ethyl 2-hydroxy-3-naphthoate	85	291	216		
Di-guaiacyl carbonate	87		274		
Dimethyl-D,L-tartrate	90	282	89		
Di-o-tolyl oxalate	91		135		
Hydroxyhydroquinone triacetate	96		76		
n-Propyl p-hydroxybenzoate	96		180		
Dimethyl fumarate	102	193	72		
Salicylaldehyde triacetate	103		89		
Dimethyl naphthalate	104		122		
Phloroglucinol triacetate	105		76		
Di-m-tolyl oxalate	105		135		
Diphenyl adipate	106		149		
β-Naphthyl benzoate	107		248		
Dimethyl mesotartrate	111		89		
Di-p-tolyl carbonate	114		242		
Cholesteryl acetate	114		416		
Resorcinol dibenzoate	117		159		
Diphenyl succinate	121	330	135		
Di-p-tolyl succinate	121		149		
Hydroquinone diacetate	124		77.5		
Triethyl trimesate	133		98		
Dimethyl terephthalate	141		97		
Tetramethyl pyromellitate	142		97		
Trimethyl trimesate	144		84		
Di-p-tolyl oxalate	148		135		
Diethyl mucate	163		133		
Dimethyl mucate	165 d.		119		
Pyrogallol triacetate	172		84		
Hydroquinone dibenzoate	199 204 corr.		159		

TABLE 1–5–B. *Esters, Liquid*

	B. Pt.	M. Pt.	Saponification Equivalent	n_D^{20}	D_4^{20}
Ethyl formate	54		74	1.3597	0.92247
Methyl acetate	57		74	1.36170	0.9274
Isopropyl formate	71		88		0.8728
Ethyl acetate	77		88	1.37005 n_D^{25}	0.90055
Methyl propionate	80		88	1.3779	0.9151
Methyl acrylate	80		86	1.3984	0.961 $D^{19.2}$
n-Propyl formate	81		88	1.37789	0.9071
tert.-Butyl formate	83		114		
Allyl formate	83.5		86		0.948 D^{18}
Isopropyl acetate	89		102	1.3740 n_D^{25}	0.8690 D_4^{25}
Dimethyl carbonate	90.5		90	1.3687	1.0694
Methyl isobutyrate	92.5		102	1.3840	0.8906
sec.-Butyl formate	97		102	1.3812 $n_D^{25.3}$	0.8820 $D_4^{21.5}$
tert.-Butyl acetate	98		116	1.3840 n_D^{25}	0.8620 D_4^{25}
Isobutyl formate	98		102	1.38564	0.8755
Ethyl propionate	99		102	1.3853	0.8889
Ethyl acrylate	101		100	1.4059 $n_D^{19.4}$	0.9136 D^{15}
Methyl pivalate	101		116	1.4228	0.891 D_4^0
n-Propyl acetate	101.5		102	1.38468	0.8834
Methyl *n*-butyrate	102.3		102	1.3879	0.8982
Allyl acetate	104		100	1.40488	0.9276
Trimethyl orthoformate	105		35	1.3793	0.9676
Methyl isocrotonate	106		100		
n-Butyl formate	106.6		102	1.38940	0.8885
Ethyl isobutyrate	111		116	1.3903	0.86930
Isopropyl propionate	111.3		116		0.8931 D^0
sec.-Butyl acetate	112		116	1.3865 n_D^{25}	0.8648 D_4^{25}
Methyl isovalerate	116.7		116	1.3900 n_D^{25}	0.8808
Isobutyl acetate	117		116	1.39008	0.8747
Ethyl pivalate	118		130	1.3912	0.856
Ethyl methacrylate	118.5[753]		114	1.41472	0.91063
Methyl crotonate	119		100		0.9806 D^4
Isopropyl isobutyrate	121		130		0.8687 D_4^0
Ethyl *n*-butyrate	121.5		116	1.39475 n_{He}^{15}	0.87917
n-Propyl propionate	123		116	1.39325	0.8809
tert.-Amyl acetate	124		114	1.392	0.8738 D^{19}
Allyl propionate	124		114		
Isoamyl formate	124		116	1.39756	0.8820
Ethyl isocrotonate	125[749]		114	1.42423	0.9182
n-Butyl acetate	126		116	1.39614 n^{15}	0.87636 D_4^{25}
tert.-Butyl isobutyrate	127		144	1.3921	
Diethyl carbonate	127		118	1.3852	0.9752
Methyl *n*-valerate	128		116	1.3993 n^{15}	0.8947 D_4^{15}
Isopropyl *n*-butyrate	128		130		0.8652 D^{13}
Methyl methoxyacetate	130		104	1.39636	1.0511

Table 1–5–B. Esters, Liquid (Cont.) 345

	B. Pt.	M. Pt.	Saponification Equivalent	n_D^{20}	D_4^{20}
Ethyl methoxyacetate	132		118		1.0118 D^{15}
n-Amyl formate	132		116	1.39916	0.8853
sec.-Amyl-(3) acetate	133		130		1.4005
sec.-Amyl-(2) acetate	133.5		130	1.3960	0.8692 D_4^{18}
Allyl isobutyrate	134		128		
Ethyl isovalerate	135		130	1.4009	0.86565
i-Propyl isobutyrate	135		130	1.3959	0.8843 D_4^0
Ethyl crotonate	137749		114	1.42524	0.91752
Methyl Pyruvate	137		102		1.154 D^0
Methyl α-hydroxyisobutyrate	137		118		
Isobutyl propionate	138		130	1.3975	0.8876 D_4^0
Allyl n-butyrate	142		128		
Isoamyl acetate	142		130	1.40034	0.8674
Isopropyl isovalerate	142		144	1.3938 n_D^{25}	0.8538 D^{17}
-Propyl n-butyrate	144		130	1.4005	0.8789 D^{15}
Methyl D,L-lactate	145		104	1.4132 n_D^{25}	1.0898 D^{19}
Triethyl orthoformate	145.5		49	1.3922	0.8909
Ethyl n-valerate	145.5		130	1.40094	0.8739
tert.-Butyl n-butyrate	145		144	1.4001 $n^{17.5}$	
-Butyl propionate	147		130	1.4038 n_D^{15}	0.8818 D_4^{15}
Diisopropyl carbonate	147		146	1.3932	0.9162
Methyl ethoxyacetate	148		118		1.0112 D_4^{15}
Isobutyl isobutyrate	149		144	1.3999	0.8752 D_4^0
-Amyl acetate	149		130	1.4031	0.8756
Ethyl α-hydroxyisobutyrate	150		132		
Methyl glycolate	151		90		1.1677 D^{18}
Methyl n-caproate	151		130	1.40699 n_{He}^{15}	0.88464
Isopropyl n-valerate	153.5		144	1.4009	0.8579
Ethyl D,L-lactate	154.5		118	1.4121 n_D^{25}	1.038 D^{19}
Ethyl pyruvate	155		116	1.408 $n_D^{15.6}$	1.0596$D_4^{15.6}$
-Hexyl formate	155.5		130	1.40898 n_{He}^{15}	0.88133
-Propyl isovalerate	155.5		144	1.40413 $n^{17.8}$	0.8643$D_4^{17.8}$
-Ethoxyethyl acetate	156		132		0.9810 D_4^{15}
Isobutyl n-butyrate	157		144	1.40295$n_D^{18.4}$	0.8634$D_4^{18.4}$
Ethyl ethoxyacetate	158		132	1.40292	0.9701
Ethyl glycolate	160		104		1.0869 D_4^{15}
Isoamyl propionate	160		144	1.4065	0.8580$D_4^{19.5}$
Cyclohexyl formate	162.5750		128		1.0057 D_4^0
Propyl n-valerate	166		144	1.4065	0.8699
Butyl n-butyrate	166.5		144	1.4087 n^{25}	0.8712 $D_4^{1.5}$
Ethyl n-caproate	168		144	1.40727	0.8710
Isopropyl D,L-lactate	166		132	1.4082 n_D^{25}	0.998 D_{20}^{20}
di-n-Propyl carbonate	168.5		146	1.4014	0.9411
Amyl propionate	169		144	1.4096 n_D^{15}	0.8761 D_4^{15}
Ethylidene diacetate	169		73		1.061 D^{12}
Isoamyl isobutyrate	169		158		0.8760 D_4^0
Isobutyl isovalerate	171		158	1.40569	0.8534

	B. Pt.	M. Pt.	Saponification Equivalent	n_D^{20}	D_4^{20}
Methyl enanthate	174		144	$1.41334\ n_{He}^{15}$	0.88011
Ethylene glycol diformate	174		59		$1.193\ D^0$
sec.-Butyl n-valerate	174.5		158	1.4081	0.8605
Cyclohexyl acetate	175		142		$0.9854\ D_4^0$
Furfuryl acetate	175		140		$1.1175\ D_2^{2(}$
n-Heptyl formate	178		144	$1.41505\ n_{He}^{15}$	0.87841
n-Hexyl acetate	178		144	$1.41122\ n^{15}$	0.87336
Isoamyl n-butyrate	179		158		$0.8657\ D_1^1$
Ethyl acetylglycolate	179		73		$1.0993\ D^{17}$
Isobutyl n-valerate	179		158	1.4099	0.8625
Ethylene glycol monformate	180		90		$1.1989\ D_4^1$
Ethyl acetoacetate	181			1.41976	1.025
Methyl pyromucate	181.5		66	1.4860	$1.1786 D_4^{21}$
Dimethyl malonate	181.5		66	1.41398	1.1539
Ethyl β-methoxyethyl carbonate	183		148	$1.4036\ n_D^{25}$	$1.0424\ D_4^2$
Methyl cyclohexanecarboxylate	183		142	$1.45372\ n_D^{15}$	$0.9954\ D_4^1$
n-Amyl n-butyrate	186		158	$1.4139\ n_D^{15}$	$0.8713\ D_4^1$
n-Butyl n-valerate	187		158	1.4123	0.8678
Ethylene glycol monoacetate	187		104		
n-Propyl n-caproate	187		158	$1.41401\ n_{He}^{15}$	0.86719
Ethyl enanthate	189		158	$1.41537\ n_{He}^{15}$	0.86856
Diisobutyl carbonate	190		174	1.4072	0.9138
n-Hexyl propionate	190		158	$1.41621\ n_{He}^{15}$	0.86980
Ethylene glycol diacetate	190		73	1.4150	1.1040
Isoamyl isovalerate	190		172	$1.41300 n_D^{18.7}$	$0.8583 D_4^{18}$
n-Heptyl acetate	192.5		158	$1.41653\ n_{He}^{15}$	$0.87070\ D$
Cyclohexyl propionate	193^{750}		156		$0.9718\ D_4^0$
Diisopropyl oxalate	193		87	1.4100	1.0097
Ethyl β-ethoxyethyl carbonate	194.5		162	$1.5064\ n_D^{25}$	$1.0115\ D_4^2$
sec.-Octyl acetate	194.5		172	1.4141	$0.8606\ D_4^1$
Methyl n-caprylate	194.5		158	$1.4069\ n_D^{45}$	$0.8942\ D_0^0$
α-Tetrahydrofurfuryl acetate	195		144	$1.4350\ n_D^{25}$	1.061
Dimethyl succinate	196	18.2	73	1.41965	1.1192
Methyl levulinate	196		130	1.42333	1.04945
Ethyl cyclohexanecarboxylate	196		156	$1.45012\ n_D^{15}$	$0.9672\ D_4$
Phenyl acetate	197		136	1.503	$1.0809\ D_1^1$
n-Octyl formate	199		158	$1.42082\ n_{He}^{15}$	0.87435
Diethyl malonate	199		80	1.41618	1.05513
Methyl benzoate	200		136	1.5164	$1.0937\ D_4^1$
Dimethyl mesaconate	203		79	1.45119	1.0914
Benzyl formate	203		136	$1.51537 n_D^{19.9}$	$1.083\ D_4^{17}$
Cyclohexyl isobutyrate	204^{750}		170		$0.9489\ D_4^0$
Dimethyl maleate	204	7.6	72	$1.44156 n^{19.9}$	$1.14513\ D$
α-Tetrahydrofurfuryl propionate	204		158		1.044
Ethyl levulinate	206		144	1.42288	1.01114
n-Amyl n-valerate	207		172	$1.4181\ n_D^{15}$	$0.8825\ D_4^0$
Di-n-butyl carbonate	207.5		174	1.4117	0.9238

Table 1–5–B. Esters, Liquid (Cont.)   347

	B. Pt.	M. Pt.	Saponification Equivalent	n_D^{20}	D_4^{20}
n-Butyl n-caproate	208		172	$1.41877\ n_{He}^{15}$	0.86530
n-Hexyl n-butyrate	208		172	$1.41875\ n_{He}^{15}$	0.86519
Dimethyl itaconate	208	38	79	1.44413	$1.12410\ D_4^{15}$
o-Tolyl acetate	208		150		
n-Propyl n-enanthate	208		172	$1.41835\ n_{He}^{15}$	0.86556
Ethyl n-caprylate	208.5		172	1.41775	0.8667
Isobutyl enanthate	209		186		0.8593
Isopropyl levulinate	209		158	1.42088	0.98724
Trimethylene glycol diacetate	210		80		$1.070\ D^{19}$
n-Octyl acetate	210		172		$0.8847\ D_0^0$
n-Heptyl propionate	210		172	$1.42605\ n_{He}^{15}$	0.86786
Dimethyl citraconate	210.5		79	1.44856	1.11531
Ethylene glycol dipropionate	211		87		$1.0544\ D_{15}^{15}$
Phenyl propionate	211	20	150		$1.0467\ D_{25}^{25}$
n-propyl pyromucate	211		154	$1.4737\ n_D^{25.9}$	$1.0745 D_4^{25.9}$
m-Tolyl acetate	212	12	150	1.4978	$1.043\ D^{26}$
Cyclohexyl n-butyrate	212^{750}		170		$0.9572\ D_4^0$
p-Tolyl acetate	212.5		150	$1.4991\ n_D^{23}$	$1.0499\ D^{23}$
Ethyl benzoate	213		150	1.506	$1.0509\ D_4^{15}$
Di-n-propyl oxalate	214		87	1.4168	1.0169
Dimethyl glutarate	214^{751}		80	1.42415	1.0874
Methyl pelargonate	214		172		$1.0384\ D_0^0$
2,6-Dimethylphenyl acetate	214		164		
Methyl-o-toluate	215		150		$1.073\ D^{15}$
Benzyl acetate	217		150	1.5200	1.055
Diethyl succinate	218		87	1.41975	1.0398
Diethyl fumarate	218		86	$1.44103 n_D^{20.1}$	$1.05721\ D_4^{15}$
Isopropyl benzoate	218.5		164	$1.4890\ n_D^{25}$	$1.0102\ D_4^{25}$
Methyl phenylacetate	220		150	$1.5091\ n_D^{16}$	$1.0633\ D_{16}^{16}$
L-Linalyl acetate	220		196	1.4460	$0.8951\ D^{20}$
Methyl m-toluate	221		150		$1.066\ D^{15}$
n-Propyl levulinate	221		158	1.42576	0.98955
Diethyl tartronate	222 d.		88		$1.152\ D^{15}$
Methyl-p-toluate	222.5		150		
Diethyl maleate	223		86	$1.44075 n_D^{19.9}$	$1.07279\ D_4^{15}$
2,5-Dimethylphenyl acetate	224^{741}		164		$1.0264\ D^{15}$
Ethyl β-n-butoxyethyl carbonate	224		190	$1.4143\ n_D^{25}$	$0.9756\ D_4^{25}$
sec.-Butyl levulinate	226		172	1.42499	0.96698
n-Heptyl n-butyrate	226		186	$1.42279\ n_{He}^{15}$	$0.86371\ D^{20}$
2,4-Dimethylphenyl acetate	226		164	$1.4990\ n_D^{15}$	$1.0298 D_4^{15.5}$
Methyl n-caprate	226		186	$1.4161\ n_D^{45}$	
D-Bornyl acetate	226	29	196	$1.4623\ n_D^{22.6}$	$0.991\ D^{15}$
n-Amyl-n-caproate	226		186	$1.42280\ n_{He}^{15}$	$0.86349\ D^{20}$
n-Butyl n-enanthate	226		186	$1.42280\ n_{He}^{15}$	$0.86382\ D^{20}$
n-Hexyl n-valerate	226		186	$1.42286\ n_{He}^{15}$	$0.86345\ D^{20}$
n-Propyl n-caprylate	226		186	$1.42351\ n_{He}^{15}$	$0.86591\ D^{20}$
Methyl β-(α-furyl) acrylate	227	27	152		

	B. Pt.	M. Pt.	Saponification Equivalent	n_D^{20}	D_4^{20}
Ethyl o-toluate	227		164	$1.507\ n_D^{21.6}$	$1.0325 D_4^{21}$•
Ethyl pelargonate	227		186	1.42200	0.8657
Ethyl phenylacetate	227.5		164	$1.49921 n_D^{18.5}$	1.0333
n-Octyl propionate	228		186	$1.42185\ n_{He}^{15}$	$0.86633\ D^{20}$
Diethyl itaconate	228		93	1.4377	1.0467
Diethyl mesaconate	229		93	1.4488	1.0453
Diisobutyl oxalate	229		101	1.4180	0.97373
Allyl benzoate	230		162		$1.0578\ D_{15}^{15}$
Isobutyl levulinate	231		172	1.42677	0.96770
Diethyl citraconate	231		93	1.4442	1.0491
n-Propyl benzoate	231		164	$1.5000\ n_D^{20.3}$	$0.9958\ D_4^{25}$
β-Phenylethyl acetate	232		164	$1.5108\ n_D$	$1.057\ D^{22.5}$
Ethyl β-(α-furyl)acrylate	232	14	166	1.5286	$1.0891\ D_4^{15}$
Di-(β-methoxyethyl) carbonate	232		178	$1.4193\ n_D^{25}$	$1.0936\ D_4^{25}$
Diisoamyl carbonate	233		202	1.4174	0.9067
Ethyl m-toluate	234		164	$1.505\ n_D^{21.6}$	$1.0265 D_4^{21}$•
Ethyl p-toluate	234.5		164	$1.5089\ n_D^{18.2}$	$1.0269 D_4^{18}$•
3,4-Dimethylphenyl acetate	235	22	164		
2,4,6-Trimethylphenyl acetate	236		178		
Ethylene glycol di-n-butyrate	235⁷⁴⁹		101	$1.42619\ n_{He}^{20}$	1.0005
Diethyl glutarate	237		94	1.42395	1.02229
n-Butyl levulinate	238		172	1.42905	0.97353
Benzyl n-butyrate	238		178		$1.016\ D_{17.5}^{16}$
Methyl hydrocinnamate	239		164		$1.0455\ D^0$
Guaiacol acetate	240		166	$1.5101\ n_D^{25}$	$1.1285\ D_4^{25}$
Dimethyl L-malate	242		81	1.4425	1.2334
Geranyl acetate	242		196	1.4660	$0.9174\ D^{15}$
Isobutyl benzoate	242		178		$1.0018\ D_4^{15}$
n-Octyl n-butyrate	244		200	$1.42674\ n_{He}^{15}$	$0.86288\ D^{20}$
Ethyl n-caprate	245		200	1.42575	0.8650
Methyl phenoxyacetate	245		166		$1.150\ D^{17.5}$
Thymyl acetate	245		192		$1.009\ D^0$
Carvacryl acetate	245		192	$1.49128\ n_D^{20}$	$0.98959\ D^{25}$
n-Butyl n-caprylate	245		200	$1.42647\ n_{He}^{15}$	$0.86278\ D^{20}$
2,4,5-Trimethylphenyl acetate	245	34	178		
n-Heptyl n-valerate	245		200	$1.42536\ n_{He}^{15}$	0.86225
n-Amyl n-enanthate	245		200	$1.42627\ n_{He}^{15}$	$0.86232\ D^{20}$
Diethyl adipate	245		101	1.42765	1.0090
n-Hexyl n-caproate	245		200	$1.42637\ n_{He}^{15}$	$0.86216\ D^{20}$
Di-(β-ethoxyethyl) carbonate	245.5		206	$1.4239\ n_D^{25}$	$1.0635\ D_4^{25}$
Di-n-butyl oxalate	245.5		101	1.4240	0.98732
Diethylene glycol diacetate	245		95	1.4348	$1.123\ D_{20}^{20}$
Ethyl hydrocinnamate	247		178	1.49542	1.0147
Di-n-propyl succinate	248		101	1.4252	1.011
Methyl o-methoxybenzoate	248		166	$1.534\ n_D^{19.5}$	$1.1571\ D_4^{19}$
Methyl undecylanate	248		198	1.43928	$0.889\ D^{15}$
Isoamyl levulinate	249		186	1.43102	0.96136
n-Butyl benzoate	250		178		$1.0111\ D_{15}^{15}$

Table 1–5–B. Esters, Liquid (Cont.)   349

	B. Pt.	M. Pt.	Saponification Equivalent	n_D^{20}	D_4^{20}
Ethyl phenoxyacetate	251		180		$1.104\ D^{17.5}$
Methoxyl m-methoxybenzoate	252		166	$1.52236\ n_D$	$1.131\ D^{20}$
Diethyl L-malate	253		95	1.4362	1.1290
n-Amyl levulinate	253		186	1.43192	0.96136
Methyl p-methoxybenzoate	255	49	166		
β-Methoxyethyl benzoate	255		180	$1.5040\ n_D^{25}$	$1.0891\ D_{25}^{25}$
Ethyl m-methoxybenzoate	260		180	1.5161	1.0993
n-Amyl-n-caprylate	260		214	$1.43019\ n_{He}^{15}$	$0.86132\ D^{20}$
n-Hexyl n-enanthate	261		214	$1.42939\ n_{He}^{15}$	$0.86114\ D^{20}$
β-Ethoxyethyl benzoate	$260^{738.5}$		194	$1.4969\ n_D^{25}$	$1.0585\ D_{25}^{25}$
Ethyl o-methoxybenzoate	261		180	1.5224	1.1124
Methyl cinnamate	261	36	162		
n-Heptyl n-caproate	261		214	$1.42934\ n_{He}^{15}$	$0.86115\ D^{20}$
n-Octyl n-valerate	261.5		214	$1.42727\ n_{He}^{15}$	$0.86148\ D^{20}$
Isoamyl benzoate	262		192	1.4950	$0.9925 D_{14.4}^{14.4}$
Dimethyl D-camphorate	263		114	$1.46334 n_D^{16.9}$	1.0747
Ethyl undecylenate	264		212	$1.4449\ n_D^{23}$	$0.88271\ D_{15}^{15}$
Diisoamyl oxalate	267		115		$0.968\ D_{11}^{11}$
Dimethyl suberate	268		101	1.43326	1.0198
Ethyl p-methoxybenzoate	269	7	180	1.5254	1.1038
Ethyl laurate	269		228	1.4321	$0.8671\ D_{19}^{19}$
Trimethyl aconitate	270		72		
Methyl piperonylate	270	51	180		
Ethyl cinnamate	271	6.5	176	1.55982	1.0490
Di-n-butyl succinate	274.5		115	1.4298	0.9760
Triethyl aconitate	275 d.		86	1.45562	1.1064
Diisopropyl D-tartrate	275^{765}		117		$1.1274\ D_4^{17}$
Diisopropyl D,L-tartrate	275^{765}	34	117		1.1166
Ethyl p-ethoxybenzoate	275		194		$1.1076\ D^{21}$
n-Octyl n-caproate	275		228	$1.43256\ n_{He}^{15}$	$0.86032\ D^{20}$
n-Heptyl n-enanthate	277		228	$1.43183\ n_{He}^{15}$	$0.86039\ D^{20}$
n-Hexyl n-caprylate	277		228	$1.43230\ n_{He}^{15}$	$0.86033\ D^{20}$
Resorcinol diacetate	278		97		
Diethyl D-tartrate	280	19	103	1.44677	1.2028
Dimethyl D,L-tartrate	282	90	89		
Diethyl suberate	282		115	1.43236	0.9807
Eugenol acetate	282	30	206	1.52069	$1.087\ D_{15}^{15}$
Isoeugenol acetate	283	79	206		
Dimethyl phthalate	284		97	1.5138	$1.188\ D_{25}^{25}$
Diethyl isophthalate	286^{733}	11.5	111		
Di-n-propyl D,L-tartrate	286^{765}	25	117		1.1256
Diethyl D-camphorate	286		128	$1.45354 n_D^{26.2}$	1.0298
Ethyl piperanylate	286	18.5	194		
Methyl β-naphthoate	290	77	186		
n-Heptyl n-caprylate	290.5		242	$1.43492\ n_{He}^{15}$	$0.85958\ D^{20}$
n-Octyl 2-enanthate	291		242	$1.43488\ n_{He}^{15}$	$0.85961\ D^{20}$
Ethyl 2-hydroxy-3-naphthoate	291	85	216		
Diethyl azelate	291		122	1.43509	0.97294

	B. Pt.	M. Pt.	Saponification Equivalent	n_D^{20}	D_4^{20}
Triethyl citrate	294		92	1.44554	1.1369
Ethyl myristate	295	12	256	1.4362	0.8573 D_4^{25}
Di-n-propyl D-tartrate	297^{765}		117		1.1390
Di-(β-n-butoxyethyl) carbonate	297		262	1.4279 n_D^{25}	0.9766 D_4^{25}
Diethyl phthalate	298		111	1.5019	1.1175
α-Tetrahydrofurfuryl benzoate	300^{750}		206		1.137 D_0^{20}
Diethyl terephthalate	302	44	111		
Ethyl β-naphthoate	304	32	200	1.596	1.117
n-Octyl n-caprylate	307		256	1.43698 n_{He}^{15}	0.85919 D^{20}
Diethyl sebacate	307		129	1.43657	0.9631
o-Tolyl benzoate	307		212		
Ethyl α-naphthoate	309		200		1.1274 D_{15}^{15}
Diisobutyl D,L-tartrate	311	58	131		
Phenyl benzoate	314	69	198		
m-Tolyl benzoate	314	55	212		
p-Tolyl benzoate	316	71	212		
Di-n-butyl D,L-tartrate	320		131		1.0879 D_4^{18}
Benzyl benzoate	323		212	1.5681 n_D^{21}	1.1224 D^{19}
Diphenyl succinate	330	12.1	135		
Di-n-butyl phthalate	341		139	1.4900	1.047 D_{20}^{20}
Di-n-butyl sebacate	345		157		0.9329 D^{15}
Dimethyl pimelate	119^{10}		94	1.43088	1.0383
3.5-Dimethylphenyl acetate	130^{26}		164		
Di-n-propyl maleate	114^6		100	1.444 $n_D^{18.3}$	1.026
Diethyl pimelate	149^{18}		108	1.42985	0.9929
Dimethyl azelate	146^{10}		108	1.43607	1.0069
Di-n-propyl adipate	155^{16}		115	1.4314	0.9790
β-n-Butoxyethyl benzoate	156.5$^{14.5}$		222	1.4925 n_D^{25}	1.0277 D_{25}^{25}

Table 1–6–A. Anhydrides, Solid 351

TABLE 1–6–A. *Anhydrides, Solid*

	B. Pt.	M. Pt.	Amide	Anilide	*p*-Toluidide
Oleic		22	76	41	43
Capric (Decanoic)		24	108	70	78
β-Methyl-β-ethylglutaric	185	25		105 mono-	
Hexahydrobenzoic	280	25	185		
α,α-Dimethylsuccinic	220	29			
Hexahydrophthalic, *cis-*	145[18]	32			
DL-Methylsuccinic	244	37	225 di-	159 mono-	164 mono-
Undecanoic		37	103	71	80
2-Methylbenzoic (*o*-Toluic)		39	143	125	144
β-Methylglutaric	276	41		200 di-	135 mono-
				121 mono-	
Lauric (Dodecanoic)		42	110	78	87
Benzoic	360	42	130	163	158
α,β-Dimethylsuccinic *trans-*		43	238 di-		
Tridecanoic		50	100	80	88
D,L-Phenylsuccinic	204[22]	54	209 di-	222 di-	175
Myristic (tetradecanoic)		54	107	84	93
Glutaric		56	175	224	218
Maleic	198	56	18 mono-	173 mono-	142 di-
Suberic, dim. (Octanedioic)		56	127 mono-	128 mono-	218 di-
Palmitic (Hexadecanoic)		64	106	90	98
Margaric (Heptadecanoic)		67	108		
Itaconic					
(Methylenesuccinic)		67	192 di-	190	
Sebacic, dim. (Decanedioic)		68	210 di-	201 di-	201
			170 mono-	122 mono-	
Stearic (Octadecanoic)		70	109	95	102
3-Methylbenzoic (*m*-Toluic)		71	94	126	118
Phenylacetic		72	156	118	136
Arachidic (Eicosanoic)		77	108	92	96
α-Methylglutaconic, *cis-*		85		148 mono-	
β-Methylglutaconic, *cis-*		86		143 mono-	
α,β-Dimethylsuccinic, *cis-*		87	148 mono-	222 di-	
			244 di-		
4-Methylphthalic	295	92	188 di-		
4-Methylbenzoic		95	160	145	160
Diphenylacetic		98	167	180	
Anisic (4-Methoxybenzoic)		99	167	169	186
D,L-Benzylsuccinic		102			
β-Phenylglutaric		105		171 mono-	154 mono-
4-Ethoxybenzoic		108	202	170	
α-Benzylcinnamic		108			
3-Methylphthalic		114			
Succinic	261	120	157 mono-	148 mono-	180 mono-
			260 di-	230 di-	255 di-
3,4-Dimethylphthalic		126			

	B. Pt.	M. Pt.	Amide	Anilide	p-Toluidide
Phthalic		132	149 mono- 220 di-	170 mono- 253 di-	160 mono-
β-Naphthoic		135	192	171	192
Cinnamic		136	148	151	168
D,L-Hexahydrophthalic, *trans-*		140	196 mono-		
Homophthalic		141	230	231	
α-Naphthoic		146	202	163	
β-Phenylglutaconic		206	138 mono-	174 mono-	184 mono-
4,5-Dimethylphthalic		208			
2,2′-Diphenic		217	191 mono- 212 di-	176 mono- 230 di-	
D-Camphoric		221	177 mono- 193 di-	209 mono- 226 di-	212 α 190 β
1,8-Naphthalene dicarboxylic		274			

TABLE 1–6–B. *Anhydrides, Liquid*

	B. Pt.	Amide	Anilide	p-Toluidide
Acetic	140	82	114	153
Propionic	167	81	106	126
Isobutyric	182	128	105	107
Pivalic (trimethylacetic)	190	154	129	120
Butyric	198	115	96	75
Citraconic	214	185 di-	175 di-	
Isovaleric	215	135		107
Valeric	218	106	63	74
Crotonic	248	161	118	132
Caproic (*n*-Hexanoic)	254	100	95	75
Heptanoic	258	96	70	81
α-Methylglutaric	272		175 di- 114 } mono- 100	174 di- 126 mono- 98
Caprylic (octanoic)	280	110	57	70
Hexahydroisophthalic, *cis-*	304		298 di-	

Table 1-7-A. Ketones, Solid 353

TABLE 1-7-A. *Ketones, Solid*

	M. Pt.	B. Pt.	Semi-carbazone	2,4-Dinitro-phenyl hydrazone	p-Nitro-phenyl hydrazone	Phenyl hydrazone	Oxime
2-Dodecanone (n-Decyl methyl ketone)	20.5	246	122	168			
Phenyl n-amyl ketone (n-Caprophenone)	25	265	131.5		145	86	68
Benzyl methyl ketone (Phenylacetone)	27	216.5	199	153	198	97	
4-Methylacetophenone	28	226	204	260		110	118
2-Hydroxyacetophenone	28	215	210				48
Phorone (Di-isopropylidene acetone)	28	198	221	112			
2-Tridecanone (n-Undecyl methyl ketone)	28	263	123	69	101		56
Furfuralacetophenone	29	317 d.		169			
2-Furyl ethyl ketone	30	183	189				
2-(1'-hydroxycyclopentyl)-cyclopentanone	31	99^{3}					78
4-Cyclohexylcyclohexanone	31	$100^{0.1}$	216				
2-Acetylfuran	32	169	150	220	185	86	104
2,3,5-Trimethyl-1,4-benzoquinone	32						184
7-Tridecanone (Di-n-hexyl ketone)	33	255			97		
Levulinic acid (3-Acetyl propionic acid)	33	245		206	174	108	45
2-Tetradecanone (n-Dodecylmethylketone)	33		115				
1-Naphthyl methyl ketone	34	302	229			146	139
1,3-Diphenyl-2-propanone (α,α'-Diphenyl acetone; dibenzyl ketone);	34	330	145	100		121	
2-Phenylcyclopentanone	37	135^{9}	214				125
Furfuralacetone	38	116^{10}		241		131	
4-Methoxyacetophenone	38	258	197	220	195	142	86
Benzylidenemethyl butyl ketone (Styryl n-butyl ketone)	39	159^{11}				98	
4,4-Dimethylcyclohexanone	40	73^{14}	204				
3,4-Methylenedioxypropiophenone (Propiopiperone)	39		187			97	104

Table 1–7–A. (Cont.)

	M. Pt.	B. Pt.	Semi-carbazone	2,4-Dinitro-phenyl hydrazone	p-Nitro-phenyl hydrazone	Phenyl hydrazone	Oxime
2-Hydroxybenzophenone	39	250^{560}				155	141 syn- 143 anti-
2-Methoxybenzophenone (o-Anisyl phenyl ketone)	39						145
Benzalacetone	41	212	187	227	166	157	115
1-Indonone (α-Hydrindone)	42	241^{739}	233	258	234	130	146
8-Pentadecanone (Di-n-heptyl ketone)	42	178					120
4-Phenyl-3-butene-2-one (Styryl methyl ketone)	42	262	186	227	165	156	115
2-Benzylfuran	44	150^{3}					122
2-Methyl-5-isopropyl-1,4-benzoquinone (Thymoquinone)	45.5	232	201 mono- 237 di-	179 mono-			160 mono-
Phenyl undecyl ketone (Laurophenone)	47						63
Benzophenone	48	306	164	238	154	137	142
2,4,6-Heptanetrione (Diacetylacetone)	49	121^{10}	203 mono-	110		142 di-	68.5 di-
5-Phenoxy-2-pentanone	50	121^{2}					
Phenyl ethynyl ketone	51			214			
3,4-Dimethoxyacetophenone (Acetoveratrone)	51	286	218		227	131	140
Diphenylacetoin	52		169				
9-Heptadecanone (Di-n-octyl ketone)	53						112
2-Naphthyl methyl ketone (2-Acetonaphthone)	53	301	234	262 d.		176	149
2,3-Dimethyl-1,4-benzoquinone (o-Xylo-p-quinone)	55						184
2-Nonadecanone (n-Heptadecyl methyl ketone)	56						77
n-Caproylresorcinal	56	243 d.					190

Table 1–7–A. Ketones, Solid (Cont.) 355

	m.p.	b.p.					
2-Indanone	57						153
3-Propionylphenanthrene	57						
9-Propionylphenanthrene	57						
Styryl phenyl ketone (Benzalacetophenone; Chalcone)	58	345	168 α 170 β 179 γ	244 d.		120	140
3-Phenyl-2,4-pentanedione	60	134^{20}					
Mesitylacetone	60	130^{10}	205				
2-Naphthyl ethyl ketone	60	312	190				133
Difurfuralacetone	60						
Desoxybenzoin (Benzyl phenyl ketone)	60	321	148	204	163		98
4-Methylbenzophenone (p-Tolyl phenyl ketone)	60	326	121	202		121 116	154
1-Phenyl-1,3-butanedione (Benzoylacetone; Phenacyl methyl ketone)	61	261		151		109	165
1,1-Diphenylacetone	61		170				
5-Isopropyl-1,3-cyclohexanedione	62						
4-Methoxybenzophenone (p-Anisyl phenyl ketone)	62	354		180 139	100	150 131	146 α 115 β
2-Phenylcyclohexanone	63	160^{15}	190			132	169
4-Methoxybenzil	63						124
1-Aceto-2-naphthol	64						
Di-n-decyl ketone (11-Heneicosanone)	64			196	198		27.5 127 α
Benzoylformic acid (Phenylglyoxylic acid)	66						145 d. β 105
Di-2-tolyl ketone	67						
1,5-Diphenyl-1,5-pentanedione (1,3-Dibenzoylpropane)	67.5					180	
Cinnamalacetone	68	198^{15}	186	222			165 d. di- 153
2-Methyl-1,4-benzoquinone (p-Toluquinone)	69		178 mono- 240 d. di-	269 di-			134 mono- 220 d. di-
Benzoyl-2-furoyl methane	68	169^{3}				130	

23*

Table 1–7–A. (Cont.)

	M. Pt.	B. Pt.	Semi-carbazone	2,4-Dinitro-phenyl hydrazone	p-Nitro-phenyl hydrazone	Phenyl hydrazone	Oxime
12-Tricosanone (Di-n-undecyl ketone; Laurone)	69.5	179					39
Diphenyl triketone	70						
Dihydroxyacetone	72			277			84
2,6-Dimethyl-1,4-benzoquinone (m-Xylo-p-quinone)	72						
3-Acetylphenanthrene	72		230	229			175
4-Methoxybenzalacetone (Anisalacetone)	73		144				
Benzylacetophenone	73						
Phenoxymethyl phenyl ketone (α-Phenoxyacetophenone)	74	187[8]	187				
9-Acetylphenanthrene	74	170[1]	201				
1-Naphthyl phenyl ketone	75	225[15]				139	161
9-Acetylfluorene	75.5					154	
2-Benzofuryl methyl ketone	76	136[11]	207				
p-Methoxyphenyl benzyl ketone	77						118
4-Methoxybenzalacetophenone (Anisal-acetophenone; 4-Methoxychalcone)	77		168 α / 190 β				
2-Naphthoxyacetone	78		203			154	123
4-Phenylcyclohexanone	78		212				
1,4-Cyclohexanedione	79	139[20]					188
Di-n-tridecyl ketone (Myristone)	79						57
Phenacyl phenyl ketone (Dibenzoylmethane)	81 keto / 78 enol		205			105 mono-	
1-Benzoylpropionic acid	83 d.					100	
Fluorenone	83	341.5		283	269	151	195
α-Hydroxyacetophenone (Phenacyl alcohol)	86	118[11]	146			112	70
Di-n-Hepadecyl ketone	88.5						67

Table 1–7–A. Ketones, Solid (Cont.)   357

2,5-Dimethyl-1,4-naphthoquinone	94					226 mono-	163
4,4′-Dimethylbenzophenone (Di-p-tolyl ketone)	95	335					
Benzil (Dibenzoyl)	95	347	140 / 174 mono- / 243 di-	229 / 189 di-	192 mono- / 290 di-	100 / 134 mono- / 235 di-	137 mono- / 237 di- / 133
β,β′-Diphenylpropiophenone	96		194				
3-Hydroxyacetophenone	96	296					
2,3-Dihydroxyacetophenone (3-Acetocatechol)	97						168 d.
Dumione	98		232 mono-			197	
2-Naphthylglyoxal	98 hyd.	183[20]					
2-Benzoylacrylic acid	99 anh. / 64 mono-hyd.		190				200 / 201 mono- / 70 di-
Di-1-naphthyl ketone	100						168
1,3-Dibenzoylbenzene	101						(see prev.)
2-Aceto-1-naphthol	102	325	245			136	225
p-Tolil (4,4′-Dimethylbenzil)	102			222			
Cinnamacetophenone	102				135 α		156
1,3-Cyclohexanedione	104						
2-Propionylphenanthrene	105						
2-Methyl-1,4-naphthoquinone	106			299 d. mono-			166 di- / 48
Benzylidene-acenaphthenone	107						
4-Hydroxyacetophenone (p-Acetyl phenol)	109		199	261.5		151	145
trans-1,2-Dibenzoylethylene	110		217 α / 168 β				211
Piperonalacetone	110					163	186
1,5-Diphenyl-3-pentadienone (Dibenzalacetone)	112		187	180	173	152	
4,4′-Dimethoxybenzoin (Anisoin)	113		185				142
1,4-Diacetylbenzene	114	130[3]					240

Table 1–7–A. Ketones, Solid (Cont.)

Table 1–7–A. (Cont.)

	M. Pt.	B. Pt.	Semi-carbazone	2,4-Dinitro-phenyl hydrazone	p-Nitro-phenyl hydrazone	Phenyl hydrazone	Oxime
Quinone	116		166 mono- 243 d. di-	186 mono-		152	240
3,4-Dihydroxyacetophenone (4-Acetocatechol)	116						184 d. 76 syn. 126 anti-
3-Hydroxybenzophenone	116						175
7-Acenaphthenone	121					90	
4-Phenylacetophenone (4-Acetylbiphenyl; p-Xenyl methyl ketone)	121	325					186
Piperonalacetophenone	122		203 α				
9-Hydroxyxanthene (Xanthydrol)	122 d.						
2-Naphthoin	124						172
1,4-Naphthoquinone (α-Naphthoquinone)	125						168 mono- 272 di-
2,5-Dimethyl-1,4-benzoquinone	125						242 d.
2,6-Diphenyl-1,4-benzoquinone	131						
3-Methoxy-4-hydroxystyryl methyl ketone (Vanillalacetone)	129			230		127	
Dianisalacetone	129			82			
4,4′-Dimethoxybenzil (Anisil)	133		254 di-				
D,L-Benzoin	133	344	205 α	245		158 α 106 β	151 α 99 β
cis-1,2-Dibenzoylethylene	134						210 d. di-
4-Hydroxybenzophenone (p-Benzoyl phenol)	134		194	242		144	81 161 α
1-Furoin	135			216		79	102 β

Table 1–7–A. Ketones, Solid (Cont.)   359

Name	M.P.					
Mesityl phenyl ketone	137					
α-Anisal-α'-cinnamalacetone	139		232			
2,5-Diphenyl-3-n-dodecyl-1,4-benzoquinone (Embelin)	143					
z-Acetylphenanthrene	143				189 di-	175 tetra-
Dicinnamalacetone	144	260	196		166	
1,2-Naphthoquinone (β-Naphthoquinone)	145	184 d. mono-		250 mono-	138 mono-	109.5 mono- 169 di-
1,2-Dibenzoylethane	147					204
2,4-Dihydroxyacetophenone (Resacetophenone)	147	218			159	198 d.
3,5-Dihydroxyacetophenone	147	205		236		
1,2-Dibenzoylbenzene	148					
9-Benzoylanthracene (9-Anthraphenone)	148					
4-Hydroxypropiophenone	148		229			150 mono-
5,5-Dimethyl-1,3-cyclohexanedione	148					176
Methone (5,5-Dimethyldihydroresorcinol)	148					
2,3,4,2'-Tetrahydroxybenzophenone	149 anh. 100 hyd.					115 mono-
3,7-Dimethyl-1,2-naphthoquinone	151					222 d.
5-Hydroxy-1,4-naphthoquinone	151					167 mono- 225 di- DANGER
Anthrone	154					
1,4-Dibenzoylbenzene	161					212 mono- 235 di-
Furil (2,2'-Bifuroyl)	165				82 mono- 184 bis-	106 mono-α 97 mono-β 100 di-α 188 di-β
Benzanthrone	170					

Table 1–7–A. (Cont.)

	M. Pt.	B. Pt.	Semi-carbazone	2,4-Dinitro-phenyl hydrazone	p-Nitro-phenyl hydrazone	Phenyl hydrazone	Oxime
Quinhydrone	171					152	161
2,3,4-Trihydroxyacetophenone (Gallacetophenone)	172		225			152	162
Xanthone (Diphenylene ketone oxide)	174						161
1,8-Dihydroxy-2-methyl-anthraquinone (2-Methylchrysazin)	175						
2-Methyl-9,10-anthraquinone	177						
D,L-Camphor	178	209	247	164	217	233	118 D
3,5-Dihydroxy-2-methyl-1,4-naphthoqui-none (Droserone)	181						151 di-
2,3,4-Trihydroxy-9,10-phenanthraquinone	185 d.		270 d. mono-				188 d.
1,2-Anthraquinone	185 d.				260 d.		
3,4,5-Trihydroxyacetophenone	187		216				128.5 mono-
7-Isopropyl-1-methyl-phenanthraquinone	197		200 mono-	36 mono-	222 mono-	160 mono-	153 mono-α 114 mono-β 201 d. di- α 248 d. di- β 136 di- γ 194 d. di- δ
Camphoroquinone	199		236 d. mono-	190 di-	239	183	
1-Hydroxy-9,10-anthraquinone	200						
1,4-Dihydroxy-9,10-anthraquinone	200						
2,4,5-Trihydroxyacetophenone	200 d.						
2,5,2′,6′-Tetrahydroxybenzophenone	200 d.						149
2,5-Dihydroxyacetophenone	202				241 d.		
2,3,5-Trihydroxyacetophenone	206						158 mono-
9,10-Phenanthraquinone	206	>360	220 d. mono-	312 d. mono-	245 mono-	165 mono-	202 d. di-

Table 1–7–A. Ketones, Solid (Cont.)   361

Compound	m.p.					
1,4-Anthraquinone	218 d.					233
2,4,6-Trihydroxyacetophenone (Phloracetophenone)	219					
3,4,3′,4′-Tetrahydroxybenzophenone	227					145
Chrysoquinone (Chrysenequinone)	239.5					161 mono-
1,2,8-Trihydroxy-9,10-anthraquinone (Hydroxychrysazin)	239					
Ninhydrin (Triketohydrindene hydrate)	243				207 di-	201
1,2,4-Trihydroxy-9,10-anthraquinone	259				179 mono- 219 di-	230
Acenaphthenequinone	261		192 mono- 271 di-	247 mono-		
1,3-Dihydroxy-4-methylanthraquinone (4-Methylpurpuroxanthin)	265					
Aceanthrenequinone	270				203 mono-	251 d. mono-
1,2,5-Trihydroxy-9,10-anthraquinone (Hydroxyanthrarufin)	273					
1,5-Dihydroxyanthraquinone (Anthrarufin)	280 subl.					
9,10-Anthraquinone	286	382				224 mono-
Alizarin (1,2-Dihydroxy-9,10-anthraquinone)	290	430				
Dianthraquinone	>300					
2-Hydroxy-9,10-anthraquinone	305					
1,2,3-Trihydroxy-9,10-anthraquinone (Anthragallol)	313 d.					
1,2,6-Trihydroxy-9,10-anthraquinone	>330					
1,2,7-Trihydroxy-9,10-anthraquinone	369					

Table 1–7–B. *Ketones, Liquid*

	B. Pt.	M. Pt.	Semi-carbazone	2,4-Dinitro-phenyl hydrazone	p-Nitro-phenyl hydrazone	Phenyl hydrazone	Oxime
Acetone	56		190	126	148	42	59
3-Buten-2-one (Vinyl methyl ketone)	81		141	116			152 B.Pt.
2-Butanone (Ethyl methyl ketone)	82		135		128		
3-Butyne-2-one	86			181	143		
Butane-2,3-dione (Biacetyl)	88		235 mono- 278 bis-	314 bis-	230 mono-	134 mono- 243 d. bis-	76 mono- 245 di-
2-Methyl-3-butanone (Isopropyl methyl ketone)	94		113	120	108		
2-Methyl-1-buten-3-one	97^{734}		173	181			
Cyclobutanone	100			146			
3-Pentanone (Diethyl ketone)	102		138	156	144		165 B. Pt.
2-Pentanone (Propyl methyl ketone)	102		112	143	117		167 B. Pt.
1-Penten-3-one (Ethyl vinyl ketone)	102^{740}			129			
3,3-Dimethyl-2-butanone (Pinacalone)	106		157	125			75
1-Methoxy-2-propanone (Methoxymethyl methyl ketone)	115^{756}			163	111		
1-Methoxy-3-butanone (1-Methoxy ethyl methyl ketone)	117			141			
4-Methyl-2-pentanone (Isobutyl methyl ketone)	117			132	95		176 B. Pt.
3-Methyl-2-pentanone (sec.-Butyl methyl ketone)	118			94	71		
2-Methyl-1-pentene-3-one	119^{751}		161	88			
2,4-Dimethyl-3-pentanone (Di-isopropyl ketone)	124		160	100			
Neopentyl methyl ketone	125			130			
3-Hexanone (Propyl ethyl ketone)	125		113	144			
2,2-Dimethyl-3-pentanone (tert.-Butyl methyl ketone)	125^{729}			106			
2-Hexanone (n-Butyl methyl ketone)	128		125		88		49

Table 1–7–B. Ketones, Liquid (Cont.) 363

Compound	B.P.					
4-Methyl-3-penten-2-one (Mesityl oxide)	130	164 α / 133 β	200	132	142	48 β
3,3-Dimethyl-2-pentanone (tert.-Amyl methyl ketone)	130^{733}		112			
Cyclopentanone	131	210	146	154	55	56.5
5-Hexen-2-one (Allylacetone)	132	102	108			
1-Methoxy-2-butanone	133^{757}		198			
2,2,4-Trimethyl-3-pentanone (tert.-Butyl isopropyl ketone)	135	132				144
4-Methyl-3-hexanone (Isobutyl ethyl ketone)	135^{735}	152				
2-Methyl-1-penten-4-one	135	192				
2-Methyl-3-hexanone (Isopropyl n-propylketone)	136	119	78			
4-Methyl-3-hexanone (sec.-Butyl ethyl ketone)	136	137				
4-Methoxy-3-pentanone	136^{750}	120				
Cyclobutyl methyl ketone	136	149				
3-Methyl-2-hexanone	137	70				
3-Methyl-1-hexen-5-one	138	112				
3-Methyl-1-penten-4-one	138	201				75
3,4-Dimethyl-2-pentanone	138	113				
4-Hexen-3-one	139	157				
2,4-Pentanedione (Acetyl acetone)	139	122 mono- / 209 di-	209			149 di-
2-Methylcyclopentanone	139	184				
3-Ethyl-2-pentanone	139^{746}	99				
3-Hydroxy-3-methyl-2-butanone (Diethyl acetyl carbinol)	140					
4-Methyl-2-hexanone	142	165				87
1-Propoxy-2-propanone	142	120	142			
D-3-Methylcyclopentanone	143	184				91 α / 67 β
3,4-Dimethyl-4-penten-2-one	144	114				

Table 1–7–B. (Cont.)

	B. Pt.	M. Pt.	Semi-carbazone	2,4-Dinitro-phenyl hydrazone	p-Nitro-phenyl hydrazone	Phenyl hydrazone	Oxime
4-Heptanone (Dipropyl ketone)	144		132	75			193 B. Pt.
2,4-Dimethyl-3-hexanone (*sec.*-Butyl isopropyl ketone)	145			71			
3-Hydroxy-2-butanone (D,L-Acetoin)	145		185	318 bis-			
3-Methylcyclopentanone	145^{755}		185				
1-Methoxy-3-methyl-2-butanone	145^{748}			163			
2,2-Dimethyl-3-hexanone (*tert.*-Butyl-*n*-propyl ketone)	145^{738}			124			
1-Hydroxy-2-propanone (Acetol)	146		196	128.5	173		
1-Hepten-4-one	146		110				
3,4-Dimethyl-3-penten-2-one	147		200				
1-Ethoxy-2-butanone	147^{752}						
2,5-Dimethyl-3,4-hexanedione (Diisobutyryl)	148						125 mono- 172 di-
3-Heptanone (*n*-Butyl ethyl ketone)	148		101				
5-Methyl-4-hexen-3-one	148		163				
5-Methyl-5-hexen-2-one (Methallylacetone)	149		137				
2-Methyl-4-heptanone (Isobutyl *n*-propyl ketone)	150^{750}		124				
4,4-Dimethyl-3-hexanone (*tert.*-Amyl ethyl ketone)	150		98				
2-Heptanone (*n*-Amyl methyl ketone)	151		123	89		207	
3-Ethyl-5-hexen-2-one	152			53			
2-Hepten-6-one	152		97				
5-Hepten-2-one (Crotylacetone)	153		105				
1-Methoxy-2-pentanone	153^{745}						
3,3-Dimethyl-1-cyclopentanone	153^{748}		178				
2,2,4,4-Tetramethyl-3-pentanone (di-*tert.*-Butyl ketone)	154						

Table 1–7–B. Ketones, Liquid (Cont.)   365

Name	B.P., °C				
Cyclopentyl methyl ketone	155				
2,2,5,5-Tetramethylcyclopentanone	155	143			
1-Methoxy-3-hexanone	155^{746}	169			
Cyclohexanone	156	166			91
4-Methyl-6-hepten-3-one	156				
2-Hepten-4-one	156	147			
2,3-Hexanedione	158				175 di-
3,4-Dimethyl-2-hexanone	158	120			
3,4-Dimethyl-3-hexen-2-one	158	142			
2,2,4-Trimethyl-3-hexanone (tert.-Butyl isobutyl ketone)	158	145			
2-Ethyl-1-hexen-3-one	158^{742}	119			
1-Methoxy-3,3-dimethylbutanone	159^{743}				
1-Isopropoxy-3-methyl-2-butanone	160				
2-Methyl-3-cyclopentanone	161	220	88		127
1-Ethylcyclopentanone	161^{755}	189			
3-Methyl-2-heptanone	162	82			
4,5-Dimethyl-5-hexen-3-one	162^{750}	110			
3,5-Dimethyl-4-heptanone (Di-sec.-butyl ketone)	162	83			
6-Methyl-3-heptanone (isoamyl ethyl ketone)	163	132			
2-Methoxy-3-methyl-2-pentanone	164^{757}				
1-Methoxy-4-methyl-2-pentanone	164^{751}				
2-Methylcyclohexanone	165	191	135.5	132	43
4-Hydroxy-4-methyl-2-pentanone (Diacetone alcohol)	166		202		58
4,5-Dimethyl-4-hexen-3-one	166^{750}	209			
2,2-Dimethyl-3-heptanone (tert.-Butyl n-butyl ketone)	166^{745}	145			
2,6-Dimethyl-4-heptanone (Di-isobutyl ketone; Isovalerone)	168	122	66		
2-Methyl-4-octanone (Isobutyl n-butyl ketone)	168	132			

Table 1–7–B. Ketones, Liquid (Cont.

Table 1–7–B. (Cont.)

Compound	B. Pt.	M. Pt.	Semi-carbazone	2,4-Dinitrophenyl hydrazone	p-Nitrophenyl hydrazone	Phenyl hydrazone	Oxime
2,5-Dimethyl-4-heptanone (Isobutyl sec.-butyl ketone)	169		133				
D-3-Methylcyclohexanone	169		180	155	119	94	43
D,L-3-Methylcyclohexanone	169.6		179				
1-Methoxy-2-hexanone	169^{744}		96				
4-Octanone (n-Butyl-n-propyl ketone)	170		152				
Methylacetoacetate	170						
2,2-Dimethylcyclohexanone	170		201	140			
6-Methyl-2-heptanone (Isohexyl methyl ketone)	171		154	77			37
trans-2,4-Dimethylcyclohexanone	171		136		128.5	109	111
4-Methylcyclohexanone	171		199				
D,L-2,5-Dimethylcyclohexanone	171		122 α / 173 β				
2-Octanone (Hexyl methyl ketone)	173		122	58	92		
5-Ethyl-3-heptanone	173		134				97
D-2,5-Dimethylcyclohexanone	174		176				
2-Methyl-3-ethylcyclopentanone	174		170				
2,6-Dimethylcyclohexanone	174						
2-Isopropylcyclopentanone	174		202			60 d.	
Acetoxyacetone	174		145		144		
2,4-Heptanedione (n-Butyrylacetone)	174						
3-Methyl-3-hepten-2-one	175		164				
cis-2,4-Dimethylcyclohexanone	176		200				98
4-Ethyl-4-hydroxy-3-hexanone	178^{742}	203	177				
2,3-Dimethylcyclohexanone	178		209	141			
2,2,6-Trimethylcyclohexanone	179^{767}		219				
3,3-Dimethylcyclohexanone	179^{748}		105				
5-Ethyl-4-hepten-3-one	179^{740}						
3-Methyl-4-ethylcyclopentanone	180		208				

Table 1–7–B. Ketones, Liquid (Cont.) 367

Name	B.P.	M.P.					
Cyclohexyl methyl ketone	180		177				60
trans-3,5-Dimethylcyclohexanone	180		193 D,L		154		
5-Hydroxy-4-octanone (Butyroin)	180						
Ethylacetoacetate	181		133	99	137		
Cycloheptanone	181		163	93			23
3,5-Dimethylcyclohexanone	182		201	148			
cis-3,5-Dimethylcyclohexanone	182		202				74
2-Propylcyclopentanone	183		214 d.				
2,2,6,6-Tetraethylcyclohexanone	184[772]	15					
3-Methyl-2,4-hexanedione	184						
5-Nonanone (di-*n*-Butylketone)	186		90				
3,4-Dimethylcyclohexanone	187		189				
3-Nonanone (*n*-Hexyl ethyl ketone)	187[751]		112				
2,5-Dimethylcyclohexen-3-one	189		165				92
3-Propylcyclopentanone	190		178				
3-Ethylcyclohexanone	192		182				
1,5-Dimethylcyclohexen-4-one	192						102
2,5-Hexanedione (Acetonylacetone)	194		185 d. (mono) 224 di-	257 bis-	210 di-	120 bis-	137 di- 165 α 123 β
D-Fenchone	195		184	140			
2-Nonanone (*n*-Heptyl methyl ketone)	195		118				
4-Methyl-1-acetylcyclohexanone	195		159 α 175 β				57
Methyl levulinate	196		143	142		96	
D,L-2-Ethyl-5-methyl-cyclohexanone	197		178				80
2-Methyl-1-acetyl-cyclohexanone	197		172				
2-Propylcyclohexanone	198[748]		133 d.				67
1-Acetyl-1-cyclohexene	200		220				59
β-Thujone	202		174	114			
Acetophenone (Phenyl methyl ketone)	205[747]	20	198	238	184	105	60
3-Methyl-5-ethyl-cyclohexanone	205[747]						

Table 1–7–B. Ketones, Liquid (Cont.)

Table 1–7–B. (Cont.)

	B. Pt.	M. Pt.	Semi-carbazone	2,4-Dinitro-phenyl hydrazone	p-Nitro-phenyl hydrazone	Phenyl hydrazone	Oxime
Ethyl levulinate	206		148	102		104	
4-Decanone	206		51			76	
1,5-Dimethylcyclohexene-3-one	208		179	146		53	
L-Methone	209	14	189				59
2-Decanone (n-Octyl methyl ketone)	211		124				
4-n-Propylcyclohexanone	212^{740}		180				61
2-Methylacetophenone (o-Tolyl methyl ketone)	214		205	159		68	79.5
1,5,5-Trimethylcyclohexene-3-one (Isophorone)	215	20	199.5 d.				54
Propiophenone (Phenyl ethyl ketone)	218		173	190			50
Phenyl n-propyl ketone	218		188				55
3-Methylacetophenone (m-Tolyl methyl ketone)	220		198	207		73	94
Isobutyrophenone (Phenyl isopropyl ketone)	222		181	163			
1-Methyl-5-ethylcyclohexene-3-one	223		162 d.				166 mono- α 114 mono- β 240 di-
Benzoyl acetyl ketone	222		229 di-		256 di-	143 α	
4-[8]-p-Menthen-3-one (Pulegone)	224		174	142			119
Pivalophenone (Phenyl tert.-butyl ketone)	224^{750}		150	194			167
1-Phenyl-2-butanone (Benzyl ethyl ketone)	226		135				
6-Undecanone (Di-n-amyl ketone)	228	15	122				
2-Undecanone (n-Nonyl methyl ketone)	228		185	63	90		44
2,4-Dimethylacetophenone	228		173				63
1-Phenoxy-2-propanone (Phenoxyacetone)	229		187				
n-Butyrophenone (Phenyl-n-propyl ketone)	230	11.5	162	190	174	72 D-α	49
d-Carvone	230		168	191			
2,5-Dimethylacetophenone	230		210				
Phenyl isobutyl ketone	235						87
4-Phenyl-2-butanone	235		142				

Table 1–7–B. Ketones, Liquid (Cont.) 369

1-Phenyl-3-methyl-1-butanone (Isovalerophenone)	236	210				76
3,5-Dimethylacetophenone	236	183		179	114	114
2-Methoxyacetophenone (o-Acetylanisole)	239	196				83
3-Methoxyacetophenone (m-Acetylanisole)	240	80				
5-Phenyl-3-pentanone	244					
5-Isopropyl-2-methyl-acetophenone (2-Acetyl-p-cymene)	245	147	140			91
3,4-Dimethylacetophenone	246	233				85
2,4,5-Trimethylacetophenone	246	204				85
1-Phenyl-1-pentanone (Phenyl butyl ketone; n-Valerophenone)	248	160	166		162	52
4-Isopropylacetophenone	252	125		161		
Ethyl benzoylacetate	265	119				
1-Phenylheptanone (Phenyl n-hexyl ketone)	283	167		127		55
3-Phenylcyclohexanone	287^{736}	289				128
1-Acetonaphthone (1-Naphthyl methyl ketone)	302				146	140
1-Naphthyl ethyl ketone	305					58
2,4,5-Trimethylbenzophenone	328					
2,4,4′-Trimethylbenzophenone	340					132
α-Methylstyryl phenyl ketone	340	151				134 syn- 78 anti-
1,5-Diphenyl-3-pentanone (Dibenzylacetone)	352					95
1-Ethoxy-2-propanone	36^{28}	96				
1-Heptene-6-one	41^{10}	108				
3-n-Propylcyclohexanone	42$^{0.7}$	169				
1-Heptene-5-one	46^{12}	82				
3-Isopropylcyclohexanone	51^{1}	195				
1-Keto propionaldehyde (Pyruvic aldehyde)	52^{12}	254 di-	299 di-			157 di-
3-Methyl-2-n-propyl-1-cyclopentanone	53^{2}	210				
3-Ethyl-2-cyclohexanone	57$^{0.9}$	186				

Table 1–7–B. Ketones, Liquid (Cont.)

Table 1–7–B. (Cont.)

	B. Pt.	M. Pt.	Semi-carbazone	2,4-Dinitro-phenyl hydrazone	p-Nitro-phenyl hydrazone	Phenyl hydrazone	Oxime
3-n-Propyl-2-cyclohexenone	$60^{0.4}$		175	156			
3-Isopropyl-2-cyclohexenone	$60^{0.3}$		179	155			
trans-3-Heptene-2-one	60^{16}		125				
3-Heptene-6-one	61^{20}		109				
7-Methyl-1-octene-5-one	62^{14}		101				
2,2,3-Trimethyl-4-cyclopentanone	66^{19}		190				
1-Cyclopentyl-2-propanone	67^{12}		150				
2-Methyl-3-octene-5-one	68^{24}		187				
2-Cyclohexenone	68^{22}		172	163			
cis-3-Heptene-2-one	70^{15}		152				
3-Methyl-2,5-hexanedione	71^{10}		220				
3-Propyl-3-hexene-2-one	72^{9}		142				
2-Acetyl-5-methylfuran	73^{8}		191				
2-Methyl-3-octene-6-one	73^{19}		131				
3-Methyl-3-hydroxy-2-pentanone	73^{50}		150				
1-Acetyl-1-cyclopentene	74^{12}		211	162			
2-Ethylcyclohexanone	76^{20}		162	88			
3-Octyne-2-one	76^{15}		109				
2,3-Dimethyl-2-heptene-6-one	76^{13}		163				
3-Methyl-3-phenyl-2-butanone	77^{15}		186				
1,3-Dimethoxy-2-propanone	78^{18}		120				
3-Methyl-2-cyclohexene-1-one	78^{14}		199				
5,5-Dimethyl-3-hexene-2-one	79^{40}		178				
3-Cyclopentyl-2-butanone	79^{17}		98				
3-Methyl-3-heptene-5-one	82^{42}		114				
D-2-Ethyl-5-methylcyclohexanone	83^{18}		152				
3-Acetofurone	84^{21}		150				
3-Methyl-3-hydroxy-2-heptanone	84^{19}		152				

Table 1–7–B. Ketones, Liquid (Cont.)   371

Compound					
4-Methoxycyclohexanone	85^{14}	178	150		
5-Methyl-5-hydroxy-3-heptanone	86^{14}	125			
5-Hydroxy-2-pentanone	86^{10}	155			
2-n-Propylcyclohexanone	88^{17}	120			
5,5-Dimethyl-3-cyclohexenone	88.5^{32}	195			
4-Isopropylcyclohexanone	91^{13}	188	123		
2,3-Dimethyl-2-cyclopentanone	92^{25}	250			
4-Methyl-2-octanone	94^{40}	70			
1,1-Dimethyl-2-tetralone	$96^{0.5}$	204			
1-Phenyl-4-hexene-1-one	97^{1}	130			
6-Isopropyl-3-cyclohexanone	98^{10}	185	137	168	
D,L-3-Methyl-1-acetylcyclohexanone	99^{38}	174			
Phenyl tert.-butyl ketone	100^{16}	150	195		166
1-Phenoxy-2-butanone	100^{5}	102			
(Phenoxymethyl ethyl ketone)					
Phenyl-2-methyl-3-butenyl ketone	$100^{2.1}$	177			
1-Propionyl-1-cyclohexene	102^{14}	195			78
1,3-Diethoxy-2-propanone	103^{35}	91			
(sym.-Diethoxy acetone)					
1-Ethyl-2-methyl-3-cyclohexenone	105^{19}	250			
2-Acetylbiphenyl	105^{1}	197			
3-Phenyl-2-butanone	107^{22}	158			
3-Phenyl-2-pentanone	110^{18}	191			
Methoxymethyl cyclohexyl ketone	111^{21}	102			
4-Methyl-1-tetralone	111^{1}	211			
Dicyclopentyl ketone	112^{12}	162			
1-Phenoxy-2-pentanone	112^{4}	108			
2,4-Dimethylacetophenone	113^{18}	234			64
4-Phenyl-2-pentanone	115^{13}	137			
cis-1-Decalone	116^{18}	220 d.			
Phenyl neopentyl ketone	116^{11}	218			114
2,2-Dimethyl-1-acetyl-1-cyclohexene	118^{49}	201			

24*

Table 1–7–B. Ketones, Liquid (Cont.)

Table 1–7–B. (Cont.)

	B. Pt.	M. Pt.	Semi-carbazone	2,4-Dinitro-phenyl hydrazone	p-Nitro-phenyl hydrazone	Phenyl hydrazone	Oxime
2-Ethylacetophenone	118[29]		180				
1,2-Dimethyl-3-cyclohexenone	118[12]		225 d.				
1-Phenoxy-2-propanone	120[19]		176				
4-Phenylhexahydroacetophenone (4-Phenyl cyclohexyl methyl ketone)	121[1]		191				
α-Ethoxyacetophenone	122[15]		128				
5-Phenyl-2-pentanone	226		130				
α-Methoxyacetophenone	126[19]		129				
2,5-Dimethylacetophenone	127[31]		169				
3-Methyl-4-phenyl-2-butanone	130[17]		112				
β-Tetralone	131[11]	18	194				88
3-Dodecanone	134[18]	19	89				
2-Methyl-1-tetralone	138[16]		205				
3-Phenyl-3-hexene-5-one	138[14]		158				
3-Phenyl-2-hexene-5-one	138[14]		185				
3-Acetylbiphenyl	138[1]		223				
4-n-Butylacetophenone	141[14]		185				
3-Propiophenone	145[20]		128				
o-Methylstyryl ethyl ketone	152[14]		178				
1-Phenyl-1-hexene-5-one	153[10]		132				
3-Phenyl-1-hexene-5-one	153[10]		132	103			
6-Acetyltetralin	156[10]		234				
Phenylacetone	161[12]		191 mono-				123 mono- 108 di-
6-Propionyltetralin	163[11]		209				
1-Tetralone	170[49]		217				102
1-Naphthoxyacetone	205[14]		103				

Table 1–8–A. Alcohols, Solid   373

TABLE 1–8–A. *Alcohols, Solid*

	M. Pt.	B. Pt.	α-Naphthyl urethan	p-Nitrobenzoate	3,5-Dinitrobenzoate	3-Nitrohydrogen phthalate
1-Phenyl ethyl alcohol (D,L-Methyl phenyl carbinol)	20	202	106	43	95	
2-Methylcyclohexanol	21	167	155		115	
1-Dodecanol (n-Dodecyl alcohol; lauryl alcohol)	24	259	80	45	60	124
1,1-Dimethyl-2-phenylethanol (Benzyl dimethyl carbinol)	24	216				
4-Methoxy benzyl alcohol (p-Anisyl carbinol)	24	259				
Cyclohexanol	25	161	129	50	112	160
tert.-Butyl alcohol (Trimethyl carbinol)	25.5	82.5	101	116	142	
2,3,3-Trimethylcyclohexanol	28	197				
2,4-Hexadien-1-ol	31	76^{12}			85	
1-Tridecanol	31 α / 28 β	155^{15}		37.5		
Cinnamyl alcohol	33	257	114	78	121	124
2-Methyl benzyl alcohol (2-Tolyl carbinol)	36	219				
trans-Octa-9-decen-1-ol (Elaidyl alcohol)	37	333	71			
D,L-Fenchyl alcohol	38	201.5	149	109	104	95
1-Tetradecanol (Myristyl alcohol)	39	170^{20}	82	51	67	123.5
1,2,2-Trimethylcyclohexanol	41	82^{20}				
Pinacol (Tetramethyl glycol)	43	172				
L-Menthol	44	216	119	61	153	
1-Pentadecanol	44 α / 39 β					
1,3,5-Trimethyl-1-cyclohexen-3-ol	46	87^{17}	72	46		122.5
D,L-α-Propyl benzyl alcohol	49	168^{100}		58		
1-Hexadecanol (Cetyl alcohol)	50	190^{18}	90	58.5	66	122
2,2,6-Trimethylcyclohexanol	51	186^{753}	82			
3,3,5-Trimethylcyclohexanol	52	201^{750}				

Table 1–8–A. (Cont.)

	M. Pt.	B. Pt.	α-Naphthyl urethan	p-Nitro-benzoate	3,5-Dinitro-benzoate	3-Nitro-hydrogen phthalate
2,2-Dimethyl-1-propanol (tert.-Butyl carbinol; Neopentyl alcohol)	52	113	100			
p-Methylbenzohydrol (Phenyl p-tolyl carbinol)	53				121.5	121
1-Heptadecanol	54	310	88.5	54		
Piperonyl alcohol	58				117	119
1-Octadecanol (Stearyl alcohol)	59.5	210.5^{15}		64	66	
4-Methyl benzyl alcohol (4-Tolyl carbinol)	59	217		58.9		
1-Nonadecanol	62			58.9		
Eicosanol	65	220^{8}		69.5		
1-(α-Naphthyl)-ethanol (D,L-Methyl α-naphthyl carbinol)	66					
1,2-Diphenylethanol (D,L-Benzyl phenyl carbinol)	67	167^{10}				
4,4'-Dimethylbenzohydrol (Di-4-tolyl carbinol)	68					
Benzohydrol (Diphenyl carbinol)	68	288	135	131	141	
Glyceryl α-phenyl ether	69					
Erythritol (1,2,3,4-D,L-Tetrahydroxybutane)	72					
Dihydroxyacetone (1,3-Dihydroxy-2-propanone)	72					
1,10-Decanediol (Decamethylene glycol)	75.5					
10-Nonadecanol (Myricyl alcohol)	85		54			
Phenacyl alcohol (α-Hydroxyacetophenone; Benzoyl carbinol)	86	118^{11}		128.5		
n-Triacontanol (1-Hydroxytriacontane)	86.5					
o-Hydroxybenzyl alcohol (Saligenin)	86					
D-Sorbitol	89					
Tri-p-tolyl carbinol	96					
meso-Erythritol	121	330				
D,L-Benzoin (Benzoyl phenyl carbinol)	137	344	140	123		
Cinchol (β-Sitosterol)	137				202	
Furoin (Furoyl furyl carbinol)	138					
Cholesterol, anh. (L-Cholesterol)	148.5	360 d.	176	185		

Table 1–8–A. Alcohols, Solid (Cont.)   375

Triphenylmethanol (Triphenyl carbinol)	161				
Ergosterol	165	380	202		202
D-Mannitol	166				
Dulcitol (1,2,3,4,5,6-Hexanehexol)	188.5				
D-Borneol	208	212	132	153	154
meso-Inositol (1,2,3,4,5,6-Hexahydroxycyclohexane)	225				
p-Quercitol (Pentahydrocyclohexane)	232				
Pentaerythritol (2,2-Bishydroxymethyl-1,3-propanediol)	262				

Table 1–8–B. Alcohols, Liquid

TABLE 1–8–B. *Alcohols, Liquid*

	B. Pt.	M. Pt.	α-Naphthyl urethan	p-Nitro-benzoate	3,5-Dinitro-benzoate	3-Nitro-hydrogen phthalate
Methanol (Methyl alcohol)	65		124	179	108	153
Ethanol (Ethyl alcohol)	78		79	57	93	158
2-Propanol (Isopropyl alcohol)	82		106	110.5	123	154
D,L-3-Buten-2-ol (Methyl vinyl carbinol)	94		108	28	49	43
2-Propen-1-ol (Allyl alcohol)	97		80	35	74	124
1-Propanol (n-Propyl alcohol)	97		97	25	76	145.5
2-Butanol (D,L-sec.-Butyl alcohol) (Ethyl methyl carbinol)	99.5		72	85	116	131
2-Methyl-2-butanol (tert.-Amyl alcohol)	102		104	69	87	180.5
2-Methyl-1-propanol (Isobutyl alcohol)	108					
3-Buten-1-ol	122.5755					
D,L-3-Methyl-2-butanol (sec.-Isoamyl alcohol; D,L-Isopropyl methyl carbinol)	114		109	17	101	127
3-Pentanol (sym.-sec.-Amyl alcohol; Diethyl carbinol)	116		95		64	121
1-Butanol (n-Butyl alcohol)	118		71	70	62	147
D,L-2-Pentanol (sec.-Amyl alcohol)	120		74.5	17		102
3,3-Dimethyl-2-Butanol (D,L-Pinacolyl alcohol; tert.-Butyl methyl carbinol)	120		101		107	
2,3-Dimethyl-2-butanol (Dimethyl isopropyl carbinol)	120.5				111	
3-Methyl-3-pentanol	123		83.5		96.5	
2-Methyl-2-pentanol (Dimethyl n-propyl carbinol)	123				72	
2-Methoxyethanol (Methyl cellosolve; ethylene glycol monomethyl ether)	124.5		112.5	50.5	85	129
2-Methyl-3-pentanol (Isopropyl ethyl carbinol)	127.5					151
2-Methyl-1-butanol (Active amyl alcohol; D-sec.-Butyl carbinol)	129		82		70	157
D,L-4-Methyl-2-pentanol (Isobutyl methyl carbinol; methyl amyl alcohol)	132		88	26	65	

Table 1–8–B. Alcohols, Liquid (Cont.)   377

3-Methyl-1-butanol (*prim.*-Isoamyl alcohol)	132	68	21	61	166.5
3-Methyl-2-pentanol (*sec.*-Butyl methyl carbinol)	134^{749}	72		43.5	
2-Ethoxyethanol (Ethylene glycol monoethyl ether)	135	67.5		75	118
3-Hexanol (*n*-Propyl ethyl carbinol)	136			97	
2,2-Dimethyl-1-butanol (*tert.*-Amyl carbinol)	137	80			51
1-Pentanol (*n*-Amyl alcohol)	138	68	11	46.5	136
D,L-2-Hexanol (*n*-Butyl methyl carbinol)	138	60.5	40	38.5	
2,4-Dimethyl-3-pentanol	140	95	155		150
Cyclopentanol	141	118			
2-Isopropoxyethanol (Ethylene glycol mono-isopropyl ether)	141.5			51.5	
3-Ethyl-3-pentanol (Triethyl carbinol)	142				
2,3-Dimethyl-1-butanol	145				
3-Hydroxy-2-butanone (D,L-Acetoin; Acetyl methyl carbinol)	145				145
1-Hydroxy-2-propanone (Acetol; Acetyl carbinol)	146				
2-Methyl-1-pentanol (2-Methyl *n*-amyl alcohol)	148	75		50.5	
2-Ethyl butanol	149			51.5	
2-*n*-Propoxyethanol (Ethylene glycol mono-*n*-propyl ether)	150^{736}				
3-Methyl-1-pentanol	151	58		38	
4-Methyl-1-pentanol (Isoamyl carbinol; Isohexyl alcohol)	152		35	72	138.5
D-1-4-Heptanol (Di-*n*-propyl carbinol)	156	78		64	
1-Hexanol (1-Hexyl alcohol)	157.5	59	5	58.5	124
D,L-2-Heptanol	159			49.5	
(*n*-Amyl methyl carbinol; *sec.*-Heptyl alcohol)					
2-Isobutoxy-1-ethanol (Ethylene glycol mono-isobutyl ether)	159^{746}	54			
2-*sec.*-Butoxy-1-ethanol (Ethylene glycol mono-*sec.*-butyl ether)	159^{746}				
2,4-Dimethyl-1-pentanol	160				154
2-Methyl-1-hexanol	164				131
2-Ethyl-1-pentanol (2-Ethyl-*n*-amyl alcohol)	164		51		127
D,L-4-Methyl-1-hexanol	165				149
cis-(β)-2-Methylcyclohexanol (Hexahydro-*o*-cresol)	165	50	65	98	
trans-(α)-2-Methylcyclohexanol	167		48	114	
4-Hydroxy-4-methyl-2-pentanone (Diacetone alcohol)	166			55	

Table 1-8–B. Alcohols, Liquid (Cont.)

Table 1–8–B. (Cont.)

	B. Pt.	M. Pt.	α-Naphthyl urethan	p-Nitro-benzoate	3,5-Dinitro-benzoate	3-Nitro-hydrogen phthalate
Furfuryl alcohol (2-Furyl carbinol) 172	172		129	76	80	120
2-n-Butoxyethanol (Ethylene glycol mono-n-butyl ether)	170743					
2,6-Dimethyl-4-heptanol (Diisobutyl carbinol)	171					82
cis-(β)-3-Methylcyclohexanol (Hexahydro-m-cresol)	173		128	65	91	
trans-(α)-3-Methylcyclohexanol (Hexahydro-m-cresol)	174		122	58	97	
cis-(β)-4-Methylcyclohexanol (Hexahydro-p-cresol)	173750			94	134	
trans-(α)-4-Methylcyclohexanol (Hexahydro-p-cresol)	173745			67	139	
2,6-Dimethylcyclohexanol	174748					
cis-2,5-Dimethylcyclohexanol	175					
trans-2,4-Dimethylcyclohexanol	175					
cis-2,4-Dimethylcyclohexanol	176					
trans-2,5-Dimethylcyclohexanol	177–					
1-Heptanol (1-Heptyl alcohol)	177		62	10	46	127
2,2-Dimethylcyclohexanol	177					
Tetrahydrofurfuryl alcohol	177743			46	83	
2-Methyl-1,2-propanediol (Isobutylene glycol)	178		63	28	32	
D,L-2-Octanol	179					
1,3,5-Trimethylcyclohexanol	181					
Cyclohexyl carbinol (Hexahydrobenzyl alcohol)	182					133
4-Methyl-1-heptanol	183		60			108
2-Ethyl-1-hexanol	185					
2,3-Butanediol (Butylene glycol-2,3)	177742 D,L 182742 *meso-*					
3,3-Dimethylcyclohexanol	185754	11		83		
cis-3,5-Dimethylcyclohexanol	187					
trans-3,5-Dimethylcyclohexanol	187					
D,L-1,2-Propanediol (α-Propylene glycol)	187					
3,4-Dimethylcyclohexanol	189					

Table 1–8–B. Alcohols, Liquid (Cont.)   379

	B.P.					
2,4,5-Trimethylcyclohexanol	191 *cis-* 196 *trans-*					
1,3,3-Trimethyl-1-cyclohexen-6-ol	193					
2-(2-Methoxyethoxy)-ethanol	194			92		91.5 anh. 87 monohyd.
(Diethylene glycol monomethyl ether)						
2,3,6-Trimethylcyclohexanol	193^{747}					
5-Nonanol	194^{743}					
1-Octanol (*n*-Octyl alcohol)	195		67	12	61	128
2-Methyl-2,4-pentanediol	196					
2-(2-Ethoxyethoxy)-ethanol						
(Diethylene glycol monoethyl ether)	196^{763}					
Glycol (1,2-Ethanediol)	198		176 bis-	140	169 d.	
D,L-2-Nonanol	198		55.5	70	43	
L-Linalool (L-Linalyl alcohol)	199		53			
Benzyl alcohol	205.5		134	85	113	176
D,L-1,3-Butanediol (D,L-Butylene glycol-1,3)	207.5		184			
D,L-2-Decanol (*n*-Octyl methyl carbinol)	211		69	60	52	125
1-Nonanol (*n*-Nonyl alcohol)	213.5		65.5			
1,3-Propanediol (Trimethylene glycol)	215		164 di-	119 di-	178 di-	
3-Methyl benzyl alcohol (*m*-Tolyl carbinol)	217		116			
p-α-Dimethyl benzyl alcohol (α-Methyl p-tolyl carbinol)	219					
1-Phenyl-*n*-propyl alcohol (D,L-Phenyl ethyl carbinol)	219		102	59		
2-Phenethyl alcohol (2-Phenylethanol)	220		119	61.5	108	123
D,L-α-Terpineol	221	35	152	139	78	
Citronellol	222					
α-Isopropylbenzyl alcohol (D,L-Isopropyl phenyl carbinol)	222		116			
D,L-2-Undecanol (*n*-Nonanyl methyl carbinol)	228					
2-(2-*n*-Butoxyethoxy)-ethanol	228					
(Diethylene glycol mono-*n*-butyl ether)						
1,4-Butanediol (Tetramethylene glycol)	230	19	199 bis-	175 di-		
Geraniol	230		47	35	62	117

Table 1–8–B. (Cont.)

	B. Pt.	M. Pt.	α-Naphthyl urethan	p-Nitro-benzoate	3,5-Dinitro-benzoate	3-Nitro-hydrogen phthalate
1-Decanol (n-Decyl alcohol)	231		73	30	58	123
2-Phenoxyethanol (Ethylene glycol monophenyl ether)	237					112
3-Phenylpropanol (Hydrocinnamyl alcohol)	237			45	92	117
1,5-Pentanediol (Pentamethylene glycol)	238		147 bis-	104 di-		
1-Undecanol (n-Undecyl alcohol)	243		149	99.5	55	123.5
Diethylene glycol (β,β′-Dihydroxy diethyl ether)	244.5		135	151		
2-Methoxy benzyl alcohol (Saligenin 2-methyl ether)	247					
2-Benzyloxyethanol (Ethylene glycol monobenzyl ether)	265					
Phenyl n-hexyl carbinol	275					
Triethylene glycol (Ethylene di-[β-hydroxyethyl]-ether)	285		191 tri-	188 tri-		
Glycerol (1,2,3-Trihydroxypropane)	290 d.	18				
3,4-Dimethoxy benzyl alcohol (Veratryl alcohol)	296^{732}					
p-Methoxyphenyl methyl carbinol (4-Anisyl methyl carbinol)	310 d.					
cis-Octa-9-decen-1-ol (Oleyl alcohol; cis-Octadecenyl alcohol)	333		44 β			

Table 1–9–A–1. Hydrocarbons, Solid, Non-Aromatic 381

TABLE 1–9–A–1. *Hydrocarbons, Solid, Non-Aromatic*

	B. Pt.	M. Pt.	n_D^{20}	D_4^{20}	2,4-Dinitrophenyl sulfenyl chloride
Pentadecane	270.7	10	1.4310	0.769	
Hexadecane (Cetane)	287	18	1.4352	0.7751	
1,4-Dihydronaphthalene	212	24	1.5740	0.998	
n-Heptadecane	302.6	28	1.4360 n^{25}	0.7767$D_{22.5}^{22.5}$	
Octadecane	317.4	28	1.4367 n^{28}		
n-Nondecane	331.6				
Eicosane	345.1	36.7	1.4307 n^{50}		
Hencicosane		40.4	1.4352 n^{45}		
Docosane		44.4			
Tricosane		47	1.4190 n^{90}		
Tetracosane		51.1	1.4303 n^{65}		
L-Camphene	159	51.3	1.46207	0.8555	121
Pentacosane		54	1.4320 n^{60}		
Heptacosane		60			
Cyclopentadecane		60	1.4592 n^{61}		
Octacosane		61.4			
Nonacosane		64	1.4361 n^{65}		
Triacontane		66	1.4266 n^{90}		
Doticontane		70			
1,4-Diphenylbutadiene		70			
Tetracontane		80.5			
Pentacontane		75			
2,2,3,3-Tetramethylbutane	106.3	100.8	1.4695 $n^{106.3}$		
Stilbene	306	125		0.970 D_{13}^{125}	
1,4-Diphenylbutadiene, *trans-*		148			

Table 1–9–A–2. Hydrocarbons, Solid, Aromatic

TABLE 1–9–A–2. *Hydrocarbons, Solid, Aromatic*

	M. Pt.	B. Pt.	Density	Nitro		2,4-Dinitrophenyl sulfenyl chloride	Picrate
				Position	M. Pt.		
1,4-Dihydronaphthalene	10	270.7	0.998				
Diphenylmethane	26	261		2,4,2',4'	172		135
2,6-Dimethylphenanthrene	33						100
1-Propylphenanthrene	34						116
2-Methylnaphthalene	34	241					
9,10-Dihydrophenanthrene	34.5	168^{15}		1	81		108
2-Isopropylphenanthrene	44						127
1,5-Dimethylphenanthrene	46	204^{15}					143.5
1,4-Dimethylphenanthrene	50						131
Pentamethylbenzene	51			6	154		
Bibenzyl (1,2-Diphenylethane)	53			4,4'	180	132	
				2,2',4,4'	169		
Methylenefluorene (Biphenylene-ethylene)	53						152
3,5-Dimethylphenanthrene	53						139
7-Methyl-3',4'-benzphenanthrene	54						134
3,3'-Dimethylstilbene (*sym*-Di-*m*-tolylethylene)	55						97
2,9-Dimethylphenanthrene	56						138
1,5-Dimethylphenanthrene	57						134
1,2-Dimethylazulene	58						129
1,7-Dimethyl-4-isopropylnaphthalene	60						92
3,4-Dimethylphenanthrene	62						129
sym-Diphenylacetylene (Tolane)	62.5						111
1-Ethylphenanthrene	62.5	198					108
9-Ethylphenanthrene	62.5						123
4-Methylfluorene	63						
1,8-Dimethylnaphthalene	63						148
8-Methyl-3',4'-benzphenanthrene	65						107

Table 1–9–A–2. Hydrocarbons, Solid, Aromatic (Cont.)　　　　383

2-Ethylphenanthrene	67					95.5
3,4-Benzphenanthrene	68					128
4,8-Dimethylazulene	69					157
Biphenyl	69		4,4' 2,2',4,4'	237 150	142	
2-Methyl-3',4'benzphenanthrene	70					192
1,4-Diphenylbutadiene	70					
3-Methylpyrene	71					211
1,4-Dimethylanthracene	74					140
9-Propylphenanthrene	74	265^{22}				134
4,9-Dimethyl-1,2-benzanthracene	75					116
Benzalfluorene (ω-Phenyldibenzofulvene)	76					115
1,3-Dimethylphenanthrene	76					153
1-Methyl-3',4'-benzphenanthrene	78	$210^{0.4}$				112
1,2'-Binaphthyl	79					127
2,3-Dimethylphenanthrene	79					146
1,2,4,5-Tetramethylbenzene (Durene)	79	195	3,6	205		
1,5-Dimethylnaphthalene	80					138
6-Methyl-3',4'-benzphenanthrene	80					118
Naphthalene	80	218	1	61	173	149
1,3-Dimethylanthracene	83					136
2,2'-Dimethylstilbene (sym-Di-o-tolylethylene)	83	176^{10}				102
1-Isopropylphenanthrene	85					125
1,7-Dimethylphenanthrene	86					132
1,6-Dimethylphenanthrene	87					134
1,9-Dimethylphenanthrene	88					163.5
1,3-Diphenylbenzene	89					
Triphenyl methane	92	363	4,4',4''	206		
2,7-Dimethylnaphthalene	92					136
5-Isopropylnaphthanthracene	92					157
Acenaphthylene	92	265				201
3,9-Dimethyl-1,2-benzanthracene	93					137

Table 1–9–A–2. Hydrocarbons, Solid, Aromatic (Cont.)

Table 1–9–A–2. (Cont.)

	M. Pt.	B. Pt.	Density	Nitro Position	Nitro M. Pt.	2,4-Dinitro-phenyl sulfenyl chloride	Picrate
5,6-Benzindan (2,3-Cyclopentenonaphthalene)	94						120
12-Isopropylnaphthanthracene	95						157
Acetnaphthene	96	277.5		5	101	187	162
2,7-Dimethylnaphthalene	96	262					136
1-Methyl-7-isopropylfluorene	96.5	390			245		124
Retene (1-Methyl-7-isopropylphenanthrene)	100	340				250	144
Phenanthrene	101						152
2,7-Dimethylphenanthrene	101						123
2,3-Dimethylnaphthalene (Guaiene)	104						155
Ethylidenefluorene	104						142
2,6-Dimethylnaphthalene	110	261					139
2,4-Dimethylphenanthrene	111						162
4,10-Dimethyl-1,2-benzanthracene	114			2	156		87
Fluorene	113.5	293		2,7	199		
5-Methylchrysene (5-Methyl-1′,2′-benzphenanthrene)	117						143
1′,10-Dimethyl-1,2-dibenzanthracene	122						147
9,10-Dimethyl-1,2-benzanthracene	122						112
trans-Stilbene	124	305^{720}	0.970 D_{13}^{125}				94
3,4-Benzfluorene	124						130
9-Isopropylnaphthanthracene	125						152
5,8-Dimethyl-1,2-benzanthracene	131						175
8-Isopropylnaphthanthracene	132						118
2-Methyl-1′,2′-benzpyrene	138						184
1,5-Dimethylanthracene	139						166
3,6-Dimethylphenanthrene	141						172
1,2-Dimethylphenanthrene	142						148
4-Methylpyrene	143						

Table 1–9–A–2. Hydrocarbons, Solid, Aromatic (Cont.) 385

Name	m.p.			
8,10-Dimethyl-1,2-benzanthracene	146			166
9-Methyl-1′,2′-benzpyrene	147			226
9-Phenylfluorene	147			179.5
1-Methylpyrene	147.5			222
3-Methyl-1′-2′,benzpyrene	148			135
1,4-Diphenylbutadiene, *trans-*	148			178 di-
Pyrene	149			133
4-Methylchrysene (4-Methyl-1′,2′-benzphenanthrene)	151			145
Cinnamalfluorene	155			210 tri-
1,2-Benzanthracene	159			170
1,1′-Binaphthyl	160.5			199
Di-1-naphthastilbene (*sym*-Di-1-naphthylethylene)	161			170
6-Methylchrysene (6-Methyl-1′,2′-benzphenanthrene)	161			164
2′,6′-Dimethyl-1,2-benzanthracene	164			167
Hexamethylenebenzene	165			181
3-Methylchrysene (3-Methyl-1′,2′-benzphenanthrene)	170			170
Cholanthrene	170			197
6-Methyl-1′,2′-benzpyrene	171			174
6,7-Dimethyl-1,2-benzanthracene	174			229
1,2-Benzpyrene	176.5			176 d.
5,10-Dimethyl-1,2-benzanthracene	177			184
4,5-Benzpyrene	178			191
9,10-Dimethylanthracene	180			127.5
2,2′-Binaphthyl	187			151
5,6-Dimethyl-1,2-benzanthracene	187			177
1,2-Benzfluorene (Chrysofluorene)	189	413		212
1,8-Dimethylphenanthrene	191			207
Bifluorenylidene (Dibiphenylene-ethylene)	194		171	
1,2,7,8-Dibenzanthracene	196			
1,2,3,4-Dibenzanthracene	200			
Di-2-fluorenylmethane	201	358	256	
sym-Tetramethylbenzene	211			

Table 1–9–A–2. (Cont.)

	M. Pt.	B. Pt.	Density	Nitro Position	Nitro M. Pt.	2,4-Dinitro-phenyl sulfenyl chloride	Picrate
1,4-Diphenylbenzene	213						207
5-Methyl-1,2′-benzpyrene	216						138
Anthracene	216						203
4-Methyl-1,2′-benzpyrene	217.5						143
2-Methylchrysene (2-Methyl-1′,2′-benzphenanthrene)	224.5						273
1,2-Benzphenanthrene (Chrysene)	254	448					215
Di-2-naphthastilbene (*sym*-Di-2-naphthylethylene)	254						
1-Methylchrysene (1-Methyl-1′,2′-benzphenanthrene)	254						
2,3,6,7-Dibenzphenanthrene	257						184
2,3,5,6-Dibenzphenanthrene	261						213 di-
1,2,5,6-Dibenzanthracene	262						214 di-
Picene (1,2,7,8-Dibenzphenanthrene)	365	518					> 250 d.
Coronene (Hexabenzobenzene)	438						

TABLE 1–9–A–3. *Ethers, Solid*

	M. Pt.	B. Pt.	n_D^{20}	D_4^{20}	3,5-Dinitro-benzoate	Picrate
Allyl-2-naphthyl ether	16	d.	$1.600\ n_D^{25}$			
Veratrole (1,2-Dimethoxybenzene)	22.5	207	$1.5287\ n^{21}$	1.080		56
Anethole (1-Methoxy-4-propenylbenzene)	22.5	235	1.558	$0.989\ D_4^{28}$		69
p-Methoxybenzyl alcohol (Anisyl alcohol)	24	151^{27}				
n-Amyl-2-naphthyl ether	24.5	327.5	$1.5587\ n^{30}$			66.5
Diphenyl ether	28	259	$1.5826\ n^{24}$	1.073		110
Isoamyl-2-naphthyl ether	28	321				
2-Methoxyphenol (Guaiacol; Pycatechol monomethyl ether)	28	205	1.5441	$1.1287\ D^{20.4}$	141	93.5
2-Methoxybiphenyl (2-Biphenyl methyl ether)	29	274				

Table 1–9–A–3. Ethers, Solid (Cont.)   387

	m.p.	b.p.	n	d	
Isobutyl-2-naphthyl ether	33	304			84
Dodecyl ether (Dilauryl ether)	33	190^{1}			
2-Biphenyl ether	34	132^{6}			86
sec.-Butyl-2-naphthyl ether	34	298.5			
3-Biphenyl ethyl ether	35	158^{8}			
n-Butyl 2-naphthyl ether	35.5	309			67
Ethyl-2-naphthyl ether (neo-Nerolin)	36	282	$1.5932 \ n^{47}$	1.064	101
Isopropyl-2-naphthyl ether	40	285			95
n-Propyl-2-naphthyl ether	40	297			81
Catechol diethyl ether (1,2-Diethoxybenzene)	43	217			69
Pyrogallol trimethyl ether (1,2,3-Trimethoxybenzene)	47	241			78.5
Phloroglucinol trimethyl ether (1,3,5-Trimethoxybenzene)	52	255.5			
Hydroquinone monomethyl ether	52.5	244^{754}			
Hydroquinone dimethyl ether (1,4-Dimethoxybenzene)	56	213			47
4-Cyclohexylphenyl methyl ether	59	116^{4}			
1,3-Diphenoxypropane (Trimethyleneglycol diphenyl ether)	61	338			
Catechol dibenzyl ether (1,2-Dibenzoxybenzene)	63				
1-Phenyl-2-phenoxymethanol	64				
α-Glyceryl phenyl ether	70	187^{15}			
Hydroquinone diethyl ether (1,4-Diethoxybenzene)	72				116.5
Methyl-2-naphthyl ether (Nerolin)	73	273			
4-Biphenyl ethyl ether	76	188^{13}			85
Benzyl-1-naphthyl ether	77	200^{12}			
2-Phenyl-2-phenoxyethanol	81				
Biphenylene oxide (Dibenzofuran)	86	288			94
4-Methoxybiphenyl (4-Phenylphenol methyl ether; 4-Phenylanisole)	90				
1,2-Diphenoxyethane (Ethylene glycol diphenyl ether)	98				
Benzyl-2-naphthyl ether (2-Benzoxynaphthalene)	101.5				123
Anisoin (p,p'-Dimethoxybenzoin)	113				
Hydroquinone dibenzyl ether (1,4-Dibenzoxybenzene)	128				
Anisil (5-Hydroxy-1,2,3-trimethoxybenzene)	148				

25*

Table 1–9–B–1. Hydrocarbons, Liquid, Aromatic

TABLE 1–9–B–1. *Hydrocarbons, Liquid, Aromatic*

	B. Pt.	M. Pt.	Density	Nitro Position	Nitro M. Pt.	2,4-Dinitro-phenyl sulfenyl chloride	Picrate
Benzene	80		0.8790	1,3	89	120	84
				1,3,5	122	139	
Δ′-Tetrahydrotoluene	107		0.8145 D_8^{18}				
Toluene	110.6		0.8670	2,4	70	102	88
Ethylbenzene	136		0.8669	2,4,6	37	97	96.5
1,4-Xylene	138		0.8611	2,3,5	139	134	90
1,3-Xylene	139		0.8642	2,4,6	183		91
1,2-Xylene	144		0.8802	4,5	118		88
Phenylacetylene	142		0.9281				
Styrene (vinylbenzene)	145		0.9056			143	
Isopropylbenzene (Cumene)	152		0.8618	2,4,6	109		
Allyl benzene	157		0.8912				
n-Propylbenzene	159		0.8620				103
1-Ethyl-3-methylbenzene (m-Ethyltoluene)	161		0.8645				
1-Ethyl-4-methylbenzene (p-Ethyltoluene)	162		0.8612				
1,3,5-Trimethylbenzene (Mesitylene)	165		0.8652	2,4	86		97
α-Methylstyrene	165		0.9106				
1-Ethyl-2-methylbenzene (o-Ethyltoluene)	165		0.8807				
m-Methylstyrene	168		0.900				
tert.-Butylbenzene	169		0.8665	2,4	62	130	
p-Methylstyrene	169		0.897				
1 4-Trimethylbenzene (Pseudocumene)	169		0.8758	3,5,6	185		97
o-Methylstyrene	171		0.916				
Isobutylene	173		0.8532			99	
sec.-Butylbenzene	173		0.8621			88	
1,2,3-Trimethylbenzene (Hemimellitene)	176		0.8944				89.5
β-Methyl-styrene	176		0.935				

Table 1–9–B–1. Hydrocarbons, Liquid, Aromatic (Cont.)   389

Compound							
4-Isopropyltoluene (p-Cymene)	177		0.8573	2,6	54		98
1,3-Diethylbenzene	181		0.8641	2,4,6	62		
Indene	182		0.9915				
n-Butylbenzene	183		0.8601			72	
m-Ethylvinylbenzene	190		0.8945				
1,2,3,5-Tetramethylbenzene (Isodurene)	198		0.8899	4,6	181		
1,2,3,4-Tetramethylbenzene	205		0.9053	5,6	176		
1,2,3,4-Tetrahydronaphthalene ("Tetralin")	206		0.971	5,7	95		92
1,3,5-Triethylbenzene	218			2,4,6	108		
n-Hexylbenzene	226		0.8575				
Cyclohexylbenzene	235		0.9502				
1-Methylnaphthalene	245		1.0200	4	71		142
2-Ethylnaphthalene	258		0.9922				72
1-Ethylnaphthalene	258	15	1.0076				98.5
1,7-Dimethylnaphthalene	261		1.0115				121
1,6-Dimethylnaphthalene	262		1.003				114
1,4-Dimethylnaphthalene	262		1.008				144
1,3-Dimethylnaphthalene	263		1.002				118
1-Isopropylnaphthalene	263^{769}						85
2-Isopropylnaphthalene	263						93
1,1-Diphenylethane	268		1.0033				
1-Propylnaphthalene	274						140
2-Propylnaphthalene	277						89
1,1-Diphenylethylene	277	8				135.5	
4,5-Benzindan (1,2-Cyclopentenonaphthalene)	294^{757}						110
Diphenylacetylene	298					206	
3-Ethylphenanthrene	oil						121.5

Table 1–9–B–2. Ethers, Liquid

TABLE 1–9–B–2. *Ethers, Liquid*

	B. Pt.	M. Pt.	n_D^{20}	D_4^{20}	3,5-Dinitro-benzoate	Picrate
Ethylene oxide (Epoxyethane)	10.7		$1.3614\ n^4$	$0.8971\ D_4^0$		
Methyl ethyl ether	11			$0.7260\ D_4^0$		
Furan	31		1.42157	0.9366		
Diethyl ether (Ethyl ether)	35		1.3526	0.71352	93	
Propylene oxide (1,2-Epoxypropane)	35		1.466	0.830		
Ethyl vinyl ether	36		1.3768	0.7589		
Methyl *n*-propyl ether	39		1.3579	$0.7356\ D_4^{13}$		
Allyl methyl ether	46					
Ethyl isopropyl ether	53			0.7211		
tert.-Butyl methyl ether	55			0.7405		
2,3-Epoxybutane	58^{745} *cis-* 53^{741} *trans-*		1.3689	$0.8226\ D_4^{25}$ *cis-* $0.8010\ D_4^{25}$ *trans-*		
α-Butylene oxide (1,2-Epoxybutane)	61		$1.385\ n^{17}$	$0.837\ D^{17}$		
Ethyl *n*-propyl ether	64		1.36948	0.7386		
2-Methylfuran (Sylvan)	64		1.434	0.913		
Tetrahydrofuran	65		1.407	0.889		
Allyl ethyl ether	66^{742}		1.3881	0.7651		
Diisopropyl ether (Isopropyl ether)	67.5		1.3688	0.726	123	
n-Butyl methyl ether	70		1.3728	0.7455		
tert.-Butyl ethyl ether	73		1.3760	0.7404		
Tetrahydrosylvan	79		1.407	0.855		
Ethyl isobutyl ether	81		$1.3739\ n^{25}$	$0.7323\ D_4^{25}$		
sec.-Butyl ethyl ether	81		1.3802	0.7503		
Isopropyl *n*-propyl ether	83		1.376	0.7370		
Ethylene glycol dimethyl ether	85		1.37965	0.8665		
Dihydropyran	86		1.440	0.923		

Table 1–9–B–2. Ethers, Liquid (Cont.)   391

Compound	B.P., °C	n	d	
tert.-Amyl methyl ether	86	1.3885	0.7703	
Tetrahydropyran	88	1.421	0.881	
Di-n-Propyl ether (n-Propyl ether)	90	1.38829	0.74698	74
n-Butyl ethyl ether	92	1.3820	0.7505	
2,5-Dimethylfuran	94	$1.4363\,n^{21.6}$	$0.888\,D_4^{20.1}$	79
n-Amyl methyl ether	99	1.3873	0.761	
tert.-Amyl ethyl ether	101	1.3912	0.7657	
1,4-Dioxane	101	1.4232	1.03361	
Ethylene glycol ethyl methyl ether (1-Ethoxy-2-methoxyethane)	102	1.38677	0.8529	
Cyclopentyl methyl ether	105	1.4206	0.862	
n-Butyl isopropyl ether	108^{738}	$1.3889\,n^{24.9}$	$0.7594\,D^{15}$	
n-Amyl ethyl ether	121	1.3927	0.762	75.5
Di-sec.-Butyl ether	121	$1.3928\,n^{25}$	0.760	
Cyclopentyl ethyl ether	122	1.423	0.853	87
Diisobutyl ether (Isobutyl ether)	123	1.39467	$0.7616\,D_{15}^{15}$	
Ethylene glycol methyl n-propyl ether (1-n-Propoxy-2-methoxyethane)	124.5	1.3972	0.8472	
n-Hexyl methyl ether	126		0.772	97
2-Methoxy-1-propanol	130^{758}			
Cyclohexyl methyl ether	134	1.435	0.875	
Ethylene glycol monoethyl ether ("Cellosolve"; 2-Ethoxy ethanol)	135	1.40797	0.9297	75
3-Ethoxy-2-methyl-2-butanol	141			
n-Hexyl ethyl ether	142	1.4008	0.772	62
n-Butyl ether	142	1.3989	0.76829	87
Cyclohexyl ethyl ether	149	1.435	0.864	64
Anisole (Methoxybenzene; Methyl phenyl ether)	154	1.52211	0.99393	
3-Methoxy-2-methyl-1-propanol	155	$1.4140\,n^{27}$		
Diethylene glycol dimethyl ether	162	1.4099	$0.944\,D_{20}^{20}$	
2-Furancarbinol	170	1.4868	1.1351	
Ethylene glycol mono-n-butyl ether (Butyl "Cellosolve")	171^{743}	1.4177	0.9188	80

Table 1–9–B–2. (Cont.)

	B. Pt.	M. Pt.	n_D^{20}	D_4^{20}	3,5-Dinitrobenzoate	Picrate
Benzyl methyl ether	170		1.5008	0.9649		115
2-Methoxytoluene (Methyl anisole; Methyl o-tolyl ether; o-Cresyl methyl ether)	171		1.505	0.9853		116
Phenyl ethyl ether (Phenetole)	172		1.5080	0.9666		92
Diisoamyl ether (Isoamyl ether)	172.5		1.409	0.778	60	88
4-Methoxytoluene (p-Cresyl methyl ether)	173		1.512	0.970		88
3-Methoxytoluene (m-Cresyl methyl ether)	173		1.513	0.972		113
Tetrahydrofurancarbinol	177		1.45167	1.0544	83	
Phenyl isopropyl ether	178		1.4992	0.975		117
2-Ethoxytoluene (Ethyl o-tolyl ether)	184		1.505	0.953		
Benzyl ethyl ether (Homophenetole)	184		1.4958	0.9478	42	
Di-n-amyl ether (n-Amyl ether)	187.5		1.416	0.78298	42	
Diethylene glycol dimethyl ether	188		1.411	0.906		
Phenyl n-propyl ether	188		1.5014	0.9494 D_{20}^{20}		110
4-Ethoxytoluene (Ethyl p-tolyl ether)	190.5		1.505	0.949		110
3-Ethoxytoluene (Ethyl m-tolyl ether)	190.5		1.506	0.949		114
Diethylene glycol monomethyl ether	194		1.4244	1.035 D_{20}^{20}		
Diethylene glycol monoethyl ether	196		1.4298	1.023 D_{20}^{20}		
n-Butyl phenyl ether	206		1.5049	0.9233		110
Benzyl isobutyl ether	210		1.4826	0.954 D_4^0		
Methyl thymyl ether	216		1.4233	0.9871 D_{20}^{20}		56
Triethylene glycol dimethyl ether	216		1.4233	1.0552 D_{25}^{25}		
Resorcinol dimethyl ether (1,3-Dimethoxybenzene)	217		1.4833	0.9227		
Benzyl n-butyl ether	219			1.0919 D_4^{25}		112
Creosol (4-Methylcatechol 2-methyl ether)	221		1.5353 n^{25}	0.9437 D_0^0		
2-Butoxytoluene (n-butyl o-tolyl-ether)	223			0.7936	54.5	
Di-n-Hexyl ether (n-Hexyl ether)	228^{761}					
4-Allyl-1,2-methylenedioxybenzene (Safrole)	233	11	1.5383	1.100		104

Table 1–9–B–2. Ethers, Liquid (Cont.)   393

Resorcinol diethyl ether	235					109
Eugenol methyl ether (2,1-Dimethoxy-4-allylbenzene)	244	12.4	1.5360	1.0336		114
trans-(β)-Isosafrole (1,2-Methylene dioxy-4-propylbenzene)	248	6.8	1.5782	1.122		74
Di-n-Heptyl ether (n-Heptyl ether)	263		1.427	$0.8056\,D_{20}^{20}$	47	
Isoeugenol methyl ether	264	16	1.5692	1.0528		42
Tetraethylene glycol dimethyl ether	266		1.432	1.009		
Methyl-1-naphthyl ether (1-Methoxynaphthalene)	271		$1.6940\,n^{25}$	1.09159		129.5
Ethyl-1-naphthyl ether (1-Ethoxynaphthalene)	280.5	5.5	$1.5973\,n^{25}$	1.074		118.5
Dibenzyl ether (Benzyl ether)	290 d.	-4		1.0428	112	77
Isoamyl-1-naphthyl ether	317.5		$1.57049\,n^{14.2}$	$1.00689\,D_{4}^{14.2}$		

TABLE 1–9–B–3. *Hydrocarbons, Liquid, Alkynes, Terpenes, etc.*

	B. Pt.	n_D^{20}	D_4^{20}	Bromo derivative	2,4-Dinitro-phenyl sulfenyl chloride
1,3-Butadiene	−4.54	$1.4292\,n^{-25}$	$0.6500\,D^{-6}$		
1-Butyne	8	1.3962	$0.6682\,D^8$		
1,2-Butadiene	11	$1.4208\,n^2$	0.652		
1,4-Pentadiene	26	1.3887	0.6607		
2-Butyne	27	1.3893	0.688	243	75
3-Methyl-1-butyne	28	1.3785	0.666		
Isoprene (2-Methyl-1,3-butadiene)	34	1.4219	0.6809		
1-Pentyne	40	1.3847	0.6945		
3-Methyl-1,2-butadiene	40	1.4166	0.680		
1,3-Cyclopentadiene	41	1.4461	0.7983		
1,3-Pentadiene (Piperylene)	42.3	1.4309	0.6803		
1,2-Pentadiene	45	1.4209	0.6926		
2,3-Pentadiene	48	1.4284	0.6950		
2-Pentyne	55	1.4045	0.710		
1,5-Hexadiene	59	1.4034	0.690		
2,3-Dimethyl-1,3-butadiene	69	1.4390	0.7263	138	
1-Hexyne	71	1.3990	0.719		
2-Methyl-2,3-pentadiene	72	1.425	0.710		
1,3,5-Hextriene	78	1.4330	0.718		
1,3-Cyclohexadiene	80	1.4740	0.8413		
2,4-Hexadiene (Dipropenyl)	81	1.4493	0.7152	185	
3-Hexyne	81	1.4115	0.724		66
Cyclohexene	83	1.4465	0.8088		117
1-Heptyne	100	1.4084	0.7338		
1-Octyne	132	1.4172	0.7470		
α-Pinene	156	1.4560	0.8600	169	
Myrcene	166	1.4706	0.7982		
Dipentene (DL-Limonene)	175	1.4727	0.8402	124	
Sylvestrene	175	1.4760	0.8479	135	
D-Limonene	177	1.4739	0.8446	104	195

Table 1–9–B–4. Hydrocarbons, Liquid, Alkenes 395

TABLE 1–9–B–4. *Hydrocarbons, Liquid, Alkenes*

	B. Pt.	n_{D}^{20}	D_4^{20}	Bromo derivative	2,4-Dinitro-phenyl sulfenyl chloride
2-Methyl propene	−6.9	1.3467	0.6266 $D^{-6.6}$		86
1-Butene	−6.3	1.3465	0.6255 $D^{-6.5}$		77.5
2-Butene, *cis*-	3.73		0.6303 D^1		
3-Methyl-1-butene	20	1.3643	0.6320D^{15}		
1-Pentene (Amylene)	30.1	1.3710	0.6410		
2-Methyl-1-butene	31	1.3778	0.6504		
trans-2-Pentene	36	1.3790	0.6486		
cis-2-Pentene	37	1.3822	0.6562		
2-Methyl-2-butene	38.5	1.3878	0.6620		
3,3-Dimethyl-1-butene	41	1.3766	0.652		
Cyclopentene	44.2	1.4225	0.7736		
3-Methyl-1-pentene	53.6	1.3835	0.6700		
2-Methyl-4-pentene	54	1.4045	0.710		
2,3-Dimethyl-1-butene	56	1.3897	0.6807		
2-Methyl-1-pentene	61.5	1.3921	0.6817		
1-Hexene	66	1.3858	0.6734		61
3-Hexene	67	1.3942	0.6816		
2-Methyl-2-pentene	67	1.4005	0.690		
2-Hexene	68	1.3928	0.6813		
4,4-Dimethyl-1-pentene	72	1.3911	0.683		
2,3-Dimethyl-2-butene (Tetramethylethylene)	73	1.4115	0.7081	121	
5-Methyl-1-hexene	84	1.3954	0.694		
1-Heptene	93.6	1.3998	0.6971		
3-Heptene	96	1.4090	0.704		
2-Heptene	98.5	1.4041	0.703		
2,4,4-Trimethyl-1-pentene	101.2	1.4082	0.7151		
2,4,4-Trimethyl-2-pentene	104	1.4158	0.721		
Cycloheptene (Suberene)	115	1.4580	0.8228		
2-Ethyl-1-hexene	120	1.4157	0.7270		
1-Octene	121.3	1.4088	0.7160		
1-Nonene	147	1.4154	0.7292		
1-Decene	170.5	1.4220	0.7408		
1-Undecene	192.6	1.4261	0.7503		
1-Dodecene	213	1.4300	0.7584		

TABLE 1–9–B–5. *Hydrocarbons, Liquid, Alkanes*

	B. Pt.	M. Pt.	n_{D}^{20}	D_{4}^{20}
Neopentane (2,2-Dimethylpropane)	9.5		1.3513	0.596
Isopentane	28		1.3580	0.620
Pentane	36		1.3577	0.626
Cyclopentane	49.3		1.4068	0.746
2,2-Dimethylbutane	49.7		1.3689	0.649
2,3-Dimethylbutane	58		1.3750	0.662
2-Methylpentane	60.3		1.3716	0.653
3-Methylpentane	63.3		1.3764	0.664
Hexane	68.3		1.3749	0.659
Methylcyclopentane	72		1.4100	0.749
2,2-Dimethylpentane	79.2		1.3823	0.674
2,4-Dimethylpentane	80.5		1.3823	0.673
Cyclohexane	80.7		1.4264	0.778
2,2,3-Trimethylbutane	80.8		1.3894	0.690
3,3-Dimethylpentane	86		1.3911	0.693
1,1-Dimethylcyclopentane	87.8		1.41357	0.75448
2,3-Dimethylpentane	89.9		1.3920	0.695
2-Methylhexane	90		1.3851	0.679
1,3-Dimethylcyclopentane, *trans-*	90.8		1.40891	0.74479
1,3-Dimethylcyclopentane, *cis-*	91.7		1.4111	0.7488
1,2-Dimethylcyclopentane, *trans-*	91.9		1.41199	0.75144
3-Methylhexane	92		1.3887	0.687
3-Ethylpentane (Triethyl methane)	93.5		1.39340	0.69818
Heptane	98.4		1.3877	0.684
2,2,4-Trimethylpentane	99.2		1.3916	0.692
1,2-Dimethylcyclopentane, *cis-*	99.5		1.42221	0.77262
Methylcyclohexane	100.9		1.4231	0.769
Ethylcyclopentane	103.5		1.41976	0.76647
1,1,3-Trimethylcyclopentane	104.9		1.41119	0.74825
2,2-Dimethylhexane	106.8		1.3930	0.695
2,5-Dimethylhexane	109.1		1.3930	0.694
1-*trans*-2-*cis*-4-Trimethylcyclopentane	109.3		1.41060	0.74727
2,4-Dimethylhexane	109.4		1.39534	0.70036
2,2,3-Trimethylpentane	110		1.4030	0.717
1-*trans*-2-*cis*-3-Trimethylcyclopentane	110.2		1.4138	0.7535
3,3-Dimethylhexane	112		1.3992	0.708
2,3,4-Trimethylpentane	113.5		1.40422	0.71905
1,1,2-Trimethylcyclopentane	113.7		1.42298	0.77252
2,3,3-Trimethylpentane	114.7		1.4074	0.726
2,3-Dimethylhexane	115.6		1.4015	0.712
3-Ethyl-2-methylpentane	115.7		1.40402	0.71931
1-*cis*-2-*trans*-4-Trimethylcyclopentane	116.7		1.41855	0.76345
1-*cis*-2-*trans*-3-Trimethylcyclopentane	117.5		1.4218	0.7704
2-Methylheptane	117.6		1.39495	0.69790
3,4-Dimethylhexane	117.7		1.4044	0.720

Table 1–9–B–5. Hydrocarbons, Liquid, Alkanes (Cont.)   397

	B. Pt.	M. Pt.	n_D^{20}	D_4^{20}
4-Methylheptane	118		1.3985	0.705
3-Ethyl-3-methylpentane	118.3		1.40162	0.72742
3-Ethylhexane	118.5		1.4440	0.71358
Cycloheptane (Suberane)	119		1.4440	0.8099
3-Methylheptane	119		1.3988	0.706
1,4-Dimethylcyclohexane, *trans-*	119.4		1.4209	0.763
1,1-Dimethylcyclohexane	119.5		1.42895	0.78094
1,3-Dimethylcyclohexane, *cis-*	120		1.4229	0.766
3-Ethyl-*trans*-1-methylcyclopentane	120.8		1.4186	0.7619
3-Ethyl-*cis*-1-methylcyclopentane	121		1.4203	0.7724
2-Ethyl-*trans*-1-methylcyclopentane	121.2		1.4219	0.7690
1-Ethyl-1-methylcyclopentane	121.5		1.42718	0.78093
2,2,4,4-Tetramethylcyclopentane	122		1.4070	0.718
1-*cis*-2-*cis*-3-Trimethylcyclopentane	123		1.4262	0.7792
1,2-Dimethylcyclohexane, *trans-*	123.5		1.4270	0.766
2,2,5-Trimethylhexane	124.1		1.39971	0.70721
1,4-Dimethylcyclohexane, *cis-*	124.3		1.4297	0.783
1,3-Dimethylcyclohexane, *trans-*	124.5		1.4308	0.784
Octane	125.7		1.3975	0.703
2,2,4-Trimethylhexane	126.5		1.4033	0.7156
2-Ethyl-*cis*-1-methylcyclopentane	128		1.42933	0.78522
1,2-Dimethylcyclohexane, *cis-*	129.7		1.4360	0.796
2,4,4-Trimethylhexane	130.6		1.40748	0.72381
n-Propylcyclopentane	130.9		1.42626	0.77633
2,3,5-Trimethylhexane	131.3		1.4061	0.7219
Ethylcyclohexane	131.7		1.4332	0.788
2,2-Dimethylheptane	132.7		1.4016	0.7105
2,4-Dimethylheptane	133		1.403	0.716
2,2,3,4-Tetramethylpentane	133		1.41471	0.73895
2,2,3-Trimethylhexane	133.6		1.4105	0.7292
4-Ethyl-2-methylhexane	133.8		1.4063	0.723
2,2-Dimethyl-3-ethylpentane	133.8		1.4123	0.7348
2,6-Dimethylheptane	135		1.4007	0.709
4,4-Dimethylheptane	135.2		1.4076	0.725
2,5-Dimethylheptane	136		1.4038	0.715
3,5-Dimethylheptane	136		1.4067	0.723
2,4-Dimethyl-3-ethylpentane	136.7		1.4137	0.7379
2,2,5,5-Tetramethylhexane	137.5		1.40550	0.71875
2,3,3-Trimethylhexane	137.7		1.4141	0.738
3,3-Dimethylheptane	138		1.4085	0.725
3-Ethyl-2-methylhexane	138		1.4106	0.731
2,3,4-Trimethylhexane	139		1.4144	0.741
2,2,3,3-Tetramethylpentane	140.3		1.42360	0.75666
4-Ethyl-3-methylhexane	140.4		1.416	0.742
3,3,4-Trimethylhexane	140.5		1.4178	0.745
2,3-Dimethylheptane	140.5		1.4085	0.7260
3,4-Dimethylheptane	140.6		1.4111	0.7314

	B. Pt.	M. Pt.	n_D^{20}	D_4^{20}
3-Ethyl-3-methylhexane	140.6		1.4142	0.741
4-Ethylheptane	141.2		1.4109	0.730
2,3,3,4-Tetramethylpentane	141.6		1.42224	0.75473
3-Ethyl-2,3-dimethylpentane	142		1.419	0.754
4-Methyloctane	142.5		1.4061	0.7199
3-Ethylheptane	143		1.4093	0.727
2-Methyloctane	144.2		1.4032	0.713
3-Methyloctane	144.2		1.4062	0.7207
3,3-Diethylpentane	146.2		1.42051	0.75359
Nonane	150.8		1.4056	0.718
Cyclooctane	150^{750}		1.4586	0.8349
Isopropylcyclohexane	154.7		1.4410	0.802
n-Butylcyclopentane	156.6		1.4316	0.7846
n-Propylcyclohexane	156.7		1.4370	0.795
2,2,3,4,4-Pentamethylpentane	159.3		1.43069	0.76703
2,7-Dimethyloctane	160		1.4080	0.724
2,2,3,3-Tetramethylhexane	160.3		1.42818	0.76446
5-Methylnonane	165		1.4122	0.7326
2,2,3,3,4-Pentamethylpentane	166.1		1.43606	0.78009
2-Methylnonane	166.8		1.4099	0.7281
3-Methylnonane	167.8		1.4125	0.7334
p-Menthane	169		1.4369	0.796
Cyclononane	170		1.4328 n_D^{16}	0.8524 D^{15}
Decane	174		1.4114	0.730
n-Butylcyclohexane	177		1.4408	0.800
Decahydronaphthalene, trans-	187.2		1.4695	0.870
Isoamylcyclohexane	193		1.4423	0.802
Decahydronaphthalene, cis- (Decalin)	195.7		1.4810	0.896
Undecane	196		1.4190	0.702
Amylcyclohexane	201		1.4442	0.804
Cyclodecane	201		1.4692	0.8577 $D^{20.4}$
Dodecane	217		1.4216	0.749
n-Tridecane	235.5		1.4256	0.7563
Tetradecane	253.5		1.4289	0.764
Pentadecane	270.7		1.4310	0.769
Hexadecane (Cetane)	287		1.4352	0.773

TABLE 2–1–1. *Acid Nitrogen Compounds. Amino Acids*

	M. Pt.	p-Toluene sulfonyl	Phenylurea	Benzoyl	3,5-Dinitrobenzoyl	Acetyl
m-Aminohydrocinnamic acid	84					162
L-(+)-Valine	93	147		127	157	156
N-Methyl-β-alanine	99					
Aminomalonic acid	109					
o-Aminophenylacetic acid	119			61		158
Anilinomalonic acid	119 d.			179		195
2-Amino-1-naphthoic acid	126					194
N-Phenylglycine	127		195	63		124 hyd.
p-Aminohydrocinnamic acid	132			194		
2-Anilinoisovaleric acid	135					
L-Ornithine	140		190	240		
2-Anilinobutyric acid	141					
Anthranilic acid	147	217	181	182	278	
2-Anilinovaleric acid	147					
Oxanilic acid	148					
m-Aminophenyl acetic acid	151					
D-(-)-Valine	156					156
ω-Amino-n-valeric acid	157			105		
o-Aminocinnamic acid	158			191		250 mono-
D,L-β-Amino-n-valeric acid	160			145		
2-Anilinopropionic acid	162					
2-Amino-p-toluic acid	165					
m-Aminobenzoic acid	174		270	248	270	279
p-Aminocinnamic acid, *trans-*	175			274		259
ω-Aminotridecylic acid	177			111		
3-Amino-p-toluic acid (Homoanthranilic acid)	177					184

Table 2–1–1. (Cont.)

	M. Pt.	p-Toluene sulfonyl	Phenylurea	Benzoyl	3,5-Dinitrobenzoyl	Acetyl
4-Amino-1-naphthoic acid	177					189
m-Aminocinnamic acid, *trans*-	181			229		237
3-Amino-1-naphthoic acid	181					254
N-Ethylglycine	182					
L-Canavanine	184			86 d. tri-		
2-Anilinoisobutyric acid	184					
L-Glutamine	185					
Acetylanthranilic acid	185					
Hippuric acid	187					
p-Aminobenzoic acid	188		300	278	290	
D,L-Canaline	190			158		
N-Methylacetylanthranilic acid	192					
Betaine (Trimethyl glycine)	193					
D,L-β-Aminobutyric acid	194	117		154		187
D,L-Glutamic acid	199			153		168
p-Aminophenyl acetic acid	199			205	202	
β-Alanine	200		168	120		
L-Isoserine	200			107		
ω-Amino-n-caproic acid	202			45		
γ-Aminobutyric acid	203		170		217	
D,L-Proline	203			150		170
γ-Amino-n-caproic acid	205					
6-Amino-1-naphthoic acid	205					
1-Amino-2-naphthoic acid	205				150	
L-Arginine	207			298		
Oxamic acid	210					199
L-Glutamic acid	211	131				
5-Amino-1-naphthoic acid	212					296

Table 2–1–1. Acid Nitrogen Compounds. Amino Acids (Cont.)   401

Sarcosine	212		102	104	153	135
L-α-Asparagine	213			132		
D,L-γ-Amino-n-valeric acid	214			99 di-		
L-Canaline	214					
β-Amino-isovaleric acid	217					
β-Hydroxyvaline	218		182	153		
L-Proline	220	130				
L-Citruline	222					
7-Amino-1-naphthoic acid	223					229
L-Lysine	224		184	235 mono- / 149 di-		
D,L-Threonine	227		177	145		
β-L-Asparagine	227	175	164	189	196	
3,5-Diaminobenzoic acid	228					
L-Serine	228					
Glycine	228	147	197	187.5	179	
D,L-Thyroxine	230			210		
D,L-β-Hydroxynorvaline	230		156	170		
D,L-β-Aminohydrocinnamic acid	231			194		161
3-Pyridylacrylic acid	233					
D,L-Homoaspartic acid (α-Amino-α-methyl succinic acid)	234					
D-β-Aminohydrocinnamic acid	234					
L-β-Aminohydrocinnamic acid	234					
3-Aminosalicylic acid	235			189		215
D,L-Allothreonine	237			176 mono- / 174 di- / 230 di- anh. / 176 di- hyd.	200	
D,L-Arginine	238					
p-Dimethylaminobenzoic acid	242					
β-Amino-β-phenyl isobutyric acid	243			205		
D,L-Isoserine	246	213	184	151		
D,L-Serine	246		169	149		

Organic Analysis

26

Table 2–1–1. (Cont.)

	M. Pt.	p-Toluene sulfonyl	Phenylurea	Benzoyl	3,5-Dinitrobenzoyl	Acetyl
p-Hydroxyphenylglycine	248			117		203 mono- 174 di-
Isoaspartic acid (α-Amino-α-methylmalonic acid)	250					
D,L-Threonine	251			147		
D,L-Aminophenylacetic acid	256			175		198.5
L-Cystine	260	204	160	181 di-	180	
D,L-α-Aminohydratropic acid (α-Phenylalanine)	260					
Glycylglycine	260		176	208	210	
D,L-Phenylalanine	264	178	182	188		
D,L-Aspartic acid	270	134		119 hyd. 176 anh.		
D,L-α-Aminooctanoic acid	270	140		128		
L-Aspartic acid	270		162	185		
D,L-α-Aminononanoic acid	273			128		
L-Hydroxyproline	274	153	175	100 mono- 92 di-	240	
D,L-Tryptophane	275	176		198		
α-Aminoisobutyric acid	280			135		
D,L-α-Aminoheptanoic acid	281			145		
D,L-Methionine	281			252		114
5-Aminosalicylic acid	283					184 di- 218 mono-
D,L-Lanthionine	283			195 di-	150 anh. 94 hyd.	
L-Methionine	283					98
L-(+)-Isoleucine	283 d.	130	121	117		
D,L-Phenylalanine	283	164	181	146	93	
L-Hexahydrotyrosine	285			117		
D-(−)-Isoleucine	283	130	121			

Compound						
L-Histidine	288	202		230 mono-	189	
L-Cysteic acid	289					
L-Tryptophane	290	176	166	183	233	
D,L-N-Methyl-α-alanine	292					
D,L-Isoleucine	292	141	120	118		
L-(+)-α-Aminobutyric acid	292			121		
D,L-Leucine	293		165	137	187	
D,L-α-Amino-α-methyl valeric acid	295					
D,L-Alanine	295	139		166	177	
D-α-Aminohydratropic acid (α-Phenylalanine)	295					
L-Alanine	297	133		151		
D,L-Norleucine	297	124				
D,L-Valine	298	110		132	158	
L-Djenkolic acid	300		164	166 mono- / 88 di-		
D-N-Methyl-α-alanine	300					
Taurine	300					
L-(+)-Norleucine	301					
D,L-Norvaline	303		117	53		
Creatine (α-Methyl guanido-acetic acid)	303					165 di-
p-Aminohexahydrobenzoic acid	303					
D,L-α-Aminobutyric acid	304		170	147		
Lanthionine, meso-	304			198		
Creatinine	305					
L-α-Aminophenylacetic acid	305					
Diaminosuccinic acid, meso-	306				212 di- hyd.	
L-(+)-Norvaline	307					191
L-Tyrosine	314	N-188	104	64		235 d.
L-(+)-Valine	315 sealed tube	147	115	N-166		137
L-Leucine	337	124		127	157	N-148
D,L-Tyrosine	340			118	187	
α-Aminohexahydrobenzoic acid	350			N-197	252 di-	

26*

Table 2–1–1. (Cont.)

	M. Pt.	p-Toluene sulfonyl	Phenylurea	Benzoyl	3,5-Dinitrobenzoyl	Acetyl
D,L-Diaminosuccinic acid						235 di-
D,L-Ornithine	278 d.	188 mono-	192	164 di- hyd. 4-N-285		
L-(+)-Alloisoleucine			151			
D,L-Lysine			196	249 mono- 146 di-		
L-Cysteine						

Note: Although all amino acids do not react acidically in the generic test, they are placed in this one table on the basis of their other reactions.

Table 2–1–2. Acid Nitrogen Compounds. Other Acids and Anhydrides   405

Table 2–1–2. Acid Nitrogen Compounds. Other Acids and Anhydrides

	M. Pt.	B. Pt.	Amide	Anilide	p-Toluidide	p-Nitrobenzyl ester	p-Bromophenacyl ester
d,l-α-Azidobutyric acid	24	$81^{0.2}$	38				
2-Azidoisovaleric acid	31	$82^{0.1}$	93				
α-Azidoisobutyric acid	45	$75^{0.2}$					
4-Cyanobutyric acid							
Cyanoacetic acid	66		69 sealed tube				
Phenylcyanoacetic acid	92		147	136			
α-Cyanohydrocinnamic acid	101		130				
3,5-Dinitrobenzoic anhydride	109		183	234			
4-Nitrophthalic anhydride	119		200 d.	192	172 mono-		
m-Nitrophenylacetic acid	120						
Nicotinic anhydride	123		128	85	150		
3-Nitrosalicylic acid	125		145				
2-Nitrobenzoic anhydride	135		176	155			
2-Pyridinecarboxylic acid (Picolinic Acid)	138		107				
m-Nitrobenzoic acid	140		143	154	162	141	132
o-Nitrophenylacetic acid	141		161				
o-Nitrobenzoic acid	146		176	155		112	107
p-Nitrophenylacetic acid	153		198	198			207
2,4-Dinitrobenzoic anhydride	160		203				
3-Nitrobenzoic anhydride	160		143	154	162		
Alloxanic acid	162–163 d.		191				
3-Nitrophthalic anhydride	162		201 di-	234 di-	226 di-		
3,5-Dinitrophthalic anhydride	163		200 d.				
4-Nitrophthalic acid	165		181	192	172 mono-		
3,5-Dinitrosalicylic acid	182		203				
2,4-Dinitrobenzoic acid	183		173			142	158
2-Cyanobenzoic acid	187						

Table 2–1–2. (Cont.)

	M. Pt.	B. Pt.	Amide	Anilide	p-Toluidide	p-Nitro-benzyl ester	p-Bromo-phenacyl ester
3-Nitroanisic acid	187			163			
4-Nitrobenzoic anhydride	189		201	211	204		
Anthroxanic acid	190		211				
trans-*m*-Nitrocinnamic acid	199		196	234		174	178
3,5-Dinitrobenzoic acid	204–205		183			157	159
3-Cyanobenzoic acid	217		280				
3-Nitrophthalic acid	218		201 d. di.	234 di-	226 di-	189	
4-Cyanobenzoic acid	219		223	179	189		
Methylimidodiacetic acid	227 d.		169				
2,4,6-Trinitrobenzoic acid	228		264 d.				
5-Nitrosalicylic acid	229		225	224	150		
3-Pyridine carboxylic acid	237–238		128	85		132	141
trans-*o*-Nitrocinnamic acid	240		185				137
4-Nitrobenzoic acid	241		201	211	204		
Azobenzene-4-carboxylic acid	241			224			
Azobenzene-2,2′-dicarboxylic acid	245		215 d. mono- / 294 d. di-	199 di-			
2-Aminoanthraquinone-1-carboxylic acid	250–252		300				
Cinchoninic acid	253–254		181				
Cinchomeronic acid	260 d.		200 d. 3-mono- / 170 d. 4-mono- / 163 d. di-				
3-Quinolinecarboxylic acid	272		198				
4-Nitrocinnamic acid	285		204			186	191
4-Pyridinecarboxylic acid	324		156				

Table 2–1–3. Acid Nitrogen Compounds. Nitrophenols   407

TABLE 2–1–3. *Acid Nitrogen Compounds, Nitrophenols*

	B. Pt.	M. Pt.	Phenyl-urethan	α-Naphthyl-urethan	p-Nitro-benzoate	3,5-Dinitro-benzoate	Acetate	Benzoate
3-Nitro-p-cresol		34						102
2-Nitro-3-methylphenol (2-Nitro-m-cresol)		41					59	79
2-Nitrophenol		45		113	141	155	40	77
4-Nitro-3-methylphenol		56					48	42
3-Nitro-2-methylphenol		70						
2-Nitro-4-methylphenol		79						
2-Nitroresorcinol		85						
3,5-Dinitro-2-methylphenol		86.5					95	135
3-Nitrocatechol		86.5						
5-Nitro-3-methylphenol		90						
5-Nitro-2-methylphenol		96						128
3-Nitrophenol		97	129	167	174	159	55	95
3,4,5-Trinitro-2-methylphenol		102						
1-Nitro-2-naphthol		103					61	
2,4,6-Trinitro-3-methylphenol		109		150		186	135	140
4-Nitrophenol		114			159		81	142.5
2,4-Dinitrophenol		114			139		72	132
4-Nitro-2-methylphenol		118					74	
4-Nitro-2-naphthol		120						
4-Nitroresorcinol		122					90 di-	110 di-
2,4,6-Trinitrophenol (Picric Acid)		122 slow heating					76	
4,5,6-Tribromo-2-nitrophenol		123						
2-Nitro-1-naphthol		127					118	
6-Nitro-3-methylphenol		129					34	74
8-Nitro-1-naphthol		130						

Table 2–1–3. Acid Nitrogen Compounds, Nitrophenols (Cont.)

Table 2–1–3. (Cont.)

	B. Pt.	M. Pt.	Phenyl-urethan	α-Naphthyl-urethan	p-Nitro-benzoate	3,5-Dinitro-benzoate	Acetate	Benzoate
2,4-Dinitro-1-naphthol		138						174
2-Amino-4-nitrophenol		142						> 200 d.
8-Nitro-2-naphthol		144						
5-Nitro-2-naphthol		147					101	
6-Nitro-2-methylphenol		147						
2,4-Dinitroresorcinol		148						
3-Nitrosalicyl acid		148						
5-Nitroresorcinol		158						
4-Nitro-1-naphthol		164						
2-Amino-4,6-dinitrophenol (Picramic acid)		169			122			
5-Nitro-1-naphthol		171					114	109
3,5-Dinitrosalicylic acid		173						
4-Nitrocatechol		176					98 di-	163 mono- 156 di-
2,4,6-Trinitroresorcinol		179						
2,4,5-Trinitro-1-naphthol		189.5						
2-Nitro-1,3,5-trihydroxybenzene (Nitrophloroglucinol)		205 anh.						
5-Nitro-2-hydroxybenzoic acid		229						

TABLE 2–1–4. *Acid Nitrogen Compounds, Azophenols*

	M. Pt.	Acetate	Benzoate
o-Hydroxyazobenzene	83		93
2-m-Tolueneazo-1-naphthol	118		
4-Hydroxy-3-methylazobenzene	128	82	
1-o-Tolueneazo-2-naphthol	131		
1-Benzeneazo-2-naphthol	134	117	
1-p-Tolueneazo-2-naphthol	137	99	
2-Benzeneazo-1-naphthol	138	121	
1-m-Tolueneazo-2-naphthol	142		
2-p-Tolueneazo-1-naphthol	145		
4-o-Tolueneazo-1-naphthol	147		
p-Hydroxyazobenzene	152	89	
2-o-Toluene-1-naphthol	156		
1-(p-Aminobenzeneazo)-2-naphthol	160		
Benzeneazocatechol	165		
Benzeneazoresorcinol	170	104 di-	
o-Azophenol	172	150 di-	
1-(o-Methoxybenzeneazo)-2-naphthol	179		
1-(m-Aminobenzeneazo)-2-naphthol	179		
2-Hydroxy-1,2'-azonaphthalene	179	117	
1-(m-Nitrobenzeneazo)-2-naphthol	194	162	
2,4-Bis-benzeneazo-1-naphthol	197	160	
4-m-Tolueneazo-1-naphthol	199 d.		
4-Benzeneazo-1-naphthol	206 d.	128	
m-Azophenol	207	144 di-	188 di-
4-p-Tolueneazo-naphthol	208	102	
1-(o-Nitrobenzeneazo)-2-naphthol	210		
p-Azophenol	216	198 di-	210 di-
2-(o-Nitrobenzeneazo)-1-naphthol	218		
2-Hydroxy-1,1'-azonaphthalene	230		
2-(p-Nitrobenzeneazo)-1-naphthol	235	180	
1-(p-Nitrobenzeneazo)-2-naphthol	250	193	
4-(p-Nitrobenzeneazo)-1-naphthol	283	166	

TABLE 2–1–5. *Acid Nitrogen Compounds. Other Nitrogen Phenols**

	M. Pt.
1-Nitroso-2-naphthol	109
p-Nitrosophenol	125
5-Nitroso-o-cresol	135
o-Hydrazophenol	148
2-Nitroso-1-naphthol	162 d.
Nitrosothymol	162
4-Nitroso-1-naphthol	194

* See also amino phenols in Table 2-2-5.

TABLE 2–2–1. *Basic Nitrogen*

	M. Pt.	B. Pt.	Acetamide
4-Aminostyrene	23.5	98[4]	142
2-Amino-β-picoline	26	224	64
Dodecylamine	27	247–249	
Di-*n*-heptylamine	30	271	
D,L-2,6-Dimethyl-1,2,3,4-tetra-hydroquinoline	31	267	
2-Methyl-1-naphthylamine	32		188
4,4′-Dimethyldibenzylamine	32.5		
2-Aminodibenzyl	33	173[11]	117
unsym.-Diphenylhydrazine	34	220[40]	184
ω-Diamino-1,4-dimethylbenzene	35		194 tetra-
4-Amino-N-methylaniline	36	258	63
Pentadecylamine	36	300	
N-Benzylaniline	37	298	58
5-Aminoindane	37		106
5,6,7,8-Tetrahydro-2-naphthylamine	38		107
2,2-Diphenylethylamine	38		88
2,3-Dimethyl-1,2,3,4-tetrahydroquinoline	38		
6-Amino-α-picoline	41		90
4-Amino-N,N-dimethylaniline	41	208	132
1,6-Diaminohexane (Hexamethylenediamine)	42	204	
1,3-Diaminoisopropyl alcohol	42	235	
4-Amino-3-methylbiphenyl	43	190[15]	165
2,4′-Diaminobiphenyl	45	363	202 di-
4-Methylaniline (*p*-Toluidine)	45	200	147
4-Aminobenzylcyanide	46		97 mono-
			152 di-
2-Aminopropiophenone	47		71
3,4-Dimethylaniline	48	224	99
4-Aminodibenzyl	48		
2-Nitro-6-ethoxyaniline	49		64
Heptadecylamine	49	335	62
2-Aminobiphenyl	49	299	121
4-Amino-2-methyldiphenylamine	49–50	196[4]	139
1-Amino oxindole	50		186
1-Naphthylamine	50		159
1-Amino-1,2,3-triazole	51		
1-Methyl-2-naphthylamine	51		188
N-Nitrosoacetanilide	51 d.		
3-Methyl-1-naphthylamine	51		175
4-Methyl-1-naphthylamine	51		166
Indole	52	253	157
2-Aminodiphenylmethane	52		135
2,2′-Ditolylamine	52	318	
4-Aminobiphenyl	53	302	171
N,N′-Methyl-1,4-diamino-benzene	53	150[17]	
Diphenylamine	53		101

Table 2–2–1. Basic Nitrogen Compounds. Primary and Secondary   411

Compounds. Primary and Secondary

Benzamide	Benzene sulfonamide	p-Toluene sulfonamide	Phenyl thiourea	α-Naphthyl thiourea	Picrate
160					
220					229
		73			
					117
103					
180					
					153
166					167
192					
193 -N,N′-di-					232
165					
107	119	148	103		48
137					
167					204
143					212
92					178
90					202
228					188
155 di-	154 di-				220
					230
189					
278 di-					
158	120	118	141	234	168
176					185
130					
	118				
170					
91					
102					
189					
160	167	157	165		163
151					130
222					
188					
238					
68	254				
116					
114					
230		255			
					186
180	124	141	152		182

	M. Pt.	B. Pt.	Acetamide
D,L-α-Aminobenzylcyanide	55		
3-Nitro-4-methoxyaniline	57		153
4-Methoxyaniline (p-Anisidine)	58	240	130
7-Methyl-1-naphthylamine	58		182
2-Aminoazobenzene	59		126
5-Methylindole	60	267	
2-Aminopyridine	60	204	
3-(3-Indolyl)-propylamine	60		
2-Methylindole	61	271	
N-Phenyl-1-naphthylamine	62		115
2-Amino-4,4′-dimethylbiphenyl	62		118
8-Amino-6-methylquinoline	62		91
1,3-Diaminobenzene (m-Phenylenediamine)	63		87 mono-
			191 di-
5-Methyl-2-naphthylamine	63		123
2,5-Diaminotoluene	64	273	220 di-
3-Aminopyridine	64	250	133
9-Aminofluorene	64		262
4-Methylphenylhydrazine	65	240 d.	121
4-Aminobenzyl alcohol	65		188 O,N-di-
1,3-Diamino-2,6-dimethylbenzene	65		> 260
Aminoacetamide	65		
2-Aminocyclohexanol	66	219	
6-Amino-3-methylbenzophenone	66		159
1,8-Diaminonaphthalene	66		311 di-
N-Nitrosodiphenylamine	66		
8-Methyl-1-naphthylamine	67		183
5-Amino-1,2,4-trimethylbenzene	68		162
2,2′-Diaminodibenzyl	68		249 di-
4-Methyl-2-naphthylamine	68		172
3-Nitro-N-methylaniline	68		95
1-Amino-5-methyl-1,2,3-triazole	70		
8-Aminoquinoline	70		103
2-Nitroaniline	71		92
3,4-Diaminotriphenylmethane	71		226 di-
4-Aminophenylurethane	73		202
4-Aminodiphenylamine	75		158
3,5-Dimethylindole	75		
Duridine	75	261	207
5-Amino-1,2,3-trimethylbenzene	75	240	163
2-Amino-1,4-dimethylnaphthalene	75	333	219
4-Nitromesidine	75		191
2-Nitro-6-methoxyaniline	76		158
2-Nitro-4,6-dimethylaniline	76		176
5-Methyl-1-naphthylamine	77		194
3-Nitro-4-methylaniline	78		148
p-Nitroso-N-ethylaniline	78		

Benzamide	Benzene sulfonamide	p-Toluene sulfonamide	Phenyl thiourea	α-Naphthyl thiourea	Picrate
159					160
154	95	114	157		
204					
122					
165					151
					216
					146
					139
152					
95					
125 mono-	194	172			184
240 di-					
155					
307	147	150			
119					
260					
146 2-N-					
68 1-N-					
150 N-					
232 di-					
118					145
195					
167	136				
255 di-					225
194					
105	83				
158					
98		154			
98	104	142		145	73
243 di-					
230					
203					
					180
169	163				
185					
173					
172	160	164	171		

	M. Pt.	B. Pt.	Acetamide
N-*p*-Tolyl-1-naphthylamine	79		124
2-Aminodiphenylamine	79		121
2,4-Diaminophenol	79		220 2,4-N-
4-Aminopyrazole	80		
2,2′-Diaminobiphenyl	81		89 2-N-
			161 di-
3-Aminoacenaphthene	81		192
2-Aminobenzylalcohol	82	270	114 N-
1-Amino-1,3,4-triazole	82–83		
4-Aminotriphenylmethane	84	248[12]	168
4-Aminobutyrophenone	84		142
p-Nitroso-N,N-diethylaniline	84		
7-Methylindole	85	266	
4-Aminoveratrol	85		133
2-Aminophenanthrene	85		225
4-Aminobenzonitrile	86		205
4-Aminoacenaphthene	87		175
p-Nitroso-N,N-dimethylaniline	87		
3-Aminoacetanilide	87		191
3-Aminophenanthrene	87.5		200
4-Amino-3-methyl-1-phenylpyrazole	88	312	94 hyd.
			120 anh.
2-Hydroxy-3-methylaniline	89		78 N-
3,4-Diaminotoluene	89	265	210 di-
			95 3-N-
			131 4-N-
2-Nitrophenylhydrazine	90		140
1-Amino-2,6-dimethylnaphthalene	91		211
3-Nitro-2-methylaniline	92		158
6-Nitro-2-methylaniline	92	305 d.	158
1,18-Diamino-octadecane	93		
4,4′-Diaminodiphenylmethane	93		236 di-
3-Nitrophenylhydrazine	93		145
7-Aminoquinoline	93		167
2-Aminodibenzfuran	94		178
3-Aminoquinoline	94		172
7-Amino-2,4-dimethylquinoline	94	> 300	212
Skatole (3-Methylindole)	95	267	68
4-Hydroxybenzylamine	95		
1-Amino-4,5-dimethyl-1,2,3-triazole	95		
8-Hydroxy-1-naphthylamine	95		181 N-
5-Amino-2-methylpyridine	96		126
6,6′-Diamino-3,3′-dimethyldiphenylmethane	96		226 di-
			152 tetra-
4-Nitro-N-ethylaniline	96		119
Benzeneazodiphenylamine	96		
8-Nitro-1-naphthylamine	97		191
3-Aminobenzyl-alcohol	97		106 N-

Benzamide	Benzene sulfonamide	p-Toluene sulfonamide	Phenyl thiourea	α-Naphthyl thiourea	Picrate
140					
136					
253 di-					120
173 di-					193
159 2-N-					
190 di-					
209					221
198 O-					110
					194
198					
84					176
177					
216					
170					150
196					190
		241			
213					
213					
181					138
263 di-	178 di-	140 4-N-			
166					
219					
168				171	
167				171	
150 di-					
151					
189					
201					
					210
					215
					170
					124
193 N-		189 N-			163
111					201
					199
98		107			
	194				
115 N-					

	M. Pt.	B. Pt.	Acetamide
2-Amino-4-methylpyridine	98		102
2-Aminophenacyl alcohol	98		141 N-
1,2-Diaminonaphthalene	98		234 di-
4'-Amino-4-methylbiphenyl	98	190[18]	221
3-Aminoacetophenone	99		128
2,4-Diaminotoluene	99		224 N-di-
4-Amino-3,2'-dimethylazobenzene	100		185 mono-
			65 di-
1,2-Diaminobenzene (o-Phenylenediamine)	102		185 di-
N-p-Tolyl-2-naphthylamine	103		85
3,4-Diaminobiphenyl	103		211 3-N-
			155 4-N-
			163 3,4-N-di-
8-Nitro-2-naphthylamine	104		196
Piperazine	104	140	52 mono-
			144 di-
3-Amino-4,4'-dimethylbiphenyl	104		156
1,3-Diamino-4,6-dimethylbenzene	105		295 di-
			165 6-N-
Triphenylmethylamine	105		207
4-Aminophenanthrene	105		190
2-Aminobenzophenone	105		72
3-Amino-6-phenylpyridine	105		148
3-Amino-4-methylpyridine	106	260	84
4-Aminoacetophenone	106	294	167
2,4-Diaminopyridine	107		
9-Phenanthrylmethylamine	107		182
5-Nitro-2-methylaniline	107		151
2,5-Diaminopyridine	107		290 di-
N-Phenyl-2-naphthylamine	108		93
2-(4-Aminophenyl)-ethyl alcohol	108		
5-Aminoacenaphthene	108		238 mono-
			122 di-
4,4'-Diamino-2,2'-dimethyl-biphenyl (m-Toluidine)	108		281 di-
4-Aminoantipyrine	109		199
3-Amino-4-methylbenzophenone	109		108
2-Aminobenzamide	109		177
5-Aminoquinoline	110	310	178
2-Nitro-4-aminostilbene	110		192
3-Aminocamphor	110		121
3'-Amino-4-methylbenzophenone	111		139
4-Amino-3-methylbenzophenone	112		175
2-Naphthylamine	112		132
β-Aminopropiophenone	112		90
2-Hydroxybenzylaniline	113		93

Benzamide	Benzene sulfonamide	p-Toluene sulfonamide	Phenyl thiourea	α-Naphthyl thiourea	Picrate
114					227
167 O,N-di-					
291 di-	215 1-N-				
		130			
224 di-	192 N-di-	192 di-			
	138 2-N-	164 4-N-			
301 di-	185	260 di-			208
139					
186 3-N-					
221 4-N-					
248 di-					
162					
75 mono-	282 di-	173 mono-			280
196 di-					
160					
258 di-		221			
160					
224					216
80					
201					
81					179
205	128	203			
191 di-					
167					241
	172				
230 di-					
148					
59 O-					
136 O,N-di-					
210					190
					225
					144
214					
		203			
141					191
158					
162	102	133	129		195
104					164

	M. Pt.	B. Pt.	Acetamide
2-Nitro-4-ethoxyaniline	113		104
3-Nitroaniline	114		155
6-Aminoquinoline	114		138
2,5-Dimethylpiperazine, cis-	114	162	
3-Amino-2-phenylquinoline	115	223[3]	124
5-Amino-3-methyl-1-phenylpyrazole	116		110
4-Aminotriphenylcarbinol	116		176
2-Nitro-4-methylaniline	117		99
5-Aminoquinaldine	117		205
2,5-Dimethylpiperazine, trans-	118	162	
5-Nitro-2-methoxyaniline	118		175
4-Hydroxypyrazole	118		
p-Nitroso-N-methylaniline	118		
6-Amino-3,4'-dimethylazobenzene	118		157
5-Nitro-1-naphthylamine	119		220
1,4-Diaminonaphthalene	120		303 di-
1,9-Diaminofluorene	120		293 di-
2-(ω-Aminoethyl)-indole	120		
2,2'-Diamino-4,4'-dimethyldiphenyl	120		189 di-
2,6-Diaminopyridine	121		203 di-
4,4'-Diaminostilbene, cis-	121		172 di-
4-Aminobenzhydrol	121		
6-Hydroxy-3-aminoacetophenone	121		165 N- 174 di-
2-Aminotriphenylcarbinol	121		192
3-Hydroxyaniline (m-Aminophenol)	121		148
2-Hydroxy-4-aminoacetophenone	122		91 N-
1-Aminoisoquinoline	122		
4,4'-Diamino-2,2'-dimethyldiphenylmethane	123		228 di-
2,2'-Diaminostilbene, cis-	123		214 di-
2,4-Dimethyl-5-nitroaniline	123		159
4-Nitro-2-aminobenzaldehyde	124		
4-Aminobenzophenone	124		153
8-Hydroxy-7-aminoquinoline	124		177 N-
5-Nitro-2-aminobiphenyl	125		133
4-Methoxy-3-hydroxyaniline (4-Aminoguaiacol)	125		116 N-
1-Nitro-2-naphthylamine	126		123
4-Aminoazobenzene	126		146
Hydrazobenzene	126		159
Benzidine	127		199 mono- 317 di-
2-Aminopyrimidine	127		
5-Aminoisoquinoline	128		
2-Aminovanillin	128		97
3,7-Dimethyl-2-naphthylamine	129		231
2-Nitro-4-methoxyaniline	129		117

Benzamide	Benzene sulfonamide	p-Toluene sulfonamide	Phenyl thiourea	α-Naphthyl thiourea	Picrate
	72	94			
155	136	138	160	161	143
169		193			
152 di-		146 di-			
					160
148	102	146			
228 di-		225 di-			
160		128			
109 di-					129
135					
	183				
280 di-		187 1-N-			
186 1-N-					
					205
173					
170 di-					
176 di-					240
253 di-					
145					
					122
174 N-		157	156		
					290
					216
					156
200	149	192			
152					
					205
		169			
162 O,N-di-					
168	156	160			
211					
126					
203 mono-	232 di-	243 di-			
352 di-					
					237
					> 200
140					

	M. Pt.	B. Pt.	Acetamide
2-Aminotriphenylmethane	129		154
2-Aminoquinoline	129		
4,4'-Diamino-3,3'-dimethylbiphenyl (o-Tolidine)	129		103 mono- 315 di- 211 tetra-
2,4-Diaminodiphenylamine	130		188 di-
3-Aminocoumarin	130		201
4-Nitro-2-methylaniline	130		202
3-Nitro-4-hydroxyaniline	131		157 N-
2-Amino-4-methylquinoline	133	320	
2,2'-Diaminobenzophenone	133		168
2,2'-Diaminoazobenzene	134		271 di-
2-Hydroxy-3,5-dimethylaniline	134		96 N-
2-Hydroxy-5-methylaniline	135		160 N- 145 O,N-di-
4-Nitro-3-methylaniline	135		102
3-Methyl-2-naphthylamine	135		181
2-Aminoacenaphthene	135		
D,L-6,6'-Diamino-2,2'-dimethylbiphenyl	136		205 di-
2-Nitro-1,4-diaminobenzene	137		186 di- 162 1-N- 189 4-N-
9-Aminophenanthrene	137		207
3,3'-Dimethoxybenzidine	137		242 di-
4-Hydroxy-3,5-dimethylaniline	137		160 di-
2,6-Dinitroaniline	138		197
2-(4-Aminophenyl)-quinoline	138		189 di-
3,6-Dimethyl-2-naphthylamine	139		207
4-Nitro-2-methoxyaniline	139		153
4-Aminopropiophenone	140		161
3-Nitro-4-aminobenzophenone	140		
2-Amino-4-methyldiphenylamine	140		161
1,4-Diaminobenzene (p-Phenylenediamine)	140	267	162 mono- 304 di-
2-Hydroxy-5-nitroaniline	142		
4-Nitro-2-aminostilbene	142		221 N-
8-Hydroxy-5-aminoquinoline	143		
2-Nitro-1-naphthylamine	144		199
5-Nitro-2-naphthylamine	144		186
5-Hydroxy-2-methylaniline	144		178 N- 128 O,N-di-
p-Nitrosodiphenylamine	144		
2,5-Dimethyl-4-nitroaniline	144		168
1-Aminophenanthrene	146		220
3,5-Dihydroxyaniline	146		119 tri-
4-Nitroaniline	147		215
5-Amino-3-methyl-1,2,4-triazole	148		> 270

Benzamide	Benzene sulfonamide	p-Toluene sulfonamide	Phenyl thiourea	α-Naphthyl thiourea	Picrate
					255
198 mono- 265 di-				167	
213 2-N- 173					
	158	174		165	
					251 164
154 O,N-di- 191 N- 190 O,N-di-					
190					
					260
182 di- 236 4-N-		162 di-			
199 236 di-					190 225 di-
234					
150 190 154	181	175			
128 mono- 300 di- > 200	247 di-	266 di- 122 O-			
205 O,N-di- 175 182					
	183 N-				
	162	185			
					204
199 285				187	225

	M. Pt.	B. Pt.	Acetamide
2,2'-Dihydroxyhydrazobenzene	148		
7-Amino-2-methylquinoline	148		
4,4'-Diamino-2,2'-dimethylazoxybenzene	148		281 di-
3-Amino-1-phenyl-1,2,4-triazole	150		168 3-N-
			118 3-N-di-
4-Aminochalkone	151		179
4-Aminopyrimidine	151		202
Pentamethylaniline	151		213
4-Nitro-N-methylaniline	152		153
4-Aminoquinoline	154		178
3-Aminobenzpyrazole	154		177 di-
4-Nitro-2,5-dihydroxyaniline	154		226
2-Nitro-4-hydroxyaniline	154		218 N-
			146 O,N-di-
3-Aminotriphenylcarbinol	155		164
L-6,6'-Diamino-2,2'-dimethylbiphenyl	156		205 di-
3,3'-Diaminoazobenzene	156		272 di-
5-Amino-1-phenyl-1,2,4-triazole	157		
4-Nitrophenylhydrazine	157		205
4-Aminopyridine	158		150 anh.
4',4-Diamino-3,3'-dimethyldiphenylmethane	158		224 di-
			119 tetra-
8-Nitro-2-aminoquinoline	159		211
3-Amino-1,2,4-triazole	159		
4'-Nitro-2-aminobiphenyl	159		199
3-Amino-2-methylquinoline	159	270	165
3-Nitro-4-hydroxy-1-naphthylamine	160		250
5-Nitro-2,4-dihydroxyaniline	160		261 N-
			176 tri-
4-Nitro-1,3-diaminobenzene	161		246 di-
			200 1-N-
3-Hydroxy-4-methylaniline	161		225 N-
			132 di-N-
2-Hydroxy-4-methylaniline	162		171 N-
4-Aminoacetanilide	162		304
4-Nitro-3-hydroxyaniline	162		221 N-
			149 O,N-di-
6-Hydroxy-2,4-dimethylaniline	163		186
			87 di-
2-Aminofluorenone	163		227
4-(2-Aminoethyl)-phenol	164		
4-Aminophenacyl alcohol	165		176 N-
			130 O-
			162 O,N-di-
2,7-Diaminonaphthalene	166		261 di-
3-Nitro-4-aminobiphenyl	167		132

Benzamide	Benzene sulfonamide	p-Toluene sulfonamide	Phenyl thiourea	α-Naphthyl thiourea	Picrate
186 di- 172 290					213
					220
					226
112 182 di-	121				274
172 di- 286 di-					
193 202 215 di-					175 119 215 192
166					257 231
161 330		163			235
222 di-		169 di-			
		111			
169 N- 162 O,N-di-					
211 N- 148 O,N-di-					
172 di- 162 N- 188 O-					206
267 di- 143					210 di-

	M. Pt.	B. Pt.	Acetamide
3,4-Diaminophenol	167		205 3,4-N,N-'di-
4,4'-Diaminotriphenylcarbinol	168		267 N,N'-di-
4-Amino-2-phenylquinoline	168		108
4-Methyl-2,6-dinitroaniline	168		195
4-Amino-2-methylquinoline	168	333	
6-Aminocoumarin	168		216
Picramic acid	169		201 N-
			193 O-
3,3'-diaminobenzophenone	173		226 di-
2-Hydroxy-4,5-dimethylaniline	173		191 N-
			157 O,N-di-
2-Hydroxyaniline	174		209
p-Nitrosoaniline	174		
4-Hydroxy-3-methylaniline	175		179 N-
6-Amino-5,7-dimethylquinoline	175	> 300	212
2,2'-Diaminostilbene, trans-	176		304 di-
5-Nitro-6-aminoquinoline	178		
6-Aminothymol	178–179		174 N-
4-Hydroxy-2-methylaniline	179		130 N-
2,4-Dinitroaniline	180		120
4-Hydroxy-2,6-dimethylaniline	181		178
4-Amino-2,6-dimethylpyrimidine	183		
4-Aminobenzamide	183		275
4-Hydroxyaniline	184		168 mono-
			150 di-
3-Hydroxy-1-naphthylamine	185		179 N-
2-Nitro-5-hydroxyaniline	185		266 N-
6,6'-Diamino-3,3'-dimethyltriphenylmethane	185	430	217 di-
4-Amino-2,6-dimethylpyridine	186	246	113
4'-Hydroxy-4-aminoazobenzene	186		236
4'-Amino-4-methylbenzophenone	186		155
6-Amino-2-methylquinoline	187		168
4-Amino-5-methyl-2,4-diethylpyrimidine	189	280 d.	59
2,4,6-Trinitroaniline (Picramide)	190		230
6-Hydroxy-1-naphthylamine	190		218 N-
			187 O,N-di-
4,4'-Diaminoazoxybenzene	190		275
3-Nitro-4-aminobenzaldehyde	191		155
1,5-Dinitro-2-naphthylamine	191		201
D,L-2,2'-Diamino-1,1'-dinaphthyl	193		235 di-
6-Nitro-8-aminoquinoline	194		224
4-Nitro-1-aminonaphthalene	195		190
2-Amino-4,6-dimethylpyrimidine	197		
4,6-Diamino-2-methylquinoline	197		250 6-N-
4-Nitro-1,2-diaminobenzene	198		205 1-N-
2,4-Dinitrophenylhydrazine	199		197
2-Hydroxy-4-Nitro-5-methyl-aniline	200		242 N-
3-Nitro-4-aminopyridine	200		

Benzamide	Benzene sulfonamide	p-Toluene sulfonamide	Phenyl thiourea	α-Naphthyl thiourea	Picrate
203 3,4-N,N′-di-					
182					
186					
					197
173	159				
300 N-		191			
218 O-					
195 N-					
152 di-					
165 N-	141	146			
194 O,N-di-		109 O-			
					182
					209
		168			270
178 N-					
92 O-					
202		219			
					214
216 N-	125	252 N-	150		
234 O,N-di-		142 O-			
309 O,N-di-		137 O-			
196 di-					
					194
196	211				
152 N-					
223 O,N-di-					170
		182			
235 di-					185
224	173	185			
					230
235 di-					
206					
					197

	M. Pt.	B. Pt.	Acetamide
4'-Nitro-4-aminobiphenyl	200		264
5-Nitro-2-aminobenzaldehyde	200		160
7-Hydroxy-2-naphthylamine	201		232 N-
			156 O,N-di
2-Hydroxy-4-nitrophenol	201–202		187 O,N-di-
4,4'-Diamino-1,1'-dinaphthyl	202		363 di-
4,4',4''-Triaminotriphenylmethane	203		201 tri-
Isatin	204		141
3-Amino-5-phenylacridine	204		256
2-Amino-1,4-naphthoquinone	204–205		202
1-Amino-2-methylanthraquinone	205		176
4,4',4''-Triaminotriphenyl-carbinol			
(Pararosaniline)	205		192 tri-
7-Hydroxy-1-naphthylamine	205–207		165 N-
4,6-Diaminoisophthaldehyde	208		270 mono-
			280 di-
4-Hydroxybenzylaniline	208		
6-Aminobenzpyrazole	210		248 6-N-
			184 di-
4,4'-Diamino-2,5,2',5'-tetramethyltriphenyl-			
methane	210		217 di-
3-Indolylpyruvic acid	211		
6-Hydroxy-2-naphthylamine	212–213		
1,4-Dihydroxy-5-aminoanthraquinone	212–213		
2-Amino-4,5-dimethylpyrimidine	214–215		
4'-Nitro-4-aminoazobenzene	216		245
2-Hydroxy-6-nitroaniline	216		172 N-
3,4-Diaminopyridine	218–219		
3,6-Dimethylcarbazole	219		129
10-Hydroxy-2-aminophenanthrene	221		182 O,N-di-
4-Nitro-5-aminoacenaphthene	222		252
2,6-Dimethylcarbazole	224		
1,8-Dinitro-2-naphthylamine	226		238
4,4'-Diaminostilbene, *trans*-	231		353 di-
3-Hydroxy-2-naphthylamine	234		188 O,N-di-
2,4-Dinitro-1-naphthylamine	242		259
4-Hydroxy-2,5-dimethylaniline	242		177
4,4'-Diaminobenzophenone	244		237 di-
Carbazole	246		69
2-Hydroxy-1-aminoanthraquinone	250		170 N-
1-Aminoanthraquinone	252		218
3-Aminocarbazole	254		217 3-N-
			200 di-
2,7-Diaminocarbazole	260		320 di-
1,8-Diaminoanthraquinone	262		284 di-
1,4-Diaminoanthraquinone	268		271 di-

Benzamide	Benzene sulfonamide	p-Toluene sulfonamide	Phenyl thiourea	α-Naphthyl thiourea	Picrate
	174				
		181			
243 N-					
181 O,N-di-					
		188 O-			
320 di-					147
246					
		218			
208 N-					
208 O,N-di-					
250 di-					
228 O,N-di-					
					250
		136 O-			
222 di-					235
225 O,N-di-					192
233					
					162
		221			
352 di-					
233 N-					
252					
		166			
98					185
255					
250 3-N-		228			
324 di-					
280 mono-					
284 di-					

	M. Pt.	B. Pt.	Acetamide
3-Nitro-2-aminofluorenone	269		245
1,1'-Diamino-2,2'-dinaphthyl	281		230 di-
1,7-Diaminoanthraquinone	290		283 di-
2,7-Diaminofluorenone	290		222 di-
1,6-Diaminoanthraquinone	292		295 di-
5-Nitro-1-aminoanthraquinone	293		275
4-Nitro-1-aminoanthraquinone	296		256 N-
5,8-Diaminoquinizarin	> 300		284 N-di-
2-Aminoanthraquinone	305	262 mono-	258 di-
2-Aminoquinizarin	313		
1,5-Diaminoanthraquinone	319		317 di-
2,7-Diaminoanthraquinone	> 330		> 350
2,5-Dianilino-p-benzoquinone	345		
2,8-Diaminoacridone	> 350		> 350 di-

Benzamide	Benzene sulfonamide	p-Toluene sulfonamide	Phenyl thiourea	α-Naphthyl thiourea	Picrate
278 di-					
325 di-					
					230 di-
275 di-					
237					
	275 N-di-				
228	271	304			
> 350 di-					
300 di-					
> 250 di-					

TABLE 2–2–2. *Basic Nitrogen Compounds.*

	B. Pt.	M. Pt.	Acetamide
Methylamine	−6		28
Dimethylamine	7		
Ethylamine	16.5		
Isopropylamine	33		
Ethylmethylamine	36		
tert.-Butyl amine	46		
n-Propylamine	49		
Methylisopropylamine	50		
Cyclopropylamine	50		
Ethyleneimine	56		
Diethylamine	56		
Allylamine	58		
D,L-*sec.*-*n*-Butylamine	63		
unsym.-Dimethylhydrazine	63		
Trimethyleneimine	63		
Isobutylamine	69		
n-Butylamine	77		
2-Amino-2-methylbutane	78		
D,L-N-Methyl-*sec.*-butylamine	78		
Ethylpropylamine	80		
sym.-Dimethylhydrazine	81		
Cyclobutylamine	82		
Di-isopropylamine	84		
Pyrrolidine	89		
N-Methyl-*n*-butylamine	90		
5-Amino-1-pentene	91		
D,L-2-Amino-*n*-pentane (*Sec.*-*n*-amylamine)	92		
Isoamylamine	96		
D-2-Methyl-*n*-butylamine (active Amylamine)	96		
2-Methylpyrrolidine	97		
3-Methylpyrrolidine	103		
n-Amylamine	104		
N-Methyl-2-amino-*n*-pentane	105		
Piperidine	106		
2,5-Dimethylpyrrolidine	106		
2-Aminodiethylether	108		
Di-*n*-propylamine	109		
Diallylamine	111		
2,4-Dimethylpyrrolidine	115		
Ethylenediamine	116	8.5	172 di-
L-2-Methylpiperidine	117		
D,L-2-Methylpiperidine	118		
D,L-1,2-Diaminopropane	119		139 di-
Isohexylamine	125		
D,L-3-Methylpiperidine	126		
2,6-Dimethylpiperidine	127		

Primary and Secondary Amines. Liquid

Benzamide	Benzene sulfonamide	p-Toluene sulfonamide	Phenyl thiourea	α-Naphthyl thiourea	Picrate
80	30	75	113	192	207
41	47	79	135	168	158
71	58	63	106	121	165
	26		101	143	
					196
134			120		198
84	36	52	63	103	135
			120		135
99	120 di-				149
					142
42	42	60	34	108	155
	39	64	98		140
76	70	55	101	137	139
					166
57	53	78	82		150
			65	108	151
					183
					78
					147
					140
		123			112
					111
			102	97	138
					106
			69	103	139
					77
48	93	96	101		152
					117
					122
	51		69	161	75
					116
244 di-	168 di-	360 di-	102		233 di-
					116
45		55			135
192 di-					135 di-
					123
					138 di-
111	50				162

	B. Pt.	M. Pt.	Acetamide
n-Hexylamine	130	−19	
3-Amino-n-hexane	130		
Morpholine	130		
Cyclohexylamine	134		104
Trimethylenediamine	136		126
2,2,6-Trimethylpiperidine	138		
Di-isobutylamine	139		86
4-Amino-n-heptane	139		
1,3-Diaminobutane	141		
2-Amino-n-heptane	142		
unsym.-Diethylenediamine	145		
Furfurylamine	145		
N-Methylcyclohexylamine	145		
2-Ethylpiperidine	146		
2,2,4-Trimethylpiperidine	148		
sym.-Diethylenediamine	149		
3-Ethylpiperidine	153		
n-Heptylamine	155	−23	
4-Ethylpiperidine	156		
Di-n-butylamine	159		
Tetramethylenediamine	159	27	137 di-
D,L-2-Hydroxy-n-propylamine	163		
Hexahydrobenzylamine	163.5		
N-Ethylcyclohexylamine	164		
2-Ethylcyclohexylamine	164		
2-Aminoethyl alcohol (Ethanolamine)	171		
3-Amino-n-pentanol-2	172		
2-Aminopropyl alcohol	173		
2-Amino-n-pentanol-3	174		
Pentamethylene diamine (Cadaverine)	178		
n-Octylamine	180		
5-Methyl-2-pyrazoline	180		
N-Methylbenzylamine	181		
Aniline	184		114
Benzylamine	184		60
D,L-α-Phenylethylamine	187		57
1,2-Diaminocyclohexane	187		260 di-
Di-isoamylamine	187	−44	
3-Aminopropylalcohol	188		
1,2,3-Triaminopropane	190		200
4-Amino-2,6-dimethylpiperidine	195		
N-Methylaniline	196		102
1-Phenylisopropylamine	196		
β-Phenylethylamine	198		51
N-Ethylbenzylamine	198		
o-Toluidine	200		110
n-Nonylamine	201		34
m-Toluidine	203		65

Benzamide	Benzene sulfonamide	p-Toluene sulfonamide	Phenyl thiourea	α-Naphthyl thiourea	Picrate
40	96		77	79	126
75	118	147	136		146
149	89		148	142	
140	96	148			250
					195
	55		113		121
					240
					211
					150
85					170
	64				133
					63
			75	68	121
			86	123	59
177 di-					250
					142
98					184
					133
	121				190
					160
135 di-	119		148		237
				72	112
156					126
		95			117
160	112	103	54	158	
105	88	116	156	172	194
120					
			72	118	94.5
					222
217					
					220
63	79	94	87	135	145
159					
116	69		135		174
		50			118
146	124	185	136	167	213
49					111
125	95	171			200

	B. Pt.	M. Pt.	Acetamide
Diamylamine	205		
D,L-2-Phenylisopropylamine	205		93
N-Ethylaniline	205		54
4-Methylpyrazole	207		
3-Methylbenzylamine (*m*-Xylylamine)	207		235
N-Methyl-2-methylaniline	208		56
2-Methylbenzylamine (*o*-Xylylamine)	208	−20	69
4-Methylbenzylamine (*m*-Xylylamine)	208	13	107
3-Methylpyrazole	208		29
1-Phenylpropylamine	208		
2-Phenylpropylamine	210		
N-Methyl-4-methylaniline	210		83
2-Ethylaniline	210		111
1-Menthylamine	212		145
2,5-Dimethylaniline	213		139
1-Phenylisobutylamine	214		
3-Methylpyridazine	215		
2,6-Dimethylaniline	215		177
4-Ethylaniline	216	−5	94
2,4-Dimethylaniline	217		133
2,4-Dimethylbenzylamine	218		
2-Amino-N,N′-dimethylaniline	219		72
3,5-Dimethylaniline	220		144
N-Ethyl-3-methylaniline	221		
3,5-Dimethylbenzylamine	221		
2,3-Dimethylaniline	221		135
1-Aminoindane	222		
3-Phenylpropylamine	222		
2-Methyl-4,5,6,7-tetrahydroindole	222		
N-*n*-Propylaniline	222		47
2-*n*-Propylaniline	222		104
α-Amino-*n*-butylbenzene	223		
9-Aminodecalin, *trans*-	223	−25	183
γ-Amino-*n*-Butylbenzene	223		
2-Methoxyaniline (*o*-Anisidine)	225	5	85
4-Isopropylaniline	225		102
4-*n*-Propylaniline	225		87
N-Isobutylaniline	227		
α-Methyl-α-phenylhydrazine	227		92
4-*tert.*-Butylaniline	228	17	169
9-Aminodecalin, *cis*-	228	−13.5	127
2-Ethoxyaniline (*o*-Phenetidine)	229		79
2,4,6-Trimethylaniline	229		216
2-Aminoindane	230		127
1,2,3,4-Tetrahydroisoquinoline	233		46
2-*tert.*-Butylaniline	233		159
4-N,N-Dimethyl-3,4-diaminotoluene	234		
4-Isobutylaniline	235		127

Benzamide	Benzene sulfonamide	p-Toluene sulfonamide	Phenyl thiourea	α-Naphthyl thiourea	Picrate
			72		
					143
60		87	89	129.5	132
					142
150					198
156			135		215
66					90
88					215
137					204
					144
115	81				
	85				182
					131
147					194
140	138	232	148		171
					166
					143
168		212	204		180
151		104			
192	130	181	152		269
					233
51					138
136			153		200
72					
					225
189					221
142					207
57					152
	86				141
	54		104		
119					151
128					
148					
108					
60	89	127	136		200
162					
115					
		122			
153	132				
134		179			
147					
104	102	164	137		
204	137	167	193		189
155					239
129	154				200
					151
		136			

	B. Pt.	M. Pt.	Acetamide
4-Aminoindane	236	–3	126
2-Aminoundecane	237		58
unsym.-Ethylphenylhydrazine	237		
sym.-Ethylphenylhydrazine	238		
1-Aminoundecane	240	15	48
2-Amino-p-cymene	241		71
N-Butylaniline	241		
Phenylhydrazine	243	19	128
ω-Diamino-m-xylene	245		118
3-Ethoxyaniline (m-Phenetidine)	248		97
4-Ethoxyaniline (p-Phenetidine)	248	2–3	137
1,2,3,4-Tetrahydroquinoline	250	20	
2-Aminoacetophenone	250 d.	20	76
3-Methoxyaniline (m-Anisidine)	251		81
4-Amino-1,2,3,5-tetramethylbenzene	255	23	215
Dicyclohexylamine	255	20	103
6-Methyl-1,2,3,4-tetrahydroisoquinoline	256		
4-Amino-N,N-diethylaniline	261		104
4-n-Butylaniline	261		105
7-Methyl-1,2,3,4-tetrahydroquinoline	264		
4-Methylindole	267	5	
D,L-3-Aminopropyleneglycol	268		
Diethanolamine	270	28	
3-Amino-N,N-dimethylaniline	272		87
5,6,7,8-Tetrahydro-1-naphthylamine	275		158
N,N-Diethyl-1-naphthylamine	290		
N-Methyl-1-naphthylamine	294		94
Dibenzylamine	300		
α-Aminodiphenylmethane	303		146
1,2-Diphenylethane	313		
2,3-Diphenylpropylamine	315		85 di-
N-Methyl-2-naphthylamine	317		51
N,N-Diethyl-2-naphthylamine	320		
2-Aminostyrene	97–98[8]		129
3-Aminostyrene	112[12]		74
2-n-Butylaniline	122[12]		100
2-Aminophenylethyl alcohol	147[3.5]		103.5
6-Amino-3,4'-dimethylbiphenyl	165[4]		104
2,2-Diphenylpropylamine	179[22]		106
4,4'-Diamino-2,3'-dimethylbiphenyl	244[12]		253 N,N'-di-
			191 tetra-

Benzamide	Benzene sulfonamide	p-Toluene sulfonamide	Phenyl thiourea	α-Naphthyl thiourea	Picrate
136					
					111
100					
60					
102					
56		56			
168	148	151	172		
107 di-	177 di-				
					185
103		157	138		158
173	143	106	136		69
75	67				
98		148			
		68			169
					200
153					173
					205
172					
126					
70					153
					194
113					
					110
163					
121		164			
112	68	159			
172					205
					212
84	107	78			145
90					
82					
245 N,N-di-					

TABLE 2–2–3. *Basic Nitrogen Compounds. Tertiary Amines, Solid*

	M. Pt.	B. Pt.	Picrate	Methyl p-toluene sulfonate	Quaternary methyl iodide	Chloroplatinate
Pyrimidine	21	123	156			103
4,6-Dimethylpyrimidine	25	160	30			
2,8-Dimethylquinoline	27	252	180		221	
Quinoxaline	30	230			176	187
5-Methylpyrimidine	30.5	154	141			
1,3,5-Trimethylpyrazole	37	170	147		117	
2,3-Dimethyl-5,6,7,8-tetrahydroquinoline	38	125^{14}	169			
7-Methylquinoline	39	252	237			
N,N-Diethyl-p-aminobenzaldehyde	41					
3-Nitropyridine	41	216	193		229	254
2,4,8-Trimethylquinoline	42	270	187			
2,6,8-Trimethylquinoline	46	264	206			206
N,N-Dimethyl-2-naphthylamine	47	305	161			
2,4,5,8-Tetramethylquinoline	48	168^{12}	143		160	226
8-Methoxyquinoline	50	283	216			
4,8-Dimethylquinoline	54	258	242			
2,3,8-Trimethylquinoline	55	281	186			
2,6-Dimethylquinoline	60	266	119	175	236	
3-Nitro-N,N-dimethylaniline	60	297	215		205	
3,4'-Bipyridyl	62	281	200		245	
2,4,6-Trimethylquinoline	65.5 anh. / 39.5 hyd.					230
3,3'-Bipyridyl	68	291	232		218	
2,3-Dimethylquinoline	68	263	230			
2,2'-Bipyridyl	69		158			
5-Nitroquinoline	72 anh.		215			
N,N-Dibenzylaniline	72		131		135	

Compound					
2,2'-*bis*-(Dimethylamino)-biphenyl	72			190	
3,4-Dimethylquinoline	73	293	215	191	
8-Hydroxyquinaldine	74	266			
4-Dimethylaminobenzaldehyde	74			143	
8-Hydroxyquinoline	75		204		160
N,N-Dimethyl-4-aminophenol	76		244		
3,4'-Biquinolyl	83	307	227		
2,2'-Dipyridylamine	84		140		
4-Nitroso-N,N-Dimethylaniline	85				
N,N-Dimethyl-3-aminophenol	85		212		
2,3,6-Trimethylquinoline	86	285	170		
6,6'-Dimethyl-2,2'-Bipyridyl	89				
4,4'-*bis*-(Dimethylamino)-diphenylmethane	91	390	185 mono- 178 di-	214 di-	
Tribenzylamine	91		190	184	
2,3,4-Trimethylquinoline	92	285	216	260	215
4-Dimethylaminobenzophenone	92			188	
N-Methyl-γ-pyridone	92				176 anh.
1,5-Dimethylbenziminazole	95	300	255		
1-Phenylisoquinoline	95	300	165		
4,4'-*bis*-(Dimethylamino)-benzohydrol	98			195 di-	242
4,4'-*bis*-(Dimethylamino)-triphenylmethane	102			231	
2,2-Biquinolylmethane	103		239	205	
2-Hydroxypyridine	106	280			
Acridine	111		208	224	
1,2-Dimethylbenziminazole	112	290	238	254	
Antipyrine	113		188		
4,4'-Bipyridyl	114 anh. 73 hyd.	257	257		
4-Dimethylaminoazobenzene	117			174	
Triphenylamine	127				

Table 2–2–3. (Cont.)

	M. Pt.	B. Pt.	Picrate	Methyl p-toluene sulfonate	Quaternary methyl iodide	Chloroplatinate
3-Hydroxypyridine	129		127			
Methyleneaminoacetonitrile	129	210				
7-Nitroquinoline	132				231	
6,8'-Biquinolyl	148		268		126 mono-	
4-Hydroxypyridine	149					
6-Nitroquinoline	154		275		245	
Quinuclidine	158					238
2,7'-Biquinolyl	160		240		263	
2,2'-Biquinolyl ketone	164		179			
6-Hydroxypyrimidine	164		190			
7,7'-Biquinolyl	171		300		310 mono-	
4,4'-(Dimethylamino)-benzophenone	174		156		105	
5,5'-Biquinolyl	175		> 300		272	
2,3'-Biquinolyl	176				286	278
6,6'-Biquinolyl	181				> 290 di-	
6-Hydroxyquinoline	193		236			
2,2'-Biquinolyl	196		210			
3-Hydroxyquinoline	198		240			
2,2'-Dipyrroyl	200					
4-Hydroxyquinoline	201 anh.					
6-Hydroxyquinaldine	213					
5-Hydroxyquinoline	224				224	230
4-Hydroxyquinaldine	232 anh.		200		201 anh.	215
7-Hydroxyquinoline	235		244		251	
5-Hydroxyquinaldine	246					
4,4'-Dipyridylamine	273		235	205	190	
Hexamethylene tetramine	280		179			> 280

Table 2–2–4. Basic Nitrogen Compounds. Tertiary Amines, Liquid   441

TABLE 2–2–4. *Basic Nitrogen Compounds. Tertiary Amines, Liquid*

	B. Pt.	Picrate	Methyl p-toluene sulfonate	Quaternary methyl iodide	Chloro-platinate
Trimethylamine	3	216		230	
Dimethylamine	37.5	193			
N-Methylpyrrolidine	78	221			233
Triethylamine	89	173			
1,2-Dimethylpyrrolidine	96	235			223
1,3-Dimethylpyrrolidine	96	181 α			58
		110 β			
Pyridine	116	167	139	117	241
1,2,5-Trimethylpyrrolidine	116	163		310	
2-Dimethylaminoethyl ether	121	119		160	
Dimethylaminoacetone	123				176
1-Methylpyrazole	127	148		190	196
N-Ethylpiperidine	128	167.5			202
2-Methylpyridine (α-Picoline)	129	169	150	230	216
β-Dimethylaminoethyl alcohol	135	96			
1,3-Dimethylpyrazole	136	138		256	
2-Methylpyrazine	136	133		129	
4-Methylpyrimidine	141	131			
2,6-Dimethylpyridine	142	168		233	208
3-Methylpyridine	143	150			202
4-Methylpyridine (γ-Piciline)	143	167			231
2-Ethylpyridine	149	187			165
Tri-n-propylamine	156.5	116		207	
2,4-Dimethylpyridine	157	183			216
2,5-Dimethylpyridine	160	169			192
1,3,4-Trimethylpyrazole	160	164			
3-Ethylpyridine	162	128			208
β-Diethylaminoethyl alcohol	163				
Tropidine	163	285		300	217
2,3-Dimethylpyridine	164	188			195
3,4-Dimethylpyridine	164	163			205
4-Ethylpyridine	164	168			213
2,4,5-Triethylpyridine	165	128			205
1,4-bis-Dimethylaminobutane	167	199			
Tropane	167	281		> 300	230
1-Diethylaminoisopropyl alcohol	167	89			
3,5-Dimethylpyridine	170	245			255
2,4,6-Trimethylpyridine	172	156			233
1,4,5-Triethylpyrazole	176	175			
2,3,6-Trimethylpyridine	176	146			250
N,N-Dimethylbenzylamine	181	93			192
2,3,5-Trimethylpyridine	184	183			227
N,N-Dimethyl-o-Toluidine	185	122			
2,6-Dimethyl-4-ethylpyridine	186	119			210
2,4-Diethylpyridine	187	98			170

	B. Pt.	Picrate	Methyl p-toluene sulfonate	Quaternary methyl iodide	Chloro-platinate
3-Diethylaminopropyl alcohol	190			175	
Methyl-2-pyridyl ketone	192	131		161	220
2,3,4-Trimethylpyridine	192	163			259
N,N-Dimethylaniline	193	163	161	228	173
3-Ethyl-4-methylpyridine	195	148			234
3,5-Dimethyl-2-ethylpyridine	198	152			189
N,N-Dimethyl-2,6-dimethylaniline	199				
N-Methyl-N-ethylaniline	201	134		125	
N,N-Dimethyl-2,5-dimethylaniline	204	158			196
N,N-Dimethyl-2,4-dimethylaniline	205	123			219
N,N-Diethyl-2-methylaniline	206	180		224	
N,N-Dimethyl-4-methylaniline	210	129	85	219	
3,4-Diethylpyridine	211	139			221
Tri-n-butylamine	211	106		180	
N,N-Dimethyl-3-methylaniline	212			177	
Methyl-4-pyridyl ketone	212	130			205
N,N-Diethylaniline	218	142		102	
Methyl-3-pyridyl ketone	220				
N,N-Diethyl-4-methylaniline	229			184	
2,3,4,5-Tetramethylpyridine	232	170			210
Quinoline	239	203	126	133	227
Isoquinoline	243	222	163	159	263
D,L-Nicotine	243	218		219	280
2-Dimethylaminobenzaldehyde	244			164	205
Tri-isoamylamine	245	125			
N,N-Dipropylaniline	245	261		156	
2-Ethylquinoline	245	148		180	188
2-Methylquinoxaline	245	215			> 250
1-Methylindole	247	150			
2-Methylquinoline (Quinaldine)	247	191		195	228
8-Methylquinoline	248	206			
L-Nicotine	248	218			275
1-Ethylisoquinoline	250	207			200
2,4-Dimethyl-5,6,7,8-tetrahydroqui-noline	250	144		157	
7-Methylquinoline	252	237			223
4,6-Dimethylquinoline	255	236			238
3-Ethylisoquinoline	257	171			180
Tri-n-amylamine	257		80		
3-Methylquinoline	257	187		221	249
6-Methylquinoline	258	229	154	219	
5-Methylquinoline	260	210		105	
N-Methyl-2-pyridone	255	145			141
4-Methylquinoline	261	210		173	226
2,4-Dimethylquinoline	264	193		263	229
2-Phenylpyridine	268	175			204
6,8-Dimethylquinoline	264	288			235
N,N-Di-n-butylaniline	271	125	180		

	B. Pt.	Picrate	Methyl p-toluene sulfonate	Quaternary methyl iodide	Chloro-platinate
4-Ethylquinoline	272	178		149	204
N,N-Dimethyl-1-naphthylamine	273	145			
5,8-Dimethylquinoline	273	198			234
3,5-Dimethyl-1-phenylpyrazole	275	103		190	186
2,4,7-Trimethylquinoline	280	232		322	272
4,7-Dimethylquinoline	283	224			227
3,4-Dimethyl-1-phenylpyrazole	285	122.5			180
2,3'-Bipyridyl	289	150			
6-Methoxyquinoline	305 d.	305		236	
N-Benzyl-N-methylaniline	306	127		164	
2,6-Diethylpyridine	71^{17}	115		142	211
β,β-Diethylphenylhydrazine	110^{14}	131			
4-Methyl-5,6,7,8-tetrahydroquinoline	122^{11}	170		183	
3-Methyl-5,6,7,8-tetrahydroquinoline	126^{17}	171		162	219
1,3-Dimethyl-1,2,3,4-tetrahydro-quinoline	130^{17}	131		204	
3-Ethylquinoline	135^{12}	197		191	
3-Dimethylaminobenzaldehyde	138^{9}	147		185	168
2-Nitro-N,N-dimethylaniline	151^{30}	102			

TABLE 2–2–5. *Basic Nitrogen Compounds. Aminophenols*

	M. Pt.	p-Nitro-benzoate	3,5-Dinitro-benzoate	p-Toluene sulfonate	Acetate	Benzoate
N,N-Dimethyl-p-aminophenol	76			130	78	
3-Aminophenol	122	143	179			
2-Amino-4-nitrophenol	142	122				> 200 d.
2,4-Dihydroxy-1-naphthyl-amine	162				0,0,N-tri- 155	
3,4-Dihydroxy-2-naphthyl-amine	164				N 170 d. 0,0,-di- > 200 d. 3–0 N-di- 195 d.	
2-Amino-4,6-dinitrophenol (Picramic acid)	169		191			
2-Aminophenol	174		146			
4,4'-Dihydroxydiphenylamine	174.5					
4-Aminophenol	184		178.5		168 mono- 150 di-	

	M. Pt.	p-Nitro-benzoate	3,5-Dinitro-benzoate	p-Toluene sulfonate	Acetate	Benzoate
3,9-Dihydroxyacridine	190					
2-Hydroxyquinoline	199					
2,3-Dihydroxyacridine	235 d.					
1,4-Dihydroxyisoquinoline	> 250				207 (4-)	
2,7-Dihydroxy-4-methyl-quinoline	290				250 (7-)	288 (7-)
2,8-Dihydroxyacridine	> 300					
3,7-Dihydroxyacridine	324					

TABLE 2–3–1. *Neutral Nitrogen Compounds. Aldehydes*

	M. Pt.	B. Pt.	Oxime	Phenyl hydrazone	p-nitro-phenyl hydrazone	2,4-Dinitro-phenyl hydrazone	Semi-carbazone
3-Pyridinealdehyde (Nicotinaldehyde)		76[4]		158			
2-Aminobenzaldehyde	40		135	221	220		
4-Diethylaminobenz-aldehyde	41	172[7]	93	103			241 d.
2-Nitrobenzaldehyde	44		102 anti-154 syn-	156	263	250 d.	256
2-Pyrrole aldehyde	50	217–219	164	139	182		183.5
Quinoline-4-aldehyde	51	123[4]	181		261		
Isoquinaldehyde	55.5						197
3-Nitrobenzaldehyde	58		120	120	247	293 d.	246
Quinoline-2-aldehyde	71		188	204	250		
4-Aminobenzaldehyde	72		124	156			153
4-Dimethylaminobenz-aldehyde	74		185	148	182	325	222
Quinoline-6-aldehyde	75		191	185			239
Quinoline-8-aldehyde	94.5		115	176			238
4-Nitrobenzaldehyde	106		133 anti-182 syn-	159	249	320	221
Indole-3-aldehyde	195			198			

TABLE 2–3–2. *Neutral Nitrogen Compounds. Carbohydrates*

	M. Pt.	Rotation		Phenyl osazone
		$[\alpha]_D$	T°C	
2-Amino-2-desoxy-D-glucose (Glucosamine)	105	+ 48		210
D-1-Aminofructose	127			210
3-Amino-3-desoxy-D-glucose		− 61 to − 78	18	207

TABLE 2–3–3. *Neutral Nitrogen Compounds. Nitriles, Solid*

	M. Pt.	B. Pt.	Acid by Hydrolysis	
			B. Pt.	M. Pt.
2-Cyanodiphenylmethane	19	313		117
Tetradecanonitrile	19			54
Cinnamonitrile	20	255		133
D,L-Mandelonitrile (Benzaldehyde cyano-hydrin)	22			118
2-Methoxybenzonitrile	24	255		100
2-Cyanopyridine	26	212		136
4-Tolunitrile	27	217		179
D-Mandelonitrile	28	170 d.		133
Malononitrile	31	218		135
Hexadecanonitrile	31			63
Maleonitrile	31			130
tert.-Butylacetonitrile (Neopentylcyanide)	32	138	186	
1-Naphthylacetonitrile	33			131
Heptadecanonitrile	34			61
1-Naphthonitrile	34	299		162
Octadecanonitrile	41	225		70
3-Cyanopyridine (Nicotinonitrile)	50	240		232
4-Cyanodiphenylmethane	51			157
Succinonitrile (di-)	53	265		186
4-Methoxybenzonitrile	61	256		184
4-Methoxycinnamonitrile	64			170
1,4-Dicyanocyclohexane (*cis-*)	65			168
2-Naphthonitrile	66			113
Phenylmalononitrile	69			152
6-Nitro-2-tolunitrile	69			184
Diphenylacetonitrile	75			148

	M. Pt.	B. Pt.	Acid by Hydrolysis	
			B. Pt.	M. Pt.
1-Cyanoisoquinoline	78			161
4-Cyanopyridine	78			315
6-Nitro-3-tolunitrile	80			219
2-Nitro-3-Tolunitrile	80			223
4-Cyanobiphenyl	85			228
2-Naphthylacetonitrile	86			142
4-Nitro-3-tolunitrile	93			134
2-Cyanoquinoline	94			157 anh.
Fumaronitrile	96			295
3-Nitro-4-tolunitrile	101			164
3-Cyanophenanthrene	102			269
4-Cyanoquinoline	102			253
5-Nitro-3-tolunitrile	104			174
4-Nitro-2-tolunitrile	105			179
2-Nitro-4-tolunitrile	107			190
9-Cyanophenanthrene	107			252
3-Cyanoquinoline	108			275
2-Cyanophenanthrene	109			259
3-Nitro-2-tolunitrile	109			151
2-Nitrobenzonitrile	110			146
4-Nitrophenylacetonitrile	116			153
3-Nitrobenzonitrile	118			140
1-Cyanoanthracene	126			245
1-Cyanophenanthrene	128			232
4-Nitro-1-naphthonitrile	133			220
1-Nitro-2-naphthonitrile	138			239
1,4-Dicyanocyclohexane (trans-)	140			300
Phthalonitrile	141			200
8-Nitro-2-naphthonitrile	143			295
4-Nitrobenzonitrile	147			241
4,4'-Dicyanodiphenylmethane	169			334
5-Nitro-2-naphthonitrile	172			295
9-Cyanoanthracene	175			207
5-Nitro-1-naphthonitrile	205			241
Biphenyl-4,4'-dicyanide	233			

Table 2–3–4. Neutral Nitrogen Compounds. Nitriles, Liquid   447

TABLE 2–3–4. *Neutral Nitrogen Compounds. Nitriles, Liquid*

	B. Pt.	Acid by Hydrolysis	
		B. Pt.	M. Pt.
Acrylonitrile	77	140	
Acetonitrile	80	165	
Methacrylonitrile	90	160	
Propionitrile	97	141	
Isobutyronitrile	104	155	
Trimethylacetonitrile	106		35
α-Ethylacrylonitrile	111	180	
Butyronitrile	117	162	
Crotononitrile	119	189	72
Allyl cyanide	119	169	
Methoxyacetonitrile	120	203	
α-Hydroxyisobutyronitrile (Acetone cyanohydrin)	120 d.		79
Isovaleronitrile	130	176	
Valeronitrile	141	186	
Diethylacetonitrile	145	190	
α-Furonitrile	147		133
Isocapronitrile	155	199	
β-Methoxypropionitrile	165	107[10]	
n-Capronitrile	165	205	
β-Ethoxypropionitrile	173	119[19]	
D,L-Lactonitrile (Acetaldehyde cyanohydrin)	182	122[15]	
Glycolonitrile (Formaldehyde cyanohydrin)	183		80
Heptanonitrile	183	223	
Benzonitrile	190		122
Dibenzylacetonitrile	200		89
2-Tolunitrile	205		104
Caprylonitrile	206	239	
3-Tolunitrile	212		113
β-Hydroxypropionitrile	220		
Phenylacetonitrile (Benzyl cyanide)	234		76
γ-Hydroxybutyronitrile	240	204	
Decanonitrile	245	269	31
Dodecanonitrile	280		44
Glutaronitrile (di-)	286		97
4-Methoxyhydrocinnamonitrile	290		104
Adiponitrile (di-)	295		153
Sebaconitrile	201[16]		134
Heptamethylenedicyanide	183[11]		106
2-Cyanobiphenyl	172[15]		114
Hexamethylenedicyanide	180[12]		141

TABLE 2–3–5. *Neutral Nitrogen Compounds. Esters*

	B. Pt.	M. Pt.	n_D^{20}	D_4^{20}
Ethyl nitrite	17			$0.900\ D_4^{15}$
Methyl nitrite	65			$1.217\ D_4^{15}$
Butyl nitrite	75			0.911
Ethyl nitrate	87			1.106
Isoamyl nitrite	99		$1.38708\ n_D^{21}$	$0.880\ D_4^{15}$
n-Propyl nitrate	110		1.3979	1.063
n-Butyl nitrate	136			$1.048\ D^0$
Methyl cyanoacetate	200			$1.0962\ D_4^{25}$
Ethyl cyanoacetate	207			
Methyl anthranalate				
(*o*-Amino methylbenzoate)	300	24.5		
Ethyl *o*-nitrobenzoate	275	30		
Diethyl-4-nitrophthalate		34		
Ethyl *o*-nitrocinnamate		44		
Diethyl-3-nitrophthalate		46		
Ethyl *m*-nitrobenzoate	296	47		
Ethyl *p*-nitrobenzoate		56		
Dimethyl-4-nitrophthalate		66		
Ethyl oxanilate		69		
Dimethyl-3-nitrophthalate		66		
Methyl *o*-nitrocinnamate		73		
Methyl *m*-nitrobenzoate	279	78		
Ethyl *m*-nitrocinnamate		79		
Ethyl-3,5-dinitrobenzoate		94		
Methyl *p*-nitrobenzoate		96		
Ethyl-3,5-dinitrosalicylate		99		
Ethyl-5-nitrosalicylate		102		
Methyl-3,5-dinitrobenzoate		108		
Ethyl oxamate		114		
Ethyl-3-nitrosalicylate		118		
Methyl-5-nitrosalicylate		119		
Methyl *m*-nitrocinnamate		124		
Methyl-3,5-nitrosalicylate		127		
Methyl-3-nitrosalicylate		132		
Ethyl *p*-nitrocinnamate		137		
Methyl *p*-nitrocinnamate		161		

TABLE 2–3–6. *Neutral Nitrogen Compounds. Ketones*

	B. Pt.	M. Pt.	Semi-carbazone	2,4-Dinitro-phenyl hydrazone	Phenyl hydrazone	Oxime
2-Pyridyl methyl ketone (2-Acetylpyridine)	190					121
4-Pyridyl methyl ketone	212					142
2-Pyridyl propyl ketone	217				82	48
3-Pyridyl methyl ketone	220				137	113
4-Pyridyl propyl ketone	229					
3-Pyridyl n-propyl ketone	246		169		182	
2-Aminoacetophenone	250 d.	20	290 d.		108	
2-Benzoylpyridine (2-Pyridyl phenyl ketone)	317			199	136	150
3-Pyridylacetone	123[1]		185			
2-Aminoacetophenone	250 d.	20	290 d.		108	109
2,2,6,6-Tetramethyl-4-piperidone		35	219			153
3-Aminopropiophenone	168[15]	42				
8-Acetylguanine	116[0.7]	43.5		253		
2-Acetylquinoline		46			54	
2-Aminopropiophenone		47		190 d.		88
3-Nitroacetophenone		81	257	228	128	132
3-Aminoacetophenone		98	196 d.			192
2-Aminobenzophenone		105				156 alk. stab. 127 acid stab.
Benzoylnitromethane		106			105	96
4-Aminoacetophenone		106	250			147
4-Aminobenzophenone		124				168
4-Aminopropiophenone		140				153
4,4′-Bis-(dimethylamino)-benzo-phenone		174			174	233
3-Acetoindazole		182		> 320		222
3-Acetoindole		190				144
2,3-(3′,4′,5′-Triphenylcyclo-pentadieno)-indone		222			246	
Phenacridone		304				

TABLE 2–3–7. *Neutral Nitrogen Compounds. Quinones*

	M. Pt.	Amine	Benzamide	Benzene-sulfonamide	Semi-carbazone	Phenyl hydrazone	Oxime
3-Methyl-2-nitro-1,4-naphthoquinone	121						
3-Nitro-1,2-naphthoquinone	156						
4-Nitrophenanthrenequinone	179					210	169 mono- 210 di-
2-Nitroanthraquinone	185	303	227				

	M. Pt.	Amine	Benzamide	Benzene-sulfonamide	Semi-carbazone	Phenyl hydrazone	Oxime
1-Nitrosoanthraquinone	224						
2,5-Dinitrophenanthrene-quinone	228						190 mono-
1-Nitroanthraquinone	230	252	255				
1,3-Dinitroanthraquinone	240	290	> 300				
1-Amino-9,10-anthraquinone	252		255				
3-Amino-9,10-phenanthra-quinone	254						
1,6-Dinitroanthraquinone	255	262	275 di-				
2-Nitrophenanthrenequinone	258	205					
3-Nitrophenanthrenequinone	279				254		240 mono- 200 di-
2,7-Dinitroanthraquinone	280	> 330	300 di-				
1,7-Dinitroanthraquinone	295	290	325 di-				
2-Amino-9,10-phenanthra-quinone	> 300						
3-Aminoalizarin (1,2-Dihy-droxy-3-amino-9,10-anthraquinone	> 300						
1,4-Dihydroxy-5,8-diamino-9,10-anthraquinone (5,8-Diaminoquinizarin)	> 300			275 N-d -			
2,7-Dinitrophenanthrene-quinone	301	> 360					246 mono-
2-Amino-9,10-anthraquinone	306		228	271			
1,8-Dinitroanthraquinone	311	262	324 di-				
1,5-Dinitroanthraquinone	384	319	> 350 di-				253

TABLE 2–3–8. *Neutral Nitrogen Compounds. Alcohols*

	B. Pt.	M. Pt.	α-Naphthyl-urethan	Benzoate	Acetate	Picrate
2-Aminoethyl alcohol (Monoethanol amine)	171		186 urea-			
m-Nitrobenzyl alcohol	175[3]	27		71		
Diethanolamine (β,β′-Dihydroxy diethylamine)	270	28				109
2-Nitrobenzyl alcohol	270	74		101		
3-Nitrophenacyl alcohol (3-Nitrobenzoyl carbinol)		92.5			53	
4-Nitrobenzyl alcohol	185[12]	93		94	78	
4-Nitrophenacyl alcohol (4-Nitrobenzoyl carbinol)		121			124	
4,4′,4″-Triamino triphenyl carbinol (Pararosaniline base)		205			192 4,4,4′-tri-	

Table 2–3–9. Neutral Nitrogen Compounds. Ethers   451

TABLE 2–3–9. *Neutral Nitrogen Compounds. Ethers*

	B. Pt.	M. Pt.	n_D^{20}	D_4^{20}
2-Methoxyaniline (o-Anisidine)	255	5		
3-Methoxyaniline (*m*-Anisidine)	251			
2-Nitroanisole	277	10	1.562	1.254
3-Nitrophenetole	284	35		
3-Aminodiphenyl ether	315	37		
m-Azoxytoluene		39		
3-Nitroanisole	258	39		1.373 D^{18}
bz-Tetrahydro-6-methoxy-quinoline	130	43	1.5718 n^{50}	
8-Methoxyquinoline	175²⁹	45		
2-Aminodiphenyl ether	173¹⁴	47		
m-Azoxyphenetole		50		
m-Azoxyanisole		52		
4-Nitroanisole	274	54	1.5707 n^{60}	1.233
4-Methoxyaniline (*p*-Anisidine)	246	57		1.071 D_4^{55}
4-Nitrophenetole		60		
2,4,6-Trinitroanisole		68		
2,4,6-Trinitrophenetole		78		
o-Azoxyanisole		81		
4-Aminodiphenyl ether	189¹⁴	83.5		
p-Hydrazophenetole		86		
2,4-Dinitrophenetole		86		
o-Hydrazophenetole		89		
2,4-Dinitroanisole		95		
o-Hydrazoanisole		102		
o-Azoxyphenetole		102		
5-Nitroso-o-anisidine		107		
m-Hydrazophenetole		119		
p-Azoxyanisole		119		
o-Azophenetole		131		
p-Azoxyphenetole		135		
p-Azophenetole		160		
Anhalamine (8-Hydroxy-6,7-di-methoxy-1,2,3,4-tetrahydroiso-quinoline)		187		
7-Methoxyquinoline	287⁷⁵⁸	210		

TABLE 2–3–10. *Neutral Nitrogen Compounds. Nitrohydrocarbons. Solid*

	M. Pt.	B. Pt.	Amine	Benzamide	Benzene sulfonamide	Picrate of amine
2-Methyl-2-nitropropane (tert.-Nitrobutane)	25	127	235 B. Pt.	134		198
3-Nitro-1,2,4-trimethyl-benzene	30		51			
3,4-Dimethyl-1-nitrobenzene (4-Nitro-o-xylene)	30		49	102		
2-Nitrobiphenyl	37	152^{14}	37	137		
5-Nitroindane	40	139^{10}	236 B. Pt.	136		189
4-Nitroindane	44		232 B. Pt.	204		
Nitromesitylene	44		98			
2-Nitroazoxybenzene	49					
4-Nitrotoluene	52	234	45	158	120	182
1-Nitronaphthalene	57	250 d.	50	160	167	163
β-Nitrostyrene	58					
2-Nitro-1-methylnaphthalene	58		51	222		
3,4-Dinitrotoluene	61		89	263 di-	178 di-	
3-Nitrobiphenyl	61		30	195		
2,3-Dinitrotoluene	63		63			
8-Nitro-1-methylnaphthalene	63		67			
2,6-Dinitrotoluene	66		105	224 di-		
2,4-Dinitrotoluene	71		99	238	191 di-	
4-Nitro-1-methylnaphthalene	71		51			
2-Nitroazobenzene	71	273	58	122		
3,5-Dimethyl-1-nitrobenzene	75					
3,5-Dinitro-1,2-dimethyl-benzene	76		63	155		
2-Nitro-5-methylnaphthalene	76					
2-Nitronaphthalene	78		112	162	102	195
2,4,6-Trinitrotoluene	80					
1-Nitro-2-methylnaphthalene	81		32	180		
4-Nitrophenanthrene	81		105	224		

Compound					
3,4-Dinitro-1,2-dimethylbenzene	82				
1-Nitro-5-methylnaphthalene	82	77	173		
2,4-Dinitro-1,3-dimethylbenzene	84	65	232 di-		
2,4-Dinitromesitylene	85				
1,3-Dinitrobenzene	90	63	240 di-	194	184
1,4-Dinitro-2,3-dimethylbenzene	90	116			
3,5-Dinitrotoluene	92				
2,3-Dinitro-1,4-dimethylbenzene	93	105	295 di-	258 di-	
4,6-Dinitro-1,3-dimethylbenzene	93	45	276 di-		
2,4′-Dinitrobiphenyl	93	56			
3-Nitroazobenzene	96	85	216		
2-Nitrophenanthrene	99	104			
2,5-Dinitro-1,3-dimethylbenzene	101	98	291 di-	215 1-N-	
1,2-Dinitronaphthalene	102	108	210		
5-Nitroacenaphthene	106				
2-Nitro-β-nitrostyrene	106				
3-Nitrodurene	112	75			
4-Nitrobiphenyl	114	53	230		
9-Nitrophenanthrene	116	137	199	185	190
1,2-Dinitrobenzene	118	102	301 di-		
2,4′-Dinitrodiphenylmethane	118	88			
4,5-Dinitro-1,2-dimethylbenzene	118	126			
2,4-Dinitrobenzene	119	117			
1,3,5-Trinitrobenzene	122				
1,3-Dinitro-2,5-dimethylbenzene	123	102			
2,2′-Dinitrobiphenyl	124	81	190 di-		190
1,4-Dinitronaphthalene	131	120	280 di-		
1,2-Dinitro-3,5-dimethylbenzene	132				
4-Nitroazobenzene	135	126	211		
2-Nitroindene	141				
2,4-Dinitrostilbene	143	119			
1,3-Dinitronaphthalene	144	96			

Table 2–3–10. (Cont.)

	M. Pt.	B. Pt.	Amine	Benzamide	Benzene sulfonamide	Picrate of amine
9-Nitroanthracene	146		145			
2,5-Dinitro-1,4-dimethylbenzene	147		150			
3-Nitroacenaphthene	151		81	209		221
4-Nitroazoxybenzene	153		138			
3,8-Dinitroacenaphthene	155		167			
2-Nitrofluorene	156		129			
2,2'-Dinitrodiphenylmethane	159		160			
1,6-Dinitronaphthalene	161		85	265 di-		
1,8-Dinitronaphthalene	170		66	311 di-		
3-Nitrophenanthrene	170		87	213		
1,4-Dinitrobenzene	173		140	128 mono- / 300 di-	247 di-	
3,3'-Dinitrodiphenylmethane	175		53			
9-Nitrofluorene	181		64	260		
4,4'-Dinitrodiphenylmethane	183		93			
2,2'-Dinitrostilbene	196		176			209
4-Nitro-β-nitrostyrene	199		94			
3,3'-Dinitrobiphenyl	200		175			
2,5-Dinitrofluorene	207		134			
2,2'-Dinitroazobenzene	209		190			
1,5-Dinitronaphthalene	214		250			
4,4'-Dinitroazobenzene	222					
2,7-Dinitronaphthalene	234		166	267 di-		210 di-
4,4'-Dinitrobiphenyl	237		128	203 mono- / 352 di-		
4,4'-Dinitrostilbene (*trans-*)	288		231	352 di-		
9,10-Dinitroanthracene	294					

TABLE 2–3–11. *Neutral Nitrogen Compounds. Nitrohydrocarbons, Liquid*

	B. Pt.	Amine	Benzamide	Benzene sulfonamide	Picrate of amine
Nitroethylene	98		71	58	165
Nitromethane	101		80	30	207
Nitroethane	114		71	58	165
2-Nitropropane	120		26		
3-Nitropropylene	125			39	140
1-Nitropropane	132		84	36	135
D,L-2-Nitrobutane	140		76	70	139
2-Methyl-1-nitropropane	140		57	53	150
2-Methyl-2-nitrobutane	150				183
D,L-2-Nitropentane	152				
1-Nitrobutane	153				151
1-Nitroisobutylene	154		57	53	150
3-Methyl-1-nitrobutane	164				138
1-Nitropentane	173				139
2-Nitrohexane	176				
1-Nitrohexane	193		40	96	126
1-Nitroheptane	193				121
2-Nitroheptane	194				
Nitrocyclohexane	205			147	
1-Nitrooctane	206				112
Nitrobenzene	210		160	112	
2-Nitrotoluene	222		146	124	213
2-Nitro-1-ethylbenzene	224		147		194
1,3-Dimethyl-2-nitrobenzene (2-Nitro-*m*-xylene)	226		168		180
Phenylnitromethane	226 d.		105	88	194
3-Nitrotoluene	233		125	95	200
1,4-Dimethyl-2-nitrobenzene (2-Nitro-*p*-xylene)	241		140	138	171
4-Nitro-1-ethylbenzene			151		
2,4-Dimethyl-1-nitrobenzene (4-Nitro-*m*-xylene)	246		192	129	209
2,3-Dimethyl-1-nitrobenzene (3 Nitro-*o*-xylene)	250		189		221
2-Nitro-*p*-cymene	264		102		
4-Nitro-*tert.*-butylbenzene	267	17	134		

TABLE 2–3–12. *Neutral Nitrogen Compounds. Miscellaneous*

	M. Pt.		B. Pt.	M. Pt.
o-Azotoluene	55	Methyl isocyanate	44	
m-Azotoluene	55	Methyl isocyanide	60	
Azobenzene	67	Ethyl isocyanate	60	
1-Benzeneazonaphthalene	70	Isopropyl isocyanate	67	
p-Dimethylaminoazo-		Ethyl isocyanide	78	
benzene	117	Isopropyl isocyanide	87	
p-Aminoazobenzene	125	Propyl isocyanide	100	
2-Benzeneazonaphthalene	131	Phenyl isocyanide	165	
1,2′-Azonaphthalene	136	Phenyl isocyanate	166	
p-Azotoluene	144	o-Tolyl isocyanide	183	
o-Azobiphenyl	145	o-Tolyl isocyanate	186	
1,1′Azonaphthalene	190	p-Tolyl isocyanate	187	
2,2′Azonaphthalene	208	α-Naphthyl isocyanate	269	
p-Azobiphenyl	250	o-Nitrophenyl isocyanate		41
		m-Nitrophenyl isocyanate		51
		β-Naphthyl isocyanate		55
Azoxybenzene	36	p-Nitrophenyl isocyanate		57
m-Azoxytoluene	39			
o-Azoxytoluene	60			
1,1′-Azoxynaphthalene	127	1-Nitroso-2,4-dimethyl-		
o-Azoxybiphenyl	158	benzene		41
2,2′-Azoxynaphthalene	168	1-Nitroso-3,4-dimethyl-		
4,4′-Dinitroazoxybenzene	200	benzene		45
p-Azoxybiphenyl	212	p-Nitrosotoluene		48
		m-Nitrosotoluene		53
		Nitrosobenzene		68
m-Hydroazotoluene	38	o-Nitrosotoluene		72
Hydrazobenzene	130	1-Nitroso-2,3-dimethyl-		
p-Hydrazotoluene	134	benzene		91
2,2′-Hydrazonaphthalene	140	1-Nitrosonaphthalene		98
1,1′-Hydrazonaphthalene	153	1-Nitroso-2,5-dimethyl-		
o-Hydrazotoluene	165	benzene		101
p-Hydrazobiphenyl	170	1-Nitroso-2,6-dimethyl-		
o-Hydrazobiphenyl	182	benzene		145

Table 3–1–A. Chlorine Compounds, Aldehydes. Solid 457

TABLE 3–1–A. *Chlorine Compounds, Aldehydes. Solid*

	M. Pt.	B. Pt.	Oxime	Phenyl hydrazone	p-Nitro-phenyl hydrazone	2,4-dinitro-phenyl hydrazone	Semi-carbazone	Dimethone
3-Chlorobenzaldehyde	17	213	70 α anti- / 118 β syn-	134	216	248	228	
3,4-Dichlorobenzaldehyde	43	247						
4-Chlorobenzaldehyde	48		110 α / 146 β	127	237	254	230	
4-Chloro-2-hydroxybenzaldehyde	52.5		155		257		212	
3-Chloro-2-hydroxybenzaldehyde	54.5		167				240	
2,3,5-Trichlorobenzaldehyde	56							
2,5-Dichlorobenzaldehyde	58	231	127.5	104				
2,4,6-Trichlorobenzaldehyde	58	235⁷⁴⁸	112					
3,5-Dichlorobenzaldehyde	65			106.5				
2,3-Dichlorobenzaldehyde	65							
2,6-Dichlorobenzaldehyde	70							
2,4-Dichlorobenzaldehyde	72		136					
2,3,6-Trichlorobenzaldehyde	86			147			252	
3,4,5-Trichlorobenzaldehyde	90–91				342 d.		227 d.	
2,3,4-Trichlorobenzaldehyde	91							
3,5-Dichloro-2-hydroxy benzaldehyde	95	281³	195	153				
3-Chloro-n-butyraldehyde (trim.)	96							
2,3,4,6-Tetrachlorobenzaldehyde	97							
2,3,4,5-Tetrachlorobenzaldehyde	106							
6-Chloro-3-hydroxybenzaldehyde	110.5			250			236	146
2,4,5-Trichlorobenzaldehyde	112							
2,4,6-Trichloro-3-hydroxy benzaldehyde	113		170					
4-Chloro-3-hydroxybenzaldehyde	121		126 anh.		272		238	
4,6-Dichloro-3-hydroxy-benzaldehyde	129				226			
3-Chloro-4-hydroxybenzaldehyde	139		144				210 d.	

Table 3–1–A. (Cont.)

	M. Pt.	B. Pt.	Oxime	Phenyl hydrazone	p-Nitro-phenyl hydrazone	2,4-dinitro-phenyl hydrazone	Semi-carbazone	Dimethone
2-Chloro-3-hydroxybenzaldehyde	139		149		244		236	
2,6-Dichloro-3-hydroxy benzaldehyde	140		188		277			
2,4-Dichloro-3-hydroxy benzaldehyde	141							
2-Chloro-4-hydroxybenzaldehyde	147		194		284 d.		214	
3,5-Dichloro-4-hydroxybenzaldehyde	158		185				236	
Pentachlorobenzaldehyde	202.5		201	152.5				

TABLE 3–1–B. *Chlorine Compounds. Aldehydes, Liquid*

	B. Pt.	Oximes	Phenyl hydrazone	p-Nitro-phenyl hydrazone	2,4-dinitro-phenyl hydrazone	Semi-carbazone	Dimethone	Dimethone anhydride
Chloroacetaldehyde	85					134 d.		
2-Chloropropionaldehyde	86							
Dichloroacetaldehyde	89.5	67^{17} B. Pt.				155		
Trichloroethanal (Chloral)	98	56		131	131	90 d.		
3-Chloropropionaldehyde	130–131							
2-Chloro-2-butenal (2-Chlorocrotonaldehyde)	147–150							
2,2,3-Trichloro-n-butyraldehyde	164.5	65						
2-Chlorobenzaldehyde	213	75 α / 101 β	86	237	214	146	205	224
3-Chlorobenzaldehyde	213							
2-Chloroacrolein	29^{17}							
D,L-2,3-Dichloropropionaldehyde	48^{14}							
4-Chloro-n-butyraldehyde	50^{13}	74.5		110	134	96		
2,3-Dichloro-n-butyraldehyde	58^{20}							
2,2,4-Trichloro-n-butyraldehyde	−7.8 M. Pt.							

Table 3–2. Chlorine Compounds. Acids and Anhydrides   459

TABLE 3–2. *Chlorine Compounds. Acids and Anhydrides*

	M. Pt.	B. Pt.	Amide	Anilide	p-Toluidide	p-Nitrobenzyl ester	p-Bromophenacyl ester
D,L-α-Chloropropionic acid		186	80	92	124		
Dichloroacetic acid		194	98	118	153		
α-Chloroisovaleric acid		210					
2-Chloro-n-valeric acid		222					
1-Chlorocyclohexane-1-carboxylic acid		138^{13}					
Dichloroacetic anhydride		216 d.	98	118	153		
α-Chloroisobutyric acid	31	118^{50}		69			
β-Chloropropionic acid	41	204					
Chloroacetic anhydride	46		121	134	162		
Trichloroacetic acid	57	167^{78}	141	97	113	80	
β-Chloroisocrotonic acid	61	195 subl.	110	108			
Chloroacetic acid	63	189	121	136	162		104
2-Chlorobenzoic anhydride	79		142	114	131		
γ-Chlorocrotonic acid	83	117^{13}	130				
3-5-Dichlorophthalic anhydride	89						
β-Chlorocrotonic acid	94	206	100	123			
o-Chlorophenylacetic acid	95		175	138.5			
3-Chlorobenzoic anhydride	95		134	122	170		
o-Chlorohydrocinnamic acid	96.5		119				
4-Chlorophthalic anhydride	99						
6-Chloro-2-methylbenzoic acid	102		167				
p-Chlorophenylacetic acid	105		175	164	190		
cis-Allo-α-chlorocinnamic acid	111		134	138			
α-Chlorodiphenylacetic acid	118		115	88			
p-Chloromandelic acid	119		122				
3,3,3-Trichlorolactic acid	124		96	164			
3-Chlorophthalic anhydride	124						

Table 3-2. (Cont.)

	M. Pt.	B. Pt.	Amide	Anilide	p-Toluidide	p-Nitrobenzyl ester	p-Bromophenacyl ester
cis-Allo-o-chlorocinnamic acid	127		112	134.5	142		
cis-Allo-β-chlorocinnamic acid	132		76	118 di-			
Chloromalonic acid	133		170 di-	118	116		
trans-α-Chlorocinnamic acid	137		121				
m-Chloromethylbenzoic acid	138		124	128	122		
trans-β-Chlorocinnamic acid	142		118	114	131		
o-Chlorobenzoic acid	142		142	121		106	106
o-Chlorophenoxyacetic acid	145		149.5				
2,5-Dichlorobenzoic acid	153		155				
2-Chloro-4-methylbenzoic acid	155		182	125			
4-Chlorophenoxyacetic acid	155		133	122			136
3-Chlorobenzoic acid	158		134			107	116
3-Chloro-4-hydroxybenzoic acid	169		180				
8-Chloro-1-naphthoic acid	171		207.5				
5-Chlorosalicylic acid	172		226				
4-Chloro-2-methylbenzoic acid	172		183				
4,5-Dichlorophthalic anhydride	188					138.5 di-	
Chlorofumaric acid	191		179	186			
4-Chlorobenzoic anhydride	194			194			
3,6-Dichlorophthalic anhydride	194						
3,4-Dichlorobenzoic acid	201		133				
4-Chloromethylbenzoic acid	203		173				
trans-2-Chlorocinnamic acid	212		168	176			
3-Chloroanisic acid	214		193				
3-Chloro-2-naphthoic acid	216		237				
4-Chloro-1-hydroxy-2-naphthoic acid	234		179	180	143		
4-Chlorobenzoic acid	243		237	194		129.5	126
7-Chloro-1-naphthoic acid	243		239	185			
5-Chloro-1-naphthoic acid	245 subl.						
Tetrachlorophthalic anhydride	256		186				
5-Chloro-2-naphthoic acid	270		317	202.5			
1-Chloroanthraquinone-2-carboxylic acid	272		>300 di-	248			
Chloroterephthalic acid	>300						

Table 3–3. Chlorine Compounds. Acyl Chlorides 461

TABLE 3–3. *Chlorine Compounds. Acyl Chlorides*

	B. Pt.	M. Pt.	D_4^{20}	n_D^{20}	Acid by hydrolysis M. Pt.
Acetyl chloride	51		$1.105\,D_4^{70}$	1.3897	
Oxalyl chloride	64		$1.488\,D_4^{13.4}$	$1.434\,n^{13}$	101 dihyd.
Acrylyl chloride	76		1.114	1.4343	
Propionyl chloride	80		1.065	1.4051	
iso-Butyryl chloride	92		1.017	1.4079	
Methacrylyl chloride	95			1.4435	15
Vinylacetyl chloride	98				163 B. Pt.
n-Butyryl chloride	101		1.028	1.4121	
Pivalyl chloride	105				35
Dichloroacetyl chloride	108				
Chloroacetyl chloride	108		$1.3997\,D_4^{18}$	1.454	63
D,L-α-Chloropropionyl chloride	110		1.285	1.440	
Methoxyacetyl chloride	113				204 B. Pt.
D,L-Methyl ethylacetyl chloride	115				176 B. Pt.
iso-Valeryl chloride	115		$0.985\,D_4^{24.3}$	$1.436\,n^{24.3}$	
Trichloroacetyl chloride	118		1.620	1.470	57
Cyclopropane carbonyl chloride	120		1.152		18
Ethoxyacetyl chloride	123				207 B. Pt.
Crotonyl chloride (*trans-*)	126		1.08	$1.45\,n^{18}$	72
n-Valeryl chloride	126		1.0004	1.420	
Allylacetyl chloride	128		$1.074\,D^{16}$		
Cyclobutane carbonyl chloride	137				195 B. Pt.
β-Methoxypropionyl chloride	138			1.424	
Diethylacetyl chloride	140			1.4234	
β-Chloropropionyl chloride	144		$1.331\,D^{13}$	1.455	42
iso-Caproyl chloride	147		0.9725		199 B. Pt.
α-Acetoxypropionyl chloride	150 d.		1.192	$1.4241\,n^{17}$	57
n-Caproyl chloride	153		0.975	1.426	
Trichloroacetyl chloride	158			$1.5271\,n^{18}$	76
Furoyl chloride	173				133
n-Heptanoyl chloride (Enanthoyl chloride)	175		0.963	$1.4345\,n^{18}$	
Hexahydrobenzoyl chloride	183		$1.096\,D_4^{15}$	$1.4766\,n^{15}$	29
Succinyl dichloride	190 d.		$1.395\,D_4^{15}$	$1.473\,n^{15}$	186
n-Capryloyl chloride (*n*-Octanoyl chloride)	196		0.949		16
Benzoyl chloride	197		1.212	$1.558\,n^{15}$	122
Diethyl malonyl dichloride	197		$1.2187\,D_{15}^{15}$	1.5537	125
Phenylacetyl chloride	210		1.1685	1.533	76
Pelargonyl chloride (*n*-Nonanoyl chloride)	215		$0.946\,D_4^{15}$		12
Glutaryl dichloride	218		1.324	1.473	97
p-Chlorobenzoyl chloride	222		1.362	1.579	240
Hydrocinnamoyl chloride	225 d.		$1.135\,D_{21}^{21}$		48
m-Chlorobenzoyl chloride	225				158
Phenoxyacetyl chloride	225				98

	B. Pt.	M. Pt.	D_4^{20}	n_D^{20}	Acid by hydrolysis M. Pt.
p-Methylbenzoyl chloride					
(p-Toluyl chloride)	225		1.1686	1.545	179
n-Decanoyl chloride	232				31
o-Chlorobenzoyl chloride	233				142
m-Methoxybenzoyl chloride	242				110
o-Methoxybenzoyl chloride	254				
Anisoyl chloride	262	22	1.261	1.58	184
Phthaloyl dichloride	276		1.406	1.569	200
α-Naphthoyl chloride	297.5				161
Fumaryl dichloride	63[13]		1.408	1.5004 n^{18}	300
Mesaconyl dichloride					
(Methylfumaryl dichloride)	64[14]				240.5
β-Ethoxypropionyl chloride	78[52]				
Hexahydrophenylacetyl chloride	98[23]				33
α-Phenoxypropionyl chloride	115[20]				115
2,4,6-Trimethylbenzoyl chloride	115[18]		1.0967 D_4^{25}	1.5263 n^{23}	152
Phenylpropionyl chloride	115[17]				136
p-Isopropylbenzoyl chloride	121[10]				256
Phenylmalonyl dichloride	122[15]				152
Benzoylformyl chloride	125[9]				64
ω-Undecenoyl chloride	128[14]				24.5
α-Phenoxybutyryl chloride	128[38]				82
m-Aldehydobenzoyl chloride	130[20]				175
Adipyl dichloride	130[18]				153
m-Ethoxybenzoyl chloride	135[16]	27			137
γ-Phenylbutyryl chloride	140[12]				52
Benzylmalonyl dichloride	141[15]				117 d.
Lauroyl chloride	145[18]			1.446 n^{20}	44
γ-Phenoxybutyryl chloride	155[20]				64
Aconitryl trichloride trans-	155[20]				194
p-Ethoxybenzoyl chloride	160[20]				198
Oleyl chloride	163[2]				16
Azelayl dichloride	166[18]				106.5
Myristoyl chloride	174[16]				54
Sebacoyl dichloride	182[16]		1.1212	1.4684	134.5
α-Naphthylacetyl chloride	188[23]				131
Benzilic acid chloride	193[27]				150
Palmitoyl chloride	194[17]				63
α-Naphthoxyacetyl chloride	194[10]				190
Dibenzylacetyl chloride	202[18]				89
Salicyloyl chloride	92[15]	19			158
Stearoyl chloride	202[6]	23			70
Cinnamoyl chloride (trans-)	258	35	1.1632 D^{37}	1.6202 n^{37}	133
iso-Phthaloyl chloride	276	43	1.388 D_4^{47}	1.570 n^{47}	345
β-Naphthoyl chloride	304	43			184
p-Aldehydobenzoyl chloride	258	48			256
β-Naphthoxy acetyl chloride		54			156
Diphenylacetyl chloride		56			148

Table 3–3. Chlorine Compounds. Acyl Chlorides (Cont.)   463

	B. Pt.	M. Pt.	D_4^{20}	n_D^{20}	Acid by hydrolysis M. Pt.
o-Benzoyl chloride		70			90 hyd.
					127 anh.
Benzylidene malonyl dichloride		77			195
Fluorene-9-carboxylic acid chloride		77			230
Terephthaloyl dichloride		83			
2,2'-Diphenic acid dichloride		94			228
α,α-Diphenylpropionyl chloride		95			173
Phenanthrene-2-carboxylic acid chloride		101			259
Phenanthrene-9-carboxylic acid chloride		102			252
Diphenyl-4-carbonyl chloride		114			228
Phenanthrene-3-carboxylic acid chloride		116			269
Fluorenone-4-carboxylic acid chloride		128			227
Fluorenone-1-carboxylic acid chloride		140			
Anthraquinone-2-carboxylic acid chloride		147			290
Di-(α-Naphthyl)-acetyl chloride		167			228.5
Anthraquinone-2,6-dicarboxylic acid dichloride		197			> 400
Anthraquinone-1,4-dicarboxylic acid dichloride		203			> 300
Anthraquinone-1,5-dicarboxylic acid dichloride		260			> 390

Table 3–4. Chlorine Compounds. Phenols

TABLE 3–4. *Chlorine Compounds. Phenols*

	B. Pt.	M. Pt.	Phenyl urethan	α-Naphthyl urethan	p-Nitro-benzoate	3,5-Dinitro-benzoate	p-Toluene sulfonate	Acetate	Benzoate	Aryl-oxyacetic acid
2-Chlorophenol	175.6	7	121	120	115	143	74		71	108
3-Chloro-4-methylphenol	196	33								
3-Chlorophenol	214	37		158	99	156	71		97	141
4-Chlorophenol	217	43	148.5	166	171	186	125		31	
2,4-Dichlorophenol	209	46								
6-Chloro-3-methylphenol	196	47					96		53	
2,4,6-Trichloro-m-cresol	265	48					92	35	71	
5-Chloro-2-methylphenol		49							55	
2-Chloro-3-methylphenol	194	56					96			
2,3-Dichlorophenol	206	58							90	
2,3,6-Trichlorophenol								206 di-		
2,5-Dichlorophenol	212	58						100.5 tri-		
2,3,5-Trichlorophenol		62							103	
3,5,6-Trichloro-2-methylphenol		62			153				110	
4-Chloro-3-methylphenol	235	66					98	37	89	
2,3,5-Trichloro-4-methylphenol		66								
3,5-Dichlorophenol	233	68					116	38	55	157
2,4,5-Trichlorophenol		68							92	
2,4,6-Trichlorophenol	245	69.5			105			45	75.5	
3,4,5-Trichloro-2-methylphenol		77								
2,3,4-Trichlorophenol		83.5							141	
2,3,6-Trichloro-4-methylphenol		85								
4-Chloro-2-nitrophenol	271^{746}	86								
3,4,5-Trichlorophenol		101								
Chlorohydroquinone	106							72 di-		

3,4,5-Trichlorocatechol	115		153 di-
Trichlorohydroquinone	136		167 tri-
Trichlorophloroglucinol	136		129
1,4,5-Trichloro-2-naphthol	157		133.5
1,3,4-Trichloro-2-naphthol	162		123
2,3,4-Trichloro-1-naphthol	168		
Pentachlorophenol	190	149	164
2,3,5,6-Tetrachlorohydroquinone	236	245 di-	233 d.

TABLE 3–5. *Chlorine Compounds. Esters*

	B. Pt.	M. Pt.	n_D^{20} (a)	D_4^{20}
Methyl chloroformate	75		1.38675	1.2231
Ethyl chloroformate	93		1.3974	1.13519
Chloromethyl acetate	111			1.094 D_4^{15}
n-Propyl chloroformate	113		1.40350	1.0901
Isobutyl chloroformate	130		1.40711 $n_{He}^{17.9}$	1.053 D^{15}
Methyl monochloroacetate	130		1.4221	1.238
n-Butyl chloroformate	145		1.417 $n_D^{8.4}$	1.079
Ethyl monochloroacetate	145		1.42274	1.158
β-Chloroethyl acetate	145		1.4234	1.178
Ethyl-α-chloropropionate	146			1.087
Benzyl chloroacetate	147		1.5246 n_D^{18}	1.2223 D_4^4
Isoamyl chloroformate	154		1.41916 n_{He}^{15}	1.032 D^{18}
Ethyl dichloroacetate	158		1.43860	1.2821
Ethyl trichloroacetate	168		1.450	1.380
n-Butyl chloroacetate	175			1.081 D_4^{15}
Methyl m-chlorobenzoate	231	21		
Methyl o-chlorobenzoate	234			
Methyl p-chlorobenzoate		44		
Ethyl trichloroacetate	162	66	1.451	1.383

TABLE 3-6. *Chlorine Compounds. Ketones*

	B. Pt.	M. Pt.	Semi-carbazone	2,4-Dinitro-phenyl hydrazone	p-Nitro-phenyl hydrazone	Phenyl hydrazone	Oxime
1-Chloro-2-propanone (Chloroacetone)	119		150	125			
1,1-Dichloro-2-propanone (1,1-Dichloroacetone)	120		163				
1-Chloro-2-butanone (Chloromethyl ethyl ketone)	138						
4-Chloro-3-methyl-2-butanone	146			116	176		88
3-Chloroacetophenone	228		232				113
2-Chloroacetophenone	229		160				95
4-Chloroacetophenone	232		202	231	239	114	130
2,5-Dichloroacetophenone	251	14					
2-Methyl-1-chloro-3-pentanone	64^9		70				
2-Ethyl-1-chloro-3-hexanone	92^{12}		115				
o-Chloropropiophenone (o-Chlorophenyl ethyl ketone)	106^{12}		173				
3-Chloroacetophenone	113^{11}		232				
4-Chloroacetophenone	126^{24}	26	204				138
3,5-Dichloroacetophenone	134^{17}	33					148
2,4-Dichloroacetophenone	140^{15}	36	177				62
4-Chloropropiophenone	118^2	41					
β-Phenylethyl chloromethyl ketone	111^5	43		147			102
3-Chlorobenzyl phenyl ketone		45					
1,3-Dichloropropanone (1,3-Dichloroacetone)	175		180				
3-Chloropropiophenone		46					
2,2'-Dichlorobenzoin		57					
4-Chloro-1,2-benzoquinone		57					
Phenacyl chloride (ω-Chloroacetophenone)	244	59	156	212			89
3-Chlorophenyl benzyl ketone		62					120
2-Chlorobenzyl phenyl ketone		71					86
4-Chlorobenzophenone		78				106	163
4-Chloro-1,2-benzoquinone		78		185			128 di-

Ketones (Cont.)	M. Pt.	
4-Chlorophenyl benzyl ketone	108	123
2-Chloro-1,4-naphthaquinone	117	198 mono-
4-Phenylphenacyl chloride	126	
p-Chlorobenzyl phenyl ketone	138	96
4,4'-Dichlorobenzophenone	147	135
3-Chloro-1,2-naphthoquinone	172	
4-Chloro-1,2-naphthoquinone	186	157 2-mono-
4-Chloro-1,2,3-trihydroxyanthraquinone	233	
Chloranilic acid (2,5-Dichloro-3,6-dihydroxy-1,4-benzoquinone)	283	
Chloranil (2,3,5,6-Tetrachloro-1,4-benzoquinone)	290	

TABLE 3-7. *Chlorine Compounds. Alcohols*

	B. Pt.	M. Pt.	α-Naphthyl urethan	p-Nitro- benzoate	3,5-Dinitro- benzoate	3-Nitro- hydrogen phthalate
1-Chloro-2-propanol	127					
2-Chloroethanol (Ethylene chlorohydrin)	131		101		77	98
D,L-2-Chloro-1-propanol	133					
Trichloroethanol	151	19	120		142	
3-Chloro-1-propanol (3-Chloropropyl alcohol)	161		76	71	76	
1,3-Dichloro-2-propanol	176		115		77	
2,3-Dichloropropanol	182		93	37		
1,1,1-Trichloroisopropanol	162^{773}	50				

30*

TABLE 3–8. *Chlorine Compounds. Ethers*

	B. Pt.	M. Pt.	n_D^{20}	D_4^{20}
Chloromethyl methyl ether	59		1.3974	1.015
Chloromethyl ethyl ether	80		1.404	1.014
α-Chloroethyl ethyl ether	98		1.404	0.966
β-Chloroethyl ethyl ether	107		1.411	0.989
α-Epichlorohydrin	115		1.438	1.181
α,α'-Dichloroethyl ether	116		1.4183 n^{24}	1.138 D_4^{12}
β,β'-Dichloroethyl ether	178		1.4568	1.220
m-Chloroanisole	194			
o-Chloroanisole	195		1.5433 n^{25}	1.1865 D_4^{25}
p-Chloroanisole	200			1.1851 $D_4^{12.8}$
o-Chlorophenetole	208			
p-Chlorophenetole	212	21	1.5227 n^{19}	1.1231 D_{20}^{20}
2,4,6-Trichlorophenetole	246	44		
2,4,6-Trichloroanisole		60		

TABLE 3–9–A. *Chlorine Compounds. Hydrocarbons, Solid*

	B. Pt.	M. Pt.	Acid by hydrolysis	Nitration product	
				M. Pt.	Position
3,4-Dichlorobenzotrichloride	283	26	202		
2-Chlorobenzotrichloride	260	29	141		
2-Chlorobenzotrichloride	264	29	142		
1,3-bis-(Chloromethyl)-benzene	250	32			
2,4,6-Trichlorotoluene		33		178	3,5
2-Chlorobiphenyl	237	34			
2,4,6-Trimethylbenzyl chloride	130[22]	37			
1,2-Dichloronaphthalene	296	35		169	di-
2,6-Dichlorobenzyl chloride		39			
2,3,4-Trichlorotoluene	231[761]	41		140	5,6
1,2,3,4-Tetrachlorobenzene	254	44		151	5,6
3,4,5-Trichlorotoluene	245[768]	44		164	2,6
2,3,5-Trichlorotoluene	232	45		149	4,6
1,6-Dichloronaphthalene		48		119	4
1,2,3,5-Tetrachlorobenzene	246	50		40	4
1,2,3-Trichlorobenzene	218	52		92	4,6
1-Chloro-2,2,3,3-tetramethyl butane		52			
1,4-Dichlorobenzene	173	53		54	2
1,2-bis-(Chloromethyl)-benzene (o-Xylylene dichloride)	239	54			
4,4'-Dichlorodiphenylmethane	337	55		198	3,3'
2-Chloronaphthalene	265	56		175	1,8
2,2'-Dichlorophenyl		60		203	5,5'

Table 3–9–A. Chlorine Compounds. Hydrocarbons, Solid (Cont.)   469

	B. Pt.	M. Pt.	Acid by hydrolysis	Nitration product	
				M. Pt.	Position
1,3-Dichloronaphthalene	291⁷⁷⁵	61		150	di-
1,3,5-Trichlorobenzene	208	63		68	2
1,7-Dichloronaphthalene	286	63		138	
1,4-Dichloronaphthalene	286⁷⁴⁰	68		92	8
2,5-Dichloro-*p*-xylene	224	68			
4-Chlorophenyl	293	77			
2,4,5-Trichlorotoluene	230⁷¹⁵	82		226	3,6
Pentachlorobenzene	276	86		143	6
1,8-Dichloronaphthalene	89				
1,4-*bis*-(Chloromethyl)-benzene					
(*p*-Xylylene dichloride)	240	98			
1,5-Dichloronaphthalene		107		142	8
1,1,1-Trichloro-2,2-*bis*-(*p*-[chlorophenyl]-ethane)					
(DDT)		108			
γ-Benzene hexachloride		112			
Triphenylmethyl chloride (Trityl chloride)		113			
2,7-Dichloronaphthalene		114		141	mono-
2,6-Dichloronaphthalene		135			
1,2,4,5-Tetrachlorbenzene	245	140		232	3,6
4,4′-Dichlorobiphenyl		149			
α-Benzene hexachloride	288	157			
5,6,7,8-Tetrachlorotetralin		174			
1,2,3,4-Tetrachlorotetralin		182			
Hexachloroethane	185	187			
Octachloronaphthalene	442	198			
9,10-Dichloroanthracene		209			
Hexachlorobenzene	309	229			
β-Benzene hexachloride		310			

TABLE 3–9–B. *Chlorine Compounds. Hydrocarbons, Liquid*

	B. Pt.	D_4^{20}	n_D^{20}	S-Naphthyl-isothiourea picrate	α-Naphtha-lide	Anilide
Methyl chloride	−24			224	160	114
Vinyl chloride	−14			104		
Ethyl chloride	13	$0.917\,D_6^6$		188	126	104
Isopropyl chloride	36.5	0.859	1.378	196		103
1-Chloropropene	37					114
Methylene dichloride						
(Dichloromethane)	41	1.336	1.4237			
Allyl chloride	44.5	0.940	1.416	155		114
n-Propyl chloride	46	0.889	1.388	181	121	92
1,2-Dichloroethylene (*trans-*)	48	1.2569	1.452			
tert.-Butyl chloride	51	0.846	1.386	160	147	128
1,1-Dichloroethane	57	1.175	1.4164			
Chloroprene	59	0.9583	1.458			
1,2-Dichloroethylene (*cis-*)	60	1.282	$1.4428\,n^{25}$			
Chloroform	61					
sec.-Butyl chloride	68	0.874	1.397	190	129	108
Isobutyl chloride	69	0.881	1.398	174	125	109
2,2-Dichloropropane	70	1.093	1.4117			
Methallyl chloride	72	0.9475	1.4340			
1,1,1-Trichloroethane	74	1.349	1.4380			
Carbon tetrachloride	77	1.595	1.4630			
n-Butyl chloride	78	0.886	1.402	180	112	63
Ethylene dichloride						
(1,2-Dichloroethane)	84	1.256	1.4443			
Neopentyl chloride	85	0.879				130
tert.-Amyl chloride	86	0.865	1.405		138	92
1,1,2-Trichloroethylene	87	1.464	1.4713			
3-Chloropentene-1	94	0.8978	1.4254			
D,L-3-Chloro-2-methylbutene-1	94	0.9088	1.4304			
Trimethylvinyl chloride	94	0.925	1.4320			
1,2-Dichloropropane	96	1.155	1.4388			
D,L-2-Chloropentane	97	0.8695	1.4079		102	94
3-Chloropentane	97	0.8723	1.4082		117	127
Isoamyl chloride	100	0.872	1.409	179	111	168
n-Amyl chloride	106	0.882	1.412	154	112	96
1-Chloropentene-2	109	$0.908\,D_4^{21.5}$	$1.435\,n^{21}$			
2-Chloro-2-methylpentane	110	0.863	1.4126		116	71
3-Chloro-2,2-dimethylbutane						
(Pinacolyl chloride)	112	0.8767	1.4181			
1,1,2-Trichloroethane	114	1.443	1.4707			
Cyclopentyl chloride	114	1.005	1.4510			
4-Chloro-2,2-dimethylbutane	115	0.8670	1.4160			138
3-Chloro-3-methylpentane	115	0.89	1.421			87
2-Chloro-2,3-dimethylbutane	117	$0.8769\,D^{22}$				
1,1,2,2-Tetrachloroethylene						
(Perchloroethylene)	121	1.623	1.5055			

Table 3–9–B. Chlorine Compounds. Hydrocarbons, Liquid (Cont.)   471

	B. Pt.	D_4^{20}	n_D^{20}	S-Naphthyl-isothiourea picrate	α-Naphtha-lide	Anilide
1,2-Dichlorobutane	123		1.440			
3-Chlorohexane	123	$0.870\,D_{20}^{20}$	1.4163			
2-Chlorohexane	123	$0.864\,D_4^{21}$	$1.4142\,n^{21}$			91
1-Chloro-2-ethylbutane	125	0.8914	1.4230			81
1,3-Dichloropropane	125	1.188	1.449			
Chlorobenzene	132	1.107	1.525			
3-Chloro-2,2,3-trimethylbutane	133					
n-Hexyl chloride	133	0.878	1.420	157	106	69
1,3-Dichloro-2-methylpropane	135	$1.131\,D_{20}^{20}$	$1.4627\,n^{19}$			
Cyclohexyl chloride	143	0.989	1.462		188	146
s-Tetrachlorethane	146	1.600	1.4942			
5-Chloro-2,3-dimethylpentane	152	0.8825	1.4299			80
1,2,3-Trichloropropane	158	1.417	1.4585			
n-Heptyl chloride	159	0.877	1.426	142	95	57
2-Chlorotoluene	159	1.082	1.524			
Pentachloroethane	161	1.681	1.504			
3-Chlorotoluene	162	1.072	1.521			
4-Chlorotoluene	162	1.071	1.521			
1,3-Dichlorobenzene	173	1.288	1.546			
1-Chloro-2-ethylbenzene	178	1.057	1.5218			
1,2-Dichlorobenzene	179	1.305	1.552			
Benzyl chloride	179	1.100	1.539	188	166	117
Octyl chloride	180	0.875	1.431	134	91	57
1-Chloro-3-ethylbenzene	184	1.053	1.5199			
1-Chloro-4-ethylbenzene	184	1.045	1.5175			
2-Chloro-1,4-dimethylbenzene	184	$1.059\,D_{20}^{20}$				
2-Chloro-1-vinylbenzene	189	1.100	1.5649			
3-Chloro-1,2-dimethylbenzene	190					
β-Phenylethyl chloride	190					97
1-Chloro-2-isopropylbenzene	191	1.0341	1.5168			
4-Methyl benzyl chloride	192	1.0512	1.5380			
4-Chloro-1,3-dimethylbenzene	192	$1.0548\,D_{20}^{20}$	$1.5230\,n^{25}$			
4-Chloro-1-vinylbenzene (p-Chlorostyrene)	192	1.0868	1.5660			
4-Chloro-1,2-dimethylbenzene	194	$1.064\,D_{15}^{15}$				
α-Phenylethyl chloride	195					133
3-Methylbenzyl chloride	195	$1.064\,D_{20}^{20}$	$1.5327\,n^{25}$			
2-Methylbenzyl chloride	197					
β-Chlorostyrene	197	1.109	$1.571\,n^{25}$			
1-Chloro-4-isopropylbenzene (p-Chlorocumene)	198	1.0208	1.5117			
2,6-Dichlorotoluene	199	1.2686	1.5510			
2,5-Dichlorotoluene	199	$1.2535\,D_{20}^{20}$				
2,4-Dichlorotoluene	200	1.249	1.549			
3,5-Dichlorotoluene	201					
n-Nonyl chloride	202	0.870	1.434			
2-Chloro-1,3,5-trimethylbenzene	204	$1.0337\,D^{30}$	$1.5212\,D^{30}$			
Benzalchloride	207	$1.295\,D^{16}$	1.5515			

	B. Pt.	D_4^{20}	n_D^{20}	S-Naphthyl-isothiourea picrate	α-Naphtha-lide	Anilide
2,3-Dichlorotoluene	207		1.5511			
3,4-Dichlorotoluene	209	1.2526	1.5471			
2-Chlorobenzyl chloride	213					
1,2,4-Trichlorobenzene	213					
4-Chlorobenzyl chloride	214					166
3-Chlorobenzyl chloride	216	$1.2695\,D_4^{15}$				
2-Chloro-p-cymene	217	$1.015\,D_4^{17}$	$1.5178\,n^{17}$			
3-Chloro-p-cymene	217	$1.018\,D_4^{18}$	1.5179^{18}			
Benzotrichloride	221	$1.374\,D_{15}^{17}$				
n-Decyl chloride	223	0.868	1.437	137		
4-Isopropylbenzyl chloride	226					
2-Chlorobenzalchloride	228	$1.399\,D_{15}^{15}$	$1.5670\,n^{16}$			
3-Chlorobenzalchloride	237					
4-Chlorobenzalchloride	237					
n-Undecyl chloride	241	0.868	1.440	139		
1-Chloronaphthalene	259	1.191	1.633			
3-Chlorobiphenyl	284					
Cetyl chloride (Hexadecyl chloride)	289 d.			155		

TABLE 4–1. *Bromine Compounds. Aldehydes*

	B. Pt.	M. Pt.	Oxime	Phenyl-hydrazone	p-Nitro-phenyl hydrazone	2,4-Dinitro-phenyl hydrazone	Semi-carbazone
2-Bromoisobutyraldehyde	115						
2,2,2-Tribromethanal (Bromal)	174		115				
3-Bromobenzaldehyde	234–236		72	141	220		205
4-Bromobenzaldehyde		57	157 syn- 111 anti-	113	207	128	228
1-Bromo-2-naphthaldehyde		118					

Table 4–2. Bromine Compounds. Acids and Anhydrides   473

TABLE 4–2. *Bromine Compounds. Acids and Anhydrides*

	M. Pt.	B. Pt.	Amide	Anilide	p-Toluidide	p-Nitro-benzyl ester	p-Bromo-phenacyl ester
D,L-α-Bromopropionic anhydride		123^{10}	123				
D,L-α-Bromobutyric anhydride		148^{10}	112				
α-Bromobutyric acid		217 d.	112	98	92		
β-Bromobutyric acid	20	122^{16}	92				
D,L-α-Bromopropionic acid	25.7	203.5	123	99	125		
Bromoacetic anhydride	41		91	131			
D,L-α-Bromoisovaleric acid	44	230 d.	133	116	124		
Dibromoacetic acid	48	232–235	156				
α-Bromoisobutyric acid	48	198	148				
Bromoacetic acid	50	208	91	131		88	
β-Bromopropionic acid	62.5		111				
α-Bromoisobutyric anhydride	63		148	83	92		
2,3-Dibromopropionic acid	67	160^{20}	130				
γ-Bromocrotonic acid	74		101				
2-Bromobenzoic anhydride	75		155				
D,L-α-Bromophenylacetic acid	86		148				
o-Bromobenzoylformic acid	93		136				
o-Bromophenylacetic acid	103		186				
4-Bromophthalic anhydride	113		181 di-				
Bromomalonic acid	113 d.		192		217 di-		
p-Bromophenylacetic acid	114		129				
cis-2-Bromoallocinnamic acid	120		155				
4-Bromopyromucic acid	129		122				
Tribromoacetic acid	131	245 d.	119				
trans-α-Bromocinnamic acid	131						
3-Bromophthalic anhydride	132						
3-Bromo-p-toluic acid	140		137				

Table 4–2. (Cont.)

	M. Pt.	B. Pt.	Amide	Anilide	p-Toluidide	p-Nitro-benzyl ester	p-Bromo-phenacyl ester
o-Bromophenoxyacetic acid	142.5		151				
3-Bromobenzoic anhydride	148		155				
2-Bromobenzoic acid	150		155	141		110	102
p-Bromophenoxyacetic acid	153						
3-Bromobenzoic acid	155		155	136		105	120
5-Bromosalicylic acid	165		232	222			
4-Bromo-2,5-dimethylbenzoic acid	171.5		209				
2,4-Dibromobenzoic acid	174		198				
8-Bromo-1-naphthoic acid	178		179	151			
5-Bromo-2,4-dimethylbenzoic acid	180		197.5				
3-Bromosalicylic acid	184		165				
5-Bromopyromucic acid	186		144				
5-Bromo-o-toluic acid	187 subl.		180				
3-Bromophthalic acid	188						
4-Bromobenzoic anhydride	218		189	197			
4-Bromo-3-hydroxy-2-naphthoic acid	233 d.			161			
5-Bromo-2-hydroxy-m-toluic acid	236		75	125			
7-Bromo-1-naphthoic acid	237		247	202			
4-Brombenzoic acid	251		189	197		180	
4-Bromocinnamic acid	251			183			
5-Bromo-1-naphthoic acid	261		241				
Tetrabromophthalic anhydride	280						
Bromoterephthalic acid	299		270 di-				

Table 4–3. Bromine Compounds. Acyl Bromides   475

Table 4–3. *Bromine Compounds. Acyl Bromides*

	B. Pt.	M. Pt.	D_4^{20}	n_D^{20}	Acid by hydrolysis
Oxalyl dibromide	64				101
Acetyl bromide	81		$1.6625\ D_4^{16}$	$1.4538\ n^{16}$	
Propionyl bromide	103				141 B. Pt.
n-Butyryl bromide	128				
iso-Valeryl bromide	138				
Bromoacetyl bromide	150		2.425		50
D,L-α-Bromopropionyl bromide	154		$2.061\ D_4^{16}$		26
α-Bromoisobutyryl bromide	162				48
D,L-α-Bromobutyryl bromide	172				
n-Caproyl bromide	175				
D,L-α-Bromoisovaleryl bromide	184				44
Benzoyl bromide	218		$1.570\ D^{15}$		122
n-Valeryl bromide	64^{66}				
Succinyl dibromide	105^{13}				186
o-Methylbenzoyl bromide	135^{37}				104
p-Bromobenzoyl bromide	136^{18}				251
m-Methylbenzoyl bromide	137^{52}				111
p-Methylbenzoyl bromide	147^{42}				179
Phenylacetyl bromide	150^{50}				76
o-Bromobenzoyl bromide	167^{18}				150
p-Methoxybenzoyl bromide	185^{27}				184
Cinnamoyl bromide (*trans-*)		48			133
Phthaloyl dibromide		80			206

TABLE 4–4. *Bromine Compounds. Phenols*

	B. Pt.	M. Pt.	α-Naphthyl-urethan	p-Nitro-benzoate	3,6-Dinitro-benzoate	p-Toluene-sulfonate	Acetate	Benzoate	Aryloxy-acetic acid
2-Bromophenol	195	5	129			78			
3-Bromophenol	108	32				52		86	108
2,4-Dibromophenol	238	36		183		120		94	
3,5-Dibromo-4-methylphenol		49		141			67	62	
3,5-Dibromo-2-methylphenol		57		136			21.5	102	
4-Bromophenol		64	169	180	191	94	68	84	
2,4,6-Tribromo-3-methylphenol		81.5				113		99	
2,4,5-Tribromophenol		87					106		
3,4,5-Tribromo-2-methylphenol		89							
3,5,6-Tribromo-2-methylphenol		91					76	133	
2,3,5-Tribromophenol		94	153	153	174	113		81	
2,4,6-Tribromophenol		95							
2,3,4-Tribromophenol		95							
2,3,5-Tribromo-4-methylphenol		102							
2,4-Dibromo-1-naphthol		105					92		
4,5,6-Tribromo-2-methylphenol		106							
Bromohydroquinone		110					72 di-		
2,4,6-Tribromoresorcinol		112					114 mono- 108 di-		
3,4,5-Tribromocatechol		144					120 di-		
Tribromophloroglucinol		152 anh.					164 mono- 181 tri-		
Tribromopyrogallol		168							
Tetrabromo-o-cresol		208					154 mono-		

Table 4–5. Bromine Compounds. Esters 477

TABLE 4–5. *Bromine Compounds. Esters*

	B. Pt.	M. Pt.	n_D^{20}	D_4^{20}
Methyl monobromoacetate	144 d			1.657
Ethyl monobromoacetate	159		1.451	1.506
Ethyl-α-bromopropionate	162			1.329
β-Bromoethyl acetate	163			1.524
Ethyl-β-bromopropionate	179			1.425
Ethyl bromomalonate	235			1.426 D_{15}^{15}
Methyl o-bromobenzoate	244			
Methyl m-bromobenzoate		32		
Methyl p-bromobenzoate		81		

Table 4–6. Bromine Compounds. Ketones

TABLE 4–6. Bromine Compounds. Ketones

	B. Pt.	M. Pt.	Semi-carbazone	2,4-Dinitrophenyl hydrazone	Phenyl hydrazone	Oxime
1-Bromo-2-propanone (Bromoacetone)	136		135 d.			36
1-Bromo-2-butanone (Bromomethyl ethyl ketone)	155			81		
6-Bromo-2-hexanone	214^{720}					
α-Bromopropiophenone	245					
1,1,1-Tribromoacetone	255 d.					
2-Bromoacetophenone	112^{10}			189		
o-Bromopropiophenone (2-Bromophenyl ethyl ketone)	118^{11}					
3-Bromoacetophenone	132^{17}					
3-Bromopropiophenone		40				
2-Bromobenzophenone		42				133
4-Bromopropiophenone	345	46	183			
2-Bromopropiophenone	140^{2}	51	171			
4-Bromoacetophenone	225	51	208		126	128
Phenacyl bromide		51	146			89.5
3-Bromophenacyl bromide	174^{14}	56	163 d.			
2-Bromo-1,4-benzoquinone						184 1-mono-; 196 4-mono-
2,4′-Dibromobenzophenone	381	62				141
3,5-Dibromoacetophenone	198^{15}	68	268 d.	230	109	
4-Bromobenzophenone		82		230	126	169
4-Bromophenacyl bromide		108				115
4-Phenylphenacyl bromide		124	265 d.		129	
3,4,5-Tribromoacetophenone		134	225 d.			
2,6-Dibromo-1,4-benzoquinone		131				170 d. 4-mono-
3,3′-Dibromobenzophenone		141				181
4,4′-Dibromobenzophenone	395	177				150
6-Bromo-1,4-dihydroxy-9,10-anthraquinone (6-Bromoquinizarin)		185.5				163 d. mono-
2-Bromo-9,10-phenanthraquinone		233				
1-Bromo-9,10-phenanthraquinone		233				
2-Bromo-1,4-dihydroxy-9,10-anthraquinone (2-Bromoquinizarin)		265				213 d. mono-
3-Bromo-9,10-phenanthraquinone		268	242 d. mono-		177 mono-	198 mono-; 212 d. di-

TABLE 4–7. *Bromine Compounds. Alcohols*

	B. Pt.	M. Pt.	α-Naphthyl urethan	p-Nitro-benzoate
2-Bromoethanol (Ethylene bromohydrin)	149 d.		86	
3-Bromo-1-propanol (Triethylene bromhydrin)	176 d.		73	
2,2-Dibromoethanol	179			
2,3-Dibromo-1-propanol	219 d.			59
2,2,2-Tribromoethyl alcohol	92^{10}	80		
1,1,1-Tribromo *tert.*-butyl alcohol (Brometone)		167		

TABLE 4–8. *Bromine Compounds. Ethers*

	B. Pt.	M. Pt.	D_4^{20}	Nitro derivative
o-Bromoanisole	210			106
p-Bromoanisole	215		$1.494\ D_4^0$	88
o-Bromophenetole	218			98
p-Bromophenetole	233			47
β-Bromoethyl phenyl ether		32		
2,4,6-Tribromophenetole		72		79
2,4,5-Tribromophenetole		73		79

480   Table 4–9. Bromine Compounds. Hydrocarbons

TABLE 4–9. *Bromine Compounds. Hydrocarbons*

	B. Pt.	M. Pt.	D_4^{20}	n_D^{20}	S-Naphthyl-isothiourea picrate	α-Naphthalide	Anilide
Methyl bromide	3.5				224	160	114
Vinyl bromide	16						104
Ethyl bromide	38		1.460	1.425	188	126	104
1-Bromopropene	60		1.4133	1.452			114
Isopropyl bromide	60		1.314	1.425	196		103
Allyl bromide	71		1.398	1.46545	155	121	114
n-Propyl bromide	71		1.353	1.4341	181	147	92
tert.-Butyl bromide	72		1.211				128
Isobutyl bromide	91		1.253	1.435	174	125	109
sec.-Butyl bromide	91		1.256	1.437	190	129	108
Dibromomethane	98		2.496	1.538			63
n-Butyl bromide	101		1.274	1.440	180	112	92
tert.-Amyl bromide	108		1.198 D_4^{18}	1.442		138	126
Neopentyl bromide	109		1.225				
1,1-Dibromomethane	112		2.055	1.5128			93
D,L-2-Pentyl bromide	117		1.212	1.442		102	124
3-Pentyl bromide	118		1.211	1.443			
Isoamyl bromide	120		1.213	1.442	179	111	108
n-Amyl bromide	129		1.219	1.445	154	112	96
1,2-Dibromoethane	132		2.179	1.5379			
Cyclopentyl bromide	137		1.387	1.489			
D,L-1,2-Dibromopropane	141		1.933	1.5203			
2-Hexyl bromide	146		1.658	1.4832 n^{25}			91
1,2-Dibromo-2-methyl propane	149		1.783	1.512			
1,2-Dibromo-1-butene	150		1.887 D^0				
Bromoform	150	8	2.890	1.598			
n-Hexyl bromide	155		1.175	1.448	157	106	69

Table 4–9. Bromine Compounds. Hydrocarbons (Cont.) 481

Compound	B.p.	Density	n_D			
1,3-Dibromopropene	156	2.097 D^0	1.538 n^{25}			
1,1-Dibromo-2-methyl propene	156	1.866 D_{20}^{20}	1.530			
Bromobenzene	156	1.494	1.560		161	
2,3-Dibromobutane	157	1.792	1.515			
Cyclohexyl bromide	165	1.336	1.495		188	146
1,2-Dibromobutane	166	1.820				
1,3-Dibromopropane	167	1.892	1.523			
1,3-Dibromo-2-butene	168	1.877	1.548			
1,3-Dibromobutane	174	1.820 D^0	1.507			
n-Heptyl bromide	180	1.140	1.451	142		
2-Bromotoluene	182	1.425			95	57
3-Bromotoluene	184	1.410				
1,1,2-Tribromoethene	189	2.6211	1.5933			
1,4-Dibromobutane	197	1.847 D^0				
Benzyl bromide	198	1.438	1.5486	188	166	117
1-Bromo-2-ethylbenzene	199	1.355				
Octyl bromide	201	1.112		134	91	57 / 133
α-Phenylethyl bromide	205	1.342	1.5448			
1-Bromo-4-ethylbenzene	205	1.4160	1.5927			
2-Bromo-1-vinylbenzene (o-Bromostyrene)	210	1.3020	1.5408			
1-Bromo-2-isopropylbenzene	210	1.398	1.5947			
4-Bromo-1-vinylbenzene (p-Bromostyrene)	212					
1-Bromo-2,3-dimethylbenzene	217					97
β-Phenylethylbromide	218	1.359	1.556			
1,3-Dibromobenzene	219	1.952	1.606			
4-Bromo-1-isopropylbenzene	219	1.2854	1.5361			
1,2-Dibromobenzene	219	1.956	1.609			
n-Nonyl bromide	220	1.090	1.454	131		
1,2,3-Tribromopropane	220	2.402	1.582			
1,5-Dibromopentane	221	1.694 D_4^{25}	1.514 n^{15}			
β-Bromostyrene	221				217	115 / 143
2-Bromocymene	234	1.267				

Organic Analysis

Table 4–9. Bromine Compounds. Hydrocarbons (Cont.)

Table 4–9. (Cont.)

	B. Pt.	M. Pt.	D_4^{20}	n_D^{20}	S-Naphthyl-isothiourea picrate	α-Naphthalide	Anilide
2,5-Dibromotoluene	236		1.811				
3,4-Dibromotoluene	240		1.81				
s-Tetrabromoethane	243	15	2.967	1.638			
1,8-Dibromooctane	270		$1.468\,D^{15}$	$1.501\,n^{15}$			
1-Bromonaphthalene	281		1.484	1.658			
1,9-Dibromononane	285	1.415^{15}					
2-Bromobiphenyl	297						
Dodecyl bromide	130^6		1.038	1.458			
n-Tetradecyl bromide	179^{20}		1.017	1.460			
n-Hexadecyl bromide (Cetyl bromide)	201^9	14			155		
4-Bromotoluene	184	28					
2-Bromobenzyl bromide		31			222		
3-Bromobenzyl bromide	263	41			205		
1,7-Dibromoheptane	281	42					
2-Bromonaphthalene		59					
4-Bromobenzyl bromide		62			219		
1,2-Dibromonaphthalene		67					
1,4-Dibromonaphthalene		82					
1,4-Dibromobenzene	219	89					
4-Bromobiphenyl	310	89					
Carbon tetrabromide	190	92					
1,3,5-Tribromobenzene	271	120					
4,4'-Dibromobiphenyl		164					
1,2,4,5-Tetrabromobenzene		180					

TABLE 5–1. *Iodine Compounds. Aldehydes and Ketones*

	M. Pt.	B. Pt.	Oxime	Phenyl hydrazone	p-Nitro-phenyl hydrazone	2,4-Dinitro-phenyl hydrazone	Semi-carbazone
2-Iodobenzaldehyde	37	129[14]	108	79			206
3-Iodobenzaldehyde	57		62	155	212		226
4-Iodobenzaldehyde	78			121	201	257	224
4-Iodoacetophenone	85	153[18]					

TABLE 5–2. *Iodine Compounds. Acids and Anhydrides*

	M. Pt.	Amide	Anilide	p-Nitro-benzyl ester	p-Bromo-phenacyl ester
Iodoacetic anhydride	46	95	143		
β-Iodopropionic acid	82	101			
Iodoacetic acid	83	95			
4-Iodophthalic anhydride	125				
3-Iodobenzoic anhydride	134	187			
3-Iodophthalic anhydride	159				
2-Iodobenzoic acid	162	110	141	111	143
3-Iodobenzoic acid	187	186		121	128
3,4-Di-iodophthalic anhydride	198				
4-Iodobenzoic anhydride	228	217			
4-Iodobenzoic acid	270	217	210	141	146
Tetraiodophthalic anhydride	318				

TABLE 5–3. *Iodine Compounds. Acyl Iodides*

	B. Pt.	D_4^{20}	Acid by Hydrolysis
Acetyl iodide	108	1.98 D^{17}	118 B. Pt.
Propionyl iodide	127		141 B. Pt.
Butyryl iodide	146		162 B. Pt.
Benzoyl iodide	109[10]		122 M. Pt.

31*

TABLE 5–4. *Iodine Compounds. Phenols*

	M. Pt.	Phenylurethan	p-Nitrobenzoate	3,5-Dinitro-benzoate	p-Toluene sulfonate	Acetate	Benzoate	Aryloxyacetic acid
3-Iodophenol	40	138	133	183	60		34 mono-	135
2-Iodophenol	43	122						
2,6-Di-iodophenol	68					107		
2,4-Di-iodophenol	72				165	70	98	
3,4-Di-iodophenol	83	148				32	123	
4-Iodophenol	93				99	70	119	
2,5-Di-iodophenol	99					79	93	
3,5-Di-iodophenol	104					123		
2,3,5-Tri-iodophenol	114					170 di-		
2,4,6-Tri-iodoresorcinol	145							
2,4,6-Tri-iodophenol	158			181		156	137	

TABLE 5–5. *Iodine Compounds. Ethers*

	B. Pt.	M. Pt.	D_4^{20}
o-Iodophenetole	246		
p-Iodophenetole (1-Iodo-4-ethoxybenzene)	252	27	
p-Iodoanisole	139	52	1.800

Table 5–6. Iodine Compounds. Hydrocarbons   485

TABLE 5–6. *Iodine Compounds. Hydrocarbons*

	B. Pt.	M. Pt.	D_4^{20}	n_4^{20}	S-Naphthyl-isothiourea picrate	α-Naphtha-lide	Anilide
Methyl iodide	43		2.282	1.532	224	160	114
Vinyl iodide	56						104
Ethyl iodide	72		1.940	1.514	188	126	104
Isopropyl iodide	90		1.703	1.499	196	121	103
n-Propyl iodide	102		1.743	1.505	181	121	92
Allyl iodide	103		1.777	1.578	155	147	114
tert.-Butyl iodide	103				188		128
sec.-Butyl iodide	120		1.592	1.499	190	129	108
Isobutyl iodide	120		1.602	1.496	174	125	109
tert.-Amyl iodide	128		1.479			138	92
n-Butyl iodide	130		1.616	1.499	180	112	63
2-Pentyl iodide	142		1.510	1.496			93
3-Pentyl iodide	142		1.511	1.497			124
Isoamyl iodide	148		1.503	1.493	179	111	108
n-Amyl iodide	155		1.512	1.496	154	112	96
Cyclopentyl iodide	166		1.7096	1.5447			
Cyclohexyl iodide	179		1.626 D_{15}^{15}		188		146
n-Hexyl iodide	179		1.437	1.493	157	106	69
Diiodomethane	181		3.325	1.7425			
Iodobenzene	188		1.831	1.620			
n-Heptyl iodide	204		1.373	1.490	142	95	57
3-Iodotoluene	204		1.698				
2-Iodotoluene	211		1.698				
Nonyl iodide	220				131		
1,3-Diiodopropane	224		2.5755	1.6423			
Octyl iodide	225		1.330	1.489	134		

Table 5–6. Iodine Compounds. Hydrocarbons (Cont.)

Table 5-6. (Cont.)

	B. Pt.	M. Pt.	D_4^{20}	n_4^{20}	S-Naphthyl-isothiourea picrate	α-Naphtha-lide	Anilide
4-Iodo-1-isopropylbenzene	236						
1-Iodonaphthalene	305						
n-Hexadecyl iodide (Cetyl iodide)		22			155		
Benzyl iodide	211	24			188	166	117
4-Iodotoluene	211	35					
5-Iodo-1,2,4-Trimethylbenzene	256	37					
1,3-Diiodobenzene	285	40					
2-Iodonaphthalene	309	55					
1,2-Diiodoethane		81					
4-Iodobiphenyl	320 d.	114					
Iodoform		119					
1,4-Diiodobenzene	289	129					

Table 6–1. Fluorine Compounds. Aldehydes and Ketones 487

Table 6–1. *Fluorine Compounds. Aldehydes and Ketones*

	B. Pt.	Oxime	Phenyl hydrazone	p-Nitrophenyl hydrazone	2,4-Dinitrophenyl hydrazone	Semicarbazone
Perfluoroacetone	− 28					153
Trifluoroacetaldehyde	− 20			149		138 d.
Perfluorobutanone	0					
Perfluoropropionaldehyde	2					
1,1,1-Trifluoroacetone	22				140	127
Perfluorocyclopentane	24					
Perfluoro-n-butyraldehyde	29					186
Perfluoropentanone	30				107	
Perfluorohexanone-3	52					
3,3,4,4,5,5-Heptafluoropentanone–2	58				78	
2,2,2-Trifluoropropionaldehyde	56^{745}				151	
Perfluoroheptanone-4	75					
Phenylperfluoromethyl ketone	152				95	
Phenylperfluoroethyl ketone	161				120	
3-Fluorobenzaldehyde	173	63	114	202		
Phenylperfluoro-n-propyl ketone	174					
4-Fluorobenzaldehyde	174.5^{753}	116 syn- 86 anti-	147	212		145
2-Fluorobenzaldehyde	175	63	90	205		
p-Tolylperfluoromethyl ketone	179				188	
p-Tolylperfluoroethyl ketone	181				163	
Phenylperfluoro-n-butyl ketone	189				136	
p-Tolylperfluoro-n-propyl ketone	193				142	
4-Fluoroacetophenone	196					
3-Trifluoromethylacetophenone	202					219
Phenylperfluoro-n-amyl ketone	204				145	
p-Tolylperfluoro-n-butyl ketone	211				153	
p-Tolylperfluoro-n-amyl ketone	217				161	

Table 6–2. *Fluorine Compounds. Acids and Anhydrides*

	B. Pt.	M. Pt.	Amide	Anilide
Trifluoroacetic anhydride	39		75	88
Perfluorosuccinic anhydride	55		207 di-	
Trifluoroacetic acid	71		75	88
Perfluoropropionic anhydride	72		95	
Perfluoroglutaric acid	72		237 di-	
Perfluoropropionic acid	96		95	
Perfluoro-*n*-butyric anhydride	108		105	93
Perfluoroisobutyric acid	118			
Perfluoro-*n*-butyric acid	120		105	93
Difluoroacetic acid	134		51	
Perfluoroisovaleric acid	137			
Perfluoro-*n*-valeric anhydride	138			
Perfluoro-*n*-valeric acid	139			
Perfluoro-*n*-caproic acid	157		117	
Fluoroacetic acid	164	31	107	
Perfluorocyclohexanoic acid	170		112	
Perfluoro-*n*-heptanoic acid	175			
Perfluoro-*n*-caproic anhydride	176		117	
Perfluoro-*n*-caprylic acid	189		138	
Perfluoro-*n*-capric acid	218		150	
Perfluoro-*n*-undecanoic acid	245			
Perfluoro-*n*-dodecanoic acid	270			
Perfluoro-*n*-pentadecanoic acid	294			
2-Fluoropropionic acid	60^8		76	
Hexafluoroglutaric acid	134^3			
Tetrafluorosuccinic acid		116	260 di-	
Octafluoroadipic acid		134	237 di-	
4-Fluorobenzoic acid		182	154	

TABLE 6–3. *Fluorine Compounds. Acyl Fluorides*

	B. Pt.	M. Pt.	Acid by hydrolysis B. Pt.
Trifluoroacetyl fluoride	−59		71
Perfluoropropionyl fluoride	−28		96
Perfluoro-*n*-butyryl fluoride	8		120
Acetyl fluoride	20		118
Propionyl fluoride	44		141
Fluoroacetyl fluoride	51		167
Butyryl fluoride	67		162.5
Phthaloyl difluoride	224	42	206 M. Pt.
Phenylacetyl fluoride	88^{17}		76 M. Pt.

TABLE 6–4. *Fluorine Compounds. Esters*

	B. Pt.	n_D^{20}	D_4^{20}
Vinyl perfluoroacetate	39	1.3151	1.203
Methyl perfluoroacetate	44		
Vinyl perfluoropropionate	58	1.3095	1.319
Methyl perfluoropropionate	61	1.2884	1.393
Ethyl perfluoroacetate	61	1.3093 n^{15}	1.195[17]
Ethyl perfluoropropionate	76	1.2990 n^{25}	1.294
Vinyl perfluoro-*n*-butyrate	79	1.3086	1.418
Methyl perfluoro-*n*-butyrate	79	1.293	1.483
Isopropyl perfluoropropionate	87	1.3090	1.224
Ethyl perfluoro-*n*-butyrate	95	1.3032	1.394
Ethyl difluoroacetate	99	1.3463	
Vinyl perfluoro-*n*-valerate	99	1.3116	1.493
n-Butyl perfluoroacetate	100	1.353 n^{22}	1.0268 D^{22}
Isopropyl perfluoro-*n*-butyrate	106	1.310	1.324
tert.-Butyl perfluoro-*n*-butyrate	116	1.318	1.278
Methyl perfluoro-*n*-caproate	122	1.297 n^{29}	1.618 D^{29}
sec.-Butyl perfluoro-*n*-butyrate	126	1.3212 n^{25}	1.284
n-Butyl perfluoro-*n*-butyrate	132	1.3249 n^{25}	1.296
Ethyl trifluoroacetoacetate	132		
Vinyl perfluorocyclohexanecarboxylate	59^{45}	1.3362	1.628
Vinyl perfluoro-*n*-caprate	$53^{0.5}$	1.3176	1.707
Vinyl perfluoro-*n*-caproate	66^{100}	1.3115	1.546
Diethyl perfluoroadipate	$71^{2.5}$	1.3541	1.4026 D^{29}
Diethyl perfluoroglutarate	76^{3}	1.3546	1.3444 D^{29}
Diethyl perfluorosuccinate	89^{15}	1.369	1.264
n-Octyl perfluoro-*n*-butyrate	108^{27}	1.3582 n^{25}	1.185
n-Dodecyl perfluoro-*n*-butyrate	158^{23}	1.3802 n^{25}	1.120
n-Octadecyl perfluoro-*n*-butyrate	185^{4}	1.4020 n^{25}	
n-Hexadecyl perfluoro-*n*-butyrate	208^{31}	1.3950 n^{25}	1.074

TABLE 6–5. *Fluorine Compounds. Alcohols*

	B. Pt.	α-Naphthyl urethan
2-Fluoroethanol	105	128
2,2,2-Trifluoroethanol	74	
2,2,3,3,3-Pentafluoro-*n*-propanol	80	
2,2,3,3,4,4,4-Heptafluoro-*n*-butanol	95	78

TABLE 6–6. *Fluorine Compounds. Ethers*

	B. Pt.	n_D^{20}	D_4^{20}
Perfluorodimethyl ether	−59		
Perfluorodiethyl ether	−1		
Perfluorotetrahydrofuran	1		
Perfluorotetrahydropyran	26		
Perfluoromethyl-perfluoro-*n*-butyl ether	36	1.240	1.58
Perfluoromethyl-perfluoro-cyclohexyl ether	80	1.273	1.74
Perfluoro-di-*n*-butyl ether	101	1.261	1.71
Perfluoro-di-*n*-hexyl	172	1.278	1.81

TABLE 6–7. *Fluorine Compounds. Hydrocarbons*

	B. Pt.	M. Pt.	n_D^{20}	D_4^{20}
Carbon tetrafluoride	−128			
Perfluoroethane	−78			
Perfluoro-*n*-propane	−37			
Perfluorocyclopropane	−33			
Perfluoro-*n*-butane	−3			
Perfluorocyclobutane	−4			
Perfluorocyclopentane	22	10		1.648 D_4^{25}
Perfluoro-*n*-pentane	29			
1,3-Difluoropropane	41		1.3190 n^{26}	1.0057 D_4^{25}
Perfluorocyclohexane	50	49		
Perfluoro-*n*-hexane	57		1.2512 n^{22}	1.6995 D_4^{25}
Perfluoro-2-methylpentane	58		1.2564 n^{22}	1.7326
1,3-Difluorobenzene	82		1.4404 n^{18}	1.413 D_4^{25}
Perfluoro-*n*-heptane	84		1.2770 n^{25}	1.801 D_4^{25}
Fluorobenzene	87		1.466	1.024
1,4-Difluorobenzene	88		1.4423 n^{18}	1.1632 D_4^{25}
1,2-Difluorobenzene	92		1.4451 n^{18}	1.1496 D_4^{25}
Perfluoro-*n*-octane	107			
2-Fluorotoluene	114			
3-Fluorotoluene	116			
4-Fluorotoluene	117		1.496	0.998
Perfluoro-*n*-nonane	127		1.2865 n^{25}	1.860 D_4^{25}
Perfluoro-*n*-decane	150	36	1.2890 n^{25}	1.873 D_4^{25}
Perfluoro-*n*-undecane	161	57	1.2960 n^{25}	1.919 D_4^{25}
Perfluoro-*n*-dodecane	178			
Perfluoro-*n*-tridecane	196			
1-Fluoronaphthalene	214		1.594	1.134
2-Fluoronaphthalene		60		

TABLE 7–1. *Sulfur Compounds. Aldehydes and Ketones*

	B. Pt.	M. Pt.	Oxime	Phenyl hydrazone	p-Nitro-phenyl hydrazone	2,4-Dinitro-phenyl hydrazone	Semi-carbazone
2-Thiophenealdehyde	198			119		242	
2-Acetylthiophene	213	10.5	81	96	181		190
(2-Thienyl ethyl ketone)							
1-Thienyl ethyl ketone	228		55				167
3-Thiophanone	85[24]						
2-Acetyl-5-methylthiophene	83[2]						
α-Thienylacetone	106[12]						
3-Methyl-2-thiophene-aldehyde	114[25]			149			
5-Methyl-2-thiophene-aldehyde	114[25]			126			
3-Acetylthianaphthene	137[3]						250
Thiobenzophenone		54					
2-Furyl-2-thenoyl methane	195[6]	55.5					
Phenyl-2-thienyl ketone	209[40]	56	93				
4-Methylthiazole-5-aldehyde	118[21]	75		159			
Benzoyl-2-thenoylmethane		78					
Di-2-thenoylmethane		100					
2-Acetyldibenzothiophene		112					235

TABLE 7–2. *Sulfur Compounds. Carboxylic Acids*

	M. Pt.	B. Pt.	Amide	Anilide	p-Toluidide	p-Bromo-phenacyl ester
Thioacetic acid		93	108	76	130	
2-Thienylacetic acid	76		148			
α-Thienylglyoxylic acid	91		88			
2-Thenoic acid	129		180			
3-Thenoic acid	138		180			130
4-Dibenzothienylacetic acid	162		206			
3-Thianaphthenecarboxylic acid	175		198	173		
2-Thianaphthenecarboxylic acid	236		177			

TABLE 7–3. *Sulfur Compounds. Thiols and Thiophenols*

	B. Pt.	M. Pt.	2,4-Dinitrophenyl thioether	2,4-Dinitrophenyl sulfone	3,5-Dinitrothiobenzoate	3-Nitrothiophthalate	Anthraquinone thioether
Methyl mercaptan	6		128	189.5			221
Ethyl mercaptan	36		115	160	62	149	184
Isopropyl mercaptan	56		94	140.5	84	145	
2-Methyl-2-propane thiol	62						
n-Propyl mercaptan	67						
2-Methyl-1-propane thiol	87						
Isobutyl mercaptan	88		76	105.5	64	136	144
Allyl mercaptan	90		72	105			
n-Butyl mercaptan	97		66	92	49	144	
tert.-Amyl mercaptan	97						
Isoamyl mercaptan	119		59	95	43	145	86
n-Amyl mercaptan	126		80	83	40	132	129
Dimethylene dithiol	147		248				
n-Hexyl mercaptan	151		74	97			114
2-Mercaptoethanol	153						
Cyclohexyl mercaptan	159		148	172			
Thienyl mercaptan	166		119	143			
Trimethylene dithiol	169						
Thiophenol (Phenyl thiol)	169		121	161	149	131	
n-Heptyl mercaptan	176		82	101	53	132	96
2-Ethyl-1-hexane thiol	185						
o-Thiocresol	194	15	101	155			
Benzyl mercaptan	194		130	182.5	120	137	
m-Thiocresol	195		91	145			
n-Octyl mercaptan	199		78	98			95
α-Phenylethyl mercaptan	199		89	133.5			
n-Nonyl mercaptan	220		86	92			117.5
2-Furanmethane thiol	39^5						
1,2-Ethane dithiol	41^{12}						
α-Toluene thiol	72^9						
2-Phenylethane thiol	83^9						
p-tert.-Butylbenzene thiol	104^8						
1-Dodecane mercaptan	130^9						
Toluene-3,4-dithiol		28					
p-Thiocresol	195	43	103	189.5			
Cetyl mercaptan		50.5	91	105			
β-Thionaphthol	162^{20}	81	145				
Biphenyl mercaptan		111	146	170			
α-Thionaphthol	161^{20}		176				
3-Mercaptosuccinic acid		146					
o-Mercaptobenzoic acid		164					
2-Mercaptobenzothiazole		177					

Table 7–4. Sulfur Compounds. Sulfides and Disulfides   493

TABLE 7–4. *Sulfur Compounds. Sulfides and Disulfides*

	B. Pt.	M. Pt.	Sulfoxide	Sulfone	Disulfide B. Pt.
Methyl sulfide	38			109	109.7
Ethyl methyl sulfide	65			36	
Vinyl sulfide	84				
Methyl isopropyl sulfide	85				
Ethyl sulfide	91			70	154
Methyl propyl sulfide	95.5				
Ethyl isopropyl sulfide	107.5				165.5
Methyl disulfide	109.7				
Ethyl propyl sulfide	118.5				174
Isopropyl sulfide	119			36	176
tert.-Butyl ethyl sulfide	120.5				176
n-Butyl methyl sulfide	122				
Propyl isopropyl sulfide	132				
sec.-Butyl ethyl sulfide	133.5				
Isobutyl ethyl sulfide	134				
Allyl sulfide	138				
Propyl sulfide	143			30	194
n-Butylethyl sulfide	143			50	
tert.-Butyl sulfide	149				
Ethyl disulfide	152				
Isobutyl sulfide	169			17	215
Butyl sulfide	189			46	231
Methyl phenyl sulfide	192			88	
Ethyl phenyl sulfide	204			42	
Isoamyl sulfide	215			31	247
Phenyl sulfide	296			128	60 M. Pt.
Isobutyl disulfide	84[10]				
Methyl *p*-tolyl sulfide	100[18]				
Ethyl *p*-tolyl sulfide	105[15]				
n-Butyl disulfide	110[13]				
Bis (2-ethyl hexyl) disulfide	120[1]				
n-Hexyl sulfide	126[9]				
Pentyl disulfide	128[12]				
n-Heptyl sulfide	143[8]				
Decyl sulfide	205[4]	22			
Dodecyl sulfide	260[4]	40			
Benzyl phenyl sulfide		41	123	146	
p-Tolyl disulfide		44			
Bis (*p*-methoxyphenyl) sulfide		46	96	130	
Tetradecyl sulfide		49			
Benzyl sulfide		50	135	152	73 M. Pt.
p-Tolyl sulfide		57	93	158	48 M. Pt.
Octyl sulfide		57		76	
Phenyl disulfide		59			
Hexadecyl sulfide (Cetyl sulfide)		61	100	103.5	
Octadecyl sulfide		68			

	B. Pt.	M. Pt.	Sulfoxide	Sulfone	Disulfide B. Pt.
Benzyl disulfide		70			
Bis (2-phenyl ethyl) sulfide		92	69	100.5	
Methyl-1-naphthyl sulfide		119			
Methyl-2-naphthyl sulfide		127			

TABLE 7–5. *Sulfur Compounds. Cyclic Thioethers*

	B. Pt.	n_D^{20}	D_4^{20}
Thiophene	84	1.5289	1.06485
2-Methylthiophene	112.5	1.5203	1.0193
3-Methylthiophene	115.5	1.52042	1.02183
2-Methylthiacyclopentane	133	1.4909	0.95552
3-Ethylthiophene	136	1.5146	0.9980
2,5-Dimethylthiophene	137	1.5129	0.9850
3-Methylthiacyclopentane	139	1.4924	0.9634
2,4-Dimethylthiophene	141	1.5104	0.9956
2,3-Dimethylthiophene	141.5	1.5192	1.0021
Thiacyclohexane	142	1.5067	0.9856
trans-2,5-Dimethylthiacyclopentane	142	1.4799	0.9222
cis-2,5-Dimethylthiacyclopentane	142	1.4799	0.9222
3,5-Dimethylthiophene	145	1.5212	1.008
2-Isopropylthiophene	153	1.5038	0.9678
2-Methylthiacyclohexane	153	1.4905	0.9428
3-Isopropylthiophene	157	1.5052	0.9733
2-Methyl-3-ethylthiophene	157		
3-Methylthiacyclohexane	158	1.4922	0.9473
2-Propylthiophene	158.5	1.5049	0.9687
4-Methylthiacyclohexane	158.5	1.4923	0.9471
5-Ethyl-2-methylthiophene	160	1.5073	0.9661
3-Propylthiophene	161	1.5057	0.9716
2-Ethyl-3-methylthiophene	161	1.5105	0.9815
2-Methyl-4-ethylthiophene	163	1.5098	0.9742
2,3,5-Trimethylthiophene	164.5	1.5112	0.9753
2,3,4-Trimethylthiophene	173	1.5208	0.995

Table 7–6. *Sulfur Compounds. Esters*

	B. Pt.	M. Pt.	D	n
Ethylene monothiocarbonate	62[1]			
Dimethyl sulfate	188		$1.3348\ D^{15}$	$1.3874\ n_D^{20}$
Diethyl sulfate	208		$1.172\ D_4^{25}$	$1.4010\ n_D^{18}$
Diethyl dithiooxalate		25		

Table 8–1. *Silicon Compounds. Silicates*

	B. Pt.	D^{20}	n_D^{20}
Methyl silicate	121	1.023	1.3683
Tetraethyl silicate	165.5	0.93975	1.38619
n-Propyl silicate	224		
n-Hexyl silicate	355	$0.8326\ D^{21}$	$1.428\ n^{23}$
Cresyl silicate	450	$1.126\ D^{25}$	$1.5587\ n^{25}$
Glycol silicate	d.	$1.2548\ D^{26}$	
Allyl silicate	135[34]		1.4336
n-Butyl silicate	141[32]	$0.913\ D^{25}$	1.4131
n-Amyl silicate	148[3]		
2-Ethyl-*n*-butyl silicate	164[1]	0.8920	1.4305
2-Ethylhexyl silicate	194[1]	0.878	1.4379
n-Octyl silicate	204[3]	0.8208	$1.435\ n^{22}$
Cyclohexyl silicate	229[10]		
Phenyl silicate	235[5]		
Dodecyl silicate	280[5]		1.4474

TABLE 8–2. *Silicon Compounds. Alkoxy Silanes*

	B. Pt.	M. Pt.	D^{20}	n_D^{20}
Trimethyl ethoxysilane	75		0.7573	1.3741
Dimethyl dimethoxysilane	82		0.8638	1.8706
Methyl trimethoxysilane	103			
Dimethyl diethoxysilane	111		0.890	1.3839
Methyl triethoxysilane	143.5		0.938	1.3869
Dimethyl di-*n*-propoxysilane	152		0.8414	1.3952
Vinyl triethoxysilane	158		0.90	1.338
Ethyl triethoxysilane	159		0.9207	1.3853

	B. Pt.	M. Pt.	D^{20}	n_D^{20}
Dimethyl di-n-butoxysilane	186		0.8434	1.4058
n-Amyl triethoxysilane	198		0.895	1.390
Methyl tri-n-propoxysilane	82[15]		0.8831	1.3992
Phenyl trimethoxysilane	100[18]			
Methyl tri-n-butoxysilane	120[15]		0.8775	1.4083
Phenyl triethoxysilane	120[15]		1.0133 D^0	1.4580 n^{25}
Phenyl tri-n-propoxysilane	128[6]		1.036	1.5025
Diphenyl dimethoxysilane	161[15]		1.077	1.5447
Diphenyldiethoxysilane	164[12]		1.0334	1.5250
Phenyl tri-n-butoxysilane	169[9]		0.9447	1.46107
Diphenyl di-n-propoxysilane	182[15]		1.0095	1.5189
Diphenyl di-n-butoxysilane	201[16]		0.9918	1.5132
Triphenyl ethoxysilane	207[3]	65		

TABLE 8–3. *Silicon Compounds. Alkoxy Siloxanes*

	B. Pt.	M. Pt.	D	n_D^{20}
Hexamethyldisiloxane	100.5		0.7619	1.3774
Hexamethylcyclotrisiloxane	134	64		
Ethyl polysilicate	150		1.05	
Octamethylcyclotetrasiloxane	175	17.5	0.9558	1.3968
Decamethylcyclopentasiloxane	210		0.9593	1.3982
Hexaethoxydisiloxane	235			1.389
Dodecamethylcyclohexasiloxane	245		0.9672	1.4015
Hexa-(2-ethylbutoxy)disiloxane	195[0.2]		0.916	1.4331
Hexa-(2-ethylhexoxy)disiloxane	250[4]		0.89	1.436
Hexaphenylcyclotrisiloxane	295[1]	190		
Octaphenylcyclotetrasiloxane	335[1]	201	1.185 solid	

TABLE 8–4. *Silicon Compounds. Silanols*

	B. Pt.	M. Pt.	D	n_D^{20}
Diphenylsilanediol	330[1]	132		
Triphenylsilanol		155		1.777

TABLE 8–5. *Silicon Compounds. Silanes*

	B. Pt.	M. Pt.	D	n_D^{20}
Tetramethylsilane	26.5		0.646	1.3556 n^{25}
Dimethyldivinylsilane	80		0.7408	1.4182 n^{25}
Trivinylsilane	92.5		0.7725	1.4498 n^{25}
Chloromethyltrimethylsilane	97			
Allyltrimethylsilane	100			
Trivinylmethylsilane	105		0.7692	1.4411 n^{25}
Tetraethylsilane	153		0.7662	1.4268
Triphenylsilane		30		
p-Biphenylyltriphenylsilane	512	159		
Di-p-biphenylyldiphenylsilane	570	170		
Tri-p-Biphenylylphenylsilane	580	174		
Tetraphenylsilane	430	237		
Tetra-p-biphenylylsilane	600 d.	283		
Hexaphenyldisilane		352		

TABLE 9–1. *Higher Orders. Acids*

	M. Pt.	Amide	Anilide	Benzoyl	Acetyl	3,5-Dinitro-benzoyl
Chlorobromoacetic acid	31.5	126				
-Chloro-2-nitrobenzoic acid	139	154	164			
-Chloro-4-nitrobenzoic acid	140	172	168			
-Chloro-3-nitrobenzoic acid	141	172				
-Chloronitrosalicylic acid	163	199				
-Chloro-3-nitrobenzoic acid	165	178				
-Bromo-3-nitrobenzoic acid	180	197	166			
-Chloro-3-nitrobenzoic acid	181	156	131			
-Chloropicolinic acid	182 d.	158				
-Bromo-3,5-dinitrobenzoic acid	188	188				
Bromo-2-nitro-p-toluic acid	203	191				
-Bromo-3-nitrobenzoic acid	203	156	156			
-Bromo-3-nitro-p-toluic acid	206	171				
-Bromo-3,5-dinitrobenzoic acid	213	216				
-Bromo-3-nitro-o-toluic acid	226	235				
-Chloro-2-nitrobenzoic acid	235		186			
-Chloroquinoline-3-carboxylic acid	240	200				
-Chlorocinchonic acid	244	334	202			
L-Methionine	281			145	114	
L-Lanthionine	283			195		
Methionine	283				98	94
anthionine	304			198		

TABLE 9–2. *Higher Orders. Phenols*

	B. Pt.	M. Pt.	*p*-Toluene sulfonate	Acetamide
3-Aminothiophenol	180[16]			97
2-Aminothiophenol	234	26		135
3-Bromo-4-chlorophenol		33		
4-Aminothiophenol	140[16]	46[33]		
4-Amino-*o*-thiocresol		47		95 N-
				125 N, S- di-
6-Bromo-2,6-dichlorophenol		68	82	
4-Chloro-2-iodophenol		78		
4-Chloro-2,6-dinitrophenol		81		
4-Chloro-2-nitrophenol		86		
2,4,6-Tribromo-3-nitrophenol		89	146	
4-Amino-1-thionaphthol		91		173
4-Chloro-2,6-dibromophenol		92	107	
3-Chloro-2,4,6-tribromophenol		105		
4-Chloro-2,6-diiodophenol		109		
4-Chloro-3,5-dibromophenol		121		
4,5,6-Tribromo-2-nitrophenol		123		
2,6-Dichloro-4-nitrophenol		127		
3,4,6-Tribromo-2-nitrophenol		127		
2,6-Dibromo-4-nitrophenol		144	128	
2,3,6-Tribromo-4-nitrophenol		151		
4,4′-Dichloroazoxybenzene		154		
1-(*m*-Chlorobenzeneazo)-2-naphthol		161		
1-(*p*-Chlorobenzeneazo)-2-naphthol		162		
1-(*o*-Bromobenzeneazo)-2-naphthol		165		
1-(*m*-Bromobenzeneazo)-2-naphthol		172		
1-(*p*-Bromobenzeneazo)-2-naphthol		175		
4-(*o*-Bromobenzeneazo)-1-naphthol		183		
4-(*o*-Chlorobenzeneazo)-1-naphthol		185		
2-(*p*-Chlorobenzeneazo)-1-naphthol		187		
2,6-Dichloro-3,5,6-tribromophenol		209		
4-(*m*-Bromobenzeneazo)-1-naphthol		211		
4-Chloro-2,3,5,6-tetrabromophenol		215		
4-(*m*-Chlorobenzeneazo)-1-naphthol		222 d.		
4-(*p*-Chlorobenzeneazo)-1-naphthol		230 d.		
4-(*p*-Bromobenzenazo)-1-naphthol		238		

Table 9–3. Higher Orders. Amino Compounds   499

Table 9–3. *Higher Orders. Amino Compounds*

	B. Pt.	M. Pt.	Acetamide	Benzamide	Benzene sulfonamide	p-Toluene sulfonamide	Phenyl thiourea	n_D^{20}	D_4^{20}	Picrate
Perfluorotrimethylamine	−11									
2,2,2-Trifluoroethylamine	38							$1.295\ n^{30}$	$1.245\ D^{30}$	
2,2,3,3-Pentafluoro-n-propylamine	50							1.297	1.400	
2,2,3,4,4,4-Heptafluoro-n-butylamine	68							1.298	1.493	
Perfluorotriethylamine	69							$1.262\ n^{25}$	$1.75\ D_4^{25}$	
Diperfluoroethylperfluoro-n-propylamine	91							$1.269\ n^{25}$	$1.76\ D_4^{25}$	
Diperfluoro-n-propylperfluoroethylamine	111							$1.273\ n^{25}$	$1.79\ D_4^{25}$	
Perfluorotri-n-propylamine	129							$1.278\ n^{25}$	$1.83\ D_4^{25}$	
4-Chloropyridine	147									135
3-Chloropyridine	149									
Diperfluoroethylperfluoro-cyclohexylamine	163							$1.304\ n^{25}$	$1.205\ D^{15}$	
2-Chloropyridine	170									
3-Bromopyridine	170							1.5694	$1.645\ D_4^{0}$	
2-Fluoroaniline	176		80							
Perfluorotri-n-butylamine	177							$1.291\ n^{25}$	$1.87\ D_4^{25}$	
4-Fluoroaniline	186		152	185				1.5195	1.1725	
3-Fluoroaniline	187		88						$1.160\ D^{16}$	
2-Bromopyridine	194								$1.657\ D^{15}$	
N,N-Dimethyl-2-chloroaniline	207									132
2-Chloroaniline	209		87	99	129	193	156	1.5895	1.2125	134
2,2'-Diaminodiethyl sulfide	213									212
2-Chloro-N-methylaniline	218								$1.1735\ D^{11}$	133

Table 9–3. (Cont.)

	B. Pt.	M. Pt.	Acetamide	Benzamide	Benzene sulfonamide	p-Toluene sulfonamide	Phenyl thiourea	n_D^{20}	D_4^{20}	Picrate
2-Chloro-4-methylaniline	223		113	137	154			$1.5798\ n^{23}$	$1.064\ D_4^{23}$	200
3-Chloroaniline	230	26	46	129					1.51	153
2-Bromo-4-methylaniline	240		118	149					$1.169\ D^{11.5}$	
N-Methyl-4-chloroaniline	240	29	92							
4-Chloro-2-methylaniline	241		140	135						
2-Chloro-6-methoxyaniline	246		123	120						
3-Bromoaniline	251	18	87	176			143	1.626	1.579	180
3-Bromo-2-methylaniline	254		163							182
Perfluorotri-n-hexylamine	256							$1.303\ n^{25}$	$1.93\ D_4^{25}$	135
3-Chloroquinoline	258									191
3-Bromo-N,N-dimethylaniline	259									190
4-Chloro-2-amino-N,N-dimethylaniline	267		90							217
3-Bromoquinoline	274									
6-Bromoquinoline	278									
8-Chloroquinoline	288									
8-Bromoquinoline	302							1.5679		223
4-Bromopyridine	$27.5^{0.3}$									
2-Aminothiophene	77^{11}	26	161	172						
2-Iodopyridine	93^{13}							1.6366	1.9735	120
2-Chloro-4-methoxyaniline	156^{31}		114							
2-Bromo-4-ethoxyaniline	160^{23}	25	97							
3-Bromo-4-methylaniline	254	29	113	132						
4-Bromoquinoline	270 d.	29								212
4-Chloroquinoline	263	31								
7-Chloroquinoline	267	31								
5-Bromo-2-methylaniline	253	32	165	116						
2-Bromoaniline	250	32	99	157		128	146			129
3 Iodoaniline		33	119							

Compound							
3-Bromo-5-methylaniline		36	171				122
8-Iodoquinoline		36					216
3-Iodo-4-methylaniline		37	130				
2-Chloroquinoline		38					
5-Bromo-2-naphthylamine		38	165	109			
2-Iodo-4-methylaniline		40	133	161			
4-Bromoisoquinoline		40					
2-Chloro-4,6-dimethylaniline		40	205	148			
6-Chloroquinoline	262	41					178
4-Chloroquinaldine		42					178
5-Chloroquinoline	256	45					
3-Bromo-4-ethoxyaniline	189³⁰	47	114				
3-Iodo-5-methylaniline		48	151				
5-Bromoquinoline		48					
4-Fluoro-1-naphthylamine		48		197			
2-Bromoquinoline		49					
2-Bromo-4,6-dimethylaniline		49	196	186			
2,5-Dichloroaniline		50	132	120			
4-Chloro-2-methoxyaniline		52	150				200
2-Iodoquinoline		52					
7-Bromoquinoline	290	52					
3-Iodopyridine		53					
2-Chloro-1-naphthylamine		56	191 mono- 88 di-				
5-Bromo-2-ethoxyaniline		57	133	162			135
5-Bromo-2-aminobiphenyl		57	130	98			
1-Chloro-2-naphthylamine	240	59	147	115			
4-Bromo-2-methylaniline		59	156	139			
2-Iodoaniline		61	109				112
3-Chloro-4-methoxyaniline		62	94				186
3-Chloro-1-naphthylamine		62	197	162	128		
2,4-Dichloroaniline		63	145	117		126	106

Table 9–3. Higher Orders. Amino Compounds (Cont.)

Table 9–3. (Cont.)

	B. Pt.	M. Pt.	Acetamide	Benzamide	Benzene sulfonamide	p-Toluene sulfonamide	Phenyl thiourea	n_D^{20}	D_4^{20}	Picrate
1-Bromo-2-naphthylamine		63	140 / 105 di-							
3-Bromo-4-methoxyaniline		64	111							
2-Bromo-6-methoxyaniline	245	65		90			148			180
4-Bromoaniline		66	168	204	134					
5-Bromo-3-aminopyridine	150[12]	67	76 hyd. / 127 anh.							212
4-Iodoaniline		67	184	222			153			
3-Bromo-1-naphthylamine		70	174	166	122	95	152			
4-Chloroaniline		72	179	192						
6-Chloro-8-aminoquinoline		73								83
2-Bromo-1,4-diaminobenzene		76	200 di-	235 di-		134				
2',4,6-Trichloroaniline		78	204	174						
2,4-Dibromoaniline		79	146	134						124
8-Bromoisoquinoline		80.5								203
2,2'-Diaminodibenzylsulfide	240	81	209 di-							
4-Bromo-3-methylaniline		81	103	119						123
4-Chloro-3-methylaniline		83	91							194
2,6-Dibromoaniline		83	210							
5-Chloro-2-methoxyaniline		84	104	77						
3-Iodo-1-naphthylamine		84	207	174						
4,4'-Diaminodiphenyl sulfide		85	205 di-	162						
4-Bromo-2-aminobenzaldehyde		85		184						
2,2'-Diaminodiphenyl sulfide		85	160 di-							189
4-Iodo-2-methylaniline		87	170							
2,2'-Diaminodibenzyl sulfide		90	202 di-	178 di-		215				
2,4-Diaminochlorobenzene		91	242 di-							
6-Iodoquinoline		91								
2,6-Dibromo-4-chloroaniline		93	226	194						

Table 9–3. Higher Orders. Amino Compounds (Cont.)

Compound	m.p.					
2-Hydroxy-3-bromo-5-methyl-aniline	93	129 N-	185 N-	157 N-		141 di-[e]
2,2'-Diaminodiphenyl disulfide	93	169 di-	166 di-	230 di-		
2,4-Dibromo-6-chloroaniline	95	156 di-	192			
6-Bromoquinaldine	96	227				
2,4-Diiodoaniline	96 (141)	181				
4,4'-Diamino-3,3'-dimethyl-diphenyl sulfide	96	220 di-	233 di-			186 di-
4-Iodoquinoline	97	160	108			
5-Bromo-2-methoxyaniline	97	193				
5-Iodoquinoline	100					
4-Bromo-1-naphthylamine	102					
6,6'-Diamino-3,3'-dimethyl-diphenyl sulfide	103	165 di-	185 di-			179 di-
4,4'-Diaminodibenzyl sulfide	104	188 di-	224 di-		146	
2-Bromo-4-nitroaniline	105	129	160			
4-Bromophenylhydrazine	106	211	254			
Iodo-1,4-diaminobenzene	110.5	104	137			
4-Bromo-2-nitroaniline	111	119 N-				
3,5-Dibromopyridine	112	200 di-				
5-Bromo-3-methyl-2-hydroxy-aniline	113	199 N-	195 N-			
5-Bromo-4-methyl-2-hydroxy-aniline	116	188 di-	223 N-			
2,3,4,6-Tetrabromoaniline	118	228				
2,4,6-Tribromo-5-hydroxyaniline	119	136	198			
2,4,6-Tribromoaniline	122	232				
3,4,5-Tribromoaniline	123	255	210			

Table 9–3. (Cont.)

	B. Pt.	M. Pt.	Acetamide	Benzamide	Benzene sulfonamide	p-Toluene sulfonamide	Phenyl thiourea	n_D^{20}	D_4^{20}	Picrate
6-Bromo-2-naphthylamine		128	192	218						
5-Bromo-2-hydroxyaniline		128	177							
4-Chloro-2-aminopyridine		130	115	120						243
4-Bromo-3-nitroaniline		131	146							
2-Aminobenzthiazole		132	186	186						256
4'-Bromo-4-aminobiphenyl		145	247			174				
4-Bromo-3-hydroxyaniline		150	210			135				
5-Bromo-2-nitroaniline		152	139							
3-Bromo-4-hydroxyaniline		165	157 N-	184 N-192 di-						
4'-Iodo-4-aminobiphenyl		166								
4,4'-Diaminodiphenyl sulfone		175	286 di-							
5-Bromo-4-hydroxy-2-methyl-aniline		215	171 di-	229 di-						
3-Aminothioxanthone		221	236							
3-Bromo-1-aminoanthra-quinone		243	214			227				
3-Bromo-2-aminoanthra-quinone		307	259	279						

Table 9–4. Higher Orders. Acyl Halides   505

TABLE 9–4. *Higher Orders. Acyl Halides*

	B. Pt.	M. Pt.	D_4^{20}	n_D^{20}	Acid by Hydrolysis
Trifluoroacetyl chloride	− 20				71 B. Pt.
Trifluoroacetyl bromide	− 5				71 B. Pt.
Perfluoropropionyl chloride	5				96 B. Pt.
Trifluoroacetyl iodide	22				71 B. Pt.
Perfluoro-*n*-butyryl chloride	39		1.55	1.288	120 B. Pt.
Perfluoro-*n*-butyryl bromide	54		1.735	1.3261	120 B. Pt.
Trichloroacetyl fluoride	66				57
Perfluoro-*n*-valeryl chloride	68				139 B. Pt.
Fluoroacetyl chloride	72				31
Chloroacetyl fluoride	73				63
Perfluoro-*n*-butyryl iodide	76		2.00	1.3652	120 B. Pt.
Perfluoro-*n*-caproyl chloride	86				157 B. Pt.
Acetyl glycyl chloride	115				206
Chloroacetyl bromide	127				63
Bromoacetyl chloride	133				50
Trichloroacetyl bromide	143		$1.90\ D_{15}^{15}$		57
D,L-α-Bromobutyryl chloride	150				217 d. B. Pt.
m-Fluorobenzoyl chloride	189				124
p-Fluorobenzoyl chloride	193				183
o-Fluorobenzoyl chloride	206				126.5
m-Bromobenzoyl chloride	245				150
Chloroacetyl iodide	37[4]			1.5903	63
Azidoacetyl chloride	50[20]				16
α-Bromoisobutyryl chloride	52[30]				48
Dichloroacetyl iodide	55[15]			1.5754	194 B. Pt.
Cyanoacetyl chloride	57[0.5]				66
D,L-α-Bromoisovaleryl chloride	59[15]				44
Trichloroacetyl iodide	74[30]			1.5711	57
β-Iodopropionyl chloride	81[15]				82
Nicotinyl chloride	90[15]				235
p-Chlorobenzoyl bromide	142[27]				240
o-Chlorobenzoyl bromide	144[37]				140
m-Chlorobenzoyl bromide	145[10]				158
o-Nitrobenzoyl chloride	148[7]				146
o-Iodobenzoyl chloride		35			162
m-Nitrobenzoyl chloride	278	35			140
p-Bromobenzoyl chloride		42			251
m-Nitrobenzoyl bromide		43			140
2,4-Dinitrobenzoyl chloride		46			183
p-Nitrophenylacetyl chloride		48			153
p-Iodobenzoyl bromide		55			270
3,5-Dinitrobenzoyl bromide		60			204
p-Nitrobenzoyl bromide		64			241
o-Nitrocinnamyl chloride		64.5			240
3,5-Dinitrobenzoyl chloride		68			204
p-Nitrobenzoyl chloride		75			241

	B. Pt.	M. Pt.	D_4^{20}	n_D^{20}	Acid by Hydrolysis
3-Nitrophthaloyl dichloride		77			218
p-Iodobenzoyl chloride		83			270
Diphenylcarbamyl chloride		86			
4-Chlorophenacyl bromide		96			
p-Nitrocinnamyl chloride		124			286
Azobenzene 4,4'-dicarboxylic acid dichloride		144			330 d.

Table 9–5. Higher Orders. Halides and Nitro Compounds · 507

TABLE 9–5. *Higher Orders. Halides and Nitro Compounds*

	B. Pt.	M. Pt.	n_D^{20}	D_4^{20}	Amine	Benzamide	Benzene sulfon- amide	Picrate
Trifluoromethyl chloride	-81							
Trifluoromethyl bromide	-59							
Perfluoroethyl chloride	-38							
Trifluoromethyl iodide	-23							
Perfluoroethyl bromide	-21							
Perfluoro-n-propyl chloride	-2							
Dichlorofluoromethane	9							
Perfluoro-n-propyl bromide	11							
Perfluoroethyl iodide	13							
Trichlorofluoromethane	24							
Perfluoro-n-butyl chloride	30			1.610 D_{25}^{25}				
1,2-Bromofluoroethylene	36			1.693				
Perfluoro-n-propyl iodide	40		1.3281	2.0566				
Perfluoro-n-amyl chloride	60		1.2736 n^{25}	1.6450				
m-Nitrobenzal chloride	65							
Chloromethyl bromide	68		1.4838	1.9344				
Perfluoro-n-butyl iodide	69							
Perfluoro-n-amyl bromide	74		1.2920 n^{28}	1.8522 D_4^{28}				
p-Nitrobenzal bromide	82							
1-Bromo-1-chloroethane	83							
Perfluoro-n-hexyl chloride	86			1.5705 D_{25}^{25}				
Perfluoro-n-amyl iodide	94		1.3243 $n^{31.5}$	2.0349 D_4^{28}				
Bromo-trichloromethane	105							
1-Bromo-2-chloroethane	106							
Trichloronitromethane	112							
Perfluoro-n-heptyl chloride	113			1.745 D_{25}^{25}				
1-Bromo-3-chloropropane	143		1.4861	1.594				

Table 9–5. (Cont.)

	B. Pt.	M. Pt.	n_D^{20}	D_4^{20}	Amine	Benzamide	Benzene sulfonamide	Picrate
o-Bromochlorobenzene	195		1.580	1.646				
1,3-Bromochlorobenzene	196		1.5773 n_D^{17}	1.6365 D_4^{15}				
o-Bromoiodobenzene	257		1.665	2.262				
3-Bromobenzyl chloride		23				185		
4-Nitro-1-fluorobenzene		25						
2-Chloro-1-nitrobenzene	258	32						
2,4-Dichloro-1-nitrobenzene		33				99	129	134
4-Bromo-3-nitrotoluene		33				115	128	106
4-Bromobenzyl chloride	236	36				173		
6-Chloro-2-nitrotoluene	238	37			21	157		
4-Chloro-2-nitrotoluene	240	38			33	116	121	129
3-Iodo-1-nitrobenzene		38			32	119		177
2-Bromo-1-nitrobenzene		43						
3-Chloro-1-nitrobenzene		45						
3-Nitrobenzyl chloride		45						
2-Nitrobenzyl bromide		46						
2-Iodo-1-nitrobenzene		49			61	139		112
4-Chlorobenzyl bromide		51						
2,4-Dinitro-1-chlorobenzene		54			50	120		
4-Iodo-3-nitrotoluene		55			48			
3-Bromo-1-nitrobenzene		56			18	120		180
3-Nitrobenzyl bromide		58						
4-Chlorobenzyl bromide		62						
1-Chloro-4-bromobenzene		67						
4-Nitrobenzyl chloride		71						
2,4-Dinitro-1-bromobenzene		75						
Picryl chloride		83			72	192	211	
4-Chloro-1-nitrobenzene		84			51	122	122	
1,4-Dibromo-2-nitrobenzene		85						

Table 9–5. Higher Orders. Halides and Nitro Compounds (Cont.)   509

4-Bromo-1-nitronaphthalene	85	102			
4-Chloro-1-nitronaphthalene	87	98			
8-Chloro-1-nitronaphthalene	94	88			
4-Chloro-2-nitroanisole	98	84	77		194
4-Nitrobenzyl bromide	99				
8-Bromo-1-nitronaphthalene	99	90			
5-Chloro-1-nitronaphthalene	111	85			
5-Bromo-1-nitronaphthalene	122	69			
2,4,6-Tribromonitrobenzene	125	122	198		
4-Bromo-1-nitrobenzene	126	66	204	134	180
2,5-Dibromo-1,4-dinitrobenzene	127				
4-Chloro-1,5-dinitronaphthalene	138				
4-Bromo-1,5-dinitronaphthalene	143				
4-Chloro-1,3-dinitronaphthalene	146				
4-Bromo-1,8-dinitronaphthalene	170				
4-Iodo-1-nitrobenzene	173	67	222		
4-Chloro-1,8-dinitronaphthalene	180				
4-Chloro-3-nitro-1,2-naphthoquinone	184				

Table 9–6. *Higher Orders. Sulfonamides*

	M. Pt.	Acid	Chloride	Anilide	S-Benzyl isothiouronium	p-Toluidine salt	o-Toluidine salt	1-Naphthylamide
3-Methyl-1-butane sulfonamide	3			42				90
2-Methyl-1-propane sulfonamide	14			38				107
N,N-Di-isopropylbenzene sulfonamide	30							
N,N-Diethylbenzene sulfonamide	40							60.5
1-Butane sulfonamide	45			10				84
1-Propane sulfonamide	52	7.5						
N-Ethylbenzene sulfonamide	56							
Ethane sulfonamide	58		178 B. Pt.	58	115			66
2-Propane sulfonamide	60			84				134
N-Ethyl-p-toluene sulfonamide	64							
Heptane sulfonamide	75		16					
2,4,5-Trimethoxybenzene sulfonamide	76		130	170				
N-Methyl-p-toluene sulfonamide	78							
3-Ethylbenzene sulfonamide	85							125
Methane sulfonamide	90	20		100				
N-Methyl-p-toluene sulfonamide	92							
Cetyl-(Hexadecane)-sulfonamide	97	54	54					
2-Ethylbenzene sulfonamide	100		12					
Benzyl sulfonamide	105		92	102				166
3-Methyl-4-fluorobenzene sulfonamide	105							
3-Toluene sulfonamide	108		12	96				
4-Ethylbenzene sulfonamide	110		12					
2-Naphthol-3-sulfonamide	110		112					
2,6-Dimethylbenzene sulfonamide	113	98	39					
2-Phenyl-1-ethane sulfonamide	122	91	33	77				
4-Fluorobenzene sulfonamide	125		36					

Table 9–6. Higher Orders. Sulfonamides (Cont.)   511

Compound								
4-Chloro-3-methylbenzene sulfonamide	128		63	92				
3-Chloro-4-methoxybenzene sulfonamide	130		82					
D-Camphor-10 sulfonamide	132	193	67	121				
2-Fluoronaphthalene-6 sulfonamide	133	105	97	129				
D,L-Camphor-8 sulfonamide	133	56	106					
3-Chloro-4-methylbenzene sulfonamide	134		38	96				
3,5-Dimethylbenzene sulfonamide	135	94	119					
o-Nitrobenzyl sulfonamide	137							
D-Camphor-8 sulfonamide	137	138						
4-Toluene sulfonamide	137		69	103	181	198	190	157
2,4-Dimethylbenzene sulfonamide	139	92	34	110	146			
3,4-Dichlorobenzene sulfonamide	140	62	22					
2-Bromo-1-naphthalene sulfonamide	140		97					
2,4,6-Trimethylbenzene sulfonamide	142		56					
m-Aminobenzene sulfonamide	142	77		109	148			
D-Camphor-3 sulfonamide	143		88					
5-Chloro-2-methylbenzene sulfonamide	143		21	124				
3,4-Dimethylbenzene sulfonamide	144	64	52		208			
4-Chlorobenzene sulfonamide	144		53	104	175	208	163	190
1-Methyl-3-naphthalene sulfonamide	144	93	125					
4-Bromo-3-methylbenzene sulfonamide	146		50					
3-Chlorobenzene sulfonamide	148				199			
2,5-Dimethylbenzene sulfonamide	148		24	112	184			
1-Naphthalene sulfonamide	150	90	68	175	137	181	237	
4,6-Dichloro-2,5-dimethyl benzene sulfonamide	150		81					
4-Methyl-3-bromobenzene sulfonamide	151		60					
o-Aminobenzene sulfonamide	153				132			
Benzene sulfonamide	153	66	14.5	112	148	205	176	170
3-Bromobenzene sulfonamide	154							
2-Iodo-1-naphthalene sulfonamide	154		110					
2,6-Dichloro-4-methylbenzene sulfonamide	154		56					

Table 9–6. (Cont.)

	M. Pt.	Acid	Chloride	Anilide	S-Benzyl isothiouronium	p-Toluidine salt	o-Toluidine salt	1-Naphthylamide
2-Toluene sulfonamide	156	57	10	136	170	203		
2,4-Dinitrobenzene sulfonamide	157	106	102					
3-Nitrobenzyl sulfonamide	159 d.	74	100					
5-Chloro-2-nitrobenzene sulfonamide	159		93					
p-Aminobenzene sulfonamide (Sulfanilic amide)	165			200	185			196
3,6-Dichloro-2,5-dimethylbenzene sulfonamide	165		71	171				
5-Chloro-3-nitrobenzene sulfonamide	165							
2-Naphthylamine-1 sulfonamide	165							
4-Bromobenzene sulfonamide	166	102	76	119	170	215	182	183
5-Bromo-2-benzene methyl sulfonamide	167		33					
3-Nitrobenzene sulfonamide	167	48	64	126	146	222	193	166
2,4-Dimethoxylbenzene sulfonamide	167	192	70					
5-Chloro-2-methyl-3-nitrobenzene sulfonamide	167		60					
2,3-Dimethylbenzene sulfonamide	167		47					
4,6-Dichloro-2-methylbenzene sulfonamide	168		43					
4-Bromo-2-methylbenzene sulfonamide	168		50					
3-Sulfobenzoic amide	170 di-		20 di-		163			
2,5-Dimethyl-3-nitrobenzene sulfonamide	172		60	143				
2-Methyl-4-fluorobenzene sulfonamide	172							
4-Methylnaphthalene-1 sulfonamide	174		81	158				
3,4-Dibromobenzene sulfonamide	175		34					
4-Chloro-3-nitrobenzene sulfonamide	175		40					
4-Bromo-3-nitrobenzene sulfonamide	176		55					
2-Chloro-5-methyl-6-nitrobenzene sulfonamide	177	122						
4-Hydroxybenzene sulfonamide	177			141	169	202	192	
4-Nitrobenzene sulfonamide	180	95	80	136	170			160
2,5-Dichlorobenzene sulfonamide	180	93	38	160	170			
1-Naphthylamine-7 sulfonamide	181			147				

Table 9–6. Higher Orders. Sulfonamides (Cont.)   513

Compound	No.					
2,4,5-Trimethylbenzene sulfonamide	181	112	61			
5-Chloro-4-methyl-2-nitrobenzene sulfonamide	181	128	99			
2,4-Dichlorobenzene sulfonamide	182		54			
4-Iodobenzene sulfonamide	183		85	143		
4,5-Dichloro-3-methylbenzene sulfonamide	183		86			
5-Nitronaphthalene-2 sulfonamide	184	118	125			
4-Chloro-2,5-dimethylbenzene sulfonamide	185	100	50	155		
2-Bromobenzene sulfonamide	186		51			
2,3-Dichloro-6-methylbenzene sulfonamide	186		49			
6-Chloro-3-nitrobenzene sulfonamide	186		90			
3,5-Dichloro-2-methylbenzene sulfonamide	186		54			
2-Chloro-4-methylbenzene sulfonamide	186		46			
4-Methylbenzene-1,3-disulfonamide	186		54	189		
1-Chloro-4-naphthalene	187		95	145		162
8-Iodo-1-naphthalene	187		115	140		162
4-Ethylbenzene-1,3-disulfonamide	187					
4-Chloronaphthalene sulfonamide	187		95	145		
2,4-Diaminobenzene-1,5-disulfonamide	187		275	236		
2-Methyl-5-nitrobenzene sulfonamide	187		44	148		
2-Chlorobenzene sulfonamide	188		28.5			
2,6-Dichloro-3-methylbenzene sulfonamide	188		19.5			
1-Methyl-6-naphthalene sulfonamide	189		120	133		
2,4-Dibromobenzene sulfonamide	190	110	79			
Phenanthrene-3 sulfonamide	190	175 anh. / 120 monohyd. / 88 dihyd.	110		222	
4-Bromonaphthalene sulfonamide	191		69			
3,5-Dichloro-4-methylbenzene sulfonamide	191		186			
2,7-Anthraquinone disulfonamide	192					
2,5-Dimethyl-6-nitrobenzene sulfonamide	192	145	110	182		
2-Nitrobenzene sulfonamide	193	70	69	115		

Table 9–6. (Cont.)

	M. Pt.	Acid	Chloride	Anilide	S-Benzyl isothiouronium	p-Toluidine salt	o-Toluidine salt	1-Naphthylamide
Phenanthrene-9 sulfonamide	193	174 anh. / 134 hyd.	127			235		
1-Bromo-4-naphthalene sulfonamide	195	87	71					
2,5-Dibromobenzene sulfonamide	195	128	122					
1-Fluoronaphthalene-5 sulfonamide	196	105	101					
8-Chloro-1-naphthalene sulfonamide	197		75	131				
2,5-Dimethyl-4-nitrobenzene sulfonamide	197	140	52	136				
4-Chloro-3-methyl-5-nitrobenzene sulfonamide	201							
p-Nitrobenzyl sulfonamide	204							
1-Iodo-4-naphthalene sulfonamide	206	100	124	144				
1-Fluoronaphthalene-1 sulfonamide	206		86					
p-Iodobenzyl sulfonamide	206							
2-Methyl-6-naphthalene sulfonamide	206		98					
1-Naphthylamine-4 sulfonamide	206		105		195 d.			
2,6-Diethyl-8-naphthalene sulfonamide	207		119	207				
3,5-Dimethylphenol-2,4-disulfonamide	208		35					
2,4,6-Trichlorobenzene sulfonamide	210 d.							
1-Nitronaphthalene-2 sulfonamide	214	105	120	202				
2,5-Dichlorobenzene-1,3-disulfonamide	215		114	153				
5-Methylbenzene-1,3-disulfonamide	216		94					
2-Naphthalene sulfonamide	217	91	76	132	191	221	213	215
4-Acetamidobenzene-1 sulfonamide	218			128				
1-Naphthylamine-6 sulfonamide	219 d.							
o-Sulfobenzoic acid imide	220	107 hyd.			206	197	127.5	
1-Naphthol-8 sulfonamide	222 d.			178				
2-Methylbenzene-1,4-disulfonamide	224		98					
5-Chlorobenzene-1,3-disulfonamide	224		106					
2,3,4-Trichlorobenzene sulfonamide	226 d.		64					
3,4-Dichloro-2-methyl-benzene sulfonamide	228		51					

Compound								
2,4,6-Tribromobenzene sulfonamide	228 d.	64	64	220	214			245
3,4-Dichloro-2-methylbenzene sulfonamide	228		52					
1,3-Benzene disulfonamide	229		63	148				
4-Biphenyl sulfonamide	230		115	125				
3,5-Dinitrobenzene sulfonamide	235		99					
1-Iodo-5-naphthalene sulfonamide	236		114					
5-Nitrophthalene-1 sulfonamide	236		113	123				
4-Sulfobenzoic imide	236 di-	94 hyd.; 260 anh.	57 di-	252 di-	213			
2,3-Dichloro-4-methylbenzene sulfonamide	237		41					
4-Chloro-2-nitrobenzene sulfonamide	237	82	75	128				
2-Naphthol-6 sulfonamide	237	167 anh.		161	217	248	208	
4-Methylbenzene-1,2-disulfonamide	237		109	190				
4,5-Dimethylbenzene-1,3-disulfonamide	239		79	200				
4-Methoxybenzene-1,3-disulfonamide	240		86	209				
Acetylnaphthionic amide	241							
2,7-Naphthalene sulfonamide	242		158	231		232		
1 5-Anthraquinone disulfonamide	246	310 d.	265	270 d.	212	299	238	
4,6-Dimethylbenzene-1,3-disulfonamide	249		130					
2,3-Dimethylbenzene-1,4-disulfonamide	251			196				
Phenanthrene-2 sulfonamide	253	150	156	157		291		
1,2-Benzene disulfonamide	254		143	241				
2-Amino-5-methylbenzene sulfonamide	257		156	192	206			
1-Naphthylamine-5 sulfonamide	260			171	179			
2-Methylbenzene-1,3 disulfonamide	> 260		88	162				
Anthracene-2 sulfonamide	261		122	201				
Anthraquinone-2 sulfonamide	261		197	193	211	308		
1,4-Naphthalene disulfonamide	273		160	179				
4,6-Dichlorobenzene-1,3-disulfonamide	276		123					
9,10-Dichloroanthracene-2 sulfonamide	279		221	248				
1,4-Benzene disulfonamide	288		131	249				
2,5-Dimethylbenzene-1,3-disulfonamide	295		81	174				

Table 9–6. (Cont.)

	M. Pt.	Acid	Chloride	Anilide	S-Benzyl isothio-uronium	p-Toluidine salt	o-Toluidine salt	1-Naphthyl-amide
1,6-Naphthalene disulfonamide	297	125	129		81	314	323	
4,4'-Biphenyl disulfonamide	300	72	203		171	330		
2,6-Naphthalene disulfonamide	305		225		256			
2,5-Dimethylbenzene-1,4-disulfonamide	310		164	223				
1,5-Naphthalene disulfonamide	310	240	183	249	257			
1,3,5-Benzene trisulfonamide	310	> 100	187 tri-	237 tri-				
1,5-Anthracene disulfonamide	> 330		249	293				
1,8-Anthracene disulfonamide	333		225	224				
1-Cyano-8-naphthalene sulfonamide	334		139	237				
1,8-Anthraquinone disulfonamide	> 340		222	237				
1,5-Anthraquinone disulfonamide	> 350		265	269				

Table 9–7. Higher Orders. Nitriles   517

TABLE 9–7. *Higher Orders. Nitriles*

	B. Pt.	M. Pt.	Acid	
			B. Pt.	M. Pt.
Fluoroacetonitrile	80		165	33
Trichloroacetonitrile	86		196	58
α-Chloroisobutyronitrile	116			31
Chloroacetonitrile	127		189	63
α-Bromoisobutyronitrile	139			48
β-Chloropropionitrile	178			41
γ-Chlorobutyronitrile	196		196[22]	16
β-Bromopropionitrile	69[7]			62
(2-Chlorophenyl)-acetonitrile	251	24		95
4-Chlorophenylacetonitrile	265	30		105
4-Fluorobenzonitrile	189	35		183
3-Bromobenzonitrile	225	38		155
3-Chlorobenzonitrile		41		158
2-Chlorobenzonitrile	232	43		141
2-Bromo-4-tolunitrile		44		204
3-Bromo-4-tolunitrile		47		140
4-Bromophenylacetonitrile		47		114
4-Iodophenylacetonitrile		50		135
2-Bromobenzonitrile	253	53		150
2-Iodobenzonitrile		55		162
2-Iodo-4-tolunitrile		57		205
3-Chloro-4-tolunitrile		61		155
Bromomalononitrile		65		113
5-Chloro-2-tolunitrile		67		172
5-Bromo-2-tolunitrile		70		187
5-Chloro-2-nitro-4-tolunitrile		93		180
4-Chlorobenzonitrile		96		240
4-Chloro-2-nitrobenzonitrile		98		142
4-Chloro-3-nitrobenzonitrile		100		181
4-Bromo-1-naphthonitrile		102		212
6-Chloro-3-nitrobenzonitrile		105		165
4-Chloro-1-naphthonitrile		110		210
4-Bromobenzonitrile	235	112		251
6-Bromo-3-nitrobenzonitrile		117		180
4-Bromo-3-nitrobenzonitrile		120		203
5-Bromo-3-nitro-4-tolunitrile		130		206
5-Bromo-2-nitro-4-tolunitrile		132		203
5-Chloro-2-naphthonitrile		144		270
5-Chloro-1-naphthonitrile		145		245
5-Bromo-1-naphthonitrile		147		261
5-Bromo-salicylonitrile		158		165

TABLE 9–8. *Higher Orders. Chlorosilanes*

	B. Pt.	D	n_{D}^{20}
Methyldichlorosilane	41	$1.105\ D_{27}^{27}$	
Trimethylchlorosilane	57	$0.8536\ D_{27}^{27}$	$1.3893\ n^{25}$
Methyltrichlorosilane	66	$1.270\ D_{25}^{25}$	$1.4085\ n^{25}$
Dimethyldichlorosilane	70	$1.06\ D_{25}^{25}$	$1.4023\ n^{25}$
Vinyltrichlorosilane	92	$1.264\ D_{27}^{27}$	
Ethyltrichlorosilane	98	$1.2388\ D^{19.4}$	$1.4257\ n^{25}$
Chloromethyldimethylchlorosilane	115		
Allyltrichlorosilane	117.5	$1.211\ D_{27}^{27}$	
Allylmethyldichlorosilane	119	$1.057\ D^{27}$	
Chloromethylmethyldichlorosilane	122		
n-Propyltrichlorosilane	123.5	$1.195\ D_{25}^{25}$	$1.4292\ n^{25}$
Diethyldichlorosilane	129	$1.106\ D^{15}$	$1.4309\ n^{25}$
n-Amyltrichlorosilane	170	$1.150\ D_{25}^{25}$	$1.4380\ n^{25}$
γ-Chloropropyltrichlorosilane	180	$1.336\ D^{25}$	1.4700
Phenyldichlorosilane	184	$1.222\ D^{20}$	
Phenyltrichlorosilane	201.5	$1.3256\ D^{18.8}$	$1.5240\ n^{25}$
Cyclohexyltrichlorosilane	206	$1.226\ D_{25}^{25}$	$1.4759\ n^{25}$
Diphenyldichlorosilane	305		1,5765
Triphenylchlorosilane	378		
Ethyldichlorosilane	75^{13}	1.0926	1.4148
Phenylvinyldichlorosilane	$84^{1.5}$		
Cyclohexenyltrichlorosilane	87^{16}	$1.259\ D^{25}$	$1.4891\ n^{25}$
Bis-Trichlorosilylethane	93^{25}	$1.475\ D^{29}$	
Nonyltrichlorosilane	116^{23}	$1.072\ D^{25}$	1.4596
Dodecyltrichlorosilane	120^{3}	$1.026\ D_{25}^{25}$	1.4521
Diphenylvinylchlorosilane	$133^{1.5}$		
Octadecyltrichlorosilane	159^{13}	$0.95\ D^{22}$	$1.4583\ n^{25}$
Bis-Trichlorosilylbenzene, meta	161.5^{30}	$1.47\ D^{25}$	
Bis-Trichlorosilylbenzene, para	168^{30}	$1.47\ D^{25}$	
Chlorophenyltrichlorosilane	230^{750}	$1.429\ D^{30}$	1.5648
Hexadecyltrichlorosilane	269^{100}	$0.996\ D_{25}^{25}$	$1.4568\ n^{25}$
Dichlorodiiododecylsilane	270^{7}		
Biphenyltrichlorosilane			
Dioctadecyldichlorosilane	314^{5}		

Table 9–9. Higher Orders. Miscellaneous 519

TABLE 9–9. *Higher Orders. Miscellaneous*

	B. Pt.	M. Pt.
Chloromethyl methyl sulfide	106	
Methyl isothiocyanate	118	
Chloromethyl ethyl sulfide	128	
Methyl thiocyanate	131	
Bromoethyl methyl sulfide	134	
tert.-Butyl isothiocyanate	140	40.5
Ethyl thiocyanate	147	
Isopropyl thiocyanate	150	
Chloromethyl propyl sulfide	150	
Isopropyl isothiocyanate	150	
Allyl isothiocyanate	152	
Chloromethyl sulfide	156	
sec.-Butyl isothiocyanate	159	
Allyl thiocyanate	161	
Propyl thiocyanate	165	
Butyl isothiocyanate	167	
Butyl thiocyanate	186	
Bis-(2-Chloroethyl)-sulfide	215	13
Phenyl isothiocyanate	220	
Phenyl thiocyanate	231	
o-Tolyl isothiocyanate	239	
3′-Methyl-2-amino diphenyl sulfide	174[1]	
p-Tolyl isothiocyanate	239	26
o-Aminothiophenol		26
Bis-(4-Chlorobenzyl)-sulfide		41
Thiopropionamide		42
Benzyl thiocyanate		43
2-Aminodiphenyl sulfide		43
p-Aminothiophenol		45
p-Chlorophenyl isothiocyanate		45
3′-Methyl-4-nitrodiphenyl sulfide		47
4′-Isopropyl-4-nitrodiphenyl sulfide		47.5
4′-Methyl-2-aminodiphenyl sulfide		48.5
2′-Methyl-4-aminodiphenyl sulfide		51.5
p-Chlorothiophenol		53
Thiobenzophenone		54
4-Nitrodiphenyl sulfide		55
1-Naphthyl isothiocyanate		56
4′-Chloro-4-aminodiphenyl sulfide		60
m-Nitrophenyl isothiocyanate		60.5
1,4-Butane dithiocyanate		61
2-Naphthyl isothiocyanate		63
2′-Methyl-2-nitrodiphenyl sulfide		64
sym-Dibutyl thiourea		64
3′-Methyl-4-(2,5-dimethyl-1-pyrryl)-diphenyl sulfide		66

	B. Pt.	M. Pt.
3-Chloro-4-nitrodiphenyl sulfide		71
o-Nitrophenyl isothiocyanate		72
4′-Methyl-4-aminodiphenyl sulfide		72
3′-Chloro-4-aminodiphenyl sulfide		72
3′-Methyl-4-aminodiphenyl sulfide		72.5
3′-Methyl-4-formylaminodiphenyl sulfide		72.5
p-Bromothiophenol		75
m-Nitrothiophenol		75
Thioacetanilide		76
2′-Chloro-4-aminodiphenyl sulfide		77
4′-Methyl-2-(2,5-dimethyl-1-pyrryl)-diphenyl sulfide		78
Allyl thiourea		78
4′-Methyl-4-nitrodiphenyl sulfide		80
2-Nitrodiphenyl sulfide		80.5
4′-Chloro-4-nitrodiphenyl sulfide		83
3′-Methyl-2-nitrodiphenyl sulfide		86
4-(2,5-Dimethyl-1-pyrryl)-diphenyl sulfide		86.5
2′-Methyl-2-nitrodiphenyl sulfide		87
4′-Methyl-2-nitrodiphenyl sulfide		89
2′-Methyl-2-aminodiphenyl sulfide		89
1,2-Ethane dithiocyanate		90
4′-Isopropyl-4-acetylaminodiphenyl sulfide		93.5
4′-Isopropyl-2,4-diaminodiphenyl sulfide		93.5
3′-Chloro-2,4-diaminodiphenyl sulfide		94
4-Aminodiphenyl sulfide		95
4′-Isopropyl-2,4-dinitrodiphenyl sulfide		95.5
3′-Methyl-2,4-dinitrodiphenyl sulfide		99.5
Thiobenzanilide		102
2′-Methyl-2-(2,5-dimethyl-1-pyrryl)-diphenyl sulfide		107
Thioacetamide		108
3′-Chloro-2,4-dinitrodiphenyl sulfide		108
2′-Methyl-4-(2,5-dimethyl-1-pyrryl)-diphenyl sulfide		111.5
Bis-(p-Bromophenyl)-sulfide		112
3′-Methyl-2,4-diaminodiphenyl sulfide		112
2′-Chloro-4-nitrodiphenyl sulfide		113
p-Nitrophenyl thiourea		113
2-(2,5-Dimethyl-1-pyrryl-)diphenyl sulfide		114
Thiobenzamide		116
Methyl thiourea		121
4′-Chloro-2,4-dinitrodiphenyl sulfide		121
3′-Methyl-4-acetylaminodiphenyl sulfide		121
o-Nitrophenyl thiourea		136
o-Nitrophenyl thiocyanate		136
4′-Chloro-2,4-diaminodiphenyl sulfide		141
p-Chlorothioacetanilide		142
o-Chlorophenyl thiourea		146
3′-Methyl-4-ureidodiphenyl sulfide		150
Phenyl thiourea		154

	B. Pt.	M. Pt.
sym-Diphenyl thiourea		154
Bis-(*p*-nitrobenzyl)-sulfide		158
as-Dimethyl thiourea		159
p-Fluorothiophenol		162
tert.-Butyl thiourea		171
β-Bromoethyl thiourea		174
p-Nitrothioacetanilide		175
sym-Di-*p*-tolyl thiourea		178
Thiourea		180
Thiosemicarbazide		184
1-Naphthyl thiourea		194
Ethylene thiourea		198

Subject Index

Druck: Adolf Holzhausens Nfg., Wien VII, Kandlgasse 19-21